SMITHSONIAN
INSTITUTION

UNITED STATES
NATIONAL MUSEUM
BULLETIN 243

WASHINGTON, D.C.

1965

PUBLICATIONS OF THE UNITED STATES NATIONAL MUSEUM

The scientific publications of the United States National Museum, which is comprised of the Museum of Natural History and the Museum of History and Technology, include two series, *Proceedings of the United States National Museum* and *United States National Museum Bulletin*.

In these series are published original articles and monographs emanating from the two Museums and dealing with their collections and work. These publications set forth newly acquired facts in the fields of anthropology, biology, geology, history, and technology. Copies of each publication are distributed to libraries and scientific organizations and to specialists and others interested in the various subjects.

The *Proceedings*, begun in 1878, are intended for the presentation, in separate form, of shorter papers. These are gathered in volumes, octavo in size, with the publication date of each paper recorded in the table of contents of the volume.

In the *Bulletin* series, the first of which was issued in 1875, appear longer, separate publications consisting of monographs (occasionally in several parts) and volumes in which are collected works on related subjects. *Bulletins* are either octavo or quarto in size, depending on the needs of the presentation.

Since 1902 papers relating to the botanical collections of the Museum have been published in the *Bulletin* series under the heading *Contributions from the United States National Herbarium*.

This work forms number 243 of the *Bulletin* series.

FRANK A. TAYLOR,
Director, United States National Museum.

II

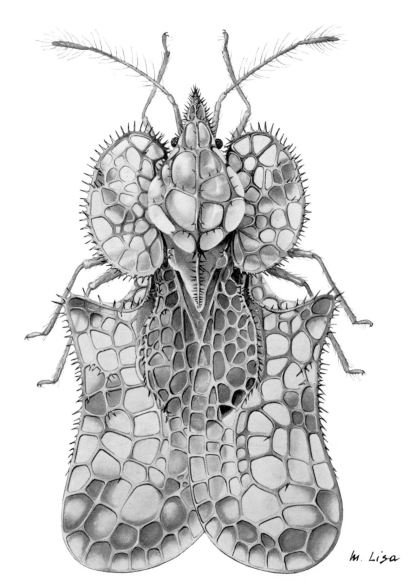

Corythucha championi Drake and Cobben

MUSEUM OF NATURAL HISTORY

Lacebugs of the World

A Catalog
(Hemiptera: Tingidae)

CARL J. DRAKE
Research Associate, Smithsonian Institution
and
FLORENCE A. RUHOFF

SMITHSONIAN INSTITUTION
WASHINGTON, 1965

CONTENTS

v

Illustrations

Figures

Plates

(1–56 follow page 444)

Lacebugs of the World
(Hemiptera: Tingidae)

Introduction

THE MEMBERS OF THE FAMILY Tingidae are purely plant-feeding bugs that live mostly on the lower surfaces of the leaves of living plants. The thin lacy outgrowths of the pronotum and the delicate lacelike texture of the forewings (pls. 36, 41, 42) have quite aptly earned for them the common name "lacebugs" all over the world. Expressed polyglotally, lacebugs are called "netzwanzen" or "gitterwanzen" in German, "netwantsen" or "netwerkwantsen" in Dutch, and "chinches de encaja" in Spanish. The vernacular name in French includes that of the host plant, such as "le tigre du poirier," "le tigre du cerisier," and "le tigre du cafféier."

Systematically, lacebugs are classified in the family Tingidae of the insect order Hemiptera. As cataloged herein, the family consists of 1,820 species arranged in 3 subfamilies and 236 genera. These figures include both living and extinct forms as far as now recorded in the literature; subgenera, subspecies, varieties, and invalid taxa are not included in the totals.

Geographically, lacebugs are widely distributed in the torrid and temperate zones on all continents and on most islands in the oceans. They are unknown in the frigid zones.

Lacebugs are relatively small insects, some nearly miniature in size (pls. 1, 14, 45) and the "giants" seldom exceed one-fourth inch in length (pls. 36, 38). The overall form varies from long and very slender (pls. 15, 16) to extremely wide (pls. 38, 40). Of the ineffable wonders of insect kinds, none surpasses the lacebugs in the diversity and oddities of forms (pls. 28, 30, 49) adorned with fancy lace designs. The lacework is original, specific, and thus peculiar to each kind of lacebug. No two species are ever dressed exactly alike. Only the adult members of the same species are clothed in identical topcoats of living lace. In size, color, markings, and general aspect, there are scarcely any differences in the outward appearances between the sexes. The classification of tribes, genera, and species is based for the most part upon the lacy outgrowths, especially the formations of the pronotum and the elytra (figs. 1–6). The buccal, sternal, and hypocostal laminae (figs. 1A, 3, 4) likewise furnish characterizing features.

Adults and nymphs alike obtain food by piercing the epidermis of the leaf blades of living plants and extracting the sap from the cellular tissue therein by means of the protrusile and retractile stylets operating from a freely movable haustellum. Only the very slender stylets of the mouth parts pierce and enter the leaves to take out the sap on which they feed.

The egg, except in the floral-gall makers, is thrust deeply into the leaf of the food plants almost up to the operculum and coated with a dark brownish adhesive material that soon hardens and forms a protective coating.   After hatching and drying, the nymphs begin to feed at once in small clusters near the empty eggshells and adults.   If disturbed and scattered, they will soon reassemble again in a cluster.

Metamorphosis is gradual.   The growth and development from egg to the unchanging imaginal stage consists of five instars separated from one another by successive moults.   Most species in the temperate zones are uni- or bivoltene and overwinter either in the imaginal or egg stage.   Not much has been printed concerning the biology and estivation of tingids in the tropical region.

Many kinds of plants, mostly the terrestrial flowering species, serve as feeding and breeding hosts.   All species are rather highly specialized in their food habits, and generation after generation live on the same kind of plant or closely related ones.   The life cycle of each species is attuned so that its breeding, egg-laying, and development period parallels in the growing time with that of the unfolding of the foliar (leaf-feeding species) or floral (gall-making species) parts of its host plant.

Much injury and plasmolysis of the foliage always accompanies the feeding activities.   Damage to the foliar tissue increases in severity with the hatching of the eggs and development of the broods.   Heavily infested leaves become badly discolored, turn yellowish to whitish, wither, and often drop prematurely.   Serious losses are effected on many cultivated and wild plants of prime importance in agriculture and horticulture.   For example, among the useful plants upon which lacebugs breed and obtain their livelihood are maize, sugarcane, cotton, castor bean, pineapple, papaya, avocado, pear, cherry, olive, tea, pepper, coffee, cinnamon, camphor, cacao, banana, coconut, cassava, rubber, walnut, oak, hazelnut, azalea, and rhododendron.

According to preliminary experiments by Nagaraj and Menon (1956), recent field tests by Shanta, et al. (1960), and by Mathen (1960), the lacebug *Stephanitis typica* (pl. 47) is accused of being a vector of a serious disease of coconut palms in Travancore-Cochin, India.   This disease (probably a virus) is called "wilt [root] of coconut palm" and seriously affects each year about one-fourth of the coconut area there under cultivation.   *S. typica* is also a pest of consequence on banana, camphor, and other plants in India and the East Indies.

As dwellers on the undersides of the leaves, tingids feed, stand, and rest in a topsy-turvy upside-down position.   In this inverted posture, the lacy topcoat serves to conceal the body, obliterate its shadow, and thus functions in ways similar to the nets or screens devised by man to hide and camouflage military installations, equipment, and troops in wartime.   Lace curtains hanging over a window provide the same sort of concealment for mankind and objects inside a room.   Diaphanous veils are worn to obscure or protect the face.   The inherent ability of tingids to stand or "sit" still and then remain motionless for long periods is vital to survival.   The least movement by the bug betrays its presence on the leaf.

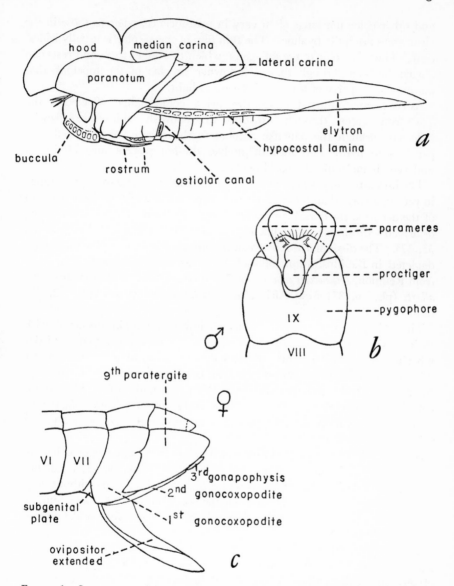

Figure 1.—Structures used in classification: *a*, *Stephanitis ligyra* Drake, lateral aspect; *b*, *Tingis cardui* (Linnaeus), ventral aspect of ♂ genital capsule; *c*, *same*, lateral aspect of ♀ genital segments.

Cryptic coloration enters into the living picture in various ways. In the species of many genera, the paranota and elytra are broadly produced outwardly beyond the body limits (pls. 38, 40, 46). In such forms, the areolae differ in size, shape, and in the degree of iridescence, translucence, and transparence. The areolae in the dark elytral bands and other color markings often vary in translucence, whereas those in the clear areas are quite hyaline. The thin film of the areolae is usually iridescent. Thus the color of the foliage on which the tingid feeds and rests can always be seen through those windowlike areolae of the topcloak that possess the property of transmitting rays of light.

As the feeding injury develops, the various color changes effected on the leaf—from green through brownish to yellowish white—are likewise reflected through the panelike areolae to the degree that the cells are pervious to light. Lacebugs themselves do not possess any ability to undergo chameleonic changes in color.

The immature stages present an altogether different external appearance in yet other ways than those of the lacy topcoats of their parents. Instead of the network, the dorsal surface of the nymph is smooth and plain (pl. 8) or armed with simple or modified spines of various kinds and sizes (pls. 31, 33, 37). The dissimilarities between the imaginal and nymphal stages are depicted in the illustrations of such forms as *Litadea delicatula* (pls. 7, 8) from Reunion, *Diconocoris capusi* (pls. 30, 31) from Viet-Nam, and *Ammianus alberti* (pls. 36, 37) from Africa, and *Australotingis franzeni* (pls. 32, 33) from Australia.

The ability of the nymphs to crouch low and remain stock-still with their bodies pressed close to the surface of the leaves are characteristics inherited from their parents. Besides these behavioral traits, the castoff skins, eggshells, scattered dots of brownish-black excrement, and the somber color of the body also tend to make them less noticeable. The spines (pls. 33, 37), tubercles, and hairs on the dorsal surface are likewise factors in concealment. The nymphal stages of some species also possess glandular spines.

Neither adults nor nymphs imitate or simulate in color, form, or behavior any animate or inanimate object in their habits. The species, in all life stages, are relatively sluggish, completely defenseless, and without any means or ways to fight back or even the speed needed to evade hungry marauders. To escape enemies, they rely entirely on behavioral features and camouflage.

The feeding activities of some species of lacebugs cause the young foliar leaves of their host plants to curl downwards. According to Horváth (1929), the African tingid *Onymochila dichapetali* (pl. 17) causes extensive leaf-curl on the foliage of its host, *Dichapetalum cymosum* (pl. 17), in the Transvaal. The attack of the Japanese tingid *Tingis comosa* on the foliage of its host plant, *Artemesia* sp., produces a similar type of down-curl (fide Takeya); and, in India, the feeding of adults and nymphs of *Corythauma ayyari* (Drake) produces a leaf-curl on *Jasminum* spp. (fide Livingston). These are the only lacebugs so far known to effect this type of leaf damage and thus may indicate their roles as vectors.

The members of two genera of lacebugs are true gall-producing insects.

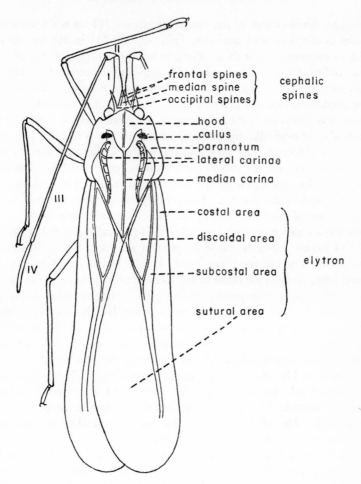

FIGURE 2.—Structures used in classification: *Leptopharsa mira* Drake and Hambleton, dorsal aspect.

The offspring, from the neonate nymph to full maturity, are confined in closed, one-celled chambers. Only the genera *Copium* and *Paracopium* of the tingines are producers and dwellers in closed galls. These genera are represented in many countries in the Old World, but are unknown in the Americas.

The gall-making lacebugs are anthophagous and induce most profound reactions on the flowers they affect. In marked contrast to the foliar feeding species that live open and free on the foliage, the gallicolous tingids cause the host plant to produce malformations known as flower cecidia or galls (pls. 20, 22, 24), within which the nymphal stages live, feed, grow and moult until they attain the imaginal stage. From a domiciliary standpoint, the closed gall forms a safe shelter and luxuriant abode for the progressive development of the immature stages. There is no reduction in the size of the legs and antennae (pls. 18, 21, 23) in the cecidogenous tingids as compared with those of free-living species (pls. 10, 11, 26).

The conformation and structure of the eggs and the method of oviposition of members of the genera *Copium* and *Paracopium* differ notably from those of the tingids that do not produce galls. According to the observations of Monod and Carayon (1958) the egg of *C. cornutum* (now *clavicorne*) has a campanular or domelike operculum, whose surface is smooth like that of the body of the egg. The time and method of laying and the fixation of the egg to the corolla are connected with floral cecidogenesis. During the laying operation, the egg is turned end for end (180°) so that the opercular pole is inserted in the corolla. Conversely, the abopercular pole is thrust into the tissue of the living leaf by the nongall-making lacebugs.

Two and a quarter centuries ago the gifted naturalist René A. F. Réamur (1737) of France wrote a classic account of an insect that produced galls on the flower buds of the plant "camedrys." He included figures of the gall and other parts of the plant as well as those of the adult and last nymphal stage of the insect that produced the galls. After opening many galls, Réamur recorded that each gall formed a one-celled chamber and confined therein was a single insect, either in the nymphal or adult stage. Years later, Geoffroy (1762) published a similar article about the same insect and its unichambered gall on the inflorescence of "chamaedras." In the 12th edition of his "Systema Naturae," Linnaeus (1767) cited the above references, clearly authenticating the identity of the species previously named and described by him as *Cimex clavicornis* (now in the genus *Copium*) from Europe. Historically, this is the first gall-making lacebug to be technically named and described (pls. 18, 19).

The tingicecidium is an abnormal growth or excrescence of the corolla of the flowerbud (pls. 20, 22, 24). The hypertropic growth contains a fairly large, closed, monothalamous cell, or chamber. The immature stages of the lacebug are confined therein from hatching until the completion of metamorphosis. At that time, the gall itself has also reached full maturity and bursts open naturally by dehiscence at the tip, thus setting free its haustellate inmate (*Copium* spp.) or inmates (*Paracopium* spp.). The adults, after escaping from the gall, become free-living like the leaf-feeding species.

An examination of 100 nearly mature cecidia of *Copium clavicorne* (pl. 20) and an equal number of galls of *C. teucrii* (pl. 22) showed each cecidium of these species to be one-chambered and inhabited by only one tingid in either the last nymphal or newly emerged imaginal stage. The cecidia were preserved in alcohol as picked in the field from the host plant, *Teucrium chamaedrys*, in Austria. Although the galls examined were almost fully grown, they were still tightly closed and showed no external signs of dehiscence.

The adults of *C. teucrii* (pl. 21) and *C. clavicorne* (pl. 18) are very similar in

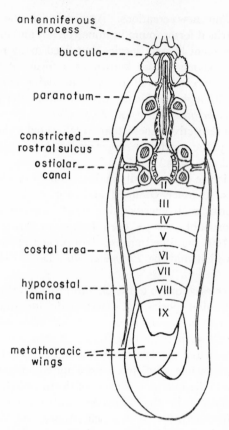

antenniferous
process

bucculo

paranotum

constricted
rostral sulcus

ostiolar
canal

II

III

IV

V

costal area

VI

VII

hypocostal
lamina

VIII

IX

metathoracic
wings

FIGURE 3.—Structures used in classification: *Vatiga illudens* (Drake), ventral aspect.

size and habitus, and their separation from each other is based largely on the antennal characters of the adults. The last nymphal stage (pl. 19) also furnishes additional characters in the pronotal carinae. However, the cecidia (pls. 20, 22) of these two species are very dissimilar and thus provide much better distinguishing characters than those of either the nymphal or imaginal forms.

The dissection of 9 nearly mature cecidia of *Paracopium hamadryas* (pl. 24) from Malagasy showed each cecidium to be monothalamous, closed, and to contain from four to seven lacebugs in the last nymphal and adult stages. A census of nine galls gave these figures: 2 galls with 2 nymphs and 2 adults; 3 galls with 3 nymphs and 2 adults; 2 galls with 3 nymphs and 3 adults; and 2 galls with 3 nymphs and 4 adults. These figures give an average population of 5.4 lacebugs per gall. From one to three young larvae of nolid moths, assumed to be scavengers, were found in four cecidia. The genera *Copium* and *Paracopium* comprise a total of 45 species (10+35) and, insofar as known, are all gall-forming tingids.

Lacebugs are no new creations. According to the geological time calendar, the petrified forms found in stone (pl. 35) and moulds engulfed in amber (pl. 3) represent bygone species that lived many million years ago. No present-day lacebug is also known as a fossil. As the illustrations depict, the extinct species as well as the forms living today wore topcoats of living lace. Although specifically different from the living forms, the zoolithic *Phatnoma baltica* (pl. 3) and *Dictyla veterna* (pl. 35) are typically members of these respective genera that were erected to hold living species (pls. 2, 7). Both of the genera are represented today by members of modern species in the Old and New Worlds.

The present picture of the fossil tingids, because of the imperfect state of our knowledge, is much confused and in need of specific and generic revision. Four forms, each described simply as " *Tingis* sp." are without trivial names and probably do not even belong to this genus. Bachofen-Echt (1949, fig. 160) published an excellent photograph of an unidentified amber lacebug which may be *Phatnoma baltica* Drake (1950) described in Baltic amber.

The lacebug species common to the Old and New Worlds are numerically low, totaling only nine species. A digest of the literature and studies of numerous collections have so far not revealed evidences of any natural faunal exchange through migration in either direction. Apparently, all the tingid species shared similarly between the two worlds made the sea voyage by ships of various kinds in transoceanic commerce. Paleontologic and chorologic data disclose no evidences of the so-called Amphiatlantic or Westarctic distribution in the Tingidae, and collections from eastern Siberia and northwestern North America (Alaska and Canada) have not as yet disclosed a single species common in these regions, even among the muscicolous genus *Acalypta*. The members of the latter genus are among the northernmost Tingidae in these regions. Apparently, perhaps, even in the present era, the Bering Strait plus unfavorable biotic factors such as low temperature and floral composition have formed a natural barrier for tingids between the Asian and North American continents.

Ballast materials, used quite extensively on sailing vessels in the colonial times, played a significant role in the transportation and introduction of certain kinds of insects and other invertebrates as well as many plants into North America from Europe (Lindroth, 1957). However, our studies of the tingifauna collected at various times in the vicinity of ballast-dumping sites near old seaports along the Atlantic and Pacific coasts of North America indicate that earthen and other sorts of ballast seem to have played no findable part in the hemispheric exchange of Tingidae.

Caloloma uhleri Drake and Bruner is an Australian indigene originally described from the West Indies (Antigua, Lesser Antilles). Specimens received recently from the Windward Islands (Saint Vincent) show that this lacebug has become established in the West Indies. From its native

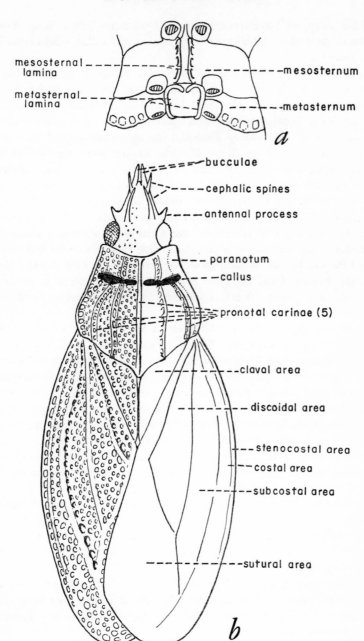

mesosternal lamina

mesosternum

metasternal lamina

metasternum

a

bucculae

cephalic spines

antennal process

paranotum

callus

pronotal carinae (5)

claval area

discoidal area

stenocostal area

costal area

subcostal area

sutural area

b

FIGURE 4.—Structures used in classification: *a, Gargaphia tiliae* (Walsh) interrupted rostra channel on metasternum; *b, Cantacader amydis* Drake, dorsal aspect.

home far away, we have specimens from Queensland, New South Wales, and South Australia. This is the only known Australian tingid colonized in the Americas.

Contrary to the usual statements, *Stephanitis rhododendri* Horváth is indigenous in the United States and Canada. It is not a European element transported to North America from Holland as generally credited. Museum specimens bearing locality and collecting dates prove that the rhododendron lacebug was widely dispersed in eastern and central parts of the United States and in southern Canada at the time the species was originally described from Holland. This indigeneity of *rhododendri* is in agreement with the findings and hypothesis proposed by Johnson (1936) relative to its native patria. Furthermore, in general aspect, *rhododendri* is systematically nearer to *S. blatchleyi* Drake of Florida than it is to members of this genus in the Old World, or even to its South American congeners. Shipments of nursery stock of the decorative rhododendrons and azaleas account for its disjunct, synathropous dispersion in the Old World. Since the tingid *rhododendri* and also *pyrioides* overwinter in the egg stage, the ericaceous hosts with persistent leaves serve as insidious conveyors of the eggs in plant shipments.

Teleonemia scrupulosa Stål is indigenous in Mexico, West Indies, Central and most of South Americas. It was experimentally introduced in the Hawaiian Islands from Mexico for the "biological control" of the noxious lantana plant. As a result of the Hawaiian tests, *scrupulosa* was intentionally transported and released in numbers for the same biological end in the East Indies, Australia, India, and Africa, where it is now firmly colonized and becoming widely spread. This is the only tingid species employed in the biological control of troublesome plants and, furthermore, the only New World lacebug intentionally imported into the Eastern Hemisphere. No lacebug has been purposely introduced into the Americas from the Old World.

Corythucha morrilli Osborn and Drake, a recent overseas transport into the Hawaiian Islands, is a native of southwestern United States, Mexico, Central America, and the West Indies. Records indicate that it was probably accidentally included in shipments of nursery plants from southwestern United States to Hawaii.

Tingis auriculata (Costa), indigenous in several European countries, was collected by Uhler many years ago in Maryland and has not been taken there since. It probably was unable to self-maintain its population in eastern United States.

Dictyonota tricornis (Schrank) is an indigene in many countries in Europe, central Asia, and northern Africa. Although discovered in eastern Canada and New England States a half a century ago, its increase and spread for an introduced species have been slow. The North American specimens from

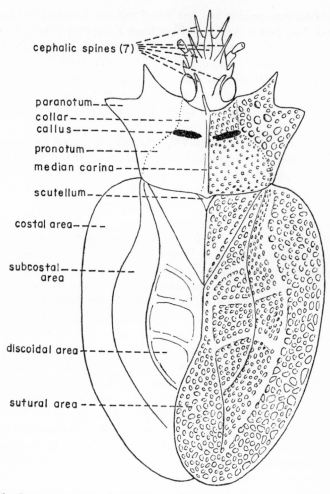

cephalic spines (7)

paranotum
collar
callus
pronotum
median carina
scutellum
costal area
subcostal area
discoidal area
sutural area

FIGURE 5.—Structures used in classification: *Phatnoma agviates* Drake and Ruhoff, dorsal aspect.

Nova Scotia and Maine are typical *tricornis* and not a variety or subspecies as described.

Dictyonota fuliginosa Costa is indigenous in several countries in eastern Europe. Scudder (1960) recently collected several specimens on broom in western Canada (British Columbia), probably introduced there on nursery stock several years ago.

Stephanitis pyrioides (Scott), originally described from Japan, is an Asian indigene and globally known as the azalea lacebug. Its synanthropic dispersal, like that of *S. rhododendri*, is associated with the wide culture and importation of azaleas and rhododendrons, both greenhouse and landscape forms and varieties, and likewise is closely bound to its ericaceous hosts.

Records show that *pyrioides* was first introduced into Europe from Japan and then later into North America either from Europe or Japan, or perhaps both. Through the transportation of nursery stock, *pyrioides* has also gained entrance into Morocco, South Africa, and Australia.

Stephanitis takeyai Drake and Maa (pl. 48) is a Japanese indigene rather recently imported into eastern United States, apparently on nursery stock from Japan. It is known from Connecticut and New Jersey in the United States.

Galeatus spinifrons (Fallén) (pl. 44), originally described from Sweden, is indigenous in many countries in Europe and Asia. It was the first lacebug accidentally transported into North America (probably New England or Newfoundland) from Europe. The synonymity of *G. angusticollis* Reuter and *G. spinifrons* (Fallén) of Europe and of *G. peckhami* (Ashmead) and *G. uhleri* Horváth of the United States and Canada gives the survivor *spinifrons* circumglobal distribution. It is the only tingid species that has encircled the world in distribution. In Europe and Asia, both macropterous and brachypterous forms are fairly common, whereas an examination of more than 500 specimens (all long-winged) from northern United States and southern Canada, indicates that perhaps only the homozygous, macropterous form was probably imported into northern United States. *Galeatus* is an Old World genus, and *G. spinifrons* is pterygopolymorphic in Eurasia.

Founded on morphologic structures from a global concept, Drake and Davis (1960) proposed the superfamily Miroidea Hahn to hold the families Tingidae Laporte and Miridae Hahn, and then systematized the Tingidae into the subfamilies Cantacaderinae Stål, Tinginae Laporte, and Vianaidinae Kormilev. In consummating these hierarchic changes, the subfamily Agrammatinae Douglas and Scott (formerly Serenthinae Stål) was suppressed as a synonym of Tinginae and the rank of the family Vianaididae Kormilev was lowered to that of subfamily and then, along with its generic taxa in totality, transferred to the Tingidae. The superfamily Miroidea falls in the higher hierarchial Cimicomorpha (Leston et al. 1954).

For almost a century, catalogs, synopses, textbooks, and other publications had either treated the Piesmatidae as a subfamily of Tingidae (Stål 1874, Horváth 1906) or as a separate family. Reuter (1912, pp. 49, 56) classified the Piesmatidae and Tingidae together in the superfamily Tingitoidea. Recently, Leston et al. (1954) and Drake and Davis (1958, 1960) have clearly shown that these two families are not so closely related to each other and that they belong to different familial groups, the Piesmatidae to the Pentamorpha and the Tingidae, as stated above, to the Cimicomorpha. Among the structural differences between these families, it should be noted that the Piesmatidae (genus *Piesma*, ventral sterna V, VI) possess trichobothria on the underside of the abdomen, whereas trichobothrial hairs are lacking in the Tingidae.

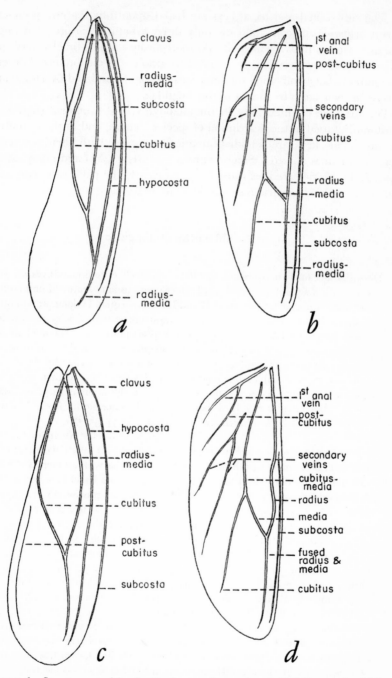

FIGURE 6.—Structures used in classification: *a*, *Cantacader afzelii* Stål, venation of forewing; *b*, same venation of hindwing; *c*, *Tingis cardui* (Linnaeus), venation of forewing; *d*, same venation of hindwing.

The subfamilial and tribal keys are based upon fully mature specimens, are worldwide in scope, and use only those structural features that apply equally well to individuals of all species regardless of sex, brachyptery (pls. 1, 45) or machroptery (pl. 46), and distribution. As dichotomized herein, the authors have embodied the higher categories formulated by Drake and Davis in their basic treatment of the Tingidae.

For the sake of uniformity in tingitaxonymy, the structures (figs. 1–6) customarily used in the description of species, genera, and in the formation of taxonomic keys are semidiagramatically figured with their respective technical names affixed. Some nymphs (pls. 31, 33, 37) and many adults (pls. 2, 43, 52, 54) are illustrated to depict clearly the habitus of representative forms found in various subfamilies and tribes.

Key to Subfamilies of Tingidae

1. Dorsal surface finely to coarsely punctate, never lacelike; compound eyes vestigial, each with a small number of poorly developed, usually scattered ommatidia; antenna with segment I shortest, II and III nearly equal, IV longest; pronotum without discal carinae, each lateral margin above with a very narrow low ridge; scutellum fairly large, triangular, exposed; ostiole and furcated ostiolar canal unusually prominent, somewhat Y-shaped, the vertical sulcus furnished with a backward projecting branch; evaporatorium enormously developed, covering entire metapleuron, hind part of mesopleuron, and then extending downward on the respective thoracic sterna to the laminar ridge of rostral sulcus; abdominal sterna II through IV fused, other sterna free. Macropterous form unknown. Myrmecetophiles (pls. 53, 54, 55, 56).

Subfamily VIANAIDINAE Kormilev (p. 443)
   Dorsal surface finely to coarsely lacelike; compound eyes fully developed; each with a large number of normal ommatidia; antenna with segment I slightly to much longer than II, II usually shortest, sometimes I and II subequal, III customarily longest, rarely III and IV subequal lengthwise, IV commonly moderately long; pronotum rarely noncarinate (pl. 1), almost always carinate with carinae present in combinations of one (pls. 4, 14), three (pls. 3, 5, 9), or five (pl. 6); scutellum small, exposed (pl. 2) or concealed (pls. 10, 12, 13) beneath hind margin or backward process of pronotum; ostiole and ostiolar canal of each metapleuron either present or absent, when present (figs. 1a, 3) with a slightly arcuate, nonbranching, nearly vertical canal, without distinct evaporatorium; abdominal sterna II and III fused, other sterna free. Pterygopolymorphic forms found in many species..........................2

2. Head always long, much produced in front of compound eyes, nearly porrect, unarmed or armed with one to nine tubercular or spiniform processes; bucculae long, wide, straight, with anterior ends extending forward beyond apex of clypeus, or shorter with ends curved inward and more or less meeting mesad in front of labium; antenna with segments I and II always short, apex of latter not reaching apex of clypeus; pronotum rarely noncarinate (pl. 1),

usually carinate with carinae arranged in combinations of one (pl. 4), three (pl. 5), or five (pl. 6); hind margin of pronotum little produced backward, wide, slightly sinuately or obtusely angulately truncate, never triangularly prolonged backward; scutellum small, either exposed or covered by hind margin of pronotum; clavus large, well developed, always entirely visible (pl. 2), often more or less fused with discoidal area (pl. 4); abdominal sterna II and III fused, other sterna free.

Subfamily CANTACADERINAE Stål (p. 22)

Head either (1) very short (pl. 50), only slightly produced in front of compound eyes, sharply declivent in front; antennal segment I mostly surpassing apex of clypeus (pls. 9, 10), or, (2) very long (pl. 51), subporrect, much produced in front of compound eyes, apex of antennal segment I and sometimes also that of II not surpassing apex of clypeus (pl. 51); unarmed or armed with one to five (rarely seven) tubercular or spinelike processes; bucculae either (1) short, with anterior ends not extending beyond lateral sides of labium, or, (2) long, with ends curved inward and almost or meeting mesad in front of labium; pronotum carinate, carinae present in combinations of either one (pls. 7, 14, 40) or three (pls. 9, 12); hind margin of pronotum triangularly prolonged backward (pl. 10), occasionally with apex much abbreviated, always completely covering scutellum and clavi of elytra in resting posture; abdominal sterna II and III fused, other sterna free.

Subfamily TINGINAE Laporte (p. 42)

The cantacaderines comprise a moderately large, sharply defined group and represent the oldest of the living lacebugs. Of the 21 known genera, *Phatnoma* is the only genus shared by the Old and New Worlds. The subfamily is unknown in the Americas north of Mexico.

Key to Tribes of Cantacaderinae

Elytron with a narrow, uniseriate stenocostal area lying between the costal area and outer margin of elytron (fig. 4; pls. 5, 6) . . . . . CANTACADERINI Stål (p. 22)
Elytron without stenocostal area, the outer margin of costal area forming the exterior boundary of elytron (fig. 5; pls. 2, 4).

PHATNOMINI Drake and Davis (p. 30)

The tingines excel by far the other subfamilies both in number of species and populations, and are well represented in all continents. Almost all the lacebugs that live at the expense of cultivated, decorative, and wild plants of importance in human welfare belong to this subfamily. The tribes may be separated thus:

Key to Tribes of Tinginae

1. Head very long, greatly prolonged in front of compound eyes, subporrect; apex of antennal segment I (sometimes also that of II) not surpassing apex of clypeus (pls. 51, 52) . . . . YPSOTINGINI, new tribe (p. 428)

Head very short, little produced in front of compound eyes, sharply declivent; antennal segment I surpassing by most of its length the apex of clypeus (pls. 9, 39) 2

2. All tarsi slender, segment II at most only slightly swollen (pls. 9, 29).
TINGINI Laporte (p. 42)

All tarsi greatly swollen; segment II enormously swollen, nearly ovate in outline, upper surface convex, beneath deeply concave, the concavity filled with short, bristlelike hairs (pls. 7, 8) . . . . LITADEINI, new tribe (p. 42)

The vianaidines are indigenous in the Neotropical region and known only from there. Four species are described, all being found inside the subterranean nests and underground passageways of ants. As to the natural history and relation between the vianaidines and ants, very little is known. All species are myrmecophiles with obsolete ommatidia, and perhaps blind. The ostiole and ostiolar canal are very prominent and provided with an extremely large evaporatorium (pl. 56).

Key to Genera and Species of Vianaidinae

1. Broadly ovate, widest behind middle of elytra, there width about two-thirds that of median length; paranotum and costal area wide, equally explanate, each with large rounded punctures, base of pronotum and elytron distinctly punctate; hypocostal lamina wide, obtusely angulately widened near base, there biseriate, thence posteriorly uniseriate (pl. 53).
Thaumamannia manni Drake and Davis (p. 444)

Elongate-ovate, elytra at widest point less than half the median length; paranotum and costal area absent; posterior part of pronotum and elytron distinctly punctate; hypocostal lamina very narrow (usually mistaken for costal area), composed of one row of tiny punctures 2

2. Backward branch of the vertical ostiolar canal situated only slightly above the hind acetabulum so as to divide the posterior part of the metapleural evaporatorium into unequal divisions (pl. 56).
Anommatocoris zeteki Drake and Froeschner (p. 444)

Backward branch of the vertical ostiolar canal placed higher on the metapleural evaporatorium so as to divide the evaporatorium into two nearly equal divisions 3

3. Compound eyes with only a small cluster of poorly developed ommatidia; elytron finely punctate for most of its length, shortly pubescent (pl. 55).
Anommatocoris coleopteratus (Kormilev) (p. 444)

Compound eyes with a few scattered, almost obsolete ommatidia; elytron punctate on basal part, thence posteriorly impunctate, inconspicuously pubescent (pl. 54) . . . . *Anommatocoris minutissimus* China (p. 444)

In this catalog an attempt has been made to record the scientific names and technical literature published on lacebugs since the beginning of systematic entomology, which dates from the publication of Linnaeus' Systema Naturae, 10th edition, 1758.

A uniform method is followed in citing references. In the text and synonymies the name of the author is followed by a year and page reference, with the full title appearing in the complete bibliography at the end of the text. In case an author has published more than one paper in a given year, the chronologic order is indicated in every case by an alphabetic affixation to the years.

The three subfamilies of Tingidae, their respective tribes, and the genera within the tribes are arranged in alphabetical sequence, each in their respective categories. The species are likewise arranged in alphabetic order in their respective genera. Synonyms, homonyms, and other errata are arranged chronologically under the valid specific name. Citations to other catalogs, faunal lists, monographs, and keys to genera or species are included in the generic citations. In addition to the original and later descriptions, specific citations include references to illustrations, morphology, biology, ecology, host plants, and distribution. Distributional records are in summary by countries. The original technical name of the type species of a genus always precedes the list of species. All elements in boldface type are regarded as of equal taxonomic value.

The incorporation of references dealing with biology, morphology, and plant injury as well as those concerned with systematic entomology makes the catalog a wide source of subject matter in different technical spheres.

To obtain the full literature for any one species, the generic references as well as those beneath the specific name should always be checked. The specific references occurring in such publications as catalogs, lists of species, and keys are listed beneath the generic names but not always beneath the trivial unless illustrations or morphologic or biologic data are involved. This combination of references (generic plus specific) includes the important citations to each species.

Information on the type (holotype or lectotype) specimen is recorded when it was included in the original description, published later, or obtainable from an institutional deposition. As will be noted in the text, the type specimens of a considerable number of species are either "lost" or "unknown." For full account of the history and type fixation of tingid genera, consult "Lacebug Genera of the World" (Drake and Ruhoff 1960a).

The information on type locality is included as it was written in the original description or as it appears on the locality label of the type specimen. Political divisions, created by events in human history of the present day, have made it ever difficult to keep pace with the changes in the names of localities and countries for distributional records. Our efforts in up-to-dateness have not been entirely successful. However, for such information we have followed the maps recently published by the National Geographic Society (Washington, D.C.), The Columbia Lippincott Gazetteer of the World, Webster's Geographic Dictionary (rev. ed., 1957), and information, current and historical, obtained from the Division of Philately and Postal

History of the United States National Museum. In the case of the Union of Soviet Socialist Republics, due to the uncertainties in some geographic boundaries, it will be noted that both general areas (Caucasus, Crimea, Siberia, etc.) and separate republics (Latvia, Dagestan, etc.) are used. The term "Ostindien," as used by Fieber (1844), is vague and can refer to either the East Indies or eastern India. Specimens from the Fieber collection deposited in the Naturhistorisches Museum, Vienna, bear simply the label "Ostindien."

As used in the text of this catalog, an asterisk (*) placed just before the scientific name means that the species is represented in the U.S. National Museum and a dagger (†) indicates that it is a fossil species. Symbols or marks used in the index only are explained immediately beneath the index caption.

Of the 1,820 valid species cataloged herein, 1,491 species are represented in the U.S. National Museum. This number includes 669 holotypes (or lectotypes) (of which 586 are in the Carl J. Drake collection and 83 in the Museum collection). The Drake collection contains 1,482 different species of lacebugs, of which 945 species are represented by a type of some kind.

Acknowledgments

For the loan of and comparison of Tingidae in their respective museums, the authors express here their most grateful thanks to Dr. S. L. Tuxen, Universitetets Zoologiske Museum, Copenhagen; Dr. E. Kjellander, Naturhistoriska Riksmuseet, Stockholm; Dr. W. E. China and Mr. R. J. Izzard, British Museum (Natural History), London; Dr. Max Beier, Naturhistorisches Museum, Vienna; Dr. Jacques Carayon, Museum National d'Histoire Naturelle, Paris; Dr. Ludvig Hoberlandt, Národni Museum, Prague; Dr. Henri Schouteden, Musée Royal de l'Afrique Centrale, Tervuren, Belgium; Dr. John W. Beardsley, Experiment Station, Hawaiian Sugar Planters Association, Honolulu, Hawaii; Dr. J. Linsley Gressitt, Bishop Museum, Honolulu, Hawaii; Dr. Hugh B. Leech, California Academy of Sciences, San Francisco, Calif.; Dr. L. Kocher, Institut Scientifique Cherifien, Rabat, Morocco.

Also to Dr. Richard Froeschner and Dr. Reece I. Sailer, U.S. Department of Agriculture, and Dr. J. F. G. Clarke, U.S. National Museum, for helpful suggestions and reading parts of the manuscript; Mr. Curtis Sabrosky, U.S. Department of Agriculture, for solving numerous nomenclatorial problems and interpreting the Code of Zoological Nomenclature; Dr. Syoiti Miyamoto, Kyushu University, Fukuoka, Japan, for microfilms and for translations of papers written in Japanese; Dr. John J. Wurdack, U.S. National Museum, Department of Botany, for checking the botanical names and placing them into families; and to Mr. Theodore B. Ruhoff,

U.S. National Museum, Division of Philately and Postal History, for assistance with geographical problems.

For the fine illustrations we are indebted to Elsie Froeschner and Caroline Lutz, both of Arlington, Va.; Maria Lisa Biganzoli and Elinor Stromberg, both of Washington, D.C.; Patricia and Robert Hogue, Alexandria, Va.; and to Arthur Smith, British Museum (Natural History), London.

Special acknowledgment is also due to Emily Bennett and Ruth Blanchard and the staff of the Smithsonian Institution Library for assistance in locating and obtaining sources of references; and for translations of papers in foreign languages, we are indebted to the late Ruth Ericson, translator, U.S. Department of Agriculture. Mr. John S. Lea and Mrs. Mary M. Ingraham, of the Smithsonian editorial staff, have been most cooperative and helpful with suggestions on format and in seeing the manuscript through the press.

This work was supported in part by National Science Foundation Grant 18721.

Family TINGIDAE Laporte

CIMICIDES Latreille 1807, p. 126 (*Tingis*, p. 139).
GEOCORISES Latreille 1829, p. 201.
TINGIDITES Laporte 1833, p. 47.
TINGIDAE Westwood 1840a, p. 447; 1840b, p. 120.—Lethierry and Severin 1896, pp. 1, 4.—China and Miller 1955, p. 261; 1959, pp. 9, 34.—Drake and Ruhoff 1960a, p. 3.—Drake and Davis 1960, p. 4 (morphology and higher classification).
DUCTIROSTRI, Group TINGIDES Amyot and Serville 1843, pp. 285, 295.
TINGIDITAE Spinola 1852b, p. 27.
TINGIDIDAE Fieber 1861, pp. 35, 116, 400.—Oshanin 1908, p. 395.
TINGITIDEA Costa 1863, p. 6.
TINGITIDAE Stål 1873, pp. 115, 116.—Horváth 1906a, p. 1; 1911d, p. 14.—Oshanin 1912, p. 42.—China 1943, p. 245.

Subfamily CANTACADERINAE Stål

CANTACADERARIA Stål 1873, p. 116.—Horváth 1906a, p. 10.—Oshanin 1908, p. 400 (as divisions).
CANTACADERINI Champion 1897, p. 2 (as group).
CANTACADERARIA Oshanin 1912, p. 42 (as tribe).
CANTACADERINAE Stichel 1926, p. 103.—China and Miller 1959, p. 34.—Drake and Ruhoff 1960a, p. 26.—Drake and Davis 1960, pp. 74, 75.
TYPE GENUS: *Cantacader* Amyot and Serville.

Tribe CANTACADERINI Stål

Cantacaderini Drake and Davis 1960, p. 77.
TYPE GENUS: *Cantacader* Amyot and Serville.

Genus ALLOCADER Drake

Allocader Drake 1950a, pp. 156, 163.—Drake and Ruhoff 1960a, p. 26.
TYPE SPECIES: *Cantacader leai* Hacker.
*Allocader cordatus (Hacker)
   Phatnoma cordata Hacker 1927, p. 19, fig. 9 [Queensland].
   Cantacader cordatus: Hacker 1928, p. 174.
   Allocader cordata: Drake 1950a, p. 156.
TYPE: Sex unknown; National Park, Queensland, Australia; Queensland Mus.
DISTRIBUTION: Australia (Queensland).
HOST PLANT: Unrecorded.

22

*Allocader leai (Hacker)

Cantacader leai Hacker 1928, p. 176, pl. 20, fig. 3 [Tasmania].

Allocader leai: Drake 1950a, p. 156.

TYPE: Sex unknown; Hobart, Tasmania, Australia; Queensland Mus.

DISTRIBUTION: Australia (Tasmania).

HOST PLANT: Unrecorded.

NOTE: Myrmecophile; adults and nymphs taken in nest of *Amblyopone australis* Erichson [Hacker].

Allocader nesiotes Drake and Ruhoff

Allocader nesiotes Drake and Ruhoff 1962b, p. 249, pl. 7, fig. 2 [Lord Howe].

TYPE: Holotype ♂, brachypterous; Lord Howe Island; So. Austr. Mus.

DISTRIBUTION: Australia (Lord Howe Island).

HOST PLANT: Unrecorded.

Genus CANTACADER Amyot and Serville

Cantacader Amyot and Serville 1843, p. 299.—Stål 1873, p. 116; 1874, p. 46.—Lethierry and Severin 1896, p. 4.—Distant 1903b, p. 123.—Horváth 1906a, p. 10.—Oshanin 1908, p. 400; 1912, p. 42.— Stichel 1935, p. 348; 1938a, p. 404; 1960a, p. 268; 1960b, p. 390; 1960c, p. 129.—Drake 1950a, p. 163.—Drake and Ruhoff 1960a, p. 26.

Taphrostethus Fieber 1844, p. 40.—Drake and Ruhoff 1960a, p. 30.

TYPE SPECIES: *Piesma quadricornis* Le Peletier and Serville.

*Cantacader abdivitus Drake

Cantacader abdivitus Drake 1950a, p. 161 [Queensland].

TYPE: Holotype ♀, macropterous; Redlynch, Queensland, Australia; Drake Coll. (USNM).

DISTRIBUTION: Australia (Queensland).

HOST PLANT: Unrecorded.

*Cantacader afzelii Stål   FIGURE 6*a, b*

Cantacader afzelii Stål 1873, p. 116 [Sierra Leone].—Lethierry and Severin 1896, p. 4 [Guinea].—Distant 1902a, p. 238, pl. 15, fig. 3.— Schouteden 1923, p. 83 [Congo].—Mancini 1939c, p. 308 [Somalia]; 1956b, p. 78 [Ethiopia].—Drake 1958a, p. 101 [Kenya; Angola; Ivory Coast; Ghana]; 1958b, p. 25.—Drake and Mamet 1956, p. 300 [Mauritius].—Mamet 1957, p. 56.

TYPE: Holotype ♂; Sierra Leone; Stockholm Mus.

DISTRIBUTION: Guinea; Sierra Leone; Ivory Coast; Liberia; Ghana; Ethiopia; Somalia; Kenya; Congo; Angola; Mascarene Islands (Mauritius).

HOST PLANT: Unrecorded.

NOTE: Taken at light [Drake 1958a].

*Cantacader agilis Drake
  Cantacader agilis Drake 1951, p. 166 [Deslac]; 1960, p. 341.
  TYPE: Holotype ♂; Deslac Island; Hungarian Mus.
  DISTRIBUTION: New Guinea Territory (Deslac Island; Northeast New Guinea).
  HOST PLANT: Unrecorded.

*Cantacader agilis var. tricarinatus Drake
  Cantacader agilis var. *tricarinata* Drake 1951, p. 167 [Deslac]; 1960, p. 342.
  TYPE: Holotype ♂, macropterous; Deslac Island; Hungarian Mus.
  DISTRIBUTION: New Guinea Territory (Deslac Island; Northeast New Guinea).
  HOST PLANT: Unrecorded.

*Cantacader amydis Drake   FIGURE 4b
  Cantacader amydis Drake 1960, p. 343, fig. 2 [Normanby].
  TYPE: Holotype ♀, macropterous; Wakaiuna, Normanby; Amer. Mus.
  DISTRIBUTION: D'Entrecasteaux Islands (Normanby; Fergusson).
  HOST PLANT: Unrecorded.

Cantacader angulipennis Horváth
  Cantacader quadricornis (not Le Peletier and Serville): Fieber 1861, p. 118 [Spain].
  Cantacader angulipennis Horváth 1906a, p. 12, fig. 3.—Lindberg 1960a, p. 13 [Tenerife].
  TYPE: Spain; sex and deposition of type unknown.
  DISTRIBUTION: Spain; Canary Islands (Tenerife).
  HOST PLANT: Unrecorded.

Cantacader attenuatus Distant
  Cantacader attenuatus Distant 1902a, p. 238 [Cape Province].
  Cantacader attenuatis [sic]: Drake 1950a, p. 163.
  TYPE: Sex unknown; Cape Colony, South Africa; British Mus.
  DISTRIBUTION: South Africa (Cape Province).
  HOST PLANT: Unrecorded.

†Cantacader avitus Drake
  Cantacader avitus Drake 1950a, p. 161, fig. 3 [fossil].—Drake and Ruhoff 1960a, p. 11.
  TYPE: Holotype, sex undeterminable; fossilized in Baltic amber; MCZ.
  DISTRIBUTION: Fossil.

*Cantacader basilewskyi Schouteden
  Canthacader [sic] *basilewskyi* Schouteden 1955b, p. 163 [Ruanda-Urundi]; 1957c, p. 312.
  Cantacader basilewski [sic]: Drake 1958a, p. 102 [Congo; Angola].
  TYPE: Sex unknown; Ruanda; Cent. Afr. Mus.
  DISTRIBUTION: Ruanda-Urundi; Congo; Angola.
  HOST PLANT: Unrecorded.

*Cantacader claratis Drake

Cantacader claratis Drake 1950a, p. 160, fig. 2 [Malaya].

TYPE: Holotype ♀, macropterous; Perak, Federation of Malaya; Drake Coll. (USNM).

DISTRIBUTION: Federation of Malaya.

HOST PLANT: Unrecorded.

*Cantacader diffidentis Drake and Poor

Cantacader diffidentis Drake and Poor 1936b, p. 141 [India].

TYPE: Holotype ♂, macropterous; New Forest, Dehra Dun, India; Drake Coll. (USNM).

DISTRIBUTION: Greater Sunda Islands (Java); India.

HOST PLANT: Unrecorded.

*Cantacader divisus Bergroth

Cantacader divisus Bergroth 1908, p. 108 [Ethiopia].—Drake 1955b, p. 85 [Angola]; 1958b, p. 26 [Kenya; Tanganyika; Congo].—Mancini 1956b, p. 78.

Cantacader dividus [sic]: Drake 1950a, p. 163.

TYPE: Ethiopia; sex and deposition of type unknown.

DISTRIBUTION: Ethiopia; Kenya; Tanganyika; Congo; Angola.

HOST PLANT: Unrecorded.

*Cantacader formosus Drake

Cantacader formosus Drake 1950a, p. 159 [Taiwan].

TYPE: Holotype ♂, macropterous; Formosa; Drake Coll. (USNM).

DISTRIBUTION: Taiwan.

HOST PLANT: Unrecorded.

Cantacader gerardi Schouteden

Canthacader [sic] *gerardi* Schouteden 1955b, p. 162 [Congo].

TYPE: Sex unknown; Mulungu, Nyunzu, Katanga, Belgian Congo; Cent. Afr. Mus.

DISTRIBUTION: Congo.

HOST PLANT: Unrecorded.

*Cantacader infuscatus Distant

Cantacader infuscatus Distant 1903b, p. 124 [Burma].

TYPE: Sex unknown; Rangoon, Burma; British Mus.

DISTRIBUTION: Burma; India.

HOST PLANT: Unrecorded.

Cantacader insularis Drake

Cantacader insularis Drake 1957e, p. 399, fig. 1 [Reunion].

TYPE: Holotype ♀; Plaine des Cafres, Réunion; Madagascar Sci. Inst.

DISTRIBUTION: Mascarene Islands (Reunion); Malagasy Republic.

HOST PLANT: Unrecorded.

*Cantacader japanicus Drake

> *Cantacader japanicus* Drake 1947d, p. 225, fig. [Japan; Viet-Nam; Thailand]; 1947f, fig. 68 (color).
>
> *Cantacader japonicus* [sic]: Takeya 1951a, p. 5.

TYPE: Holotype ♂, macropterous; Shimabara Peninsula, Japan; Drake Coll. (USNM).

DISTRIBUTION: Japan; Viet-Nam; Thailand.

HOST PLANT: Unrecorded.

*Cantacader laratanus Drake

> *Cantacader laratanus* Drake 1947d, p. 226 [Larat].

TYPE: Holotype ♂, macropterous; Larat, South Pacific; Drake Coll. (USNM).

DISTRIBUTION: Tanimbar Islands (Larat).

HOST PLANT: Unrecorded.

Cantacader laticollis Horváth

> *Cantacader quadricornis* var. *staudingeri* (not von Baerensprung): Puton 1879c, p. 88 [Algeria].
>
> *Cantacader laticollis* Horváth 1906a, p. 11, fig. 1.

TYPE: Sex unknown; Bône, Algeria; Paris Mus.

DISTRIBUTION: Algeria.

HOST PLANT: Unrecorded.

*Cantacader lethierryi Scott

> *Cantacader lethierryi* Scott 1874, pp. 291, 443 [Japan].—Uhler 1896, p. 265.—Esaki 1932, p. 1634, fig.; 1954, p. 235, fig. 606.—Drake 1950a, p. 164 [China].—Takeya 1951a, p. 5; 1953d, p. 167.

TYPE: Sex unknown; Japan; British Mus.

DISTRIBUTION: Japan; China.

HOST PLANT: Unrecorded.

*Cantacader nocturnis Hacker

> *Cantacader nocturnis* Hacker 1929, p. 324, pl. 32, fig. 1 [Queensland].—Drake 1960, p. 341 [New Guinea].
>
> *Cantacader nocturnus* [sic]: Drake 1950a, p. 164.

TYPE: Sex unknown; Brisbane, Queensland, Australia; Queensland Mus.

DISTRIBUTION: Australia (Queensland); New Guinea (Northeast).

HOST PLANT: Unrecorded.

NOTE: Taken at light [Hacker].

*Cantacader quadricornis (Le Peletier and Serville)

> *Piesma quadricornis* Le Peletier and Serville 1828, p. 653.—Brullé 1835, p. 343.
>
> *Cantacader quadricornis:* Amyot and Serville 1843, p. 299 [Spain].—Puton 1879c, p. 88 [France; Corsica; Greece; Caucasus].—Bolivar and Chicote 1879, p. 166.—Horváth 1906a, p. 12 [Algeria; Mauritania].—Oshanin 1908, p. 400 [Crimea; Morocco].—Moroder Sala 1920, p. 12.—de Seabra 1931, pp. 410, 444, figs. 482, 483 [Portu-

gal].—Vidal 1937, p. 197.—Gulde 1938, p. 241, fig.—Drake 1950a, p. 164 [Turkey].—Kiritshenko 1951, p. 243, fig. 323.—Mancini 1952, p. 12.—Priesner and Alfieri 1953, p. 63 [Egypt].—Gomez-Menor 1956a, p. 109, fig. 5 (fig. only); 1956b, p. 81, fig.—Drake and Davis 1960, figs. 6, 11, 13–15, 19, 20, 24, 28.—Drake and Ruhoff 1960a, pl. 2.

Taphrostethus staudingeri von Baerensprung 1858, p. 205, pl. 2, fig. 10.
Cantacader staudingeri: Fieber 1861, p. 118.—Ferrari 1878, p. 65.—Jakovlev 1880b, p. 99.
Cantacader staudingeri var. *doriae* Ferrari 1874, p. 169 [Italy].
Cantacader cuadricornis [sic]: González 1948, p. 49.
Cantacader quadricornis quadricornis: Stichel 1960a, p. 268, fig. 32.

TYPE: Unknown.
DISTRIBUTION: Portugal; Spain; France; Corsica; Italy; Greece; Turkey; U.S.S.R. (Crimea; Caucasus); Egypt; Algeria; Morocco; Mauritania.
HOST PLANT: Unrecorded.
NOTE: Taken at light [Priesner and Alfieri].

*Cantacader quadricornis var. nubilis Horváth

Cantacader quadricornis var. *nubilis* Horváth 1906a, p. 12, fig. 2 [Caucasus; Turkey].—Kiritshenko 1951, p. 243.—Priesner and Alfieri 1953, p. 63 [Egypt].—Hoberlandt 1955, p. 86.
Cantacader quadricornis nubilus [sic]: Stichel 1960a, p. 268.

TYPE: Unknown.
DISTRIBUTION: U.S.S.R. (Caucasus); Turkey; Egypt.
HOST PLANT: Unrecorded.
NOTE: Taken at light [Priesner and Alfieri].

†Cantacader quinquecarinatus (Germar and Berendt)

Tingis quinquecarinata Germar and Berendt 1856, p. 23, pl. 3, fig. 19 [fossil].
Eotingis quinquecarinata: Scudder 1890, p. 359; 1891, pp. 406, 449 [Horizon: Ligurian].
Cantacader quinquecarinatus: Drake and Ruhoff 1960a, p. 10.

TYPE: Sex undeterminable; fossilized in Prussian amber; deposition of type unknown.
DISTRIBUTION: Fossil.

*Cantacader quinquecostatus (Fieber)

Taphrostethus quinquecostatus Fieber 1844, p. 41, pl. 3, figs. 18–22 [Ostindien].—Herrich-Schaeffer 1850, p. 150, pl. 311, figs. c–e.—Walker 1873b, p. 2 [India].
Monanthia subovata Motschulsky 1863, p. 91 [Ceylon].—Kirby 1891, p. 109.
Cantacader subovatus: Stål 1873, p. 116.
Cantacader quinquecostatus: Stål 1873, p. 117.—Distant 1903b, p. 123, fig. 88; 1910a, p. 100.—Kirkaldy 1908c, p. 12.—Horváth 1912c, p. 341

[Java; Sumatra]; 1926, p. 327 [Malaya].—Bergroth 1921, p. 103.—
Drake and Poor 1936b, p. 141; 1937a, p. 1 [Philippines].—Blöte
1945, p. 78.—Drake 1956d, p. 106, fig. 1 [Penang; Palau].—Drake
and Davis 1960, fig. 25.—Drake 1960, p. 341, fig. 1 [New Guinea].

TYPE: "Ostindien"; sex and deposition of type unknown.

DISTRIBUTION: India; Ceylon; Burma; Greater Sunda Islands (Java;
Sumatra); New Guinea; Federation of Malaya; Penang Island; Philippine
Islands; Palau Islands.

HOST PLANT: Unrecorded.

NOTE: Taken at light [Distant 1910a].

*Cantacader tener Bergroth   PLATE 6

Cantacader tener Bergroth 1894, p. 167 [Malagasy].—Drake 1958c, p. 315.
Cantacader tenei [sic]: Drake 1950a, p. 164.

TYPE: Holotype ♂; Madagascar; deposition unknown.

DISTRIBUTION: Malagasy Republic; Kenya.

HOST PLANT: Unrecorded.

*Cantacader tenuipes Stål

Cantacader tenuipes Stål 1865, p. 26 [Sierra Leone]; 1873, p. 116.—
Distant 1902a, p. 238, pl. 15, fig. 2.—Schouteden 1923, p. 83
[Congo].—Mancini 1949a, p. 229 [Somalia].—Drake 1954e, p. 1;
1957a, p. 415 [Aden]; 1958a, p. 102 [Guinea; Angola]; 1958b, p. 26
[Kenya; Ghana].

TYPE: Holotype ♂; Sierra Leone; Stockholm Mus.

DISTRIBUTION: Aden Protectorate; Somalia; Sierra Leone; Guinea;
Ghana (?); Congo; Angola; Kenya.

HOST PLANT: Unrecorded.

NOTE: Taken at light [Drake 1958a].

Cantacader tenuipes var. **furtivus** Drake

Cantacader tenuipes var. infuscatus Schouteden 1916b, p. 290 [Congo];
1923, p. 83.

Cantacader tenuipes var. furtivus Drake 1950a, p. 153 [Republique du
Congo].

TYPE: Sex unknown; Vankerckhovenville, Belgian Congo; Cent. Afr.
Mus.

DISTRIBUTION: Congo; Republique du Congo.

HOST PLANT: Unrecorded.

*Cantacader uniformis Distant

Cantacader uniformis Distant 1902b, p. 353 [India]; 1903b, p. 124.—
Drake 1950a, p. 164 [Burma].

TYPE: Sex unknown; India; British Mus.

DISTRIBUTION: India; Burma.

HOST PLANT: Unrecorded.

Cantacader vandenplasi Schouteden

Cantacader vandenplasi Schouteden 1923, p. 83 [Congo].

TYPE: Sex unknown; Belgian Congo; Cent. Afr. Mus.

DISTRIBUTION: Congo.

HOST PLANT: Unrecorded.

Genus CERATOCADER Drake

Ceratocader Drake 1950a, pp. 157, 164.—Drake and Ruhoff 1960a, p. 27.

TYPE SPECIES: *Cantacader armatus* Hacker.

*Ceratocader armatus (Hacker) PLATE 5

Cantacader armatus Hacker 1928, p. 174, pl. 20, fig. 1 [South Australia].

Ceratocader armatus: Drake 1950a, pp. 158, 164.—Drake and Davis 1960, fig. 30.

TYPE: Sex unknown; Murray Bridge, South Australia, Australia; Queensland Mus.

DISTRIBUTION: Australia (South Australia).

HOST PLANT: Unrecorded.

Ceratocader dentatus (Hacker)

Cantacader dentatus Hacker 1928, p. 175, pl. 20, fig. 2 [Tasmania].

Ceratocader dentatus: Drake 1950a, pp. 158, 164.

TYPE: Sex unknown; Burnie, Tasmania, Australia; Queensland Mus.

DISTRIBUTION: Australia (Tasmania).

HOST PLANT: Unrecorded.

Genus NECTOCADER Drake

Nectocader Drake 1928a, p. 41; 1944b, p. 141; 1950a, p. 165.—Monte 1937d, p. 111; 1941e, p. 71.—Drake and Ruhoff 1960a, p. 28.

TYPE SPECIES: *Cantacader gounellei* Drake.

*Nectocader gounellei (Drake)

Cantacader gounellei Drake 1923b, p. 81, fig. 1 [Brazil].

Nectocader gounellei: Drake 1928a, p. 42.—Drake and Hambleton 1934, p. 436.—Monte 1937a, p. 30, fig. 1 [*Vernonia*]; 1937d, p. 112, fig. 10; 1939b, p. 63.

TYPE: Holotype ♂, macropterous; Novo Friburgo, near Rio de Janeiro, Brazil; Drake Coll. (USNM).

DISTRIBUTION: Brazil.

HOST PLANT: *Vernonia* sp.

Genus TERATOCADER Drake

Teratocader Drake 1950a, pp. 158, 166.—Drake and Ruhoff 1960a, p. 30.

TYPE SPECIES: *Cantacader magnificus* Drake.

*Teratocader magnificus (Drake)

Cantacader magnifica Drake 1923b, p. 83 [Malaya].

Teratocader magnificus: Drake 1950a, pp. 158, 166.

TYPE: Holotype ♂, macropterous; Perak, Malay Peninsula; Drake Coll. (USNM).

DISTRIBUTION: Federation of Malaya.

HOST PLANT: Unrecorded.

Tribe PHATNOMINI Drake and Davis

Phatnomini Drake and Davis 1960, p. 78.

TYPE GENUS: *Phatnoma* Fieber.

Genus ALLOEODERES Drake

Alloeoderes Drake 1961a, p. 115.

TYPE SPECIES: *Alloeoderes davao* Drake.

Alloeoderes davao Drake   PLATE 1

Alloeoderes davao Drake 1961a, p. 116, fig. 43 [Mindanao].

TYPE: Holotype ♂; Mt. McKinley, Davao, Mindanao, Philippine Islands; Chicago Museum Natural History.

DISTRIBUTION: Philippine Islands (Mindanao).

HOST PLANT: Unrecorded.

Genus ANGIOCADER Drake

Angiocader Drake 1950a, pp. 159, 163.—Drake and Ruhoff 1960a, p. 26.

TYPE SPECIES: *Phatnoma obesa* Distant.

Angiocader obesus (Distant)

Phatnoma obesa Distant 1902a, p. 239, pl. 15, fig. 16 [Cape Province].

Gonycentrum obesum: Bergroth 1903, p. 297.

Sinalda obesa: Distant 1904, p. 427.

Angiocader obesus: Drake 1950a, pp. 159, 163.

TYPE: Sex unknown; Cape Colony, South Africa; British Mus.

DISTRIBUTION: South Africa (Cape Province).

HOST PLANT: Unrecorded.

Genus ASTOLPHOS Distant

Astolphos Distant 1904, p. 428.—Drake 1950a, p. 163.—Drake and Ruhoff 1960a, p. 26.

TYPE SPECIES: *Astolphos capitatus* Distant.

*Astolphos capitatus Distant

Astolphos capitatus Distant 1904, p. 429, pl. 8, fig. 5 [Cape Province].

TYPE: Sex unknown; Cape Town, South Africa; British Mus.

DISTRIBUTION: South Africa (Cape Province).

HOST PLANT: Unrecorded.

Genus CNEMIANDRUS Distant

Cnemiandrus Distant 1902a, p. 239.—Drake 1950a, p. 164.—Drake and Ruhoff 1960a, p. 27.

TYPE SPECIES: *Cnemiandrus typicus* Distant.

*Cnemiandrus typicus Distant

Cnemiandrus typicus Distant 1902a, p. 240, pl. 15, fig. 18 [Cape Province].
TYPE: Sex unknown; Cape Colony, South Africa; So. Afr. Mus.
DISTRIBUTION: South Africa (Cape Province).
HOST PLANT: Unrecorded.

Genus CYCLOTYNASPIS Montandon

Cyclotynaspis Montandon 1892, p. 265.—Lethierry and Severin 1896, p. 4.—Drake and Ruhoff 1960a, p. 27.

TYPE SPECIES: *Cyclotynaspis acalyptoides* Montandon.

Cyclotynaspis acalyptoides Montandon

Cyclotynaspis acalyptoides Montandon 1892, p. 265 [Singapore].—Drake 1955a, p. 78, fig. 25.
TYPE: Holotype ♀, brachypterous; Singapore; Bucharest Mus.
DISTRIBUTION: Singapore.
HOST PLANT: Unrecorded.
NOTE: Type specimen redescribed and figured [Drake].

Genus CYPEROBIA Bergroth

Cyperobia Bergroth 1927, p. 673.—Drake 1950a, p. 164.—Drake and Ruhoff 1960a, p. 27.

TYPE SPECIES: *Cyperobia carectorum* Bergroth.

Cyperobia carectorum Bergroth

Cyperobia carectorum Bergroth 1927, p. 674 [New Zealand; *Cassinia leptophylla;* sedges].
Cyperobia correctorum [sic]: Drake and Davis 1960, fig. 31.
TYPE: Holotype ♀; Gollan's Valley, Wellington, New Zealand; deposition unknown.
DISTRIBUTION: New Zealand.
HOST PLANTS: *Cassinia leptophylla;* sedges.

Genus EOCADER Drake and Hambleton

Eocader Drake and Hambleton 1934, p. 436; 1944b, p. 121.—Monte 1941e, p. 71; 1942d, p. 104.—Hurd 1946, p. 439.—Drake 1950a, p. 164.—Drake and Ruhoff 1960a, p. 27.
Montea Bruner 1940, p. 246.—Drake and Ruhoff 1960a, p. 28.

TYPE SPECIES: *Eocader vegrandis* Drake and Hambleton.

*Eocader bouclei (Bruner)

Montea bouclei Bruner 1940, p. 246, pl. 43 [Cuba; *Casuarina equisetifolia*].
Eocader bouclei: Monte 1942d, p. 104.—Bruner, Scaramuzza and Otero
1945, p. 33.—Hurd 1946, p. 439 [Casuarina bark].

TYPE: Holotype ♂, macropterous; Vedado, Havana, Cuba; USNM.

DISTRIBUTION: Cuba.

HOST PLANTS: *Casuarina equisetifolia;* " Casuarina bark".

*Eocader vegrandis Drake and Hambleton

Eocader vegrandis Drake and Hambleton 1934, p. 436, fig. 1 [Brazil;
Bombax munguba].—Araujo e Silva 1936, p. 7.—Costa Lima 1936,
p. 126.

TYPE: Holotype ♀, brachypterous; Viçosa, Minas Gerais, Brazil; Drake
Coll. (USNM).

DISTRIBUTION: Brazil.

HOST PLANT: *Bombax munguba.*

Genus GONYCENTRUM Bergroth

Gonycentrum Bergroth 1898, p. 9.—Distant 1903b, p. 125.—Drake 1950a,
p. 165.—Drake and Ruhoff 1960a, p. 28.
Teleia Fieber 1844, p. 55.—Walker 1873b, p. 3.—Lethierry and
Severin 1896, p. 4.—Drake and Ruhoff 1960a, p. 30.
Sinalda Distant 1904, p. 426.—Drake and Ruhoff 1960a, p. 30.

TYPE SPECIES: *Teleia coronata* Fieber.

*Gonycentrum aethiops (Distant)

Phatnoma aethiops Distant 1902a, p. 238, pl. 15, fig. 12 [Cape Province].
Gonycentrum aethiops: Bergroth 1903, p. 297.—Drake 1956f, p. 421.
Sinalda aethiops: Distant 1904, p. 427.

TYPE: Sex unknown; Cape Colony, South Africa; So. Afr. Mus.

DISTRIBUTION: South Africa (Cape Province).

HOST PLANT: Unrecorded.

*Gonycentrum afrum Drake and Ruhoff

Gonycentrum afrum Drake and Ruhoff 1961b, p. 126, fig. 1 [Cape
Province].

TYPE: Holotype ♂, macropterous; Grahamstown, South Africa; Drake
Coll. (USNM).

DISTRIBUTION: South Africa (Cape Province).

HOST PLANT: Unrecorded.

*Gonycentrum angustatum Drake

Gonycentrum angustatum Drake 1956c, p. 15 [Tanganyika].

TYPE: Holotype ♂, macropterous; Arusha, Tanganyika Territory;
Drake Coll. (USNM).

DISTRIBUTION: Tanganyika.

HOST PLANT: Unrecorded.

Gonycentrum coronatum (Fieber)

Teleia coronata Fieber 1844, p. 56, pl. 4, figs. 26–32 [Ostindien].— Herrich-Schaeffer 1850, p. 149, pl. 311, figs. 954f–k.—Stål 1873, p. 117 [India orientalis].

Gonycentrum coronatum: Distant 1903b, p. 125, fig. 89.

TYPE: "Ostindien"; sex and deposition of type unknown.

DISTRIBUTION: India.

HOST PLANT: Unrecorded.

Gonycentrum elegans (Distant)

Sinalda elegans Distant 1904, p. 427, pl. 8, fig. 2 [Cape Province].

Gonycentrum elegans: Drake 1950a, p. 165.

TYPE: Sex unknown; Cape Town, South Africa; British Mus.

DISTRIBUTION: South Africa (Cape Province).

HOST PLANT: Unrecorded.

***Gonycentrum engistum** Drake and Ruhoff

Gonycentrum engistum Drake and Ruhoff 1961b, p. 127, fig. 3* [New Guinea].

TYPE: Holotype ♀, brachypterous; Mt. Lamington, New Guinea; Drake Coll. (USNM).

DISTRIBUTION: New Guinea.

HOST PLANT: Unrecorded.

NOTE: * In Drake and Ruhoff 1961b, the illustration in figure 3 is that of *engistum*, not figure 2 as listed in text and figure citation.

***Gonycentrum nebulosum** (Distant)

Sinalda nebulosa Distant 1904, p. 428, pl. 8, fig. 4 [Cape Province].

Gonycentrum nebulosum: Drake 1950a, p. 165.

TYPE: Sex unknown; Grahamstown, Cape Colony, South Africa; British Mus.

DISTRIBUTION: South Africa (Cape Province).

HOST PLANT: Unrecorded.

***Gonycentrum reticulatum** (Distant)

Sinalda reticulata Distant 1904, p. 427, pl. 8, fig. 3 [Cape Province].

Gonycentrum reticulatum: Drake 1950a, p. 165.

TYPE: Sex unknown; Cape Colony, South Africa; So. Afr. Mus.

DISTRIBUTION: South Africa (Cape Province).

HOST PLANT: Unrecorded.

***Gonycentrum socium** Drake and Ruhoff

Gonycentrum socium Drake and Ruhoff 1961b, p. 128, fig. 2* [Tasmania]; 1962b, p. 249, pl. 7, fig. 1 [South Australia].

TYPE: Holotype ♂, brachypertous; Launceston, Tasmania, Australia; Drake Coll. (USNM).

DISTRIBUTION: Australia (Tasmania; South Australia).

HOST PLANT: Unrecorded.

NOTE: *In Drake and Ruhoff 1961b, the illustration in figure 2 is that of *socium*, not figure 3 as listed in the text and figure citation.

*Gonycentrum testaceum (Distant)

> *Phatnoma testacea* Distant 1902a, p. 238, pl. 15, fig. 13 [Cape Province].
> *Gonycentrum testaceum:* Bergroth 1903, p. 297.
> *Sinalda testacea:* Distant 1904, p. 427.

TYPE: Sex unknown; Cape Colony, South Africa; So. Afr. Mus.

DISTRIBUTION: South Africa (Cape Province).

HOST PLANT: Unrecorded.

*Gonycentrum thomasi Drake

> *Gonycentrum thomasi* Drake 1956c, p. 14 [Kenya].

TYPE: Holotype ♂, macropterous; Nairobi, Kenya Colony; Drake Coll. (USNM).

DISTRIBUTION: Kenya.

HOST PLANT: Unrecorded.

*Gonycentrum tindalei (Hacker)

> *Phatnoma tindalei* Hacker 1928, p. 177, pl. 21, fig. 5 [South Australia; moss; lichens].
> *Sinalda tindalei:* Hacker 1929, p. 333.
> *Gonycentrum tindalei:* Drake 1950a, p. 165.—Drake and Ruhoff 1962b, p. 249.

TYPE: Sex unknown; Mount Lofty Ranges, South Australia, Australia; Queensland Mus.

DISTRIBUTION: Australia (South Australia).

HOST PLANTS: Moss; lichens.

Genus MALALA Distant

> *Malala* Distant 1910a, p. 101.—Drake 1950a, p. 165.—Drake and Ruhoff 1960a, p. 28.

TYPE SPECIES: *Malala bulliens* Distant.

*Malala bulliens Distant

> *Malala bulliens* Distant 1910a, p. 101, fig. 48 [Ceylon].

TYPE: Sex unknown; Peradeniya, Ceylon; British Mus.

DISTRIBUTION: Ceylon; India.

HOST PLANTS: Tobacco; "swept from short grass."

Genus ORANOMA Drake

> *Oranoma* Drake 1951, p. 165.—Drake and Ruhoff 1960a, p. 29.

TYPE SPECIES: *Oranoma biroi* Drake.

*Oranoma biroi Drake

> *Oranoma biroi* Drake 1951, p. 166 [New Guinea]; 1960, p. 344, fig. 4.— Drake and Davis 1960, fig. 29.

Type: Holotype ♀, brachypterous; Sattelberg, Huon Gulf, New Guinea; Hungarian Mus.

Distribution: New Guinea (Northeast).

Host Plant: Unrecorded.

Genus PHATNOMA Fieber

Phatnoma Fieber 1844, p. 57.—Walker 1873b, p. 3.—Lethierry and Severin 1896, p. 5.—Champion 1897, p. 2.—Gibson 1919a, pp. 181–185 (key).—Monte 1941e, p. 72; 1946d, pp. 247–254 (key).—Drake 1944b, p. 141; 1950a, p. 165.—Hurd 1946, p. 438.—Drake and Ruhoff 1960a, p. 29.

Type Species: *Phatnoma laciniata* Fieber.

*Phatnoma agviates** Drake and Ruhoff   Figure 5

Phatnoma agviates Drake and Ruhoff 1961b, p. 130, fig. 5 [Bougainville].

Type: Holotype ♂, brachypterous; Bougainville, Solomon Islands; Drake Coll. (USNM).

Distribution: Solomon Islands (Bougainville).

Host Plant: Unrecorded.

*Phatnoma amazonica** Drake and Hambleton

Phatnoma amazonica Drake and Hambleton 1944b, p. 120 [Brazil].

Type: Holotype ♀, macropterous; Pará, Brazil; Drake Coll. (USNM).

Distribution: Brazil.

Host Plant: Unrecorded.

*Phatnoma annulipes** Champion

Phatnoma annulipes Champion 1897, p. 4, pl. 1, fig. 2 [Mexico; Guatemala; Panama].—Gibson 1919a, p. 184.—Drake and Hambleton 1945, p. 356 [Costa Rica; *Vernonia*].—Swezey 1945, p. 371 [Venezuela].—Hurd 1946, p. 438 [Peru].—Drake 1948c, p. 21.

Type: Sex unknown; Volcan de Chiriqui, Panama; British Mus.

Distribution: Mexico; Honduras; Guatemala; Costa Rica; Panama; Venezuela; Peru.

Host Plant: *Vernonia* sp.

Note: Intercepted in orchid packing from Venezuela, at port-of-entry, Washington, D.C. [Swezey].

*Phatnoma annulipes** var. **concisa** Drake

Phatnoma annulata [sic] var. *concisa* Drake 1948c, p. 21 [Venezuela].

Type: Holotype ♂, macropterous; Caracas, Venezuela; Drake Coll. (USNM).

Distribution: Venezuela.

Host Plant: Unrecorded.

*†Phatnoma baltica** Drake   Plate 3

Phatnoma baltica Drake 1950a, p. 153, fig. 1 [fossil].—Drake and Ruhoff 1960a, p. 11.

Type: Holotype ♀; fossilized in Baltic amber; Drake Coll. (USNM).

Distribution: Fossil.

*Phatnoma barberi Drake

Phatnoma barberi Drake 1941a, p. 141 [Colombia].

TYPE: Holotype ♀, macropterous; Colombia; USNM.

DISTRIBUTION: Colombia.

HOST PLANT: Unrecorded.

NOTE: Intercepted on *Cattleya schroederae* at port-of-entry, San Francisco, Calif. [Drake].

*Phatnoma costalis Distant

Phatnoma costalis Distant 1909a, p. 113 [Burma]; 1910a, p. 102, fig. 49.— Gibson 1919a, p. 184.—Drake and Poor 1936a, p. 439 [Hainan Island].

TYPE: Sex unknown; Myitta, Tenasserim, Burma; British Mus.

DISTRIBUTION: Burma; China (Hainan Island).

HOST PLANT: Unrecorded.

*Phatnoma coyazana Drake

Phatnoma coyazana Drake 1948d, p. 15 [Brazil].

TYPE: Holotype ♀, macropterous; Jutahy, Goyaz Province, Brazil; Drake Coll. (USNM).

DISTRIBUTION: Brazil.

HOST PLANT: Unrecorded.

*Phatnoma ecuadoris Drake

Phatnoma ecuadoris Drake 1941a, p. 141 [Ecuador].

TYPE: Holotype ♂, macropterous; Ecuador; USNM.

DISTRIBUTION: Ecuador.

HOST PLANT: Unrecorded.

NOTE: Intercepted on bananas at port-of-entry, New York City [Drake].

*Phatnoma guatemalana Drake

Phatnoma guatemalana Drake 1948c, p. 20 [Guatemala].

TYPE: Holotype ♀, macropterous; Guatemala City, Guatemala; USNM.

DISTRIBUTION: Guatemala.

HOST PLANT: Unrecorded.

NOTE: Intercepted on *Epidendrum cochleatum* at port-of-entry, San Francisco, Calif. [Drake].

*Phatnoma hackeri Drake

Phatnoma pacifica (not Kirkaldy): Hacker 1928, p. 176, pl. 20, fig. 4 [Australia].

Phatnoma hackeri Drake 1950a, p. 154.

TYPE: Holotype ♀, brachypterous; Cairns District, Queensland, Australia; Drake Coll. (USNM).

DISTRIBUTION: Australia (Queensland).

HOST PLANT: Unrecorded.

Phatnoma hova Schouteden
Phatnoma hova Schouteden 1957a, p. 82 [Malagasy].
TYPE: Sex unknown; Madagascar; Paris Mus.
DISTRIBUTION: Malagasy Republic.
HOST PLANT: Unrecorded.

*Phatnoma jinjana Drake
Phatnoma jinjana Drake 1956c, p. 13 [Uganda].
TYPE: Holotype ♀, macropterous; Jinja, Uganda; Drake Coll. (USNM).
DISTRIBUTION: Uganda.
HOST PLANT: Unrecorded.

Phatnoma laciniata Fieber
Phatnoma laciniata Fieber 1844, p. 57, pl. 4, figs. 33–38 [Ostindien].—
Herrich-Schaeffer 1850, p. 149, pl. 311, figs. 952a–b.—Stål 1873,
p. 117 [India orientalis].—Distant 1903b, p. 126, fig. 90 [Ceylon].—
Gibson 1919a, p. 183 [East Indies].
TYPE: "Ostindien"; sex and deposition of type unknown.
DISTRIBUTION: India; Ceylon; East Indies(?).
HOST PLANT: Unrecorded.

*Phatnoma maculata Monte
Phatnoma maculata Monte 1946d, p. 252, figs. 1, 8 [Brazil].—Kormilev
1955a, p. 63 [Argentina].
TYPE: Holotype ♀; São Paulo, Brazil; Monte Coll. (Mus. Nacional).
DISTRIBUTION: Brazil; Argentina.
HOST PLANT: Unrecorded.

*Phatnoma marmorata Champion
Phatnoma marmorata Champion 1897, p. 3, pl. 1, figs. 1, 1a [Panama].—
Gibson 1919a, p. 183.—Drake 1922c, p. 352 [Brazil].—Monte 1941d,
p. 93 [Costa Rica]; 1941e, p. 72 [Honduras; cacao].—Drake and
Hambleton 1944b, p. 120 [Trinidad; pineapple].
Phatnoma filetia Gibson 1919a, p. 185.
Phatnoma spinosa Gibson 1919a, p. 185.
TYPE: Sex unknown; David, Chiriqui, Panama; British Mus.
DISTRIBUTION: Trinidad; Honduras; Costa Rica; Panama; Brazil;
Ecuador.
HOST PLANTS: Cacao; cultivated pineapple.

Phatnoma maynei Schouteden
Phatnoma maynei Schouteden 1916b, p. 289 [Congo].
Phatnoma magnei [sic]: Drake 1950a, p. 165.
TYPE: Sex unknown; Congo da Lemba, Belgian Congo; Cent. Afr. Mus.
DISTRIBUTION: Congo.
HOST PLANT: Unrecorded.

*Phatnoma ovata Champion

Phatnoma ovata Champion 1897, p. 4, pl. 1, figs. 3, 3a [Guatemala].— Gibson 1919a, p. 182.—Monte 1943d, p. 263 [Brazil].—Drake 1944b, p. 141 [Mexico].

TYPE: Sex unknown; San Isidro, Guatemala; British Mus.

DISTRIBUTION: Mexico; Guatemala; Brazil.

HOST PLANT: Unrecorded.

*Phatnoma pacifica Kirkaldy   PLATE 2

Phatnoma pacifica Kirkaldy 1908b, p. 363 [Fiji].—Drake and Poor 1943, p. 191.

TYPE: Holotype ♀; Fiji Islands; Hawaii. Sugar Plant. Assn.

DISTRIBUTION: Fiji Islands.

HOST PLANT: Unrecorded.

*Phatnoma takasago Takeya

Phatnoma takasago Takeya 1933, p. 32, text fig. 1; pl. 3, fig. 1 [Taiwan]; 1951a, p. 6.—Drake and Poor 1939c, p. 203 [India; *Lantana*].

TYPE: Holotype ♂; Makazayazaya, Heitô, Formosa; Kyushu Univ.

DISTRIBUTION: Taiwan; India.

HOST PLANT: *Lantana* sp.

*Phatnoma togularis Drake

Phatnoma togularis Drake 1950a, p. 154 [India].

TYPE: Holotype ♀, macropterous; Dehra Dun, India; Drake Coll. (USNM).

DISTRIBUTION: India.

HOST PLANT: Unrecorded.

*Phatnoma tonkinana Drake and Maa

Phatnoma tonkinana Drake and Maa 1955, p. 1 [Viet-Nam].

TYPE: Holotype ♀, macropterous; Hoa Binh, Tonkin; Drake Coll. (USNM).

DISTRIBUTION: Viet-Nam.

HOST PLANT: Unrecorded.

*Phatnoma trinidadana Drake

Phatnoma trinidadana Drake 1948c, p. 21 [Trinidad].

TYPE: Holotype ♀, macropterous; Trinidad, British West Indies; Drake Coll. (USNM).

DISTRIBUTION: Trinidad.

HOST PLANT: Cultivated pineapple.

*Phatnoma uichancoi Drake

Phatnoma pacifica (not Kirkaldy): Drake and Poor 1937b, p. 397 [Philippines].

Phatnoma uichancoi Drake 1950a, p. 155; 1960, p. 343 [New Guinea].— Drake and Ruhoff 1962b, p. 249 [Papua].

TYPE: Holotype ♂, macropterous; Los Banos, Philippine Islands; Drake Coll. (USNM).

DISTRIBUTION: Philippine Islands (Los Banos; Mindanao); Solomon Islands; New Guinea (Papua).

HOST PLANT: Unrecorded.

*Phatnoma varians Drake

Phatnoma varians Drake 1922c, p. 352 [French Guiana].—Swezey 1945, p. 371 [Colombia].

TYPE: Holotype ♀; Env. de St. Georges, Oyapock, French Guiana; Paris Mus.

DISTRIBUTION: French Guiana; Colombia.

HOST PLANT: Unrecorded.

NOTE: Intercepted at port-of-entry, California, on *Cattleya schroederae* from Colombia [Swezey].

*Phatnoma varians var. **unicarinata** Drake

Phatnoma varians var. unicarinata Drake 1922c, p. 353 [French Guiana].

TYPE: Holotype ♀, macropterous; Env. de St. Georges, Oyapock, French Guiana; Drake Coll. (USNM).

DISTRIBUTION: French Guiana.

HOST PLANT: Unrecorded.

*Phatnoma veridica Drake and Maa

Phatnoma takasago (not Takeya): Drake 1950a, p. 156 [New Guinea].

Phatnoma veridica Drake and Maa 1955, p. 2 [Palau; Papua; *Glochidion*].—Drake 1956d, p. 107, fig. 2 [Caroline Islands]; 1960, p. 344, fig. 3 [*Pipturus*].

TYPE: Holotype ♂, macropterous; New Guinea; Drake Coll. (USNM).

DISTRIBUTION: New Guinea (Papua, Northeast; Netherlands); Palau Islands (Koror; Peleiu; Aurapusheparu; Babelthuap; Ngiramaous; Ulebsehel; Ngarmalk); Caroline Islands.

HOST PLANTS: *Pipturus* sp.; taken on bark of *Glochidion* sp.

*Phatnoma vernoniae Drake and Hambleton

Phatnoma veroniae [sic] Drake and Hambleton 1938b, p. 51, pl. 9, fig. a [Brazil; *Vernonia polyanthes*].

Phatnoma vernoniae: Monte 1942d, p. 107.

TYPE: Holotype ♂, macropterous; Campinas, São Paulo, Brazil; Drake Coll. (USNM).

DISTRIBUTION: Brazil.

HOST PLANT: *Vernonia polyanthes.*

Genus PLESIONOMA Drake

Plesionoma Drake 1950a, pp. 157, 166; 1954f, p. 2.—Drake and Ruhoff 1960a, p. 29.

TYPE SPECIES: *Phatnoma humeralis* Distant.

*Plesionoma eteosa Drake

Plesionoma eteosa Drake 1954f, p. 2 [Cape Province].

TYPE: Holotype ♂, brachypterous; Cape Recife, South Africa; Drake Coll. (USNM).

DISTRIBUTION: South Africa (Cape Province).

HOST PLANT: Unrecorded.

*Plesionoma humeralis (Distant)

Phatnoma humeralis Distant 1902a, p. 239, pl. 15, fig. 14 [Cape Province].—Bergroth 1903, p. 297.

Plesionoma humeralis: Drake 1950a, p. 157.

TYPE: Sex unknown; Cape Colony, South Africa; So. Afr. Mus.

DISTRIBUTION: South Africa (Cape Province).

HOST PLANT: Unrecorded.

Plesionoma leroyi Schouteden

Plesionoma leroyi Schouteden 1955a, p. 25 [Ruanda].

TYPE: Sex unknown; Ruanda; Cent. Afr. Mus.

DISTRIBUTION: Ruanda-Urundi.

HOST PLANT: Unrecorded.

Genus PSEUDOPHATNOMA Blöte

Pseudophatnoma Blöte 1945, p. 78.—Drake 1950a, p. 166.—Drake and Ruhoff 1960a, p. 29.

TYPE SPECIES: *Pseudophatnoma corniculata* Blöte.

Pseudophatnoma corniculata Blöte

Pseudophatnoma corniculata Blöte 1945, p. 78, fig. 1 [Rhio-Archipelago].

TYPE: Sex unknown; Durian, Rhio-Archipelago; Leiden Mus.

DISTRIBUTION: Rhio-Archipelago, Netherlands Indies.

HOST PLANT: Unrecorded.

Genus STENOCADER Drake and Hambleton

Stenocader Drake and Hambleton 1944b, p. 120.—Drake 1944b, p. 142; 1950a, p. 166.—Drake and Ruhoff 1960a, p. 30.

TYPE SPECIES: *Piesma tingidoides* Spinola.

*Stenocader tingidoides (Spinola)

Piesma tingidoides Spinola 1852a, p. 200 [Chile].—Stål 1873, p. 134.

Cantacader tingidoides: Signoret 1863, p. 575.—Walker 1873b, p. 1.—Lethierry and Severin 1896, p. 4.—Reed 1900, p. 176 (p. 86 separate).

Cantacader ? germainii Signoret 1863, p. 586.—Stål 1873, p. 134.—Walker 1873b, p. 1.

Cantacader germaini [sic]: Lethierry and Severin 1896, p. 25.—Reed 1900, p. 179 (separate, p. 86).

Nectocader germaini [sic]: Drake 1928a, p. 41.—Porter 1933, p. 236.

Nectocader tingitoides [sic]: Drake 1928a, p. 42; 1939c, p. 332.—Porter 1933, p. 236.—Monte 1937d, p. 114.

Nectocader tingidoides: Monte 1942d, p. 107.

Stenocader tingidoides: Drake and Hambleton 1944b, p. 120.

Lacebugs of the World: A Catalog
(Hemiptera: Tingidae)

C. J. Drake & F. A. Ruhoff

United states national museum

213

Smithsonian institution

Washington

1965

follow spine

color; $56 Green

TYPE: Holotype ♂; Chile; deposition unknown.
DISTRIBUTION: Chile.
HOST PLANT: Unrecorded.

Genus ULMUS Distant

Ulmus Distant 1904, p. 425.—Drake 1950a, p. 166.—Drake and Ruhoff 1960a, p. 30.

TYPE SPECIES: *Ulmus testudineatus* Distant.

*Ulmus engaeus Drake and Ruhoff

Ulmus engaeus Drake and Ruhoff 1961b, p. 129, fig. 4 [Congo].

TYPE: Holotype ♂, brachypterous; Kasango, Kivu Province, Congo; Drake Coll. (USNM).

DISTRIBUTION: Congo.
HOST PLANT: Unrecorded.

*Ulmus testudineatus Distant

Ulmus testudineatus Distant 1904, p. 426, pl. 8, figs. 1, 1a [Transvaal].—Drake 1956f, p. 421.

TYPE: Sex unknown; Pretoria District, Transvaal, South Africa; British Mus.

DISTRIBUTION: South Africa (Transvaal).
HOST PLANT: Unrecorded.

Genus ZETEKELLA Drake

Zetekella Drake 1944b, pp. 139, 142; 1950a, p. 166.—Hurd 1946, p. 439.—Drake and Ruhoff 1960a, p. 31.

Minitingis Barber 1954, p. 7.—Drake and Ruhoff 1960a, p. 28.

TYPE SPECIES: *Zetekella zeteki* Drake.

*Zetekella minuscula (Barber)

Minitingis minusculus Barber 1954, p. 7, fig. 1 [So. Bimini].

Zetekella minuscula: Drake and Ruhoff 1960a, p. 28.

TYPE: Holotype ♂; South Bimini Island, Bahamas; Amer. Mus.

DISTRIBUTION: Bahama Islands (So. Bimini Island).
HOST PLANT: Unrecorded.

*Zetekella pulla Drake and Plaumann   PLATE 4

Zetekella pulla Drake and Plaumann 1956, p. 17 [Brazil].

TYPE: Holotype ♂, macropterous; Nova Teutonia, Brazil; Drake Coll. (USNM).

DISTRIBUTION: Brazil.
HOST PLANT: Unrecorded.

*Zetekella zeteki Drake

Zetekella zeteki Drake 1944b, p. 140, fig. 1 [Canal Zone].

TYPE: Holotype ♀, brachypterous; Barro Colorado Island, Panama Canal Zone; USNM.

DISTRIBUTION: Panama (Canal Zone).
HOST PLANT: Unrecorded.

Subfamily TINGINAE Laporte

TINGIDITES Laporte 1833, p. 47.
AGRAMMIDAE Douglas and Scott 1865, pp. 24, 242 (as family).
TINGIDIDAE Douglas and Scott 1865, pp. 24, 243 (as family).
SERENTHIARIA Stål 1873, pp. 116, 117; 1874, p. 46.—Distant 1903b, p. 126.—Horváth 1906a, p. 107.—Oshanin 1908, p. 457; 1912, p. 46 (as divisions).
TINGITARIA Stål 1873, p. 118; 1874, p. 47.—Distant 1903b, p. 130.—Horváth 1906a, p. 13.—Oshanin 1908, p. 401; 1912, p. 42 (as divisions).
AXIOKERSOSARIA Distant 1909a, p. 124 (as division).
AIDONEUSARIA Distant 1909a, p. 125 (as division).
GALEATINI Blatchley 1926, p. 451 (as tribe).
ACALYPTINI Blatchley 1926, p. 479 (as tribe).
PHYSATOCHEILINI Blatchley 1926, p. 483 (as tribe).
AGRAMMINAE China and Miller 1955, p. 261; 1959, p. 9 (as subfamily).
AGRAMMATINAE Drake and Ruhoff 1960a, p. 23 (as subfamily).
TINGINAE China and Miller 1955, p. 261; 1959, p. 9.—Drake and Ruhoff 1960a, p. 31 (as subfamily).—Drake and Davis 1960, pp. 74, 78 (new concept of subfamily).
AIDONEUSINAE Menon and Hakk 1959a, p. 392 (as subfamily).
AXIOKERSOSINAE Menon and Hakk 1959a, p. 392 (as subfamily).
TYPE GENUS: *Tingis* Fabricius.

Tribe LITADEINI, new tribe

TYPE GENUS: *Litadea* China.

Genus LITADEA China

Litadea China 1924, p. 438.—Drake and Ruhoff 1960a, p. 66.
TYPE SPECIES: *Litadea delicatula* China.

*Litadea delicatula China   PLATES 7, 8
   Litadea delicatula China 1924, p. 439, figs. 2a, c [Rodriguez].—Drake and Davis 1960, figs. 39, 40.
TYPE: Sex unknown; Rodriguez Island; British Mus.
DISTRIBUTION: Mascarene Islands (Rodriguez).
HOST PLANT: Unrecorded.

Tribe TINGINI Laporte

TYPE GENUS: *Tingis* Laporte.

Genus ABDASTARTUS Distant

Abdastartus Distant 1910a, p. 103.—Bergroth 1911, p. 185.—Drake 1956b, p. 110.—Drake and Ruhoff 1960a, p. 31.

TYPE SPECIES: *Abdastartus tyrianus* Distant=*Monanthia atra* Motschulsky.

*Abdastartus atrus (Motschulsky)

Monanthia atra Motschulsky 1863, p. 91 [Ceylon].—Stål 1873, p. 134.— Kirby 1891, p. 109.—Lethierry and Severin 1896, p. 25.

Teleonemia atra: Distant 1902b, p. 356; 1903b, p. 143.—Bergroth 1921, p. 104.

Abdastartus tyrianus Distant 1910a, p. 103, fig. 50 [India].—Drake 1930c, p. 15.

Abdastartus atrus: Drake 1956b, p. 110.

TYPE: Sex unknown; Mount Patannas, Ceylon; Moscow Univ.

DISTRIBUTION: Ceylon; India.

HOST PLANT: Unrecorded.

*Abdastartus longulus Drake

Abdastartus longulus Drake 1953b, p. 95 [India].

TYPE: Holotype ♂, macropterous; Dehra Dun, India; Drake Coll. (USNM).

DISTRIBUTION: India.

HOST PLANT: Unrecorded.

*Abdastartus sacchari Drake

Abdastartus tyrianus (not Distant): Drake 1927d, p. 307 [Java; Taiwan; sugar].

Abdastartus sacchari Drake 1930c, p. 15 [Sumatra].—Box 1953, p. 37.

TYPE: Holotype ♂, macropterous; Randoeblatoeng, Java; Drake Coll. (USNM).

DISTRIBUTION: Greater Sunda Islands (Java; Sumatra); Taiwan.

HOST PLANT: Sugarcane.

Genus ACALYPTA Westwood

Acalypta Westwood 1840b, p. 121.—Stål 1873, pp. 118, 122; 1874, p. 51.—Saunders 1875, pp. 245, 251.—Horváth 1906a, pp. 13, 24 (key); 1906e, p. 498.—Mužik 1907, pp. 50, 52 (key).—Oshanin 1908, p. 406; 1912, p. 42.—Banks 1910, p. 55.—Jensen-Haarup 1912, p. 150 (key).—Osborn and Drake 1916a, p. 220 (key).—Van Duzee 1916, p. 25; 1917b, p. 211.—Lindberg 1919, p. 42.—Torre-Bueno 1924, p. 93.—Stichel 1926, pp. 103, 106 (key); 1935, p. 348; 1938a, p. 404; 1960a, p. 274; 1960b, p. 391; 1960c, p. 130.—Drake 1928c, pp. 1–9.—Börner 1935, pp. 73–75 (key).—Scholte 1935, p. 43 (key).— Gulde 1938, pp. 242, 249 (key).—Hoberlandt 1942, p. 124.—China 1943, p. 245.—Blöte 1945, p. 80.—Hurd 1946, p. 462.—Bailey 1951,

p. 32.—Kiritshenko 1951, pp. 240, 244 (key).—Singer 1952, p. 48.—
Drake and Ruhoff 1959, p. 138; 1960a, p. 31.—Southwood and Leston
1959, p. 141.
Orthosteira Fieber 1844, p. 46.—Sahlberg 1848, p. 128.—China 1941,
p. 130.—Drake and Ruhoff 1960a, p. 73.
Orthostira [sic]: Fieber 1861, p. 130.—Douglas and Scott 1865, p. 260.—
Thomson 1871, p. 398.—Ferrari 1878, p. 82 (key).—Reuter 1882b,
p. 114 (key).—Saunders 1892, p. 125.—Lethierry and Severin 1896,
p. 6.
Fenestrella Osborn and Drake 1916a, p. 222.—Parshley 1917a, p. 14.—
Drake and Ruhoff 1960a, p. 57.
Drakella Bergroth 1922, p. 152.—Blatchley 1926, p. 481.—Drake and
Ruhoff 1960a, p. 54.
TYPE SPECIES: *Tingis carinata* Panzer.

*Acalypta acutangula (Jakovlev)

Orthostira acutangula Jakovlev 1880a, p. 127 [Russia]; 1893, pp. 293, 302.
Acalypta acutangula: Horváth 1901, p. 475 [Turkey]; 1906a, p. 31
[Siberia].—Kiritshenko 1951, p. 244.—Hoberlandt 1955, p. 86.
TYPE: Holotype ♀, macropterous; Russia; Leningrad Inst.
DISTRIBUTION: U.S.S.R. (Siberia); Turkey.
HOST PLANT: Unrecorded.

*Acalypta barberi Drake

Acalypta barberi Drake 1934a, p. 196 [N.Y.].—Drake and Ruhoff 1959,
p. 137 [N.B.; moss; hops].
Acalypta mera Drake 1941a, p. 142 [B.C.; Oreg.].
TYPE: Holotype ♀, brachypterous; Merrifield, New York, U.S.; USNM.
DISTRIBUTION: U.S. (N.Y.; Oreg.); Canada (B.C.; N.B.).
HOST PLANTS: Moss; hops.

*Acalypta brunnea (Germar)

Tingis brunnea Germar 1836, fasc. 18, tab. 23 [Austria].
Monanthia brunnea: Herrich-Schaeffer 1837, p. 25, pl. 118, fig. 374.
Orthosteira brunnea: Fieber 1844, p. 48, pl. 3, figs. 43–45.—Scholz 1847,
p. 118 [Germany].—Herrich-Schaeffer 1850, p. 158.
Orthostira concinna Douglas and Scott 1863, p. 143, fig. 5 [England];
1865, p. 260 [moss on oak].—Fieber 1864, p. 211.
Orthostira brunnea: Ferrari 1878, p. 82.—Puton 1879c, p. 95 [France].—
Saunders 1892, p. 126, pl. 11, fig. 7.—Hüeber 1893, p. 305.
Acalypta brunnea: Stål 1874, p. 51.—Saunders 1875, p. 251 [moss].—
Horváth 1906a, p. 28 [Belgium; Switzerland].—Muzik 1907, p. 53
[Czechoslovakia].—Butler 1923, p. 201 [Scotland; Ireland].—Stichel
1926, p. 106; 1960a, p. 276 [Sweden].—Scholte 1935, p. 44 [Nether-
lands].—Hoberlandt 1943b, pp. 120, 121, 122; 1944, pp. 33, 35.
TYPE: Austria; sex and deposition of type unknown.

DISTRIBUTION: Ireland; Scotland; England; Netherlands; Belgium; France; Switzerland; Austria; Czechoslovakia; Germany; Sweden.

HOST PLANTS: MOSS; moss on oak.

NOTE: Life history study [Butler].

*Acalypta carinata (Panzer)

Tingis carinata Panzer 1806, heft 99, tab. 20 [Germany].—Le Peletier and Serville 1828, p. 653.—Curtis 1839, tab. 741 [England].— Fieber 1844, p. 52, pl. 4, fig. 10.

Tingis cassidae Fallén 1807, p. 37 [Sweden]; 1829, p. 146.—Herrich-Schaeffer 1835, p. 59.—Zetterstedt 1840, p. 269 [Lapland].

Monanthia carinata: Burmeister 1835, p. 262.

Tingis cervina Germar 1836, fasc. 18, tab. 22.

Monanthia cervina: Herrich-Schaeffer 1837, p. 26, pl. 118, fig. 375; pl. 129, fig. G.—Vollenhoven 1878, p. 279, pl. 9, figs. 11, 11a [Netherlands].

?Monanthia fracta Herrich-Schaeffer 1838, pp. 53, 63.

?Monanthia acuminata Herrich-Schaeffer 1838, p. 63.

Acalypta carinata: Westwood 1840a, p. 477; 1840b, p. 121.—Horváth 1906a, p. 29 [Rumania].—Oshanin 1908, p. 407 [Belgium].—Jensen-Haarup 1912, p. 152 [Denmark].—Sahlberg 1920, p. 78.—Stichel 1926, p. 106; 1938a, p. 404 [Poland]; 1960a, p. 278, fig. 55 [Norway].— Drake 1928c, p. 1.—Lindberg 1932b, p. 211.—Scholte 1935, p. 44, fig. 8.—Hoberlandt 1943b, pp. 121, 122 [Czechoslovakia].—González 1948, p. 49 [Spain].—Kiritshenko 1951, p. 244.—Bator 1953, p. 324, pl. 2, fig. 2.—Southwood and Leston 1959, p. 142, pl. 21, fig. 2, text figs. 43, 48.—Štušak 1961, p. 80, fig. 20.

Orthosteira cervina: Fieber 1844, p. 48, pl. 4, figs. 1–3 [Austria].—Scholz 1847, p. 118.—Sahlberg 1848, p. 129 [Finland].—Herrich-Schaeffer 1850, p. 159.—Mayr 1858, p. 569.—China 1941, p. 130.

Orthosteira cassidea: Mayr 1858, p. 569 [moss].

Monanthia (Orthosteira) cervina: Flor 1860, p. 341 [Latvia; Estonia].

Orthostira cervina: Fieber 1861, p. 130; 1864, p. 212.—Douglas and Scott 1865, p. 262.—Frey-Gessner 1865, p. 233 [Switzerland].—Horváth 1874b, p. 432 [Hungary].—Jakovlev 1876b, p. 70 [Russia]; 1893, p. 301.—Reiber and Puton 1876, p. 68.—Puton 1879c, p. 96 [France].—Reuter 1882b, p. 114.—Dubois 1888, p. 120.— d' Antessanty 1890, p. 31.—Saunders 1892, p. 126, pl. 11, fig. 8.— Hüeber 1893, p. 305.

Orthostira cassidea: Frey-Gessner 1865, p. 233.—Garbiglietti 1869, p. 275 [Italy].—Thomson 1871, p. 399.

Acalypta cassidea: Stål 1874, p. 52.

Acalypta cervina: Reuter 1874, p. 563.—Saunders 1875, p. 252.— Reichensperger 1920, p. 61.—Butler 1923, p. 202, fig. [Wales; Scotland; Ireland].—Blöte 1945, p. 80 [Yugoslavia; Algeria].

TYPE: Mannheim, Germany; sex and deposition of type unknown.

DISTRIBUTION: England; Scotland; Wales; Ireland; Netherlands; Belgium; France; Spain; Italy; Switzerland; Czechoslovakia; Austria; Hungary; Yugoslavia; Rumania; Germany; Denmark; Poland; U.S.S.R. (Latvia; Estonia); Finland; Sweden; Norway; (Lapland); Algeria.

HOST PLANT: Moss.

NOTE: Nymphs [Butler]; eggs [Štusak].

Acalypta carinata var. angustula Horváth

Acalypta cervina var. *angustula* Horváth 1898a, p. 69 [Hungary; France].

Acalypta carinata var. *angustula:* Horváth 1906a, p. 30 [Germany; Austria; Rumania; Finland; Estonia; Latvia; Lapland].—Sahlberg 1920, p. 79.—Scholte 1935, p. 44 [Netherlands].—Stichel 1960a, p. 278.

TYPE: Unknown.

DISTRIBUTION: Netherlands; France; Germany; Austria; Hungary; Rumania; U.S.S.R. (Estonia; Latvia); Finland; (Lapland).

HOST PLANT: Unrecorded.

Acalypta carpathica Horváth

Acalypta carpathica Horváth 1905b, p. 561 [Rumania]; 1906a, p. 30.— Stichel 1960a, p. 278.

TYPE: Sex unknown; Sinaia, Rumania; Hungarian Mus.

DISTRIBUTION: Rumania.

HOST PLANT: Unrecorded.

*Acalypta cooleyi Drake

Acalypta cooleyi Drake 1917a, p. 213 [Mont.]; 1928c, p. 9.

TYPE: Holotype ♀, macropterous; Bozeman, Montana, U.S.; Drake Coll. (USNM).

DISTRIBUTION: U.S. (Mont.; Oreg.; Calif.).

HOST PLANT: Unrecorded.

*Acalypta duryi Drake

Fenestrella ovata Osborn and Drake 1916a, p. 223, fig. 3 [Ohio]; 1917a, p. 155, pl. 8, fig. d.

Drakella [ovata]: Bergroth 1922, p. 152.

Drakella ovata: Blatchley 1926, p. 482, fig. 112.

Acalypta ovata: Drake 1928c, p. 3, fig. 1a [moss].

Acalypta duryi Drake 1930d, p. 268.

TYPE: Holotype ♀, brachypterous; Cincinnati, Ohio, U.S.; Ohio State Univ.

DISTRIBUTION: U.S. (Ohio; N.C.; Tenn.).

HOST PLANT: Moss.

Acalypta elegans Horváth

Acalypta elegans Horváth 1906a, p. 32 [Siberia].

TYPE: Sex unknown; Siberia, Russia; Helsin. Mus.

DISTRIBUTION: U.S.S.R. (Siberia).

HOST PLANT: Unrecorded.

Acalypta elinoides (Jakovlev)

Orthostira elinoides Jakovlev 1893, pp. 294, 302 [Russia].

Acalypta elinoides: Horváth 1906a, p. 31 [Siberia].

TYPE: Sex and locality unknown; Leningrad Inst.

DISTRIBUTION: U.S.S.R. (Siberia).

HOST PLANT: Unrecorded.

Acalypta finitima (Puton)

Orthostira finitima Puton 1884, p. 313 [France].

Acalypta finitima: Horváth 1906a, p. 29.

TYPE: Sex unknown; St. Martin-Lantosque, France; Paris Mus.

DISTRIBUTION: France.

HOST PLANT: Unrecorded.

*Acalypta gracilis (Fieber)

Orthosteira gracilis Fieber 1844, p. 54, pl. 4, figs. 19–21 [Czechoslovakia; *Thymus serpyllus*].—Scholz 1847, p. 118 [Germany].—Herrich-Schaeffer 1850, p. 159.—Mayr 1858, p. 569 [Austria; *Echium vulgare*].

Monanthia (Orthosteira) parvula (not Fallén): Flor 1860, pp. 333, 335 [Estonia; Latvia; Sweden].

Orthostira gracilis: Fieber 1861, p. 131 [*Thymus*].—Horváth 1874b, p. 432 [Hungary].—Reiber and Puton 1876, p. 68.—Ferrari 1878, pp. 65, 83.—Puton 1879c, p. 99 [France].—Reuter 1882b, p. 116 [Finland; moss].—Jakovlev 1893, p. 293 [Russia].—Hüeber 1893, p. 310.

Orthostira biseriata Thomson 1871, p. 402.

Orthostira reticosta Thomson 1871, p. 402.

Orthostira propinqua Ferrari 1874, p. 171 [Italy; *Plantago cynops*].

Acalypta gracilis: Puton 1874a, p. 227.—Reuter 1874, p. 564; 1880b, p. 165.—Horváth 1906a, p. 33 [Denmark; Rumania; Siberia].—Jensen-Haarup 1912, p. 152.—Schumacher 1914, p. 257 [*Artemisia; Calluna*].—Sahlberg 1920, p. 80.—Stichel 1926, p. 107; 1938a, p. 404 [Poland]; 1960a, p. 281 [*Erodium cicutarium;* Norway; Switzerland].—Scholte 1935, p. 46, figs. 11, 12 [Netherlands].—Börner 1935, p. 75, figs. 113, 119a.—Gulde 1938, p. 258, fig. [*Artemisia campestris*].—Hoberlandt 1943b, p. 122.—Kiritshenko 1951, p. 244.

Orthostira parvula var. *biseriata:* Ferrari 1878, p. 83.

Orthostira parvula var. *reticosta:* Ferrari 1878, p. 83.

Orthostira parvula var. *propinqua:* Ferrari 1878, p. 83.

TYPE: Sex unknown; Prague, Czechoslovakia; Vienna Mus.

DISTRIBUTION: Netherlands; France; Switzerland; Germany; Czechoslovakia; Italy; Austria; Hungary; Rumania; Poland; Denmark; Norway; Sweden; Finland; U.S.S.R. (Latvia; Estonia; Siberia).

HOST PLANTS: *Artemisia campestris; Artemisia* sp.; *Calluna* sp.; *Echium vulgare; Erodium cicutarium; Plantago cynops; Thymus serpyllus; Thymus* sp.; moss.

*Acalypta hellenica Reuter

Acalypta hellenica Reuter 1888, p. 224 [Greece]; 1891a, p. 25.—Horváth 1889, p. 329 [Russia]; 1906a, p. 33 [France; Corsica; Italy; Yugoslavia]; 1911b, p. 584 [Sicily].—Oshanin 1912, p. 42 [Austria].— Lindberg 1936b, p. 29 [Canary Islands].—Stichel 1938a, p. 404 [Turkey]; 1960a, p. 281 [Sardinia].—Kiritshenko 1951, p. 245.— Mancini 1953d, p. 15.—Gomez-Menor 1955b, p. 249 [Spain; Quercus].

TYPE: Sex unknown; Greece; Helsin. Mus.

DISTRIBUTION: France; Corsica; Spain; Sardinia; Italy; Sicily; Austria; Yugoslavia; Greece; Turkey; U.S.S.R.; Canary Islands.

HOST PLANT: Quercus sp.

Acalypta heteropepla Horváth

Acalypta heteropepla Horváth 1907, p. 303 [Algeria].

TYPE: Holotype ♀; Mons Babor, Algeria; Oxford Mus.

DISTRIBUTION: Algeria.

HOST PLANT: Unrecorded.

Acalypta hoberlandti Roubal

Acalypta hoberlandti Roubal 1958, p. 54, fig. 1 [France].—Stichel 1960a, p. 274, fig. 42.

TYPE: Sex unknown; France; Roubal Coll.

DISTRIBUTION: France.

HOST PLANT: Unrecorded.

*Acalypta lillianis Torre-Bueno

Acalypta lillianus Torre-Bueno 1916, p. 39 [N.Y.; Maine; Mich.].— Osborn and Drake 1916a, p. 221, figs. 1, 2 [Ohio; N.H.;Ont.].—Van Duzee 1917b, p. 212 [N.J.].—Parshley 1917a, p. 14; 1917b, p. 53; 1923b, p. 698.—Barber 1922a, p. 17 [moss].—McAtee 1923, p. 145 [D.C.].—Blatchley 1926, p. 481, fig. 111 [Ind.; Climacium americanum].—Drake 1928b, p. 100; 1928c, p. 6 [Iowa; Ill.; Pa.; Que.].— Froeschner 1944, p. 669.—Hurd 1946, p. 463 [N. Dak.].—Bailey 1951, p. 32 [Polytrichum].—Lindberg 1958b, p. 14 [Nfld.; Dryas; Oxytropis].—Byers 1959, p. 191.

Acalypta ovata Osborn and Drake 1916b, p. 9, fig. 1.—Drake 1932, p. 100 [Tenn.].

Acalypta grisea Heidemann 1917, p. 218, pl. 17, fig. 2 [Mass.; N.C.; Md.].—McAtee 1917b, p. 78.

Acalypta modesta Parshley 1921, p. 16 [B.C.].—Downes 1925, p. 14; 1927a, p. 10.—Drake 1928c, p. 7.

TYPE: Lectotype ♀; White Plains, New York, U.S.; Snow Mus.

DISTRIBUTION: U.S. (Maine; N.H.; Vt.; Mass.; Conn.; R.I.; N.Y.; N.J.; Pa.; Md.; D.C.; Va.; N.C.; Tenn.; Ohio; Ill.; Ind.; Mich.; Wis.; Nebr.; Iowa.; Minn.; N. Dak.; Idaho; Alaska); Canada (Nfld.; Que.; Ont.; B.C.).

HOST PLANTS: *Climacium americanum; Dryas* sp.; *Oxytropis* sp.; *Polytrichum* sp.; moss.

NOTE: Lectotype designated [Byers].

*Acalypta marginata (Wolff)

Acanthia marginata Wolff 1804, p. 131, pl. 13, fig. 126 [Hungary].— Fieber 1844, p. 50, pl. 4, fig. 8.

Tingis pusilla Herrich-Schaeffer 1835, p. 59.

Monanthia pusilla: Herrich-Schaeffer 1837, p. 24, pl. 118, fig. 373; 1838, p. 64, pl. 129, fig. F.

Orthosteira macrophthalma Fieber 1844, pp. 49, 110, pl. 4, figs. 4–7 [Sweden; Germany; Czechoslovakia; Austria].—Sahlberg 1848, p. 129 [Finland].—Herrich-Schaeffer 1850, p. 159.

Orthosteira pusilla: Fieber 1844, p. 51, pl. 4, fig. 9 [moss].

Monanthia (Orthosteira) cinerea (not Fieber): Flor 1860, pp. 333, 337 [Latvia; Estonia].

Orthostira pusilla: Fieber 1861, p. 131.—Garbiglietti 1869, p. 275 [Italy].—Ferrari 1878, p. 83.

Orthostira cylindricornis Thomson 1871 p. 401.

Acalypta macrophthalma: Reuter 1874, p. 564.—Saunders 1875, p. 253.— Butler 1923, p. 203.

Orthostira macrophthalma: Reiber and Puton 1878, p. 68.—Puton 1879c, p. 98 [France].—Chicote 1880, p. 189 [Spain].—Reuter 1882b, p. 116 [Lapland].—Saunders 1892, p. 128.—Hüeber 1893, p. 309 [Switzerland; *Thymus; Artemisia campestris*].—Jakovlev 1893, p. 293 [Russia].

Orthostira acutispinis Reuter 1886, p. 233.

Acalypta marginata: Horváth 1906a, pp. 26, 31, pl. 1, fig. 5 [Yugoslavia; Bulgaria; Armenia].—Oshanin 1908, p. 410 [Caucasus].— Sahlberg 1920, p. 80.—Stichel 1926, p. 107, fig. 296; 1938a, p. 404 [Norway]; 1938b, p. 454; 1960a, p. 280, fig. 60 [Portugal; *Calluna vulgaris*].—Scholte 1935, p. 46, fig. 9 [Netherlands].—Poisson 1938, p. 589 [*Erodium*].—China 1943, p. 246.—Kiritshenko 1951, p. 244.— Stehlik 1952, p. 205.—Bator 1953, p. 324, pl. 2, fig. 5.—Štušak 1957b, p. 135, fig. 2; 1961a, p. 79, figs. 4a, b, 7; pl. 1, fig. c.—Cobben 1958b, p. 16 [*Hieracium pilosella*].

TYPE: Hungary; sex and deposition of type unknown.

DISTRIBUTION: Netherlands; France; Spain; Italy; Portugal; Switzerland; Czechoslovakia; Germany; Austria; Hungary; Bulgaria; Yugoslavia; Poland; Norway; Sweden; Finland; (Lapland); U.S.S.R. (Latvia; Estonia; Armenia; Siberia; Caucasus).

HOST PLANTS: *Artemisia campestris; Calluna vulgaris; Erodium* sp.; *Hieracium pilosella; Thymus* sp.; moss.

NOTE: Records from England incorrect [China]. Associated with ants [Stichel 1960].

*Acalypta mniophila Drake and Ruhoff

   Acalypta mniophila Drake and Ruhoff 1959, p. 136, fig. 1 [Mexico].

TYPE: Holotype ♀, brachypterous; Mexico; USNM.

DISTRIBUTION: Mexico.

HOST PLANT: Moss.

Acalypta montana Hoberlandt

   Acalypta montana Hoberlandt 1944, p. 34, fig. [Czechoslovakia].—
   Stichel 1960a, p. 276, fig. 49.

TYPE: Holotype ♂; Savinské Alps, Montes Alpinum, Czechoslovakia;
Prague Mus.

DISTRIBUTION: Czechoslovakia.

HOST PLANT: Unrecorded.

*Acalypta musci (Schrank)

   Cimex musci Schrank 1781, p. 265 [Austria; moss].

   Orthosteira cassidea (not Fallén): Fieber 1844, p. 47, pl. 3, figs. 39–42
   [Germany; Czechoslovakia; Italy].—Herrich-Schaeffer 1850, p. 159.

   Campylosteira (Orthosteira) cassidea: Kolenati 1856, p. 430 [Caucasus].

   Orthostira cassidea: Fieber 1861, p. 130 [France].

   Orthostira musci: Reiber and Puton 1876, p. 68.—Ferrari 1878, p. 82.—
   Puton 1879c, p. 94 [Hungary].—Chicote 1880, p. 189 [Spain].—
   Jakovlev 1880b, p. 100 [Russia].—Hüeber 1893, p. 303 [Switzerland].

   Acalypta musci: Horváth 1906a, p. 28 [Yugoslavia; Rumania; Bulgaria;
   Belgium].—Mužik 1907, p. 53, fig. 3.—Stichel 1926, p. 106; 1960a,
   p. 275, fig. 46 [Andorra; Poland; *Coriolus versicolor; Trametes gibbosa;*
   Polyporus unicolor].—Scholte 1935, p. 44, fig. 7 [Netherlands].—
   Hoberlandt 1943b, p. 122.—Kiritshenko 1951, p. 244, fig. 329.—
   Bator 1953, p. 324, pl. 2, fig. 1.—Mancini 1953c, p. 22; 1954b,
   p. 11.—Štušak 1957b, pp. 134, 140, figs. 1, 13b, 15c; 1958, p. 365,
   figs. 5–7.

TYPE: Austria; sex and deposition of type unknown.

DISTRIBUTION: Andorra; Spain; France; Belgium; Netherlands; Germany; Czechoslovakia; Switzerland; Austria; Hungary; Italy; Yugoslavia;
Rumania; Poland; U.S.S.R. (Caucasus); Sweden.

HOST PLANTS: *Coriolus versicolor; Polyporus unicolor; Trametes gibbosa;* moss.

NOTE: Eggs [Štušak].

*Acalypta musci var. **ditata** (Puton)

   Acalypta musci (not Schrank): Stål 1874, p. 51.

   Orthostira musci var. *ditata* Puton 1879b, p. 297; 1879c, p. 94 [France;
   Austria; moss].—Chicote 1880, p. 189 [Spain].

   Acalypta musci var. *ditata:* Horváth 1906a, p. 28 [Switzerland; Italy;
   Germany; Hungary; Yugoslavia; Bulgaria; Rumania].—Muˇik
   1907, p. 53 [Czechoslovakia].—Scholte 1935, p. 44 [Netherlands].—
   Blöte 1945, p. 81 [Tunisia].—Bator 1953, p. 324.—Mancini 1954b,
   p. 11.

Acalypta musci var. *dilatata* [sic]: Gomez-Menor 1955b, p. 249 [Andorra].
TYPE: Unknown.

DISTRIBUTION: Spain; Andorra; France; Belgium; Netherlands; Germany; Czechoslovakia; Austria; Hungary; Switzerland; Italy; Yugoslavia; Bulgaria; Rumania; U.S.S.R. (Caucasus); Tunisia.

HOST PLANT: Moss.

Acalypta musci var. triseriata Stichel

Acalypta musci var. *triseriata* Stichel 1960a, p. 275.

TYPE: Unknown.

DISTRIBUTION: Unknown.

HOST PLANT: Unknown.

*Acalypta nigrina (Fallén)

Tingis nigrina Fallén 1807, p. 37 [Finland]; 1829, p. 145.—Herrich-Schaeffer 1830, heft 118, tab. 16 [Germany].—Zetterstedt 1840, p. 269 [Lapland].

Tingis pusilla Fallén 1807, p. 38 [Sweden]; 1829, p. 146.—Curtis 1839, tab. 741 [England].

Tingis nigrinus: Herrich-Schaeffer 1835, p. 58.

Monanthia pusilla: Burmeister 1835, p. 262.

Monanthia nigrina: Herrich-Schaeffer 1838, pp. 52, 62, pl. 125, fig. G.

Monanthia (Phyllontocheila) nigrina: Fieber 1844, p. 63, pl. 5, figs. 23–24.—Herrich-Schaeffer 1850, p. 156.

Orthosteira cinerea Fieber 1844, pp. 52, 110, pl. 4, figs. 11–14 [Czechoslovakia; moss].—Sahlberg 1848, p. 130.—Herrich-Schaeffer 1850, p. 159.—Mayr 1858, p. 569 [Austria].

Monanthia (Orthosteira) nigrina: Flor 1860, p. 334 [Estonia; Latvia].

Orthostira nigrina: Fieber 1861, p. 131.—Frey-Gessner 1865, p. 233 [Switzerland].—Jakovlev 1871, p. 26 [Russia].—Thomson 1871, p. 400.—Horváth 1874b, p. 432 [Hungary].—Ferrari 1874, p. 172 [Italy; *Spartium junceum*]; 1878, p. 83.—Reiber and Puton 1876, p. 68.—Puton 1879c, p. 98 [France].—Saunders 1892, p. 127, pl. 11, fig. 9.—Hüeber 1893, p. 307.

Orthostira pusilla: Frey-Gessner 1865, p. 233.—Gredler 1870, p. 76.

Acalypta nigrina: Stål 1874, p. 52.—Reuter 1874, p. 564.—Saunders 1875, p. 252.—Horváth 1906a, p. 31 [*Thymus serpyllus*].—Reichensperger 1920, p. 61.—Sahlberg 1920, p. 79.—Butler 1923, p. 203 [Scotland].—Stichel 1926, p. 107 [*Hieracium murorum*]; 1938a, p. 404 [Norway; Poland]; 1960a, p. 279 [Iceland; Denmark; *Calluna vulgaris*].—Poisson 1938, p. 589 [*Erodium*].—Blöte 1945, p. 81 [Tunisia].—Kiritshenko 1951, p. 244.—Stehlik 1952, p. 205.—Bator 1953, p. 324, pl. 2, fig. 4.—Southwood and Leston 1959, p. 144, pl. 21, fig. 3, text fig. 49.

Monanthia carinata (not Panzer): Vollenhoven 1878, p. 280, pl. 10, figs. 1, 1a [Netherlands].

52 U.S. NATIONAL MUSEUM BULLETIN 243

Type: Sex unknown; Finland; Lund Zool. Inst.

Distribution: England; Scotland; Netherlands; France; Germany; Italy; Switzerland; Czechoslovakia; Austria; Hungary; Poland; Denmark; Norway; Sweden; Finland; (Lapland); Iceland; U.S.S.R. (Estonia; Latvia); Tunisia.

Host Plants: *Calluna vulgaris; Erodium* sp.; *Hieracium murorum; Spartium junceum; Thymus serpyllus;* moss.

*Acalypta nigrinervis Stål

Acalypta nigrinervis Stål 1874, p. 52 [Spain].—Horváth 1906a, p. 28.

Orthostira nigrinervis: Ferrari 1878, p. 82.—Puton 1879c, p. 95 [France].—Chicote 1880, p. 189.

Type: Sex unknown; Spain; Stockholm Mus.

Distribution: Spain; France.

Host Plant: Unrecorded.

*Acalypta nyctalis Drake

Acalypta nyctalis Drake 1928c, pp. 3, 5 [N.H.; Alta.].—Bailey 1951, p. 35.—Lindberg 1958b, p. 13 [Nfld.; Alaska; moss].

Type: Holotype ♀, brachypterous; Franconia, New Hampshire, U.S.; USNM.

Distribution: U.S. (N.H.; Alaska); Canada (Alta.; Nfld.).

Host Plant: Mosses.

*Acalypta parvula (Fallén)

Tingis parvula Fallén 1807, p. 37 [Sweden]; 1829, p. 145.—Curtis 1839, tab. 741 [England].—Fieber 1861, p. 384.

Monanthia obscura Herrich-Schaeffer 1837, p. 23, pl. 118, fig. 372 [Germany; moss].—Vollenhoven 1878, p. 281, pl. 10, fig. 2.

Orthosteira obscura: Fieber 1844, p. 54, pl. 4, figs. 22–25 [Czechoslovakia; Austria; *Thymus serpyllus*].—Sahlberg 1848, p. 130.—Herrich-Schaeffer 1850, p. 160.—Mayr 1858, p. 569 [Hungary].

Monanthia (Phyllontocheila) parvula: Fieber 1844, p. 66.

Orthostira obscura: Fieber 1861, p. 131.—Douglas and Scott 1865, p. 263.—Frey-Gessner 1865, p. 233 [Switzerland].—Garbiglietti 1869, p. 275 [Italy].

Orthostira parvula: Thomson 1871, p. 401.—Reiber and Puton 1876, p. 68.—Puton 1879c, p. 99 [France; Corsica].—Reuter 1882b, p. 116 [Finland].—Saunders 1892, p. 127, pl. 11, figs. 10, 10a.—Hüeber 1893, p. 312.—de Walsche 1960, p. 38.

Acalypta parvula: Stål 1874, p. 52.—Reuter 1874, p. 564; 1880b, p. 165.—Saunders 1875, p. 252.—Horváth 1906a, p. 33 [Spain; Belgium].—Oshanin 1908, p. 412 [Portugal; Algeria].—Jensen-Haarup 1912, p. 152, fig. 95 [Denmark].—Reichensperger 1920, p. 61.—Sahlberg 1920, p. 81 [*Thymus*].—Butler 1923, p. 204 [Scotland; Ireland; *Herniaria*].—Stichel 1926, p. 107, fig. 297; 1938a, p. 404

[Norway; Russia; Poland; Yugoslavia]; 1960a, p. 282, fig. 65 [Bulgaria; Sardinia; *Calluna vulgaris; Coriolus versicolor; Trametes gibbosa; Polyporus hirsutus; Pholiota mutabilis*].—de Seabra 1931, p. 412, figs. 484, 485.—Scholte 1935, p. 46, fig. 10.—Börner 1935, p. 75, fig. 119b.—Poisson 1938, p. 589 [*Erodium*].—China 1938, p. 20 [Madeira].—Kiritshenko 1951, p. 245.—Novak and Wagner 1951, p. 70.—Leston 1953, p. 132, fig. 1.—Mancini 1953d, p. 15; 1954b, p. 11.—Gomez-Menor 1955b, p. 249.—Štušak 1957b, pp. 135, 140, figs. 3, 15d; 1961a, p. 80, fig. 17.—Southwood and Leston 1959, p. 144, pl. 25, fig. 4; fig. 42.—Lindberg 1960b, p. 92.

Orthostira parvula var. *macroptera* Ferrari 1878, p. 83.

Orthostira parvula var. *pallescens* Ferrari 1878, p. 83.

Orthostira parvula var. *major* Ferrari 1878, p. 83.

Orthostira parvula var. *minor* Ferrari 1878, p. 83.—Puton 1879c, p. 99.

Monanthia parvula: Vollenhoven 1878, p. 278, pl. 9, figs. 10, 10a [Netherlands].

Campylostira parvula var. *fuscicornis* Rey 1893, p. 97.

Campylostira parvula var. *minor:* Rey 1893, p. 97.

TYPE: Sex unknown; Scania, Sweden; Lund Zool. Inst.

DISTRIBUTION: England; Scotland; Ireland; Netherlands; Belgium; France; Portugal; Spain; Italy; Sardinia; Corsica; Switzerland; Czechoslovakia; Austria; Hungary; Bulgaria; Yugoslavia; Poland; Germany; Denmark; Norway; Sweden; Finland; U.S.S.R.; Algeria; Madeira Islands.

HOST PLANTS: *Calluna vulgaris; Climacium dendroides; Erodium* sp.; *Herniaria* sp.; *Thymus serpyllus; Thymus* sp.; moss; fungi (*Coriolus versicolor; Pholiota mutabilis; Polyporus hirsutus; Trametes gibbosa*).

NOTE: Study of eggs [Leston; Štušak]. Found in association with ants [Stichel 1960a].

*Acalypta platycheila (Fieber)

Orthosteira platycheila Fieber 1844, p. 53, pl. 4, figs. 15-18 [Austria; Czechoslovakia].—Herrich-Schaeffer 1850, p. 159.

Monanthia (Orthosteira) intermedia Flor 1860, p. 339 [Estonia; Latvia].

Orthostira platychila [sic]: Fieber 1861, p. 130.—Thomson 1871, p. 400 [Sweden].—Ferrari 1878, p. 83.—Puton 1879c, p. 97 [France].—Reuter 1882b, p. 115 [Lapland; moss].—Jakovlev 1893, p. 301 [Russia].—Hüeber 1893, p. 306.

Acalypta platychila [sic]: Reuter 1874, p. 563.—Sahlberg 1878, p. 21 [Germany; Finland]; 1920, p. 79.—Butler 1923, p. 203 [*Carex*].—Stichel 1938a, p. 404 [Denmark; Belgium].—Southwood and Leston 1959, p. 142, pl. 21, fig. 7; fig. 50.

Monanthia nigrina (not Fallén): Vollenhoven 1878, p. 277, pl. 9, figs. 9, 9a [Netherlands].

Acalypta platycheila: Horváth 1906a, p. 30, pl. 1, fig. 4 [England; Hungary; Siberia].—Stichel 1926, p. 107, fig. 295; 1960a, p. 279 [Norway; Poland; Yugoslavia].—Kiritshenko 1951, p. 244.—Bator 1953, p. 324.—Massee 1954, p. 259.—Mancini 1954b, p. 11 [Italy].— Cobben 1958b, p. 16.

TYPE: Unknown.

DISTRIBUTION: England; Netherlands; Belgium; France; Italy; Czechoslovakia; Austria; Hungary; Yugoslavia; Poland; Germany; Denmark; Sweden; Norway; (Lapland); Finland; U.S.S.R. (Estonia; Latvia; Siberia).

HOST PLANTS: *Carex* sp.; moss.

*Acalypta pulchra Štušak

Acalypta pulchra Štušak 1961b, p. 261, figs. 1–3 [Bulgaria; moss].

TYPE: Holotype ♂, brachypterous; Borovec, Rila Planina, Bulgaria; Štušak Coll., Prague, Czechoslovakia.

DISTRIBUTION: Bulgaria.

HOST PLANT: Moss.

*Acalypta samara (Puton)

Orthostira samara Puton 1887, p. 98 [Switzerland].

Acalypta samara: Horváth 1906a, p. 27.—Roubal 1958, p. 54 [France].— Stichel 1960a, p. 274, fig. 44 [Austria].

TYPE: Sex unknown; Lugano, Switzerland; Paris Mus.

DISTRIBUTION: Switzerland; France; Austria.

HOST PLANT: Unrecorded.

*Acalypta saundersi (Downes)

Drakella saundersi Downes 1927b, p. 60 [B.C.].

Acalypta saundersi: Drake 1928c, p. 4, fig. 1b; 1930d, p. 268 [moss; Wash.].

TYPE: Holotype ♀, macropterous; Goldstream, British Columbia, Canada; Canada. Coll.

DISTRIBUTION: Canada (B.C.); U.S. (Wash.; Oreg.).

HOST PLANT: Moss.

*Acalypta sauteri Drake

Acalypta sauteri Drake 1942a, p. 14 [Japan].—Takeya 1951a, p. 6.

TYPE: Holotype ♂, brachypterous; Oayama, Japan; Drake Coll. (USNM).

DISTRIBUTION: Japan.

HOST PLANT: Unrecorded.

NOTE: Intercepted at port-of-entry, New York City, on packing mosses.

Acalypta sejuncta Horváth

Acalypta sejuncta Horváth 1905b, p. 561 [Armenia]; 1906a, p. 30 [Syria].— Oshanin 1908, p. 409 [Transcaucasus].—Hoberlandt 1955, p. 86 [Turkey].

TYPE: Sex unknown; Vallis Araxis, Armenia, Russia; Hungarian Mus.
DISTRIBUTION: U.S.S.R. (Armenia; Transcaucasus); Syria; Turkey.
HOST PLANT: Unrecorded.

Acalypta sibirica Jakovlev
Acalypta sibirica Jakovlev 1903a, p. 4 [Siberia].—Horváth 1906a, p. 30.
TYPE: Holotype ♂, brachypterous; Irkoutsk, Siberia, Russia; Leningrad Inst.
DISTRIBUTION: U.S.S.R. (Siberia).
HOST PLANT: Unrecorded.

Acalypta sordida (Jakovlev)
Orthostira sordida Jakovlev 1893, pp. 293, 301, 302 [Siberia].
Acalypta sordida: Reuter 1902, p. 151.—Horváth 1906a, p. 30.
TYPE: Sex unknown; Siberia, Russia; Leningrad Inst.
DISTRIBUTION: U.S.S.R. (Siberia).
HOST PLANT: Unrecorded.

Acalypta subtilis (Reuter)
Orthosteira subtilis Reuter 1882a, p. cxxx [Transcaucasus].
Acalypta subtilis: Horváth 1906a, p. 34.
TYPE: Sex unknown; Lenkoran, Russia; Helsin. Mus.
DISTRIBUTION: U.S.S.R. (Transcaucasus; Caucasus).
HOST PLANT: Unrecorded.

Acalypta suturalis (Puton)
Orthostira suturalis Puton 1879b, p. 297 [Spain]; 1879c, p. 95.—Chicote 1880, p. 189.
Acalypta suturalis: Horváth 1906a, p. 29.—Stichel 1960a, p. 277.
TYPE: Sex unknown; Irun, Spain; Paris Mus.
DISTRIBUTION: Spain.
HOST PLANT: Unrecorded.

*Acalypta thomsonii Stål
Acalypta thomsonii Stål 1873, p. 122 [Carolina].—Osborn and Drake 1916a, p. 220 [S.C.; Va.].—Heidemann 1917, p. 220, pl. 17, fig. 3 (fig. only).—Parshley 1923b, p. 699.—Blatchley 1926, p. 480, fig. 110.—Bailey 1951, p. 35 [R.I.; Md.].
Acalypta thomsoni [sic]: Drake 1926b, p. 377, pl. 34, fig. d; 1928c, p. 4, fig. 2 [D.C.; moss; sphagnum].
Acalypta madelinae Torre-Bueno 1926b, p. 117 [Mass.].
TYPE: Lectotype ♂, brachypterous; "Carolina meridionalis," U.S.; Stockholm Mus.
DISTRIBUTION: U.S. (Mass.; R.I.; N.J.; Md.; D.C.; Va.; N.C.; S.C.; Ga.; Fla.).
HOST PLANTS: Moss; sphagnum.

*Acalypta uniseriata (Puton)

Orthostira uniseriata Puton 1879b, p. 297 [Caucasus]; 1879c, p. 94.
Acalypta uniseriata: Horváth 1906a, p. 28.—Kiritshenko 1951, p. 244.—
Stichel 1960a, p. 275.
TYPE: Sex unknown; Caucasus, Russia; Paris Mus.
DISTRIBUTION: U.S.S.R. (Caucasus).
HOST PLANT: Unrecorded.

*Acalypta vanduzeei Drake

Acalypta vanduzeei Drake 1928c, pp. 3, 8 [Calif.].
TYPE: Holotype ♂, brachypterous; Green Point Ranch, Humboldt
County, California, U.S.; Cal. Acad.
DISTRIBUTION: U.S. (Calif.).
HOST PLANT: Moss.

*Acalypta vandykei Drake

Acalypta vandykei Drake 1928c, pp. 3, 8 [Calif.].—Hurd 1946, p. 463
[Oreg.].
TYPE: Holotype ♂; San Francisco County, California, U.S.; Cal. Acad.
DISTRIBUTION: U.S. (Calif.; Oreg.).
HOST PLANT: Unrecorded.

Genus ACANTHOCHEILA Stål

Monanthia (Acanthocheila) Stål 1858, p. 61.
Acanthochila [sic]: Stål 1873, p. 127.—Lethierry and Severin 1896, p.
14.—Banks 1910, p. 55.
Acanthocheila: Van Duzee 1916, p. 26; 1917b, p. 219.—Blatchley
1926, p. 479.—Monte 1939b, p. 64; 1941e, p. 73.—Hurd 1946, p.
469.—Drake and Ruhoff 1960a, p. 32.
TYPE SPECIES: Monanthia (Acanthocheila) armigera Stål.

*Acanthocheila abducta Buchanan-White

Acanthocheila abducta Buchanan-White 1879, p. 485 [Brazil].
Acanthocheila kahavalu Kirkaldy 1905, p. 216 [Peru].—Drake 1922b, p. 42
[Bolivia].—Monte 1940e, p. 287.—Blöte 1945, p. 85.
Acanthocheila kahavala [sic]: Drake 1931b, p. 511.
TYPE: Holotype ♀; Brazil; deposition unknown.
DISTRIBUTION: Brazil; Peru; Bolivia.
HOST PLANT: Unrecorded.

*Acanthocheila armigera (Stål)

Monanthia (Acanthocheila) armigera Stål 1858, p. 61 [Brazil].
Monanthia (Acanthocheila) spinuligera Stål 1858, p. 61.
Acanthochila armigera: Stål 1873, p. 127.—Distant 1888, p. lxxxiii.—
Champion 1897, p. 28, pl. 2, figs. 19, 19a, 20 [Mexico; Guatemala;
Panama]; 1898b, p. 60.—Van Duzee 1907, p. 20 [Jamaica].—
Osborn and Drake 1915b, p. 536.—Drake and Poor 1937d, p. 306

[Haiti; Peru; Bolivia; Colombia; Nicaragua; Puerto Rico; Cuba; Tex.].

Acanthochila spinuligera: Stål 1873, p. 127.

Acanthocheila armigera: Drake and Bruner 1924a, p. 146 [Trinidad].— Drake 1926b, p. 377; 1928e, p. 5 [Honduras].—Drake and Hambleton 1934, p. 442 [*Pisonia*]; 1945, p. 359 [Ecuador].—Costa Lima 1936, p. 124.—Monte 1938b, p. 128 [Argentina; Venezuela]; 1940d, p. 100 [*Nicotiana tabacum*]; 1942d, p. 108.—Singh 1953, p. 117.—Silva 1956, p. 15, fig. 1 [*Ouratea*].

Acanthocheila nigrescens (not Drake and Bondar): Monte 1937a, p. 31 [*Pisonia tomentosa*].

Type: Sex unknown; Rio de Janeiro, Brazil; Stockholm Mus.

Distribution: Argentina; Bolivia; Brazil; Peru; Ecuador; Colombia; Venezuela; Panama; Nicaragua; Honduras; Guatemala; Mexico; U.S. (Tex.); Cuba; Puerto Rico; Trinidad; Jamaica; Haiti.

Host Plants: *Nicotiana tabecum; Ouratea* sp.; *Pisonia tomentosa; Pisonia* sp.

*Acanthocheila comentis Drake

Acanthochila comentis Drake 1953a, p. 13 [Brazil].

Type: Holotype ♂, macropterous; Viçosa, Minas Gerais, Brazil; Drake Coll. (USNM).

Distribution: Brazil.

Host Plant: Unrecorded.

*Acanthocheila comitis Drake

Acanthocheila comitis Drake 1948c, p. 23 [Maria Magdalena Island].

Type: Holotype ♀; Magdalena Island, Tres Marias; Cal. Acad.

Distribution: Mexico, Los Tres Marias Islands (Maria Magdalena).

Host Plant: Unrecorded.

Acanthocheila denieri Monte

Acanthocheila denieri Monte 1940e, p. 287, fig. 1 [Argentina].

Type: Holotype ♂; Clorinda, Formosa, Argentina; Monte Coll. (Mus. Nacional).

Distribution: Argentina.

Host Plant: Unrecorded.

*Acanthocheila dira Drake and Hambleton

Acanthocheila dira Drake and Hambleton 1945, p. 359 [Guatemala].

Type: Holotype ♀, macropterous; El Porvenir, Guatemala; Drake Coll. (USNM).

Distribution: Guatemala.

Host Plant: Unrecorded.

*Acanthocheila exquisita Uhler

Acanthocheila exquisita Uhler 1889, p. 143 [Fla.].—Barber 1914, p. 507.—
Drake 1919a, p. 421.—Blatchley 1926, p. 479.—Monte 1940e, p.
288, fig. 2.

TYPE: Holotype ♀, macropterous; Cape Florida, Florida, U.S.; Cornell
Univ.

DISTRIBUTION: U.S. (Fla.); Bahama Islands.

HOST PLANT: Unrecorded.

*Acanthocheila hollandi Drake

Acanthocheila hollandi Drake 1935, p. 16 [Brazil; Paraguay]; 1947a, p.
2.—Drake and Hambleton 1938a, p. 46 [Bignoniaceae].—Monte
1940e, p. 287 [Argentina].

TYPE: Holotype ♀; Chapalo, Brazil; Carnegie Mus.

DISTRIBUTION: Brazil; Argentina; Paraguay.

HOST PLANT: Bignoniaceae.

*Acanthocheila nexa Drake

Acanthocheila nexa Drake 1936b, p. 701, fig. 1 [Argentina].—Monte
1940e, p. 288.

TYPE: Holotype ♀, macropterous; Loreto, Argentina; Leningrad Inst.

DISTRIBUTION: Argentina; Brazil.

HOST PLANT: Unrecorded.

*Acanthocheila nigrescens Drake and Bondar

Acanthocheila nigrescens Drake and Bondar 1932, p. 88 [Brazil; Sapotaceus
tree].—Costa Lima 1936, p. 124.

TYPE: Holotype ♂, macropterous; Bahia, Brazil; Drake Coll. (USNM).

DISTRIBUTION: Brazil.

HOST PLANT: Sapotaceus tree.

*Acanthocheila rustica Monte

Acanthocheila rustica Monte 1942, p. 91 [Brazil].

TYPE: Holotype ♂; Palmeiras, Ipaussú, São Paulo, Brazil; Monte Coll.
(Mus. Nacional).

DISTRIBUTION: Brazil.

HOST PLANT: Unrecorded.

*Acanthocheila rustica var. **plana** Drake

Acanthochila rustica var. *plana* Drake 1953a, p. 13 [Argentina].

TYPE: Holotype ♀, macropterous; Loreto, Misiones, Argentina; Drake
Coll. (USNM).

DISTRIBUTION: Argentina.

HOST PLANT: Unrecorded.

*Acanthocheila sigillata Drake and Bruner

Acanthocheila sigillata Drake and Bruner 1924a, p. 147 [Cuba; *Pisonia
aculeata*].—Drake 1926a, p. 86.—Bruner, Scaramuzza, and Otero
1945, p. 141.

TYPE: Holotype ♂, macropterous; Taco Taco, Pinar del Rio, Cuba; Drake Coll. (USNM).
DISTRIBUTION: Cuba.
HOST PLANT: *Pisonia aculeata*.

*Acanthocheila spinicosta Van Duzee

Acanthochila spinicosta Van Duzee 1907, p. 20 [Jamaica].
Acanthocheila spinicosta: Drake and Bruner 1924a, p. 146, fig. 1 [Dominican Republic].—Barber 1939, p. 370 [St. Thomas; Haiti; *Pisonia domingensis*].
Acanthocheila spinocosta [sic]: Gowdy 1926, p. 35.
TYPE: Sex unknown; Mandeville, Jamaica; Cal. Acad.
DISTRIBUTION: Jamaica; Haiti; Dominican Republic; Puerto Rico; Virgin Islands (St. Thomas).
HOST PLANTS: *Pisonia domingensis; Torrubia fragrans*.

*Acanthocheila thaumana Drake and Cobben

Acanthocheila thaumana Drake and Cobben 1960, pp. 67, 81, fig. 82 [St. Eustatius; St. Martin].
TYPE: Holotype ♂, macropterous; Koolbaai, St. Martin; Drake Coll. (USNM).
DISTRIBUTION: Leeward Islands (St. Eustatius; St. Martin).
HOST PLANT: Unrecorded.

*Acanthocheila tumida Drake

Acanthocheila tumida Drake 1924, p. 94 [Bolivia].—Drake and Hambleton 1938a, p. 46 [Brazil; *Anemopaegma prostratum*].—Monte 1938b, p. 128.
TYPE: Holotype ♀, macropterous; Cochabamba, Bolivia; Drake Coll. (USNM).
DISTRIBUTION: Bolivia; Brazil.
HOST PLANT: *Anemopaegma prostratum*.

*Acanthocheila visenda Drake and Hambleton

Acanthocheila visenda Drake and Hambleton 1934, p. 442 [Brazil].—Monte 1937a, p. 32 [*Bignonia exoleta*]; 1940e, p. 287 [Argentina]; 1943a, p. 105 [Peru].—Drake and Davis 1960, fig. 34.
TYPE: Holotype ♂, macropterous; Viçosa, Minas Gerais, Brazil; Drake Coll. (USNM).
DISTRIBUTION: Argentina; Brazil; Peru.
HOST PLANT: *Bignonia exoleta*.

Genus ACANTHOTINGIS Monte

Acanthotingis Monte 1940a, p. 13.—Drake and Ruhoff 1960a, p. 32.
TYPE SPECIES: *Acanthotingis apicicornis* Monte.

Acanthotingis apicicornis Monte

Acanthotingis apicicornis Monte 1940a, p. 15, fig. [Brazil]; 1940e, p. 300; 1941e, p. 149 [Rubiaceae].

TYPE: Holotype ♂; São Paulo, Brazil; Monte Coll. (Mus. Nacional).
DISTRIBUTION: Brazil.
HOST PLANT: Rubiaceae.

Genus ACONCHUS Horváth

Galeatus (*Aconchus*) Horváth 1905b, p. 566.
Aconchus: Horváth 1906a, pp. 14, 54.—Oshanin 1908, p. 424; 1912, p. 43.—Stichel 1926, pp. 104, 109.—Drake and Ruhoff 1960a, p. 32.

TYPE SPECIES: *Galeatus* (*Aconchus*) *urbanus* Horváth.

*****Aconchus urbanus** (Horváth)

Galeatus (*Aconchus*) *urbanus* Horváth 1905b, p. 565 [Italy].
Aconchus urbanus: Horváth 1906a, p. 54; 1912c, p. 341 [Java].—Drake and Poor 1937a, p. 17 [Malaya].—Drake and Ruhoff 1962d, p. 497.
Aconchus ghesquierei Schouteden 1923, p. 89 [Congo].—Mayné and Ghesquière 1934, p. 19 [papaya].

TYPE: Sex unknown; Turin, Italy; Paris Mus.
DISTRIBUTION: Italy; Congo; Kenya; South Africa; Mozambique; India; Ceylon; Federation of Malaya; Philippine Islands; Greater Sunda Islands (Java).
HOST PLANTS: *Urochloa reptans*; papaya.

Genus ACYSTA Champion

Acysta Champion 1898a, p. 46.—Costa Lima 1936, p. 124.—Monte 1939b, p. 64; 1941e, p. 76.—Hurd 1946, p. 458.—Drake and Ruhoff 1960a, p. 32.

TYPE SPECIES: *Acysta integra* Champion.

*****Acysta australica** Drake

Acysta australica Drake 1942a, p. 15 [Australia].
TYPE: Holotype ♀, macropterous; National Park, Australia; Drake Coll. (USNM).
DISTRIBUTION: Australia (Queensland).
HOST PLANT: Unrecorded.

*****Acysta hubbelli** Drake

Acysta hubbelli Drake 1928e, p. 2, fig. 1 [Honduras].
TYPE: Holotype ♂; Rio Sangrelaya, Honduras; Michigan Univ.
DISTRIBUTION: Honduras; Mexico (Vera Cruz).
HOST PLANT: Unrecorded.
NOTE: Collected on banana bits about to be planted.

Acysta integra Champion

Acysta integra Champion 1898a, p. 46, pl. 3, fig. 22 [Guatemala].
TYPE: Sex unknown; Cerro Zunil, Guatemala; British Mus.
DISTRIBUTION: Guatemala.
HOST PLANT: Unrecorded.

Acysta interrupta Champion

Acysta interrupta Champion 1898a, p. 47, pl. 3, fig. 23 [Panama].
TYPE: Sex unknown; Bugaba, Panama; British Mus.
DISTRIBUTION: Panama.
HOST PLANT: Unrecorded.

*Acysta myrocarpi Drake and Poor

Acysta myrocarpi Drake and Poor 1938a, p. 31 [Brazil].—Monte 1941e, p. 76 [*Myrocarpus fastigiatus*].
TYPE: Holotype ♂, macropterous; Belo Horizonte, Brazil; Drake Coll. (USNM).
DISTRIBUTION: Brazil.
HOST PLANT: *Myrocarpus fastigiatus.*

*Acysta nectandrae Drake and Hambleton

Acysta nectandrae Drake and Hambleton 1934, p. 439 [Brazil; *Nectandra*].
TYPE: Holotype ♂, macropterous; Viçosa, Minas Gerais, Brazil; Drake Coll. (USNM).
DISTRIBUTION: Brazil.
HOST PLANT: *Nectandra* sp.

*Acysta neivai Drake and Hambleton

Acysta neivai Drake and Hambleton 1940, p. 534 [Brazil].
TYPE: Holotype ♂, macropterous; Guarujá, São Paulo, Brazil; Drake Coll. (USNM).
DISTRIBUTION: Brazil.
HOST PLANT: Unrecorded.

*Acysta ocoteae Drake and Hambleton

Acysta ocoteae Drake and Hambleton 1935, p. 144 [Brazil; *Ocotea pretiosa*].
TYPE: Holotype ♂, macropterous; Viçosa, Minas Gerais, Brazil; Drake Coll. (USNM).
DISTRIBUTION: Brazil.
HOST PLANT: *Ocotea pretiosa.*

*Acysta praeclara Drake and Hambleton

Acysta praeclara Drake and Hambleton 1934, p. 439 [Brazil; Boraginaceae].—Drake and Davis 1960, fig. 70.
TYPE: Holotype ♂, macropterous; Viçosa, Minas Gerais, Brazil; Drake Coll. (USNM).
DISTRIBUTION: Brazil.
HOST PLANT: Boraginaceae.

Genus AEPYCYSTA Drake and Bondar

Aepycysta Drake and Bondar 1932, p. 93.—Monte 1939b, p. 65; 1941e, p. 77.—Hurd 1946, p. 478.—Drake and Ruhoff 1960a, p. 33.

TYPE SPECIES: *Aepycysta undosa* Drake and Bondar.

Aepycysta decorata Monte

Aepycysta decorata Monte 1941d, p. 93, fig. 1 [Costa Rica].

TYPE: Holotype ♂; San Isidro de Coronado, Alajuela, Costa Rica; Monte Coll. (Mus. Nacional).

DISTRIBUTION: Costa Rica.

HOST PLANT: Unrecorded.

*Aepycysta schwarzi (Drake)

Galeatus schwarzi Drake 1922b, p. 39, fig. 1 [Canal Zone].

Aepycysta schwarzi: Drake and Hambleton 1935, p. 153.

Aepycysta schwartzi [sic]: Drake and Davis 1960, fig. 59.

TYPE: Holotype ♂, macropterous; Paraíso, Panama Canal Zone; USNM.

DISTRIBUTION: Panama (Canal Zone).

HOST PLANT: Unrecorded.

*Aepycysta undosa Drake and Bondar

Aepycysta undosa Drake and Bondar 1932, p. 94, fig. 1 [Brazil; *Ichnanthus leiocarpus*].—Drake and Hambleton 1935, p. 153.—Costa Lima 1936, p. 125.—Monte 1938b, p. 127.—Silva 1956, p. 16, fig. 2.

TYPE: Holotype ♂, macropterous; Bahia, Brazil; Drake Coll. (USNM).

DISTRIBUTION: Brazil; Paraguay.

HOST PLANT: *Ichnanthus leiocarpus.*

Genus AFRAMIXIA Drake and Ruhoff

Aframixia Drake and Ruhoff 1960a, p. 33.

TYPE SPECIES: *Epimixia roboris* Drake.

*Aframixia roboris (Drake)

Epimixia roboris Drake 1942a, p. 12 [Malagasy].

Aframixia roboris: Drake and Ruhoff 1960a, p. 33.

TYPE: Holotype ♀, macropterous; Madagascar; Drake Coll. (USNM).

DISTRIBUTION: Malagasy Republic.

HOST PLANT: Unrecorded.

Genus AGACHILA Drake and Gomez-Menor

Agachila Drake and Gomez-Menor 1954, p. 89.—Drake and Ruhoff 1960a, p. 34.

TYPE SPECIES: *Agachila biafrana* Drake and Gomez-Menor.

Agachila biafrana Drake and Gomez-Menor

Agachila biafrana Drake and Gomez-Menor 1954, p. 90, fig. 1 [Spanish Guinea].

TYPE: Holotype ♀; Biafra, Cabo San Juan, Escalera, Spanish Guinea; Inst. Ent. Madrid.

DISTRIBUTION: Spanish Guinea.

HOST PLANT: Unrecorded.

Genus AGAOTINGIS Drake

Agaotingis Drake 1954b, p. 13.—Drake and Ruhoff 1960a, p. 34.

TYPE SPECIES: *Tingis australis* Montrouzier.

*****Agaotingis australis** (Montrouzier)

Tingis australis Montrouzier 1864, p. 235 [New Caledonia].—Stål 1873, p. 134.

Agaotingis australis: Drake 1954b, p. 13.

TYPE: Holotype ♂, macropterous; New Caledonia; Drake Coll. (USNM).

DISTRIBUTION: New Caledonia.

HOST PLANT: Unrecorded.

Genus AGLOTINGIS Drake

Aglotingis Drake 1954a, p. 232.—Drake and Ruhoff 1960a, p. 34.

TYPE SPECIES: *Aglotingis nimbana* Drake.

Aglotingis affinis Schouteden

Aglotingis affinis Schouteden 1955a, p. 32 [Congo].

TYPE: Sex unknown; Kikongo, Belgian Congo; Cent. Afr. Mus.

DISTRIBUTION: Congo.

HOST PLANT: Unrecorded.

Aglotingis basilewskyi Schouteden

Aglotingis basilewskyi Schouteden 1955a, p. 31 [Congo; Ruanda]; 1957c, p. 313.

TYPE: Unknown.

DISTRIBUTION: Congo; Ruanda-Urundi.

HOST PLANT: Unrecorded.

*****Aglotingis nimbana** Drake

Aglotingis nimbana Drake 1954a, p. 233 [French Guinea]; 1955b, p. 90 [Angola].

TYPE: Holotype ♀, macropterous; Mt. Nimba, French Guinea; Inst. Fr. Afr. N.

DISTRIBUTION: Guinea; Angola.

HOST PLANT: Unrecorded.

Genus AGRAMMA Stephens

Agramma Stephens 1829a, p. 64; 1829b, p. 336.—Westwood 1840b, p. 120.—Fieber 1844, p. 36; 1861, p. 118.—Garbiglietti 1869, p. 272.— Walker 1873b, p. 2.—Horváth 1874b, p. 432.—China 1943, p. 248.—Hoberlandt 1955, p. 96.—Drake 1955d, p. 1.—Drake and Maa 1955, p. 10.—Drake and Ruhoff 1960a, p. 23.—Stichel 1960a, p. 344 (key); 1960b, p. 402; 1960c, p. 141.

Serenthia Spinola 1837, p. 168.—Herrich-Schaeffer 1838, p. 47.— Stål 1873, p. 117; 1874, p. 46.—Lethierry and Severin 1896, p. 5.— Horváth 1906a, pp. 13, 107 (key).—Mužik 1907, p. 49 (key).— Oshanin 1908, p. 457; 1912, p. 46.—Schumacher 1914, p. 259; 1919, p. 202.—Stichel 1926, p. 116 (key); 1935, p. 349; 1938a, p. 408.—Börner 1935, p. 78 (key).—Gulde 1938, p. 321 (key).— Wagner 1941, pp. 1–27 (key; subgenera).—Blöte 1945, p. 79.— Kiritshenko 1951, pp. 243, 254 (key).—Mancini 1953b, p. 186; 1953d, p. 16.—Drake 1954b, p. 13; 1956a, p. 7; 1958a, p. 107.— Gomez-Menor 1955b, p. 248.—Drake and Ruhoff 1960a, p. 25.

Wombalia Schouteden 1919, p. 139.—Drake and Ruhoff 1960a, p. 25.

Serenthia (*Agramma*): Wagner 1941, pp. 6, 26.

Serenthia (*Paraserenthia*) Wagner 1941, pp. 6, 26.—Drake and Ruhoff 1960a, p. 25.

Serenthia (*Serenthiella*) Wagner 1941, pp. 6, 24, 26.—Drake and Ruhoff 1960a, p. 25.

Drakea Schouteden 1953d, p. 166.—Drake and Ruhoff 1960a, p. 24.

TYPE SPECIES: *Tingis laeta* Fallén.

*Agramma afranum Drake and Ruhoff

Agramma angolana Drake 1958a, p. 107, fig. (not 1955) [Angola].

Agramma afrana Drake and Ruhoff 1960c, p. 36.

TYPE: Holotype ♂; Alto Chicapa, Angola; Cent. Afr. Mus.

DISTRIBUTION: Angola.

HOST PLANT: Unrecorded.

*Agramma aliwalanum (Drake)

Serenthia aliwalana Drake 1954b, p. 14 [Cape Province].

Agramma aliwalanum: Drake 1958a, p. 107.

TYPE: Holotype ♂; North Aliwal, Cape Province, South Africa; British Mus.

DISTRIBUTION: South Africa (Cape Province).

HOST PLANT: Unrecorded.

*Agramma angolanum (Drake)

Serenthia angolana Drake 1955b, p. 90 [Angola].

Agramma angolanum: Drake 1958a, p. 107.

TYPE: Holotype ♂; Serra do Moco, Luimbale, Angola; Cent. Afr. Mus.

DISTRIBUTION: Angola.

HOST PLANT: Unrecorded.

*Agramma atricapillum (Spinola)

Serenthia atricapilla Spinola 1837, p. 168 [Sardinia].—Herrich-Schaeffer 1838, p. 48.—Amyot and Serville 1843, p. 300.—Costa 1847a, p. 24; 1847c, p. 164.—Garbiglietti 1869, p. 272 [Italy].—Stål 1874, p. 47.— Puton 1879c, p. 89 [France; Corsica].—Bolivar and Chicote 1879, p. 166 [Spain].—Jakovlev 1880b, p. 100 [Caucasus].—Horváth 1889, p. 329; 1892b, p. 131; 1906d, p. 2; 1916, p. 9.—Reuter 1891a, p. 25 [Greece; Albania; Crete]; 1908, p. 89 [*Juncus*].—Lethierry and Severin 1896, p. 5 [Algeria].—Oshanin 1908, p. 457 [Morocco].— Moroder Sala 1920, p. 13.—de Seabra 1924, p. 18, fig. 32 [Portugal]; 1931, p. 442, figs. 512(1–4), 513.—Lindberg 1932a, p. 45 [*Scirpus holoschoenus*]; 1948, p. 60 [Sicily; Egypt; Bulgaria; *Juncus acutus*].— Wagner 1941, pp. 6, 13, 26, figs. 2d, 3e, 4d, 5f, 6d.—Hoberlandt 1949, p. 8 [Tunisia].—Kiritshenko 1951, p. 254 [Ukraine; Crimea].— Novak and Wagner 1951, p. 71 [*Typha latifolia*].—Seidenstücker 1954, p. 236.

Agramma atricapilla: Fieber 1844, p. 39; 1861, p. 118 [Yugoslavia].— Mayr 1858, p. 569 [Hungary].—Jakovlev 1871, p. 7; 1876b, p. 66.— Hoberlandt 1955, p. 96 [Israel; Iraq].—Gomez-Menor 1956b, p. 82, fig.—Stichel 1960a, p. 345, figs. 183–186 [*Juncus maritumus*].

Serenthia brevirostris Jakovlev 1901, p. 35.

Serenthia antricapilla [sic]: Horváth 1906a, p. 110 [Rumania; Turkestan; Turkey].

TYPE: Sardinia; sex and deposition of type unknown.

DISTRIBUTION: Portugal; Spain; France; Corsica; Italy; Sicily; Sardinia; Hungary; Bulgaria; Rumania; Yugoslavia; Albania; Greece; Crete; Turkey; Iraq; Israel; U.S.S.R. (Caucasus; Ukraine; Crimea; Turkestan); Egypt; Morocco; Algeria; Tunisia.

HOST PLANTS: *Juncus acutus; Juncus maritimus; Juncus* sp.; *Scirpus holoschoenus; Typha latifolia.*

Agramma atricapillum var. **mendax** (Horváth)

Serenthia antricapilla [sic] var. *mendax* Horváth 1906a, pp. 107, 111 [Turkestan].

TYPE: Sex unknown; Michailovo, Turkestan, Russia; Hungarian Mus.

DISTRIBUTION: U.S.S.R. (Turkestan).

HOST PLANT: Unrecorded.

Agramma atricapillum var. **pallens** (Horváth)

Serenthia antricapilla [sic] var. *pallens* Horváth 1906a, p. 111 [Egypt].

Serenthia atricapilla var. *pallens:* Priesner and Alfieri 1953, p. 66 [Gramineae].

TYPE: Sex unknown; Fayum, Egypt; Hungarian Mus.

DISTRIBUTION: Egypt.

HOST PLANT: Gramineae.

*Agramma basilicorne (Drake)

Serenthia basilicornis Drake 1951, p. 167 [Tanganyika].

TYPE: Holotype ♂; Shirati, Africa orientalis; Hungarian Mus.

DISTRIBUTION: Tanganyika; Egypt.

HOST PLANT: Unrecorded.

*Agramma blandulum (Horváth)

Serenthia blandula Horváth 1905b, p. 558 [Caucasus]; 1906a, p. 116 [Turkey].—Kiritshenko 1951, p. 255 [Crimea].

Serenthia (Serenthiella) blandula: Wagner 1941, p. 25.

Agramma (Serenthiella) blandula: Hoberlandt 1955, p. 97.

Agramma blandula: Stichel 1960a, p. 35, fig. 217 [Greece].

TYPE: Sex unknown; Caucasus, Russia; Paris Mus.

DISTRIBUTION: U.S.S.R. (Caucasus; Crimea); Turkey; Greece.

HOST PLANT: Unrecorded.

*Agramma carinatum (Distant)

Serenthia carinata Distant 1911b, p. 269 [Ceylon; *Juncus*].

TYPE: Sex unknown; Ambalangoda Lake, Ceylon; British Mus.

DISTRIBUTION: Ceylon.

HOST PLANT: *Juncus* sp.

*Agramma confusum (Puton)

Serenthia laeta (not Fallén): Herrich-Schaeffer 1838, p. 49, pl. 122, fig. 388.—Amyot and Serville 1843, p. 300 (in part) [France].—Costa 1847a, p. 24; 1847c, p. 164.

Sercuthia [sic] *femoralis* var. *confusa* Puton 1879b, p. 297.

Serenthia femoralis var. *confusa:* Puton 1879c, p. 90 [Corsica].—Chicote 1880, p. 189 [Spain].—Horváth 1906d, p. 2.

Serenthia confusa: Reuter 1885, p. 43.—Horváth 1906a, pp. 109, 114 [Italy; Germany; Hungary; Yugoslavia; Greece; Rumania; Russia; Turkey; *Juncus*]; 1916, p. 9 [Albania]; 1918, p. 334.—Stichel 1926, p. 117 [*Plantago maritima*].—Börner 1935, p. 79, fig. 121 [*Juncus gerardi*].—Gulde 1938, p. 326, fig. [Cyperaceae].—Kiritshenko 1951, p. 254 [Ukraine; Crimea].—Mancini 1953b, p. 186 [Turkestan].

Serenthia (Agramma) confusa: Wagner 1941, pp. 7, 15, 26, figs. 7a, 8a, 9a, 11a.—Hoberlandt 1942, p. 126 [Czechoslovakia].

Agramma confusa: Hoberlandt 1955, p. 96 [Transcaucasus].—Stichel 1960a, p. 349, figs. 206–207 [Bulgaria; Poland; Austria].

TYPE: Unknown.

DISTRIBUTION: Spain; France; Germany; Austria; Czechoslovakia; Poland; Hungary; Italy; Corsica; Rumania; Bulgaria; Albania; Yugoslavia; Greece; Turkey; U.S.S.R. (Caucasus; Ukraine; Crimea; Transcaucasus; Turkestan).

HOST PLANTS: *Juncus gerardi; Juncus* sp.; *Plantago maritima;* Cyperaceae.

Agramma confusum var. **antennatum** (Horváth)

Serenthia femoralis var. *antennata* Horváth 1905b, p. 556 [Rumania].
Serenthia confusa var. *antennata:* Horváth 1906a, p. 114 [Hungary; Turkestan].
TYPE: Sex unknown; Rumania; Hungarian Mus.
DISTRIBUTION: Rumania; Hungary; U.S.S.R. (Turkestan).
HOST PLANT: Unrecorded.

Agramma confusum var. **thoracicum** (Horváth)

Serenthia femoralis var. *thoracica* Horváth 1905b, p. 557 [Hungary].
Serenthia confusa var. *thoracica:* Horváth 1906a, p. 114.—Hoberlandt 1943, pp. 116, 117 [Czechoslovakia].
TYPE: Sex unknown; Hungary; Hungarian Mus.
DISTRIBUTION: Hungary; Czechoslovakia.
HOST PLANT: Unrecorded.

*Agramma dilectulum (Drake)

Serenthia dilectula Drake 1951, p. 168 [Ethiopia].
Agramma dilectula: Drake 1956f, p. 429 [Cape Province]; 1958a, p. 107.
TYPE: Holotype ♂; Maraquo, Abyssinia; Hungarian Mus.
DISTRIBUTION: Ethiopia; South Africa (Cape Province).
HOST PLANT: Unrecorded.

*Agramma dubium (Horváth)

Serenthia ruficornis var. *dubia* Horváth 1905b, p. 556 [Algeria].
Serenthia dubia: Horváth 1906a, p. 112.—Lindberg 1932a, p. 45 [Spain].
Agramma dubia: Drake 1958a, p. 107 [Mauritania].—Stichel 1960a, p. 347 [Morocco].
TYPE: Sex unknown; Philippeville, Algeria; Hungarian Mus.
DISTRIBUTION: Algeria; Mauritania; Tunisia; Spain.
HOST PLANT: Unrecorded.

Agramma dubium var. **imbecillum** (Horváth)

Serenthia femoralis var. *imbecilla* Horváth 1905b, p. 557 [Mauritania].
Serenthia dubia var. *imbecilla:* Horváth 1906a, p. 113.—Lindberg 1932a, p. 45 [Spain; Morocco; *Scirpus holoschoenus*].
Agramma dubia var. *imbecilla:* Stichel 1960a, p. 347.
TYPE: Sex unknown; Mauritania; Hungarian Mus.
DISTRIBUTION: Mauritania; Morocco; Spain.
HOST PLANT: *Scirpus holoschoenus.*

Agramma ecmeles Drake and Ruhoff

Agramma ecmeles Drake and Ruhoff 1962a, p. 164 [Western Australia].
TYPE: Holotype ♂, macropterous; Kimberley District, north Western Australia, Australia; Stockholm Mus.
DISTRIBUTION: Australia (Western Australia).
HOST PLANT: Unrecorded.

*Agramma elegans Kiritshenko

Agramma elegans Kiritshenko 1952, p. 180, fig. 26 [Russia].

TYPE: Sex unknown; Tadshikistan, Russia; Leningrad Inst.

DISTRIBUTION: U.S.S.R.

HOST PLANT: Unrecorded.

Agramma fallax (Horváth)

Serenthia confusa var. *fallax* Horváth 1906a, p. 114 [Hungary; Russia].

Serenthia fallax: Stichel 1926, p. 117 [Germany].—Börner 1935, p. 79 [*Juncus*].

Serenthia (*Agramma*) *fallax:* Wagner 1941, pp. 7, 17, 26.

Agramma fallax: Stichel 1960a, p. 349.

TYPE: Unknown.

DISTRIBUTION: Germany; Hungary; U.S.S.R.

HOST PLANT: *Juncus* sp.

*Agramma femorale Thomson

Agramma laetum (not Fallén): Flor 1860, p. 324 [Sweden; Germany; France; England; Italy; Spain; *Schoenus albus*].

Agramma femoralis Thomson 1871, p. 397.—Stichel 1960a, p. 351 [*Rhynchospora alba*].

Serenthia femoralis: Stål 1874, p. 46.—Reuter 1874, p. 562 [Finland; *Eriophorum angustifolium*]; 1882b, p. 111; 1885, p. 43; 1890a, p. 249.— Sahlberg 1878, p. 20 [Latvia]; 1920, p. 86.—Hüeber 1893, p. 299 [Hungary; Austria].

Serenthia femorata [sic]: Jakovlev 1893, p. 293 [Russia].

Serenthia laeta var. *femoralis:* Horváth 1906a, p. 115 [Siberia].—Oshanin 1908, p. 461 [Morocco; Rumania].—Kiritshenko 1951, p. 254.

Serenthia (*Agramma*) *laeta* var. *femoralis:* Wagner 1941, p. 24, fig. 10e.

TYPE: Unknown.

DISTRIBUTION: Sweden; Finland; U.S.S.R. (Latvia; Siberia); Hungary; Austria; Germany; France; Rumania; Italy; Spain; England; Morocco.

HOST PLANTS: *Eriophorum angustifolium; Rhynchospora alba; Schoenus albus.*

Agramma femorale var. **poppii** (Horváth)

Serenthia laeta var. *poppii* Horváth 1906a, p. 116 [Siberia].—Stichel 1926, p. 118.—Gulde 1938, p. 327.

Serenthia femoralis var. *poppiusi:* Sahlberg 1920, p. 86 [Finland].

Serenthia laeta var. *poppiusi:* Stichel 1935, p. 350; 1938b, p. 455.

Agramma femoralis var. *poppiusi:* Stichel 1960a, p. 351.

TYPE: Sex unknown; Saoneskje Kosmosero, Siberia, Russia; Helsin. Mus.

DISTRIBUTION: U.S.S.R. (Siberia); Finland.

HOST PLANT: Unrecorded.

Agramma formosanum (Matsumura)

Serenthia formosana Matsumura 1910, p. 24, pl. 12, fig. 10 [Taiwan]; 1911, p. 138.—Esaki 1926, p. 163; 1932, p. 1637, fig.—Takeya 1951a, p. 23 [*Saccharum officinarum*].—Box 1953, p. 37.

TYPE: Holotype ♀; Rinkiho, Formosa; deposition unknown.
DISTRIBUTION: Taiwan.
HOST PLANT: *Saccharum officinarum.*

*Agramma gibbum Fieber

Agramma gibba Fieber 1844, p. 38, pl. 3, figs. 7–11 [Ostindien].
Serenthia gibba: Stål 1873, p. 117 [India orientalis].—Distant 1903b,
p. 127, fig. 91 [India].—Drake 1938b, p. 195 [East Indies; Hainan
Island].—Blöte 1945, p. 79.
TYPE: Sex unknown; "Ostindien"; Vienna Mus.
DISTRIBUTION: India; East Indies(?); China (Hainan Island); Ceylon.
HOST PLANT: Unrecorded.

Agramma globiceps (Horváth)

Serenthia globiceps Horváth 1906a, p. 111 [Syria].
TYPE: Sex unknown; Jaffa, Syria; Hungarian Mus.
DISTRIBUTION: Syria.
HOST PLANT: Unrecorded.

*Agramma gracilicorne (Wagner)

Serenthia (Paraserenthia) gracilicornis Wagner 1941, pp. 6, 11, 26, figs. 2b,
3b, 4 c, f, 5b, 6b [Germany].
Agramma gracilicornis: Stichel 1960a, p. 346, figs. 193–196 [Austria;
Poland].
TYPE: Sex unknown; Germany; Wagner Coll.
DISTRIBUTION: Germany; Austria; Poland.
HOST PLANT: Unrecorded.

*Agramma hupehanum (Drake and Maa)

Serenthia hupehana Drake and Maa 1954, p. 111 [China].
TYPE: Holotype ♂; Suisapa, Western Hupeh, China; Cal. Acad.
DISTRIBUTION: China; India (Bengal).
HOST PLANT: Unrecorded.

*Agramma intermedium (Wagner)

Serenthia (Agramma) intermedia Wagner 1941, pp. 7, 20, 26, figs. 7c, 8c, 9c,
10 a, c, 11c [Trieste].
Serenthia intermedia: Novak and Wagner 1951, p. 71 [Yugoslavia; *Typha
latifolia*].—Mancini 1953b, p. 186 [Italy; Germany; Hungary;
Greece].
Agramma intermedia: Hoberlandt 1955, p. 96 [Turkey].—Stichel 1960a,
p. 348, figs. 197–200 [France; Austria; Czechoslovakia; Poland].
TYPE: Sex unknown; Trieste; Wagner Coll.
DISTRIBUTION: Trieste; Yugoslavia; Greece; Turkey; Hungary; Austria;
Italy; Czechoslovakia; Germany; Poland; France.
HOST PLANT: *Typha latifolia.*

*Agramma japonicum (Drake)

Serenthia japonica Drake 1948g, p. 174 [Japan].—Takeya 1951a, p. 23.—
Drake and Maa 1953, p. 88 [China].

TYPE: Holotype ♀, brachypterous; Sapporo, Japan: Drake Coll. (USNM).
DISTRIBUTION: Japan; China.
HOST PLANT: Unrecorded.

*Agramma karisimbiense (Schouteden)

Serenthia karisimbiensis Schouteden 1953d, p. 165 [Ruanda].
Agramma karisimbiensis: Drake 1958a, p. 107.

TYPE: Sex unknown; Nya Muzinga, Volcan Karisimibi, Ruanda; Cent.
Afr. Mus.
DISTRIBUTION: Ruanda-Urundi; Kenya.
HOST PLANT: Unrecorded.

*Agramma kivuanum (Drake)

Serenthia kivuana Drake 1956a, p. 8 [Congo].
Agramma kivuanum: Drake 1958a, p. 107.

TYPE: Holotype ♂; lac Magera, Kivu, Belgian Congo; Parcs Nat. Inst.
DISTRIBUTION: Congo.
HOST PLANT: Unrecorded.

*Agramma laetum (Fallén)

Tingis laeta Fallén 1807, p. 40 [Sweden; Germany]; 1829, p. 151.—
Germar 1835, fasc. 10, tab. 14.—Herrich-Schaeffer 1835, p. 59.—
Brullé 1835, p. 340.—Blanchard 1840, p. 112.

Agramma laeta: Stephens 1829a, p. 64 [England]; 1829b, p. 336.—
Westwood 1840b, p. 120.—Fieber 1844, p. 37, pl. 2, figs. 22–28
[Czechoslovakia; Italy]; 1861, p. 119.—Mayr 1858, p. 569 [Hungary;
Austria; moss].—Frey-Gessner 1865, p. 231 [Switzerland; *Carex*].—
Douglas and Scott 1865, p. 242.—Jakovlev 1869, p. 111 [Russia].—
Gredler 1870, p. 75.—Štušak 1958, p. 362, figs. 1–4.—Southwood
and Leston 1959, p. 151, pl. 18, fig. 1.—Drake and Ruhoff 1960a,
pl. 1.—Stichel 1960a, p. 350, figs. 212–214 [Sardinia; Poland].

Piesma tricolor Laporte 1833, p. 48 [France].

Piesma laetum: Burmeister 1835, p. 257.

Serenthia laeta: Herrich-Schaeffer 1838, p. 49, pl. 122, figs. b–f; pl. 125,
fig. c.—Amyot and Serville 1843, p. 300 (in part).—Stål 1874, p. 46.—
Saunders 1875, p. 246; 1892a, p. 123, pl. 11, fig. 5 [heath].—Reiber
and Puton 1876, p. 67.—Puton 1879c, p. 90 [Corsica].—Bolivar and
Chicote 1879, p. 166 [Spain; Portugal].—Jakovlev 1880b, p. 100
[Caucasus]; 1893, p. 293.—Reuter 1882b, p. 111 [*Juncus*]; 1890a,
p. 249; 1891a, p. 25 [Greece].—Dubois 1888, p. 120.—Hüeber 1893,
p. 297.—Rey 1893, p. 97.—Horváth 1905b, p. 557 [Trieste]; 1906a,
pp. 110, 115 [Siberia; *Schoenus albus*].—Mužik 1907, p. 49, fig. 2.—
Oshanin 1908, p. 460 [Belgium; Yugoslavia].—Jensen-Haarup 1912,

p. 149, fig. 93 [Denmark].—Reichensperger 1920, p. 61.—Butler
1923, p. 200 [Wales; rushes].—Stichel 1926, p. 118, fig. 309 [*Rhynchospora alba*]; 1938a, p. 408 [Finland; Norway].—de Seabra 1931, p. 443,
figs. 512(6), 515.—Scholte 1935, p. 92, fig. 27 [*Luzula campestris*].—
Poisson 1938, p. 589 [*Juncus maritimus*].—Blöte 1945, p. 80.—Kiritshenko 1951, p. 254, fig. 330.—Gomez-Menor 1956a, p. 115, fig. 10
(fig. only).
Agramma laetum: Vollenhoven 1878, p. 285, pl. 22, fig. 11 [Netherlands].
Serenthia (Agramma) laeta: Wagner 1941, pp. 6, 21, 26, figs. 1, 6g, 7d,
8d, 9d, 10d, 11d.—Hoberlandt 1942, p. 126.
TYPE: Unknown.
DISTRIBUTION: England; Wales; Netherlands; Belgium; France; Portugal;
Spain; Corsica; Sardinia; Italy; Switzerland; Germany; Austria; Czecho-
slovakia; Hungary; Trieste; Yugoslavia; Greece; U.S.S.R. (Caucasus;
Siberia); Poland; Finland; Denmark; Norway; Sweden; Mongolia
Republic.
HOST PLANTS: *Carex* sp.; *Juncus maritimus; Juncus* sp.; *Luzula campestris;*
Rhynchospora alba; Schoenus albus; heath; rushes; moss.
NOTE: Eggs [Štusak].

*Agramma laetum var. apicicorne (Horváth)

Serenthia laeta var. *apicicornis* Horváth 1905b, p. 557 [Trieste]; 1906a,
p. 115.
TYPE: Holotype ♀; Trieste; Hungarian Mus.
DISTRIBUTION: Trieste.
HOST PLANT: Unrecorded.

Agramma leleupi (Schouteden)

Drakea leleupi Schouteden 1953d, p. 166 [Congo].
TYPE: Sex unknown; Kundelungu, Belgian Congo; Cent. Afr. Mus.
DISTRIBUTION: Congo.
HOST PLANT: Unrecorded.

*Agramma lineatum (Horváth)

Serenthia lineata Horváth 1929, p. 326 [Natal].
Agramma lineatum: Drake 1958a, p. 107.
TYPE: Sex unknown; Weenan, Natal, South Africa; British Mus.
DISTRIBUTION: South Africa (Natal).
HOST PLANT: Unrecorded.

*Agramma longum (Drake)

Serenthia longa Drake 1954b, p. 13 [Cape Province].
Agramma longum: Drake 1958a, p. 107.
TYPE: Holotype ♂; Ceres, Cape Province, South Africa; British Mus.
DISTRIBUTION: South Africa (Cape Province).
HOST PLANT: Unrecorded.

*Agramma longurium Drake

Agramma longuria Drake 1958b, p. 30 [Congo].
TYPE: Holotype ♂; Lusinga, Belgian Congo; Parcs Nat. Inst.
DISTRIBUTION: Congo.
HOST PLANT: Unrecorded.

*Agramma maynei (Schouteden)

Serenthia maynei Schouteden 1916b, p. 291 [Congo]; 1923, p. 84.
Agramma maynei: Drake 1958a, p. 107.
TYPE: Sex unknown; Congo da Lemba, Belgian Congo; Cent. Afr. Mus.
DISTRIBUTION: Congo.
HOST PLANT: Unrecorded.

*Agramma melanoscele (Horváth)

Serenthia melanoscelis Horváth 1906a, p. 114 [Algeria].—Blöte 1945, p. 80
    [Tunisia].
Serenthia (Agramma) melanoscelis: Wagner 1941, pp. 7, 18, 26, figs. 7b,
    8b, 9b, 11b [Germany; *Juncus*].
Agramma malonascelis [sic]: Drake 1958a, p. 107.
Agramma melanoscelis: Stichel 1960a, p. 348, figs. 201–204.
TYPE: Sex unknown; Tlemcen, Algeria; Hungarian Mus.
DISTRIBUTION: Algeria; Tunisia; Upper Volta; Germany.
HOST PLANT: *Juncus* sp.

Agramma melanoscele var. muelleri (Wagner)

Serenthia (Agramma) melanoscelis var. *muelleri* Wagner 1941, p. 19
    [Germany].
Agramma melanoscelis var. *muelleri:* Stichel 1960a, p. 348.
TYPE: Sex unknown; Nurnburg, Germany; Wagner Coll.
DISTRIBUTION: Germany.
HOST PLANT: Unrecorded.

Agramma minor (Distant)

Lullius? minor Distant 1904, p. 430, pl. 8, fig. 8 [Cape Province].
Agramma minor: Drake and Ruhoff 1960a, p. 24.
TYPE: Sex unknown; Cape Colony, South Africa; British Mus.
DISTRIBUTION: South Africa (Cape Province).
HOST PLANT: Unrecorded.

*Agramma minutum Horváth

Agramma minutum Horváth 1874a, p. 333 [Hungary].
Agramma depressa Jakovlev 1874b, p. 265 [Russia].
Serenthia depressa: Puton 1876, p. 290.—Jakovlev 1893, p. 293.
Serenthia minuta: Hüeber 1893, p. 300 [Austria].—Horváth 1906a, p. 116
    [Siberia; Rumania].—Oshanin 1908, p. 462 [Caucasus].—Hober-
    landt 1943, pp. 116, 117.—Kiritshenko 1951, p. 255 [Ukraine].—
    Remold 1959, p. 1, fig. 1.

Serenthia (Serenthiella) minuta: Wagner 1941, pp. 8, 25, 26, figs. 7f, 8f, 11e.—Hoberlandt 1942, p. 126 [Germany; Czechoslovakia].
Agramma minuta: Wagner 1958, p. 241 [France].—Stichel 1960a, p. 351 [Bulgaria].

TYPE: Sex unknown; Hungary; Hungarian Mus.

DISTRIBUTION: France; Germany; Czechoslovakia; Austria; Hungary; Rumania; Bulgaria; U.S.S.R. (Siberia; Caucasus; Ukraine).

HOST PLANT: Unrecorded.

*Agramma nexile (Drake)

Serenthia nexilis Drake 1948g, p. 174 [Taiwan; Japan].—Takeya 1951a, p. 23; 1953d, p. 167.—Esaki 1954, p. 238, fig. 615.

TYPE: Holotype ♂, macropterous; Formosa; Drake Coll. (USNM).

DISTRIBUTION: Taiwan; Japan.

HOST PLANT: Unrecorded.

Agramma nigrellum Drake

Agramma nigrella Drake 1958a, p. 108, fig. [Angola].

TYPE: Holotype ♂; Vila Luso, Angola; Cent. Afr. Mus.

DISTRIBUTION: Angola.

HOST PLANT: Unrecorded.

NOTE: Taken in light trap [Drake].

*Agramma nigrum Fieber

Agramma nigra Fieber 1844, p. 40, pl. 3, figs. 12–17 [Sicily; *Statice*]; 1861, p. 118.—Herrich-Schaeffer 1850, p. 150.—Drake 1958a, p. 107.—Stichel 1960a, p. 347.
Serenthia nigra: Garbiglietti 1869, p. 272.—Stål 1874, p. 46.—Horváth 1906a, p. 113 [Tunisia; Algeria].

TYPE: Sex unknown; Sicily; Vienna Mus.

DISTRIBUTION: Sicily; Algeria; Tunisia.

HOST PLANT: *Statice* sp.

Agramma nigrum var. collare (Horváth)

Serenthia nigra var. *collaris* Horváth 1905b, p. 558 [Sicily; Algeria]; 1906a, p. 114.
Agramma nigra var. *collaris:* Stichel 1960a, p. 347.

TYPE: Unknown.

DISTRIBUTION: Sicily; Algeria.

HOST PLANT: Unrecorded.

*Agramma onar Drake   PLATE 14

Agramma onar Drake 1961c, p. 130, pl. 9 [Natal].

TYPE: Holotype ♂, brachypterous; Cathedral Peak Forestry Reserve, Natal Drakensberg, headwaters of the Indumeni River, South Africa; Natal Museum, Pietermaritzburg, Natal, South Africa.

DISTRIBUTION: South Africa (Natal).

HOST PLANT: Unrecorded.

Agramma pallidulum (Schouteden)

Serenthia pallidula Schouteden 1955a, p. 26 [Congo].
Agramma pallida [sic]: Schouteden 1957c, p. 312 [Ruanda].
Agramma pallidulum: Drake 1958a, p. 107.
TYPE: Sex unknown; Rutshuru, Belgian Congo; Cent. Afr. Mus.
DISTRIBUTION: Congo; Ruanda-Urundi.
HOST PLANT: Unrecorded.

Agramma pallidulum var. **pictum** (Schouteden)

Serenthia pallidula var. *picta* Schouteden 1955a, p. 27 [Congo].
TYPE: Sex unknown; Belgian Congo; Cent. Afr. Mus.
DISTRIBUTION: Congo.
HOST PLANT: Unrecorded.

*Agramma peringueyi (Distant)

Serenthia peringueyi Distant 1904, p. 429, pl. 8, fig. 6 [South Africa].—
  Drake 1956a, p. 7 [Ruanda].
Agramma peringueyi: Drake 1956f, p. 429 [Basutoland]; 1958a, p. 107;
  1958c, p. 316 [Malagasy; Kenya].
TYPE: Sex unknown; South Africa; So. Afr. Mus.
DISTRIBUTION: South Africa; Basutoland; Kenya; Ruanda-Urundi;
Malagasy Republic.
HOST PLANT: Unrecorded.

Agramma pictipenne (Horváth)

Serenthia pictipennis Horváth 1902b, p. 604 [New South Wales].
Agramma pictipennis: Drake and Ruhoff 1961b, p. 180, fig. 21.
TYPE: Sex unknown; Glen Innes, New South Wales, Australia; Hungarian Mus.
DISTRIBUTION: Australia (New South Wales).
HOST PLANT: Unrecorded.

Agramma pullum Drake

Agramma pulla Drake 1958b, p. 30, fig. 1 [Congo].
TYPE: Holotype ♂; Mukana-Lusinga, Belgian Congo; Parcs Nat.
Mus.
DISTRIBUTION: Congo.
HOST PLANT: Unrecorded.

*Agramma ruficorne (Germar)

Tingis ruficornis Germar 1835, fasc. 15, tab. 12 [Switzerland].—Herrich-
  Schaeffer 1835, p. 59.
Serenthia ruficornis: Herrich-Schaeffer 1838, p. 48 [Germany].—Stål
  1874, p. 47.—Puton 1879c, p. 90 [France].—Dubois 1888, p. 119.—
  Hüeber 1893, p. 297.—Horváth 1906a, pp. 108, 112.—Oshanin 1908,
  p. 458 [Turkestan].—Schumacher 1914, p. 259 [*Carex;* sphagnum].—
  Stichel 1926, p. 117 [*Juncus*]; 1938a, p. 408 [Poland].—de Seabra

1931, p. 442, figs. 512(5), 514 [Portugal].—Scholte 1935, p. 92 [Netherlands].—Bator 1953, p. 327, pl. 4, fig. 7.

Agramma ruficornis: Fieber 1844, p. 38, pl. 3, figs. 1–6 [Italy; Austria; Czechoslovakia]; 1861, p. 118.—Mayr 1858, p. 569 [Hungary].— Frey-Gessner 1865, p. 231 [moss].—Stichel 1960a, p. 346, figs. 191–192 [Sardinia].

Scraulia ruficornis: Lethierry and Severin 1896, p. 8.

Serenthia (Paraserenthia) ruficornis: Wagner 1941, pp. 6, 10, 26, figs. 2c, 3c, 4 b, e, 5c, 6c.—Hoberlandt 1942, p. 126.

TYPE: Switzerland; sex and deposition of type unknown.

DISTRIBUTION: Netherlands; France; Switzerland; Germany; Hungary; Czechoslovakia; Austria; Italy; Sardinia; Portugal; Poland; U.S.S.R. (Turkestan).

HOST PLANTS: *Carex* sp.; *Juncus* sp.; moss; sphagnum.

Agramma rwindianum (Drake)

Serenthia rwindiana Drake 1956a, p. 7 [Congo].

Agramma rwindianum: Drake 1958a, p. 107.

TYPE: Holotype ♂; lac Edouard, East Rwindi, Belgian Congo; Parcs Nat. Inst.

DISTRIBUTION: Congo.

HOST PLANT: Unrecorded.

*Agramma scitulum Drake and Maa

Agramma scitula Drake and Maa 1955, p. 11 [India].

TYPE: Holotype ♂, brachypterous; Tanjore District, South India; Drake Coll. (USNM).

DISTRIBUTION: India.

HOST PLANT: Unrecorded.

*Agramma sedale (Drake)

Serenthia sedalis Drake 1927d, p. 312 [Luzon].—Drake and Poor 1937a, p. 2; 1937b, p. 397.

TYPE: Holotype ♂, macropterous; Manila, Philippine Islands; USNM.

DISTRIBUTION: Philippine Islands (Luzon); Ceylon; Greater Sunda Islands (Java).

HOST PLANT: Unrecorded.

*Agramma singulum (Drake)

Serenthia singula Drake 1954b, p. 14 [Cape Province].—Drake and Slater 1955, p. 49 [Zululand].

Agramma singulum: Drake 1958a, p. 107.

TYPE: Holotype ♂; Somerset East, Cape Province, South Africa; British Mus.

DISTRIBUTION: South Africa (Zululand; Cape Province).

HOST PLANT: Unrecorded.

*Agramma sociale (Drake)

Serenthia socialis Drake 1951, p. 169 [Tanganyika; Ethiopia].

Agramma sociale: Drake 1958a, p. 107 [Kenya].

TYPE: Holotype ♂; Arusha-Ju, Africa orientalis; Hungarian Mus.

DISTRIBUTION: Tanganyika; Kenya; Ethiopia.

HOST PLANT: Unrecorded.

*Agramma striolum (Drake)

Serenthia striola Drake 1951, p. 168.

Agramma striola: Drake 1955d, p. 1 [Urundi; Ethiopia].

TYPE: Holotype ♂; Hungarian Mus.; type locality unknown.

DISTRIBUTION: Ruanda-Urundi; Ethiopia.

HOST PLANT: Unrecorded.

*Agramma tropidopterum Flor

Agramma tropidopterum Flor 1860, p. 326 [Estonia].

Serenthia tropidoptera: Stål 1874, p. 47.—Horváth 1906a, p. 111, pl. 1, fig. 1 [Russia].—Stichel 1926, p. 117, fig. 308 [*Juncus; Eriophorum;* Germany].—Kiritshenko 1951, p. 254.

Scraulia tropidoptera: Lethierry and Severin 1896, p. 9.

Serenthia (Paraserenthia) tropidoptera: Wagner 1941, pp. 6, 9, 26, figs. 2a, 3a, 4a, 5a, 6a.

Agramma tropidoptera: Stichel 1960a, p. 345, figs. 187, 188.

TYPE: Estonia; sex and deposition of type unknown.

DISTRIBUTION: U.S.S.R. (Estonia; Latvia); Germany.

HOST PLANTS: *Juncus* sp.; *Eriophorum* sp.

*Agramma turanicum (Horváth)

Serenthia turanica Horváth 1905b, p. 556 [Turkestan]; 1906a, p. 113.

TYPE: Sex unknown; Ilysk, Turkestan, Russia; Hungarian Mus.

DISTRIBUTION: U.S.S.R. (Turkestan).

HOST PLANT: Unrecorded.

*Agramma umbrosum (Horváth)

Serenthia umbrosa Horváth 1906a, p. 113 [Algeria].

Agramma umbrosum: Drake 1958a, p. 107.

TYPE: Holotype ♂; Madjez-Amar, Algeria; Hungarian Mus.

DISTRIBUTION: Algeria; West Africa; Senegal.

HOST PLANT: Unrecorded.

Agramma vanderysti (Schouteden)

Wombalia vanderysti Schouteden 1919, p. 140 [Congo].

Serenthia vanderysti: Drake 1954b, p. 13.

Agramma vanderysti: Drake 1958a, p. 107.

TYPE: Sex unknown; Wombali, Belgian Congo; Cent. Afr. Mus.

DISTRIBUTION: Congo.

HOST PLANT: Unrecorded.

*Agramma vicinale (Drake)
Serenthia vicinalis Drake 1927d, p. 311 [Luzon]; 1930e, p. 166.—Drake
and Poor 1937a, p. 1.
TYPE: Holotype ♂, macropterous; Mount Maquiling, Luzon, Philippine
Islands; Drake Coll. (USNM).
DISTRIBUTION: Philippine Islands (Luzon).
HOST PLANT: Unrecorded.

*Agramma vulturnum (Kirkaldy)
Serenthia vulturna Kirkaldy 1908a, p. 778 [Queensland].—Hacker 1927,
p. 20, fig. 17.
TYPE: Holotype ♂; Bundaberg, Queensland, Australia; Hawaii. Sugar
Plant. Assn.
DISTRIBUTION: Australia (Queensland).
HOST PLANT: Unrecorded.

Genus AIDONEUS Distant

Aidoneus Distant 1909a, p. 122; 1910a, p. 125.—Drake and Ruhoff
1960a, p. 34.
TYPE SPECIES: Aidoneus dissimilis Distant.

Aidoneus dissimilis Distant
Aidoneus dissimilis Distant 1909a, p. 123 [India]; 1910a, p. 126, fig. 66.
TYPE: Sex unknown; Bengal, India; British Mus.
DISTRIBUTION: India.
HOST PLANT: Unrecorded.

Genus ALLOEOCYSTA Drake

Alloeocysta Drake 1961b, p. 109.
TYPE SPECIES: Alloeocysta approba Drake.

Alloeocysta approba Drake   PLATE 12
Alloeocysta approba Drake 1961b, p. 109, pl. 5 [New South Wales].
TYPE: Holotype ♂; Bogan River, New South Wales, Australia; Austr.
Mus.
DISTRIBUTION: Australia (New South Wales).
HOST PLANT: Unrecorded.

Genus ALLOIOTHUCHA Drake

Alloiothucha Drake 1927a, p. 58.—Drake and Poor 1937a, p. 18 (in part);
1939c, p. 207 (in part).—Drake and Ruhoff 1960a, p. 34.
TYPE SPECIES: Alloiothucha philippinensis Drake.

*Alloiothucha artocarpi (Horváth)

  Holophygdon artocarpi Horváth 1926, p. 327, figs. 1–2 [Java; *Artocarpus integrifolia*].—Poisson 1951, p. 1798, fig. 1591a (fig. only).
  Alloiothucha artocarpi: Drake and Poor 1939c, p. 207.

TYPE: Holotype ♀; Buitenzorg, Java; Hungarian Mus.
DISTRIBUTION: Greater Sunda Islands (Java; Sumatra).
HOST PLANT: *Artocarpus integrifolia.*

*Alloiothucha necopinata Drake

  Alloiothucha necopinata Drake 1927a, p. 59 [Palawan].—Drake and Poor 1939c, p. 207.
  Holophygdon necopinata: Drake and Poor 1937a, p. 18.

TYPE: Holotype ♂, macropterous; Puerto Princesa, Palawan, Philippine Islands; Drake Coll. (USNM).
DISTRIBUTION: Philippine Islands (Palawan); Greater Sunda Islands (Borneo).
HOST PLANT: Unrecorded.

*Alloiothucha philippinensis Drake

  Alloiothucha philippinensis Drake 1927a, p. 58 [Luzon].—Drake and Poor 1939c, p. 207, fig. 1.
  Holophygdon philippinensis: Drake and Poor 1937a, p. 18.

TYPE: Holotype ♂, macropterous; Mount Maquiling, Luzon, Philippine Islands; Drake Coll. (USNM).
DISTRIBUTION: Philippine Islands (Luzon).
HOST PLANT: Unrecorded.

Genus ALLOTINGIS Drake

  Allotingis Drake 1930d, p. 269.—Hurd 1946, p. 471.—Drake and Ruhoff 1960a, p. 35.

TYPE SPECIES: *Leptobyrsa binotata* Drake and Bruner.

*Allotingis binotata (Drake and Bruner)

  Leptobyrsa binotata Drake and Bruner 1924b, p. 155 [Cuba; *Thrinax wendlandiana*].
  Allotingis binotata: Drake 1930d, p. 270.

TYPE: Holotype ♂, macropterous; La Machorra, Peninsula de Guanahacabibes, Cuba; Drake Coll. (USNM).
DISTRIBUTION: Cuba.
HOST PLANT: *Thrinax wendlandiana.*

*Allotingis insulicola Drake and Poor

  Allotingis insulicola Drake and Poor 1939a, p. 31 [Haiti].

TYPE: Holotype ♂, macropterous; Fond-des-Negres, Haiti; Drake Coll. (USNM).
DISTRIBUTION: Haiti.
HOST PLANT: Unrecorded.

Genus ALVEOTINGIS Osborn and Drake

Alveotingis Osborn and Drake 1916a, p. 245; 1917b, p. 305 (key).—Van
Duzee 1917b, pp. 221, 818.—Parshley 1917a, p. 24; 1923b, p. 707.—
Blatchley 1926, p. 486.—Hurd 1946, p. 445.—Bailey 1951, p. 20.—
Drake and Ruhoff 1960a, p. 35.

TYPE SPECIES: *Alveotingis grossocerata* Osborn and Drake.

*Alveotingis brevicornis Osborn and Drake

Alveotingis brevicornis Osborn and Drake 1917b, p. 305, fig. 2c [Iowa].—
Froeschner 1944, p. 670 [Mo.].

TYPE: Holotype ♀, macropterous; Little Rock, Iowa, U.S.; Drake Coll.
(USNM).

DISTRIBUTION: U.S. (Iowa; Mo.; Minn.).

HOST PLANT: Unrecorded.

*Alveotingis grossocerata Osborn and Drake

Alveotingis grossocerata Osborn and Drake 1916a, p. 245, fig. 9 [Maine];
1917b, pp. 305, 306, fig. 2a [N.H.].—Van Duzee 1917b, p. 221
[Pa.].—Parshley 1917a, p. 25; 1917b, p. 57; 1920a, p. 274; 1922a,
p. 236 [Conn.]; 1923b, p. 707.—Blatchley 1926, p. 486, fig. 113.—
Drake 1928b, p. 103 [N.Y.; thistle].—Torre-Bueno 1931, p. 149
[Mass.].—Bailey 1951, p. 20.—Drake and Davis 1960, fig. 67.

TYPE: Holotype ♂, brachypterous; Orono, Maine, U.S.; Drake Coll.
(USNM).

DISTRIBUTION: U.S. (Maine; N.H.; Mass.; Conn.; N.Y.; Pa.; Kans.).

HOST PLANT: Unrecorded.

NOTE: Netted on thistle.

*Alveotingis minor Osborn and Drake

Alveotingis minor Osborn and Drake 1917b, p. 305, fig. 2h [Iowa].

TYPE: Holotype ♂, brachypterous; Ames, Iowa, U.S.; Drake Coll.
(USNM).

DISTRIBUTION: U.S. (Iowa).

HOST PLANT: Unrecorded.

Genus AMBLYSTIRA Stål

Amblystira Stål 1873, pp. 120, 129.—Champion 1897, p. 29 (key).—
Monte 1939b, p. 65; 1941e, p. 77.—Hurd 1946, p. 455.—Drake and
Ruhoff 1960a, p. 35.

TYPE SPECIES: *Monanthia pallipes* Stål.

*Amblystira amica Drake and Ruhoff

Amblystira solida Drake 1942a, p. 17 (not p. 16) [Haiti].
Amblystira dozieri Drake and Hambleton 1944a, p. 94.
Amblystira amica Hurd 1946, p. 456 (nom. nud.).—Drake and Ruhoff
1960c, p. 31.

TYPE: Holotype ♀, macropterous; Hinche, Haiti; Drake Coll. (USNM).
DISTRIBUTION: Haiti.
HOST PLANT: Unrecorded.

Amblystira angella Drake and Ruhoff

Amblystira angella Drake and Ruhoff 1962c, p. 137, fig. 1 [Peru].
TYPE: Holotype ♀, macropterous; Monson Valley, Tingo Maria, Peru;
Cal. Acad.
DISTRIBUTION: Peru.
HOST PLANT: Unrecorded.

*Amblystira atrinervis Champion

Amblystira atrinervis Champion 1897, p. 31, pl. 2, fig. 24 [Mexico].
TYPE: Holotype ♂; Atoyac, Vera Cruz, Mexico; British Mus.
DISTRIBUTION: Mexico.
HOST PLANT: Unrecorded.

*Amblystira fuscitarsis Champion

Amblystira fuscitarsis Champion 1897, p. 30, pl. 2, figs. 21–22 [Guate-
mala; Panama].—Drake and Bruner 1924a, p. 148 [Cuba].—Monte
1938b, p. 128 [Brazil].—Bruner, Scaramuzza and Otero 1945, p. 100
[*Lonchocarpus sericeus*].—Drake and Hambleton 1945, p.358 [Colom-
bia; Haiti; *Derris elliptica*].
TYPE: Sex unknown; Volcan de Atitlan, Guatemala; British Mus.
DISTRIBUTION: Mexico; Guatemala; Panama; Colombia; Brazil; Haiti;
Cuba.
HOST PLANTS: *Derris elliptica; Longchocarpus sericeus*.

*Amblystira laevifrons Champion

Amblystira laevifrons Champion 1897, p. 31, pl. 2, fig. 25 [Mexico].
TYPE: Sex unknown; Atoyac, Vera Cruz, Mexico; British Mus.
DISTRIBUTION: Mexico.
HOST PLANT: Unrecorded.

*Amblystira machalana Drake

Amblystira machalana Drake 1948c, p. 22 [Ecuador].
TYPE: Holotype ♂, macropterous; Machala, Ecuador; Drake Coll.
(USNM).
DISTRIBUTION: Ecuador; Peru.
HOST PLANTS: Teak; cacao.

Amblystira maculata Van Duzee

Amblystira maculata Van Duzee 1907, p. 21 [Jamaica].—Drake and
Bruner 1924a, p. 148, fig. 2.—Gowdy 1926, p. 35.
TYPE: Sex unknown; Richmond Village, Jamaica; Cal. Acad.
DISTRIBUTION: Jamaica.
HOST PLANT: Unrecorded.

*Amblystira marginata Drake

Amblystira marginata Drake 1922c, p. 362, pl. 39, fig. 7 [Canal Zone].—
Hurd 1946, p. 456 [Costa Rica].

TYPE: Holotype ♂, brachypterous; Paraiso, Panama Canal Zone;
USNM.

DISTRIBUTION: Panama (Canal Zone); Costa Rica.

HOST PLANT: Unrecorded.

*Amblystira melanosoma Monte

Amblystira melanosoma Monte 1941d, p. 95, fig. 2 [Costa Rica].

TYPE: Holotype ♀; San Isidro de Coronado, Alajuela, Costa Rica;
Monte Coll. (Mus. Nacional).

DISTRIBUTION: Costa Rica.

HOST PLANT: Unrecorded.

*Amblystira morrisoni Drake

Amblystira morrisoni Drake 1922c, p. 360 [Dominican Republic].—Drake
and Bruner 1924a, p. 148.

TYPE: Holotype ♂, macropterous; San Domingo City, San Domingo;
USNM.

DISTRIBUTION: Dominican Republic.

HOST PLANT: Unrecorded.

*Amblystira nyctalis Drake

Amblystira nyctalis Drake 1922c, p. 360 [Brazil].

TYPE: Holotype ♂; Chapada, Brazil; Carnegie Mus.

DISTRIBUTION: Brazil.

HOST PLANT: Unrecorded.

*Amblystira opaca Champion

Amblystira opaca Champion 1897, p. 30, pl. 2, fig. 23 [Guatemala].—
Hurd 1946, p. 456 [Panama].

TYPE: Sex unknown; San Isidro, Guatemala; British Mus.

DISTRIBUTION: Guatemala; Panama; Nicaragua.

HOST PLANT: *Derris elliptica.*

*Amblystira pallipes (Stål)

Monanthia (Tropidocheila) pallipes Stål 1858, p. 62 [Brazil].

Monanthia pallipes: Walker 1873a, p. 192.

Amblystira pallipes: Stål 1873, p. 129.—Champion 1898b, p. 61, pl. 2,
fig. 12.—Drake and Hambleton 1935, p. 141 [*Serjania*]; 1944b, p. 124
[Venezuela]; 1945, p. 358 [Peru].—Drake and Poor 1937d, p. 304
[Colombia].—Monte 1938b, p. 128; 1939b, p. 65 [*Bredemeyera*].

TYPE: Sex unknown; Rio de Janeiro, Brazil; Stockholm Mus.

DISTRIBUTION: Brazil; Colombia; Peru; Venezuela.

HOST PLANTS: *Serjania* sp.; *Bredemeyera* sp.

*Amblystira peltogyne Drake and Hambleton

Amblystira peltogyne Drake and Hambleton 1935, p. 141, fig. 1 [Brazil; Peltogyne].—Monte 1939b, p. 65 [Hymenaea stigonocarpa].

TYPE: Holotype ♂, macropterous; Viçosa, Minas Gerais, Brazil; Drake Coll. (USNM).

DISTRIBUTION: Brazil.

HOST PLANTS: Peltogyne sp.; Hymenaea stigonocarpa.

*Amblystira pensa Drake and Hambleton

Amblystira pensa Drake and Hambleton 1939, p. 155 [Brazil].—Monte 1941e, p. 78 [Roupala].

TYPE: Holotype ♂, macropterous; Belo Horizonte, Minas Gerais, Brazil; Drake Coll. (USNM).

DISTRIBUTION: Brazil.

HOST PLANT: Roupala sp.

*Amblystira scita Drake and Hambleton

Amblystira scita Drake and Hambleton 1944b, p. 124 [Costa Rica].

TYPE: Holotype ♀, macropterous; Mercedes, Costa Rica; Drake Coll. (USNM).

DISTRIBUTION: Costa Rica.

HOST PLANT: Unrecorded.

*Amblystira silvicola Drake

Amblystira silvicola Drake 1922c, p. 361, pl. 39, fig. 6 [Bolivia; Brazil; British Guiana]; 1935, p. 11 [Paraguay]; 1936b, p. 699 [Argentina].— Monte 1938b, p. 128; 1939b, p.65 [Serjania; Bignoniaceae].—Silva 1956, p. 18, fig. 3.

TYPE: Holotype ♂; Rio Machupe, Bolivia; Carnegie Mus.

DISTRIBUTION: Bolivia; Brazil; British Guiana; Argentina; Paraguay.

HOST PLANTS: Serjania sp.; Bignoniaceae.

*Amblystira socia Drake

Amblystira socia Drake 1942a, p. 17 [Paraguay].

TYPE: Holotype ♂, macropterous; Chaco, Paraguay; Drake Coll. (USNM).

DISTRIBUTION: Paraguay; Peru; Bolivia.

HOST PLANT: Unrecorded.

*Amblystira solida Drake

Amblystira solida Drake 1942a, p. 16 [Brazil].—Drake and Davis 1960, fig. 66.

TYPE: Holotype ♀, macropterous; Guaruja, Brazil; Drake Coll. (USNM).

DISTRIBUTION: Brazil.

HOST PLANT: Unrecorded.

Genus AMBOTINGIS Drake and Ruhoff

Ambotingis Drake and Ruhoff 1960c, p. 29.

TYPE SPECIES: *Monanthia senta* Drake and Hambleton.

*Ambotingis senta (Drake and Hambleton) PLATE 10

Monanthia senta Drake and Hambleton 1942a, p. 329 [Peru]; 1945, p. 356 [Ecuador].

Ambotingis senta: Drake and Ruhoff 1960c, p. 31, fig. 1; 1960e, p. 80.

TYPE: Holotype ♂, macropterous; Sullena, Peru; Drake Coll. (USNM).

DISTRIBUTION: Peru; Ecuador.

HOST PLANT: Unrecorded.

Genus AMBYCYSTA Drake and Hurd

Ambycysta Drake and Hurd 1945b, p. 129.—Hurd 1946, p. 475.—Drake and Ruhoff 1960a, p. 36.

TYPE SPECIES: *Megalocysta championi* Drake.

*Ambycysta championi (Drake)

Megalocysta championi Drake 1922b, p. 38 [Brazil].—Monte 1941e, p. 123; 1942c, p. 302.

Ambycysta championi: Drake and Hurd 1945b, p. 130.

TYPE: Holotype ♂, macropterous; Brazil; Drake Coll. (USNM).

DISTRIBUTION: Brazil.

HOST PLANT: Unrecorded.

NOTE: This species is known only from the holotype, which was erroneously recorded as a female in the original description.

Ambycysta cornuta (Monte)

Megalocysta cornuta Monte 1942c, p. 302, figs. 1–3 [Peru].

Ambycysta cornuta: Drake and Hurd 1945b, p. 130.

TYPE: Holotype ♂; Hacienda San Juan, Col. Perene, Peru; Monte Coll. (Mus. Nacional).

DISTRIBUTION: Peru.

HOST PLANT: Unrecorded.

*Ambycysta enodis Drake

Ambycysta enodis Drake 1948j, p. 430.

TYPE: Holotype ♀, macropterous; Pachitea, Peru; Drake Coll. (USNM).

DISTRIBUTION: Peru.

HOST PLANT: Unrecorded.

*Ambycysta gibbifera (Picado)

Leptostyla gibbifera Picado 1913, pp. 303, 306, pl. 13, fig. 5; figs. 29, 30 [Costa Rica; *Aechmea*].

Megalocysta gibbifera: Drake 1928d, p. 23.—Monte 1942c, p. 302.

Ambycysta gibbifera: Drake and Hurd 1945b, p. 130.

TYPE: Sex unknown; Orosi, Costa Rica; Paris Mus.

DISTRIBUTION: Costa Rica.

HOST PLANT: *Aechmea* sp.

Genus AMMIANUS Distant

Ammianus Distant 1903b, p. 136; 1910a, p. 115.—Drake 1955d, p. 5; 1957c, p. 31.—Drake and Ruhoff 1960a, p. 36.

Monanthia (Phyllontocheila) Fieber 1844, p. 59 (in part).

Phyllontochila (emendation): Stål 1873, pp. 120, 128.—Horváth 1909b, p. 632; 1910, p. 62.

Sakuntala Kirkaldy 1902, p. 298.—Horváth 1909b, p. 632; 1910, p. 62.— Drake and Ruhoff 1960a, p. 80.

Phyllontocheila: Horváth 1911a, p. 327 (key).—Schouteden 1923, p. 95.— Drake and Ruhoff 1960a, p. 76.

Phyllontocheila (Kitoko) Schouteden 1923, p. 95.—Drake 1955c, p. 105.— Drake and Ruhoff 1960a, p. 63.

TYPE SPECIES: *Monanthia (Phyllontocheila) erosa* Fieber.

*Ammianus admirandus (Drake)

Phyllontocheila admiranda Drake 1931d, p. 96 [Borneo; Malaya]; 1934b, p. 107, fig.

Ammianus admirandus: Drake 1955d, p. 5.

TYPE: Sex unknown; Borneo; Paris Mus.

DISTRIBUTION: Greater Sunda Islands (Borneo); Federation of Malaya.

HOST PLANT: Unrecorded.

*Ammianus alaticollis (Stål)

Phyllontocheila alaticollis Stål 1855a, p. 37 [Natal].—Horváth 1911a, pp. 329, 331.

Monanthia (Phyllontochila) alaticollis: Stål 1865, p. 27 [Caffraria].

Monanthia alaticollis: Walker 1873a, p. 195.

Phyllontochila alaticollis: Stål 1873, p. 128.—Distant 1902a, p. 241, pl. 15, fig. 5.

Phyllontochila (Sinuessa) alaticollis: Horváth 1910, p. 63 [Tanganyika].

Ammianus alaticollis: Drake 1957c, p. 32.

TYPE: Sex unknown; Natal, South Africa; Stockholm Mus.

DISTRIBUTION: South Africa (Natal); Tanganyika; Mozambique.

HOST PLANT: Unrecorded.

*Ammianus alberti (Schouteden)   PLATES 36, 37

Phyllontocheila alberti Schouteden 1916a, p. 275 [Congo]; 1916b, p. 293.— Drake 1954e, p. 4.

Phyllontocheila (Kitoko) alberti: Schouteden 1923, p. 96.—Mayné and Ghesquière 1934, p. 20 [*Vernonia conferta;* cacao].

Kitoko alberti: Schouteden 1953d, p. 170.

Ammianus alberti: Drake 1955d, p. 5.

TYPE: Sex unknown; Uelé, Belgian Congo; Cent. Afr. Mus.

DISTRIBUTION: Congo.

HOST PLANTS: *Vernonia conferta;* cacao.

*Ammianus alberti var. tricarinatus (Schouteden)

Kitoko alberti var. tricarinata Schouteden 1953d, p. 170 [Congo].
Phyllontocheila alberti subsp. tricarinata: Drake and Gomez-Menor 1954, p. 93 [Spanish Guinea].—Drake 1955c, p. 105 [Cameroun; Vernonia].
Ammianus alberti var. triseriatus [sic]: Drake 1955d, p. 5.
Piesma pupla (not Puton): Gomez-Menor 1956a, p. 119, fig. 15 (fig. only).

TYPE: Sex unknown; Belgian Congo; Cent. Afr. Mus.
DISTRIBUTION: Congo; Spanish Guinea; Cameroun.
HOST PLANT: Vernonia sp.

Ammianus basilewskyi Schouteden

Ammianus basilewskyi Schouteden 1957c, p. 315 [Ruanda].
TYPE: Sex unknown; Ruanda; Cent. Afr. Mus.
DISTRIBUTION: Ruanda-Urundi.
HOST PLANT: Unrecorded.

*Ammianus bobangensis (Schouteden)

Phyllontocheila bobangensis Schouteden 1923, p. 96 [Congo].
Ammianus bobangensis: Drake 1955d, p. 5; 1958b, p. 29.
TYPE: Sex unknown; Bolobo, Belgian Congo; Cent. Afr. Mus.
DISTRIBUTION: Congo.
HOST PLANT: Unrecorded.

*Ammianus burgeoni (Schouteden)

Phyllontocheila burgeoni Schouteden 1923, p. 97 [Congo].
TYPE: Sex unknown; Mabao, Haut Uelé, Belgian Congo; Cent. Afr. Mus.
DISTRIBUTION: Congo.
HOST PLANT: Unrecorded.

*Ammianus corticinus (Horváth)

Phyllontocheila corticina Horváth 1911a, pp. 328, 329 [Cameroun].—
Schouteden 1923, p. 99 [Congo].
Ammianus corticinus: Drake 1955d, p. 5.
TYPE: Sex unknown; Vallis N'Goko, Cameroun; Hungarian Mus.
DISTRIBUTION: Cameroun; Congo.
HOST PLANT: Unrecorded.

*Ammianus depictus (Schouteden)

Phyllontocheila burgeoni var. depicta Schouteden 1923, p. 98 [Congo].
Ammianus depictus: Drake and Ruhoff 1962a, p. 156.
TYPE: Sex unknown; Belgian Congo; Cent. Afr. mus.
DISTRIBUTION: Congo.
HOST PLANT: Unrecorded.

*Ammianus dilatatus (Guérin-Méneville)   PLATE 38

Tingis dilatata Guérin-Méneville 1831, p. 8, fig. [Senegal].—Stål 1873, p. 134.

Phyllontochila dilatata: Distant 1902a, p. 241 [West Africa; Rhodesia]; 1902b, p. 355 [Sierra Leone].

Phyllontocheila dilatata: Horváth 1911a, pp. 328, 331.—Drake 1954a, p. 232 [Ivory Coast]; 1954e, p. 4 [Congo]; 1955b, p. 90 [Angola;] 1955c, p. 105 [Cameroun; Nigeria].

Ammianus dilatatus: Drake 1955d, p. 5.

TYPE: Senegal; sex and deposition of type unknown.

DISTRIBUTION: Senegal; Sierra Leone; Guinea; Ivory Coast; Ghana; Nigeria; Cameroun; Spanish Guinea; Angola; Congo; Rhodesia; West Africa.

HOST PLANT: Unrecorded.

Ammianus dilatatus var. obscurus (Schumacher)

Phyllontocheila dilatata var. *obscura* Schumacher 1912, p. 320 [Cameroons].

TYPE: Barombi, Cameroons; sex and deposition of type unknown.

DISTRIBUTION: Cameroons.

HOST PLANT: Unrecorded.

*Ammianus elisabethae (Schouteden)

Phyllontocheila elisabethae Schouteden 1916a, p. 274 [Congo]; 1916b, p. 293; 1923, p. 99 [Tanganyika].

Ammianus elisabethae: Drake 1955d, p. 5.

TYPE: Sex unknown; Belgian Congo; Cent. Afr. Mus.

DISTRIBUTION: Congo; Tanganyika.

HOST PLANT: Unrecorded.

*Ammianus erosus (Fieber)

Monanthia (Phyllontocheila) erosa Fieber 1844, p. 71, pl. 6, figs. 5–9 [Ostindien].—Herrich-Schaeffer 1850, p. 155.

Tingis erosa: Stål 1870a, p. 671 [Philippines].—Walker 1873a, p. 181 [India].

Phyllontocheila erosa: Stål 1873, p. 128 [Penang].—Distant 1902b, p. 355.—Drake and Poor 1937a, p. 15 [Luzon].—Drake 1937a, p. 387 [Sumatra]; 1938b, p. 196 [China].

Ammianus erosus: Distant 1903b, p. 137, fig. 100 [Burma].—Drake 1955d, p. 5; 1957c, p. 32.

Phyllontocheila erosa: Blöte 1945, p. 92.

TYPE: Sex unknown; "Ostindien"; Vienna Mus.

DISTRIBUTION: India; Burma; Thailand; Penang; China; Greater Sunda Islands (Sumatra; Java); Philippine Islands (Luzon).

HOST PLANT: Unrecorded.

*Ammianus flabilis (Bergroth)

Phyllontochila flabilis Bergroth 1894, p. 167 [Malagasy].
Ammianus flabilis: Drake 1955d, p. 5.
Ammianus flavilis [sic]: Drake 1957f, p. 131.
TYPE: Sex unknown; Madagascar; Helsin. Mus.
DISTRIBUTION: Malagasy Republic.
HOST PLANT: Unrecorded.

*Ammianus ghesquierei (Schouteden)

Phyllontocheila ghesquierei Schouteden 1923, p. 99 [Congo].—Drake 1954e, p. 4.
TYPE: Sex unknown; Luebo, Kasai, Belgian Congo; Cent. Afr. Mus.
DISTRIBUTION: Congo.
HOST PLANT: Unrecorded.

*Ammianus junodi (Distant)

Phyllontochila junodi Distant 1904, p. 431, pl. 8, fig. 10 [Transvaal].
Phyllontochila (Sinuessa) junodi: Horváth 1910, p. 64 [Tanganyika].
Phyllontocheila junodi: Horváth 1911a, pp. 329, 332.—Drake 1956f, p. 424 [Cape Province; Uganda; Kenya; Natal; Zanzibar].
Ammianus janodi [sic]: Drake 1957c, p. 32.
TYPE: Sex unknown; Shilouvane, Zoutpansberg District, Transvaal, South Africa; British Mus.
DISTRIBUTION: South Africa (Transvaal; Natal; Cape Province); Uganda; Kenya; Tanganyika; Zanzibar.
HOST PLANT: Unrecorded.

*Ammianus kassianoffi Drake

Ammianus kassianoffi Drake 1955d, p. 4 [Congo; Uganda].
TYPE: Holotype ♂; Lukolo, Belgian Congo; Brussels Mus.
DISTRIBUTION: Congo; Uganda.
HOST PLANT: Unrecorded.

*Ammianus laminatus (Horváth)

Phyllontocheila laminata Horváth 1911a, pp. 328, 330 [Uganda].—Schouteden 1916b, p. 293 [Congo]; 1923, p.100.—Drake and Gomez-Menor 1954, p.93 [Cameroun].
Ammianus laminatus: Drake 1955d, p. 5.
TYPE: Entebbe, Uganda; sex and deposition of type unknown.
DISTRIBUTION: Uganda; Cameroun; Congo; Tanganyika; Kenya.
HOST PLANT: Unrecorded.

Ammianus maseruanus (Drake)

Phyllontocheila maseruana Drake 1956f, p. 424 [Basutoland].
TYPE: Holotype ♂; Mount Machache, Basutoland; Lund Zool. Inst.
DISTRIBUTION: Basutoland.
HOST PLANT: Unrecorded.

*Ammianus mayri (Haglund)

Phyllontochila mayri Haglund 1895, p. 471 [Cameroun].—Distant 1902a, p. 241 [West Africa].

Phyllontocheila mayri: Horváth 1911a, p. 331 [Dahomey].

Ammianus mayri: Drake 1955d, p. 5.

TYPE: Sex unknown; Cameroun; Stockholm Mus.

DISTRIBUTION: Cameroun; Dahomey; West Africa.

HOST PLANT: Unrecorded.

*Ammianus mayri subsp. **septuosus** Drake and Ruhoff

Phyllontocheila mayri var. *obscura* Schouteden 1916a, p. 276 [Congo].

Ammianus mayri var. *obscura:* Drake 1955d, p. 5.

Ammianus mayri subsp. *septuosus* Drake and Ruhoff 1962a, p. 161.

TYPE: Sex unknown; Belgian Congo; Cent. Afr. Mus.

DISTRIBUTION: Congo; Nigeria; Sierra Leone.

HOST PLANT: Unrecorded.

*Ammianus mussolinii (Mancini)

Phyllontocheila mussolinii Mancini 1939a, p. 214, tab. 5, fig. 2 [Ethiopia].

Ammianus amoenus Drake 1956b, p. 112 [Kenya].

Ammianus mussolinii: Drake and Ruhoff 1961c, p. 145.

TYPE: Holotype ♂; Neghelli, Ethiopia; Mancini Coll.

DISTRIBUTION: Ethiopia; Kenya.

HOST PLANT: Unrecorded.

*Ammianus perakensis (Distant)

Phyllontochila perakensis Distant 1902b, p. 355 [Malaya].

Phyllontocheila perakensis: Blöte 1945, p. 92 [Sumatra].

Ammianus parakensis [sic]: Drake 1955d, p. 5.

Ammianus perakensis: Drake 1957c, p. 32.

TYPE: Sex unknown; Perak, Malay Peninsula; British Mus.

DISTRIBUTION: Federation of Malaya; Greater Sunda Islands (Sumatra; Sarawak).

HOST PLANT: Unrecorded.

*Ammianus philippinensis (Distant)

Phyllontochila philippinensis Distant 1902b, p. 355 [Philippines].—Drake and Poor 1937a, p. 15 [Luzon].

Phyllontocheila philippinensis: Drake and Poor 1937b, p. 403.

Ammianus philippinensis: Drake 1957c, p. 32.

TYPE: Sex unknown; Philippine Islands; British Mus.

DISTRIBUTION: Philippine Islands (Luzon; Mindanao); Greater Sunda Islands (Java).

HOST PLANT: Unrecorded.

*Ammianus ravanus (Kirkaldy)

Sakuntala ravana Kirkaldy 1902, p. 299 [Ceylon].—Blöte 1945, p. 86 [Lombok].

Phyllontocheila ravana: Distant 1903a, p. 51; 1903b, p. 136, fig. 99 [Vitrex trifolia]; 1910a, p. 115 [India].—Drake 1926e, p. 335 [Vitrex pubescens; Java]; 1933, p. 1016.—Drake and Poor 1936b, p. 146; 1937a, p. 15 [Singapore; Philippines].—Singh 1953, p. 118.

Ammianus ravanus: Drake 1957c, p. 31.

TYPE: Peradeniya, Ceylon; sex and deposition of type unknown.

DISTRIBUTION: India; Ceylon; Singapore; Lesser Sunda Islands (Lombok); Greater Sunda Islands (Java; Sumatra); Philippine Islands.

HOST PLANTS: Vitrex pubescens; Vitrex trifolia.

*Ammianus schoutedeni Distant

Ammianus schoutedeni Distant 1908a, p. 220 [Congo].—Drake 1955d, p. 5.

Phyllontocheila schoutedeni: Horváth 1911a, p. 333.—Schouteden 1916a, p. 276; 1916b, p. 293; 1923, p. 101.—Mayné and Ghesquière 1934, p. 20 [Triumfetta rhombeaefolia].—Drake and Gomez-Menor 1954, p. 93 [Rio Muni].

Stephanitis pyrioides (not Scott): Gomez-Menor 1956a, p. 117, fig. 12 (fig. only).

TYPE: Sex unknown; Popocabacca, Belgian Congo; British Mus.

DISTRIBUTION: Congo; Rio Muni; Ghana; Liberia.

HOST PLANT: Triumfetta rhombeaefolia.

*Ammianus spinosus (Schouteden)

Phyllontocheila spinosa Schouteden 1923, p. 100 [Congo].

Ammianus spinosus: Drake 1955d, p. 5.

TYPE: Sex unknown; Madyu, Haut Uelé, Belgian Congo; Cent. Afr. Mus.

DISTRIBUTION: Congo.

HOST PLANT: Unrecorded.

Ammianus tellinii (Schouteden)

Phyllontocheila tellinii Schouteden 1916a, p. 273 [Eritrea].

TYPE: Sex unknown; Adi Ugri, Eritrea; Cent. Afr. Mus.

DISTRIBUTION: Eritrea.

HOST PLANT: Unrecorded.

*Ammianus toi (Drake)

Phyllontochila toi Drake 1938b, p. 196 [China]; 1947d, p. 228 [Viet-Nam].

Ammianus toi: Drake 1955d, p. 5; 1957c, p. 32.

TYPE: Holotype ♂; Canton, P'an-yu District, China; Lingnan Surv.

DISTRIBUTION: China; Viet-Nam; Greater Sunda Islands (Java).

HOST PLANT: Unrecorded.

Ammianus urundicus Schouteden

Ammianus urundicus Schouteden 1957c, p. 313 [Urundi].

TYPE: Sex unknown; Urundi; Cent. Afr. Mus.

DISTRIBUTION: Ruanda-Urundi.

HOST PLANT: Unrecorded.

*****Ammianus vanderijsti** (Schouteden)

Phyllontocheila vanderijsti Schouteden 1923, p. 101 [Congo].

TYPE: Sex unknown; Belgian Congo; Cent. Afr. Mus.

DISTRIBUTION: Congo; Kenya; Tanganyika.

HOST PLANT: Unrecorded.

Ammianus vicinus Schouteden

Ammianus vicina Schouteden 1957c, p. 315 [Ruanda].

TYPE: Sex unknown; Ruanda; Cent. Afr. Mus.

DISTRIBUTION: Ruanda-Urundi.

HOST PLANT: Unrecorded.

*****Ammianus wahlbergi** (Stål)

Phyllontocheila wahlbergi Stål 1855a, p. 37 [Natal].—Horváth 1911a, p. 331.—Schouteden 1923, p. 103 [Congo].—Mancini 1939a, p. 214 [Ethiopia].—Drake 1954a, p. 232 [Guinea].

Monanthia (Phyllontochila) wahlbergi: Stål 1865, p. 27 [Caffraria].

Monanthia wahlbergi: Walker 1873a, p. 195.

Phyllontochila wahlbergii [sic]: Stål 1873, p. 128.—Distant 1902a, p. 241.

TYPE: Sex unknown; Natal, South Africa; Stockholm Mus.

DISTRIBUTION: South Africa (Natal); Nigeria; Guinea; Congo; Ethiopia.

HOST PLANT: Unrecorded.

Genus ANGOLOTINGIS Drake

Angolotingis Drake 1955b, p. 88.—Drake and Ruhoff 1960a, p. 37.

TYPE SPECIES: *Angolotingis vilhenai* Drake.

*****Angolotingis vilhenai** Drake

Angolotingis vilhenai Drake 1955b, p. 88, fig. 2 [Angola]; 1958a, p. 104, fig. 1.

TYPE: Holotype ♂; Serra do Moco, Luimbale, Angola; Cent. Afr. Mus.

DISTRIBUTION: Angola; Southern Rhodesia.

HOST PLANT: Unrecorded.

Genus ANGOLUSA Drake

Angolusa Drake 1958a, p. 104.—Drake and Ruhoff 1960a, p. 37.

TYPE SPECIES: *Angolusa machadoi* Drake.

Angolusa machadoi Drake

Angolusa machadoi Drake 1958a, p. 105.

TYPE: Holotype ♀; Vila Luso, Angola; Cent. Afr. Mus.

DISTRIBUTION: Angola.

HOST PLANT: Unrecorded.

Genus APHELOTINGIS Drake

Aphelotingis Drake 1948g, p. 176.—Drake and Ruhoff 1960a, p. 37.
TYPE SPECIES: *Abdastarus muiri* Drake.

*Aphelotingis muiri (Drake)

Abdastartus muiri Drake 1927d, p. 307 [Java; Singapore].
Aphelotingis muri [sic]: Drake 1948g, p. 176.
TYPE: Holotype ♂, macropterous; Pekalongan, Java; Drake Coll. (USNM).
DISTRIBUTION: Singapore; Greater Sunda Islands (Java).
HOST PLANT: Unrecorded.

*Aphelotingis perinetana Drake

Aphelotingis perinetana Drake 1957f, p. 130 [Malagasy].
TYPE: Holotype ♀; Périnet, Madagascar; Madagascar Sci. Inst.
DISTRIBUTION: Malagasy Republic.
HOST PLANT: Unrecorded.

Aphelotingis tacsa Drake

Aphelotingis tacsa Drake 1957f, p. 129 [Malagasy].
TYPE: Holotype ♂; Périnet, Madagascar; Madagascar Sci. Inst.
DISTRIBUTION: Malagasy Republic.
HOST PLANT: Unrecorded.

Genus ARISTOBYRSA Drake and Poor

Aristobyrsa Drake and Poor 1937c, p. 164.—Monte 1941e, p. 79.—
Hurd 1946, p. 472.—Drake and Ruhoff 1960a, p. 37.
TYPE SPECIES: *Leptobyrsa latipennis* Champion.

*Aristobyrsa latipennis (Champion)

Leptobyrsa latipennis Champion 1897, p. 25, pl. 2, figs. 13, 13a [Panama].
Aristobyrsa latipennis: Drake and Poor 1937c, p. 164 [Brazil; Peru].—
Monte 1940b, p. 375; 1943a, p. 105; 1947b, p. 432 [*Lucuma* sp.].—
Silva 1956, p. 19.
TYPE: Sex unknown; Bugaba, Panama; British Mus.
DISTRIBUTION: Panama; Brazil; Peru.
HOST PLANT: *Lucuma* sp.

Genus ARUSHIA Drake

Arushia Drake 1951, p. 170.—Drake and Ruhoff 1960a, p. 37.
TYPE SPECIES: *Arushia horvathi* Drake.

*Arushia connata Drake

Arushia connata Drake 1951, p. 170 [Tanganyika; Kenya].
TYPE: Holotype ♀; Arusha-Ju, Africa orientalis; Hungarian Mus.
DISTRIBUTION: Tanganyika; Kenya.
HOST PLANT: Unrecorded.

*Arushia horvathi Drake

Arushia horvathi Drake 1951, p. 170 [Tanganyika]; 1954g, p. 663 [Ethiopia; Congo]; 1956a, p. 5.

TYPE: Holotype ♀; Arusha-Ju, Africa orientalis; Hungarian Mus.

DISTRIBUTION: Tanganyika; Congo; Ethiopia; Guinea.

HOST PLANT: Gramineae.

Genus ATHEAS Champion

Atheas Champion 1898a, p. 44.—Heidemann 1909, p. 231 (key).—Banks 1910, p. 55.—Van Duzee 1916, p. 26; 1917b, p. 222.—Blatchley 1926, p. 494 (key).—Monte 1939b, p. 65; 1941e, p. 80.—Hurd 1946, p. 460.—Drake and Ruhoff 1960a, p. 38.

TYPE SPECIES: *Atheas nigricornis* Champion.

*Atheas austroriparius Heidemann

Atheas austroriparius Heidemann 1909, p. 235, fig. [Tex.; Fla.].—Barber 1914, p. 507.—Drake 1925c, p. 39 [Miss.; *Desmodium*].—Blatchley 1926, p. 496, fig. 119c.—Froeschner 1944, p. 670 [Mo.].

TYPE: Holotype ♀, brachypterous; Duval, Florida, U.S.; USNM.

DISTRIBUTION: U.S. (Fla.; Miss.; Tex.; Mo.; S.C.); Mexico.

HOST PLANTS: *Desmodium* sp.; *Schrankia* sp.

Atheas cearanus Monte

Atheas cearana Monte 1947b, p. 430 [Brazil; *Manihot*].

TYPE: Holotype ♂; Baturité, Ceará, Brazil; Monte Coll. (Mus. Nacional).

DISTRIBUTION: Brazil.

HOST PLANT: *Manihot* sp.

*Atheas exiguus Heidemann

Atheas exiguus Heidemann 1909, p. 233, fig. [Fla.].—Barber 1914, p. 507.—Blatchley 1926, p. 496, fig. 119b; 1928, p. 5.

TYPE: Holotype ♂, macropterous; Sevenoaks, Florida, U.S.; USNM.

DISTRIBUTION: U.S. (Fla.; Miss.; Tex.).

HOST PLANT: Unrecorded.

*Atheas flavipes Champion

Atheas flavipes Champion 1898a, p. 45, pl. 3, figs. 19, 19a [Panama].—Drake and Hambleton 1938a, p. 46, fig. 7 [Brazil; *Machaerium angustifolium*].

TYPE: Sex unknown; Bugaba, Panama; British Mus.

DISTRIBUTION: Panama; Brazil.

HOST PLANT: *Machaerium angustifolium*.

*Atheas fuscipes Champion

Atheas fuscipes Champion 1898a, p. 45, pl. 3, fig. 20 [Mexico; Guatemala].—Drake and Hambleton 1934, p. 438 [Brazil; Leguminosae].—Costa Lima 1936, p. 125.—Drake 1942a, p. 15 [Bolivia; Paraguay].

TYPE: Sex unknown; Rio Naranjo, Guatemala; British Mus.

DISTRIBUTION: Mexico; Guatemala; El Salvador; Brazil; Bolivia; Paraguay.

HOST PLANT: Leguminosae.

*Atheas insignis Heidemann

Atheas insignis Heidmann 1909, p. 232, fig. [Md.; D.C.].—Osborn and Drake 1917b, p. 295 [Va.].—McAtee 1923, p. 146 [Stylosanthes biflora].—Drake 1925c, p. 39 [Miss.; Desmodium].—Blatchley 1926, p. 495, fig. 119a.

TYPE: Holotype ♀, macropterous; Bladensburg, Maryland, U.S.; USNM.

DISTRIBUTION: U.S. (Md.; D.C.; Va.; Miss.).

HOST PLANTS: Desmodium sp.; Stylosanthes biflora.

*Atheas laetantis Drake and Hambleton

Atheas laetantis Drake and Hambleton 1944b, p. 124 [Brazil; Machaerium angustifolium; Machaerium].

TYPE: Holotype ♂, macropterous; Viçosa, Minas Gerais, Brazil; Drake Coll. (USNM).

DISTRIBUTION: Brazil.

HOST PLANTS: Machaerium angustifolium; Machaerium sp.

*Atheas mimeticus Heidemann

Atheas mimeticus Heidemann 1909, p 234, fig. [Wis.; Minn.; Kans.].—Osborn and Drake 1917b, p. 295 [Colo.; N. Mex.].—Drake 1925c, p. 39 [Miss.; Desmodium].—Blatchley 1926, p. 496, fig. 119d.—Froeschner 1944, p. 670 [Mo.; Petalostemon purpureum].—Hurd 1946, p. 460 [Wyo.].

Atheas annulatus Osborn and Drake 1917b, p. 295 [Ark.].—Froeschner 1944, p. 670.

Atheas sordidus Osborn and Drake 1917b, p. 296 [Iowa].

TYPE: Holotype ♂, brachypterous; Onaga, Kansas, U.S.; USNM.

DISTRIBUTION: U.S. (Wyo.; Colo.; N. Mex.; Nebr.; Kans.; Iowa; Minn.; Wis.; Mo.; Ark.; La.; Miss.; Fla.).

HOST PLANTS: Desmodium sp.; Petalostemon purpureum.

*Atheas mirabilis Drake

Atheas mirabilis Drake 1938a, p. 70 [Mexico].

TYPE: Holotype ♂; Temescaltepec, Mexico; Cal. Acad.

DISTRIBUTION: Mexico.

HOST PLANT: Unrecorded.

*Atheas nigricornis Champion

Atheas nigricornis Champion 1898a, p. 45, pl. 3, fig. 21 [Mexico; Guatemala].—Osborn and Drake 1915b, p. 536; 1917b, p. 296 [Ariz.].—Drake 1938a, p. 70.—Hurd 1946, p. 461 [Alnus acuminata; Parosela citriodora].

TYPE: Sex unknown; Cerro Zunil, Guatemala; British Mus.
DISTRIBUTION: Ecuador; Honduras; Guatemala; Mexico; U.S. (Tex.; Ariz.).
HOST PLANTS: *Alnus acuminata; Parosela citriodora.*

*Atheas ornatipes Drake and Hambleton

Atheas ornatipes Drake and Hambleton 1935, p. 143 [Brazil; *Aeschynomene falcata*].

TYPE: Holotype ♂, macropterous; Guarujá, São Paulo, Brazil; Drake Coll. (USNM).
DISTRIBUTION: Brazil.
HOST PLANT: *Aeschynomene falcata.*

*Atheas paganus Drake

Atheas paganus Drake 1942a, p. 15 [Brazil; *Aeschynomene*].

TYPE: Holotype ♂, macropterous; Viçosa, Minas Gerais, Brazil; Drake Coll. (USNM).
DISTRIBUTION: Brazil.
HOST PLANT: *Aeschynomene* sp.

*Atheas placentis Drake and Poor

Atheas fuscipes (not Champion): Monte 1939b, p. 66 [*Celtis brasiliensis*].
Atheas placentis Drake and Poor 1940, p. 226 [Brazil].—Drake and Hambleton 1944b, p. 124.

TYPE: Holotype ♀, macropterous; Belo Horizonte, Minas Gerais, Brazil; Drake Coll. (USNM).
DISTRIBUTION: Brazil.
HOST PLANT: *Celtis brasiliensis.*

*Atheas tristis Van Duzee

Atheas tristis Van Duzee 1923, p. 143 [Mexico; *Aeschynomene nivea*].

TYPE: Holotype ♂; Concepcion Bay, Lower California, Mexico; Cal. Acad.
DISTRIBUTION: Mexico.
HOST PLANT: *Aeschynomene nivea.*

Genus AULOTINGIS Drake and Poor

Aulotingis Drake and Poor 1943, p. 194.—Drake and Ruhoff 1960a, p. 38.
TYPE SPECIES: *Aulotingis moalae* Drake and Poor.

Aulotingis moalae Drake and Poor

Aulotingis moalae Drake and Poor 1943, p. 195, fig. 2 [Fiji].
TYPE: Holotype ♂; Naroi, Moala Island, Fiji Islands; Bishop Mus.
DISTRIBUTION: Fiji Islands (Moala).
HOST PLANT: Unrecorded.

Genus AUSTRALOTINGIS Hacker

Australotingis Hacker 1927, p. 29.—Drake and Ruhoff 1960a, p. 38.
TYPE SPECIES: *Australotingis franzeni* Hacker.

*Australotingis franzeni Hacker PLATES 32, 33
Australotingis franzeni Hacker 1927, p. 29, pl. 10, fig. 15 [Queensland].
TYPE: Holotype ♀; Nanango, Queensland, Australia; Queensland Mus.
DISTRIBUTION: Australia (Queensland).
HOST PLANT: Unrecorded.

*Australotingis vinnula Drake
Australotingis vinnula Drake 1953c, p. 152 [Queensland].
TYPE: Holotype ♂; Lankelly Creek, Cape York, Queensland, Australia;
MCZ.
DISTRIBUTION: Australia (Queensland).
HOST PLANT: Unrecorded.

Genus AXIOKERSOS Distant

Axiokersos Distant 1909a, p. 121; 1910a, p. 124.—Drake and Ruhoff
1960a, p. 38.
TYPE SPECIES: *Axiokersos ovalis* Distant.

*Axiokersos ovalis Distant
Axiokersos ovalis Distant 1909a, p. 122 [India]; 1910a, p. 124, fig. 65·
TYPE: Sex unknown; Calcutta, India; Indian Mus.
DISTRIBUTION: India.
HOST PLANT: Unrecorded.

Genus BAEOCHILA Drake and Poor

Cysteochila (Baeochila) Drake and Poor 1937b, p. 400.
Baeochila: Drake 1948e, p. 151.—Drake and Ruhoff 1960a, p. 39.
TYPE SPECIES: *Cysteochila elongata* Distant.

*Baeochila dehrana Drake and Maa
Baeochila dehrana Drake and Maa 1954, p. 113 [India].
TYPE: Holotype ♂, macropterous; Dehra Dun, India; Drake Coll.
(USNM).
DISTRIBUTION: India; Ceylon.
HOST PLANT: Unrecorded.

*Baeochila elongata (Distant)
Cysteochila elongata Distant 1903a, p. 49 [India]; 1903b, p. 138, fig.
102.—Drake and Poor 1937a, p. 7.
Cysteochila (Baeochila) elongata: Drake and Poor 1937b, p. 400 [Taiwan].
Baeochila elongata: Drake 1948e, p. 151.—Takeya 1951a, p. 21.

TYPE: Sex unknown; Margherita, Assam, India; British Mus.
DISTRIBUTION: India; Burma; Taiwan.
HOST PLANT: Unrecorded.

Baeochila nexa (Distant)

Cysteochila nexa Distant 1903a, p. 49 [India]; 1903b, p. 139.—Drake and Poor 1937a, p. 7.
Baeochila nexa: Drake and Ruhoff 1960c, p.29.—Drake and Davis 1960, fig. 53.

TYPE: Sex unknown; Margherita, Assam, India; British Mus.
DISTRIBUTION: India.
HOST PLANT: Unrecorded.

*Baeochila perinetana Drake

Baeochila perinetana Drake 1958c, p. 320 [Malagasy].

TYPE: Holotype ♂; Périnet, Madagascar; Madagascar Sci. Inst.
DISTRIBUTION: Malagasy Republic.
HOST PLANT: Unrecorded.

*Baeochila scitula Drake

Baeochila scitula Drake 1948e, p. 151 [Taiwan].—Takeya 1951a, p. 21.

TYPE: Holotype ♂, macropterous; Formosa; Drake Coll. (USNM).
DISTRIBUTION: Taiwan.
HOST PLANT: Unrecorded.

Genus BAEOTINGIS Drake and Poor

Baeotingis Drake and Poor 1939b, p. 96.—Drake and Ruhoff 1960a, p. 39.
TYPE SPECIES: Baeotingis ogloblini Drake and Poor.

*Baeotingis ogloblini Drake and Poor

Baeotingis ogloblini Drake and Poor 1939b, p. 96, fig. [Argentina].—
Kormilev 1955a, p. 64.

TYPE: Holotype ♂, brachypterous; San Ignacio, Misiones, Argentina; Drake Coll. (USNM).
DISTRIBUTION: Argentina.
HOST PLANT: Unrecorded.

*Baeotingis silvestrii Drake

Baeotingis silvestrii Drake 1948e, p. 153 [Argentina].

TYPE: Holotype ♂; Rio Santa Cruz, Patagonia, Argentina; Hungarian Mus.
DISTRIBUTION: Argentina.
HOST PLANT: Unrecorded.

*Baeotingis vianai Kormilev

Baeotingis vianai Kormilev 1955a, p. 65, fig. 1 [Argentina].

TYPE: Holotype ♀, brachypterous; La Falda, Córdoba, Argentina; Drake Coll. (USNM).
DISTRIBUTION: Argentina.
HOST PLANT: Unrecorded.

Genus BAICHILA Drake and Slater

Baichila Drake and Slater 1955, p. 50.—Drake and Ruhoff 1960a, p. 39.
TYPE SPECIES: *Baichila capeneri* Drake and Slater.

*Baichila capeneri Drake and Slater

Baichila capeneri Drake and Slater 1955, p. 51 [Transvaal].
TYPE: Holotype ♂, macropterous; Rustenburg, Union of South Africa;
Drake Coll. (USNM).
DISTRIBUTION: South Africa (Transvaal).
HOST PLANT: Unrecorded.

*Baichila pulla Drake and Slater

Baichila pulla Drake and Slater 1955, p. 52 [Transvaal].
TYPE: Holotype ♂, macropterous; Rustenburg, Union of South Africa;
Drake Coll. (USNM).
DISTRIBUTION: South Africa (Transvaal).
HOST PLANT: Unrecorded.

*Baichila vulsa Drake and Slater

Baichila vulsa Drake and Slater 1955, p. 51 [Transvaal].
TYPE: Holotype ♀, macropterous; Rustenburg, Union of South Africa;
Drake Coll. (USNM).
DISTRIBUTION: South Africa (Transvaal).
HOST PLANT: Unrecorded.

Genus BAKO Schouteden

Bako Schouteden 1923, p. 91.—Drake 1954f, p. 8; 1956e, pp. 63–66.—
Drake and Ruhoff 1960a, p. 39.
Galeotingis Drake 1947b, p. 1.—Drake and Ruhoff 1960a, p. 58.
TYPE SPECIES: *Bako lebruni* Schouteden.

*Bako capeneri Drake

Bako capeneri Drake 1956e, p. 65 [Transvaal].
TYPE: Holotype ♀, macropterous; Johannesburg, South Africa; Drake
Coll. (USNM).
DISTRIBUTION: South Africa (Transvaal).
HOST PLANT: Unrecorded.

*Bako dieides Drake and Ruhoff

Bako dieides Drake and Ruhoff 1961b, p. 181, figs. 22 a, b [Cape
Province].
TYPE: Holotype ♂, macropterous; Grahamstown, South Africa; Drake
Coll. (USNM).
DISTRIBUTION: South Africa (Cape Province).
HOST PLANT: Unrecorded.

*Bako editus Drake

Bako editus Drake 1956e, p. 65 [Transvaal].

TYPE: Holotype ♀, macropterous; Johannesburg, South Africa; Drake Coll. (USNM).

DISTRIBUTION: South Africa (Transvaal); Malagasy Republic.

HOST PLANT: Unrecorded.

*Bako lebruni Schouteden

Bako lebruni Schouteden 1923, p. 91 [Congo].—Drake 1954f, p. 8; 1956e, p. 64.—Drake and Ruhoff 1962a, p. 156.

Galeotingis usumburana Drake 1947b, p. 2, fig. 1.

Bako usumburana: Drake 1954f, p. 8; 1956e, p. 64.

TYPE: Sex unknowm; Kwamouth, Belgian Congo; Cent. Afr. Mus.

DISTRIBUTION: Congo.

HOST PLANT: Unrecorded.

*Bako malayanus (Drake)

Galeotingis malayana Drake 1947b, p. 2 [Malaya].

Bako malayanus: Drake 1954f, p. 8; 1956e, p. 64.—Drake and Mohana-sundarum 1961, p. 113 [India; *Panicum repens; Cynadon dactylon; Cenchurus glaucus; Oriza sativa*].

TYPE: Holotype ♂, macropterous; Parit Butan, Malay Peninsula; Drake Coll. (USNM).

DISTRIBUTION: Federation of Malaya; Philippine Islands (Luzon); India.

HOST PLANTS: *Cenchrus glaucus; Cynodon dactylon; Oryza sativa; Panicum repens.*

Genus BANAHAONA Drake and Ruhoff

Banahaona Drake and Ruhoff 1961b, p. 170.

TYPE SPECIES: *Banahaona exalla* Drake and Ruhoff.

*Banahaona exalla Drake and Ruhoff

Banahaona exalla Drake and Ruhoff 1961b, p. 171, figs. 16 a, b [Luzon].

TYPE: Holotype ♂, macropterous; Mount Banahao, Luzon, Philippine Islands; Drake Coll. (USNM).

DISTRIBUTION: Philippine Islands (Luzon).

HOST PLANT: Unrecorded.

Genus BELENUS Distant

Belenus Distant 1909a, p. 116; 1910a, p. 115.—Horváth 1910, p. 62.—Drake 1957c, pp. 31–35.—Drake and Ruhoff 1960a, p. 39.

TYPE SPECIES: *Monanthia dentatus* Fieber.

*Belenus adocetus Drake

Belenus adocetus Drake 1957c, p. 32 [Uganda].

TYPE: Holotype ♂, macropterous; Jinja, Uganda; Drake Coll. (USNM).

DISTRIBUTION: Uganda.

HOST PLANT: Unrecorded.

Belenus angulatus Distant

Belenus angulatus Distant 1909a, p. 116 [Burma]; 1910a, p. 116, fig. 59.

TYPE: Sex unknown; Burma; British Mus.

DISTRIBUTION: Burma.

HOST PLANT: Unrecorded.

*Belenus bengalensis Distant

Belenus bengalensis Distant 1909a, p. 117 [India]; 1910a, p. 117.

TYPE: Sex unknown; India; British Mus.

DISTRIBUTION: India; Thailand.

HOST PLANT: Unrecorded.

*Belenus dentatus (Fieber)

Monanthia (Phyllontocheila) dentata Fieber 1844, p. 71, pl. 6, figs. 2–4 [Ostindien].—Herrich-Schaeffer 1850, p. 155.

Phyllontochila dentata: Stål 1873, p. 128 [India orientalis].—Distant 1903b, p. 136.

Belenus dentatus: Distant 1909a, p. 116 [India; Borneo]; 1910a, p. 116, fig. 58.—Horváth 1912c, p. 342 [Java].—Esaki 1926, p. 163.—Drake 1923a, p. 104 [Taiwan]; 1937a, p. 387 [Thailand; Viet-Nam; Sumatra]; 1957c, p. 32.—Drake and Poor 1936b, p. 147 [Malaya]; 1937a, p. 15 [Luzon]; 1937b, p. 402.—Blöte 1945, p. 86.—Takeya 1951a, p. 15.

TYPE: "Ostindien"; sex and deposition of type unknown.

DISTRIBUTION: India; Thailand; Viet-Nam; Federation of Malaya; Taiwan; Greater Sunda Islands (Borneo; Java; Sumatra); Philippine Islands (Luzon; Mindanao); Marianas Islands (Guam).

HOST PLANT: Unrecorded.

NOTE: Taken at light.

*Belenus laplumei (Schouteden)

Phyllontocheila laplumei Schouteden 1916a, p. 271 [Congo]; 1916b, p. 292.

Belenus laplumei: Drake 1957c, p. 32.

TYPE: Sex unknown; Api, Belgian Congo; Cent. Afr. Mus.

DISTRIBUTION: Congo; Sierra Leone; Central African Republic.

HOST PLANT: Unrecorded.

*Belenus thomasi Drake

Belenus thomasi Drake 1957c, p. 33 [Kenya].

TYPE: Holotype ♂, macropterous; Limuru, Kenya Colony; Drake Coll. (USNM).

DISTRIBUTION: Kenya.

HOST PLANT: Unrecorded.

Genus BEROTINGIS Drake

Berotingis Drake 1956d, pp. 106, 113.—Drake and Ruhoff 1960a, p. 40.

TYPE SPECIES: *Berotingis rugiana* Drake.

*Berotingis guamensis (Drake)

Tingis (*Tingis*) *guamensis* Drake 1941a, p. 142 [Guam].

Tingis guamensis: Usinger 1946a, p. 39 [*Premna gaudichaudii*].

Berotingis guamensis: Drake 1956d, pp. 106, 115.

TYPE: Holotype ♀, macropterous; Guam; USNM.

DISTRIBUTION: Marianas Islands (Guam).

HOST PLANT: *Premna gaudichaudii.*

*Berotingis rugiana Drake

Berotingis rugiana Drake 1956d, pp. 106, 113, fig. 7b [Rota].

TYPE: Holotype ♂, macropterous; Rugi, Rota, Marianas Islands; USNM.

DISTRIBUTION: Marianas Islands (Rota; Guam).

HOST PLANT: Unrecorded.

*Berotingis yapensis (Drake)

Eteoneus yapensis Drake 1946, p. 27 [Yap; *Premna gaudichaudii*].—Takeya 1951a, p. 18.

Berotingis yapensis: Drake 1956d, pp. 106, 113, fig. 7a.

TYPE: Holotype ♂; Dogor-Kanif-Rul, Yap; Kyushu Univ.

DISTRIBUTION: Caroline Islands (Yap).

HOST PLANT: *Premna gaudichaudii.*

Genus BIRABENA Drake and Hurd

Birabena Drake and Hurd 1945b, p. 127.—Drake and Ruhoff 1960a, p. 40.

TYPE SPECIES: *Birabena birabeni* Drake and Hurd.

*Birabena angusta (Drake and Hambleton)

Atheas angusta Drake and Hambleton 1940, p. 535 [Brazil].—Monte 1941e, p. 80.

Birabena angusta: Drake and Hurd 1945b, p. 128.

TYPE: Holotype ♀, macropterous; S. José dos Campos, São Paulo, Brazil; Drake Coll. (USNM).

DISTRIBUTION: Brazil.

HOST PLANT: Unrecorded.

*Birabena birabeni Drake and Hurd

Birabena birabeni Drake and Hurd 1945b, p. 127, fig. 1 [Argentina].—Kormilev 1955a, p. 64.

TYPE: Holotype ♀, macropterous; Puna, S. del Estero, Argentina; La Plata Mus.

DISTRIBUTION: Argentina.

HOST PLANT: Unrecorded.

Birabena carvalhoi Monte

Birabena carvalhoi Monte 1947b, p. 429 [Brazil].

TYPE: Holotype ♂; Brazil; Monte Coll. (Mus. Nacional).

DISTRIBUTION: Brazil.

HOST PLANT: Unrecorded.

*Birabena elongata (Drake)

Atheas elongata Drake 1922c, p. 367, pl. 39, fig. 1 [Brazil].—Monte 1941e, p. 80; 1942a, p. 97.

Birabena elongata: Drake and Hurd 1945b, p. 128.

TYPE: Sex unknown; Chapada, Brazil; Carnegie Mus.

DISTRIBUTION: Brazil.

HOST PLANT: Unrecorded.

Genus BUNIA Schouteden

Bunia Schouteden 1955b, p. 167.—Drake and Ruhoff 1960a, p. 41.

TYPE SPECIES: *Bunia ituriensis* Schouteden.

Bunia ituriensis Schouteden

Bunia ituriensis Schouteden 1955b, p. 167 [Congo].

TYPE: Sex unknown; Bunia, Ituri, Belgian Congo; Cent. Afr. Mus.

DISTRIBUTION: Congo.

HOST PLANT: Unrecorded.

Genus BUNOTINGIS Drake

Bunotingis Drake 1948e, p. 152.—Drake and Ruhoff 1960a, p. 41.

TYPE SPECIES: *Cysteochila* (*Parada*) *camelinus* Hacker.

*Bunotingis camelina (Hacker)

Cysteochila (*Parada*) *camelinus* Hacker 1927, p. 24, pl. 8, fig. 10 [New South Wales].

Bunotingis camelina: Drake 1948e, p. 152.

TYPE: Sex unknown; Tooloom, New South Wales, Australia; Queensland Mus.

DISTRIBUTION: Australia (New South Wales; Queensland).

HOST PLANT: Unrecorded.

Genus CALLITHRINCUS Horváth

Callithrincus Horváth 1925a, p. 10.—Drake and Ruhoff 1960a, p. 42.

TYPE SPECIES: *Callithrincus serratus* Horváth.

*Callithrincus serratus Horváth

Callithrincus serratus Horváth 1925a, p. 10, fig. 6 [Queensland].—Hacker 1928, p. 181.—Drake 1942b, p. 361.

TYPE: Holotype ♀; Mt. Tambourine, Queensland, Australia; Stockholm Mus.

DISTRIBUTION: Australia (Queensland).

HOST PLANT: Unrecorded.

*Callithrincus signatus Drake

Callithrincus signatus Drake 1942b, p. 361 [Queensland].

TYPE: Holotype ♂, macropterous; Mount Glorious, Queensland, Australia; Drake Coll. (USNM).

DISTRIBUTION: Australia (Queensland).

HOST PLANT: Unrecorded.

Genus CALOLOMA Drake and Bruner

Caloloma Drake and Bruner 1924a, p. 152.—Drake 1945, p. 98.—Hurd 1946, p. 472.—Drake and Ruhoff 1960a, p. 42.

TYPE SPECIES: *Caloloma uhleri* Drake and Bruner.

*Caloloma uhleri Drake and Bruner

Caloloma uhleri Drake and Bruner 1924a, p. 153 [Antigua].—Drake 1945, p. 98 [Australia]; 1961b, p. 112.—Drake and Ruhoff 1961b, p. 183, fig. 24.

TYPE: Holotype ♀, macropterous; San Juan, Antigua, Lesser Antilles; USNM.

DISTRIBUTION: Leeward Islands (Antigua); Windward Islands (St. Vincent); Australia (Queensland; New South Wales; South Australia).

HOST PLANT: Unrecorded.

NOTE: Australian indigene. Contrary to previous statements in the literature, this species now appears to be permanently established in the West Indies.

Genus CALOTINGIS Drake

Calotingis Drake 1918d, p. 86.—Hacker 1929, p. 334.—Hurd 1946, p. 454.—Drake and Ruhoff 1960a, p. 42.

Neopachycysta Hacker 1928, p. 183.—Drake and Ruhoff 1960a, p. 70.

TYPE SPECIES: *Calotingis knighti* Drake.

*Calotingis knighti Drake

Calotingis knighti Drake 1918d, p. 87 [Tex.; *Malvaviscus drummondii*].—Van Duzee 1923, p. 141 [Mexico].—Drake and Davis 1960, fig. 68.

TYPE: Holotype ♂, macropterous; Helotes, Texas, U.S.; Drake Coll. (USNM).

DISTRIBUTION: U.S. (Tex.); Mexico.

HOST PLANT: *Malvaviscus drummondii*.

Calotingis subopaca (Hacker)

Neopachycysta subopaca Hacker 1928, p. 184, pl. 22, figs. 11, 12 [Queensland].

Calotingis subopaca: Hacker 1929, p. 334.

TYPE: Sex unknown; Maleny, Queensland, Australia; Queensland Mus.

DISTRIBUTION: Australia (Queensland).

HOST PLANT: Unrecorded.

Genus CAMPYLOSTEIRA Fieber

Campylosteira Fieber 1844, p. 42.—Horváth 1906a, pp. 13, 15 (key).—
Mužik 1907, pp. 49, 51 (key).—Jensen-Haarup 1912, p. 150.—
Stichel 1926, pp. 103, 105 (key); 1960a, p. 269 (key); 1960b, p.
390; 1960c, p. 129.—Gulde 1938, pp. 242, 245 (key).—China 1943,
p. 245.—Kiritshenko 1951, pp. 240, 243 (key).—Drake and Ruhoff
1960a, p. 43.

Campylostira [sic]: Fieber 1861, p. 131.—Douglas and Scott 1865,
p. 257.—Stål 1874, p. 52.—Puton 1887, p. 100 (key).—Horváth
1892, p. 309.—Lethierry and Severin 1896, p. 9.—Oshanin 1908,
p. 402; 1912, p. 42.—Stichel 1935, p. 348; 1938a, p. 404.

TYPE SPECIES: *Campylosteira falleni* Fieber.

Campylosteira bosnica Horváth

Campylostira bosnica Horváth 1892a, pp. 309, 311 [Yugoslavia].
Campylosteira bosnica: Horváth 1906a, pp. 15, 19.—Stichel 1926, p.
105; 1960a, p. 269.

TYPE: Sex unknown; Bosnia; Hungarian Mus.
DISTRIBUTION: Yugoslavia.
HOST PLANT: Unrecorded.

Campylosteira bosnica var. diluta Horváth

Campylostira bosnica var. *diluta* Horváth 1892a, pp. 309, 312 [Yugoslavia].
Campylosteira bosnica var. *diluta:* Horváth 1906a, p. 19.—Stichel 1960a,
p. 269.

TYPE: Sex unknown; Bosnia; Hungarian Mus.
DISTRIBUTION: Yugoslavia.
HOST PLANT: Unrecorded.

Campylosteira ciliata Fieber

Campylosteira ciliata Fieber 1844, p. 44, pl. 3, figs. 33–37 [Czechoslo-
vakia].—Herrich-Schaeffer 1850, p. 160.—Horváth 1906a, p. 23.—
Stichel 1926, p. 106; 1960a, p. 273, fig. 38a.—Hoberlandt 1943b,
p. 120.

Campylostira ciliata: Fieber 1861, p. 132 [moss].—Puton 1887, p. 100.—
Horváth 1892a, pp. 309, 311.—Hüeber 1893, p. 300.

Monanthia ciliata: Walker 1873a, p. 190.

TYPE: Prague, Czechoslovakia; sex and deposition of type unknown.
DISTRIBUTION: Czechoslovakia.
HOST PLANT: Moss.

Campylosteira dispar Horváth

Campylosteira dispar Horváth 1905b, p. 558 [Algeria; Tunisia]; 1906a,
p. 22.—Hoberlandt 1955, p. 86 [Turkey].

TYPE: Unknown.
DISTRIBUTION: Algeria; Tunisia; Turkey.
HOST PLANT: Unrecorded.

*Campylosteira eximia Horváth

Campylostira eximia Horváth 1892a, pp. 311, 313 [Turkestan].
Campylosteira eximia: Horváth 1906a, p. 22.
TYPE: Holotype ♀; Taschkent, Turkestan, Russia; Hungarian Mus.
DISTRIBUTION: U.S.S.R. (Turkestan).
HOST PLANT: Unrecorded.

*Campylosteira falleni Fieber

Campylosteira falleni Fieber 1844, p. 43, pl. 3, figs. 23-26 [Czechoslovakia].—Horváth 1906a, p. 20.—Stichel 1926, p. 105; 1960a, p. 270, fig. 34a.—Kiritshenko 1951, p. 243 [Russia].
Campylosteira fallenii [sic]: Herrich-Schaeffer 1850, p. 160.
Campylostira falleni: Fieber 1861, p. 132 [moss].—Puton 1879c, p. 93.—Lethierry and Severin 1896, p. 9 [Hungary; Yugoslavia; Rumania; Caucasus].—Blöte 1945, p. 82.
Monanthia falleni: Walker 1873a, p. 190.
Campylostira fallenii [sic]: Hüeber 1893, p. 302.
TYPE: Sex unknown; Prague, Czechoslovakia; Vienna Mus.
DISTRIBUTION: Czechoslovakia; Hungary; Yugoslavia; Rumania; U.S.S.R. (Caucasus).
HOST PLANT: Moss.

Campylosteira horvathi Drake

Campylosteira horvathi Drake 1951, p. 171 [Tanganyika].
TYPE: Holotype ♂, brachypterous; Arusha-Chini, Africa orientalis; Hungarian Mus.
DISTRIBUTION: Tanganyika.
HOST PLANT: Unrecorded.

Campylosteira libanotica Horváth

Campylosteira libanotica Horváth 1906a, p. 21 [Lebanon].
TYPE: Sex unknown; Lebanon; Hungarian Mus.
DISTRIBUTION: Lebanon.
HOST PLANT: Unrecorded.

Campylosteira moroccana Puton

Campylostira moroccana Puton 1887, p. 100 [Morocco].
Campylostira maroccana [sic]: Horváth 1892a, p. 310.
Campylosteira maroccana [sic]: Horváth 1906a, p. 20 [Mauritania].
TYPE: Sex unknown; Morocco; Paris Mus.
DISTRIBUTION: Morocco; Mauritania.
HOST PLANT: Unrecorded.

*Campylosteira orientalis Horváth

Campylostira orientalis Horváth 1881a, p. 223 [Hungary; Caucasus; Yugoslavia].—Oshanin 1912, p. 42 [Austria; Crimea].—Stichel 1938a, p. 404 [Turkey; Albania].

Campylostira falleni var. *orientalis:* Horváth 1892a, p. 310 [Rumania; Transcaucasus].
Campylosteira orientalis: Horváth 1906a, p. 20.—Kiritshenko 1951, p. 243.—Stichel 1960a, p. 270.
TYPE: Unknown.
DISTRIBUTION: Hungary; Austria; Yugoslavia; Albania; Turkey; Rumania; U.S.S.R. (Caucasus; Transcaucasus; Crimea).
HOST PLANT: Unrecorded.

*Campylosteira orientalis var. miridita Horváth
Campylosteira falleni var. *miridita* Horváth 1905b, p. 558 [Albania].
Campylosteira orientalis var. *miridita:* Horváth 1906a, p. 20.—Mancini 1953b, p. 185.—Stichel 1960a, p. 270.
Campylostira orientalis var. *miridita:* Horváth 1916, p. 9.
TYPE: Sex unknown; Velipoja, Albania; Hungarian Mus.
DISTRIBUTION: Albania.
HOST PLANT: Unrecorded.

Campylosteira orientalis var. suspecta Horváth
Campylostira falleni (not Fieber): Horváth 1892a, p. 310.
Campylostira falleni var. *suspecta* Horváth 1892a, pp. 310, 312 [Rumania].
Campylosteira orientalis var. *suspecta:* Horváth 1906a, p. 20 [Hungary].—Stichel 1960a, p. 271.
TYPE: Sex unknown; Rumania; Hungarian Mus.
DISTRIBUTION: Rumania; Hungary.
HOST PLANT: Unrecorded.

Campylosteira parvula Ferrari
Campylostira parvula Ferrari 1874, p. 172 [Iran].—Horváth 1892a, p. 310.
Serenthia parvula: Lethierry and Severin 1896, p. 5.
Campylosteira parvula: Horváth 1906a, p. 23.
TYPE: Sex unknown; Persia; Genova Mus.
DISTRIBUTION: Iran.
HOST PLANT: Unrecorded.

*Campylosteira perithrix Puton
Campylostira perithrix Puton 1887, p. 99 [Algeria].—Horváth 1892a, p. 309.
Serenthia perithrix: Lethierry and Severin 1896, p. 5.
Campylosteira perithrix: Horváth 1906a, p. 23.
TYPE: Sex unknown; Algeria; Paris Mus.
DISTRIBUTION: Algeria; Tunisia.
HOST PLANT: Unrecorded.

Campylosteira perithrix var. cognata Horváth

Campylosteira cognata Horváth 1905b, p. 559 [Algeria].

Campylosteira perithrix var. *cognata:* Horváth 1906a, p. 23.

TYPE: Sex unknown; St. Charles, Algeria; Hungarian Mus.

DISTRIBUTION: Algeria.

HOST PLANT: Unrecorded.

*Campylosteira pilicornis Horváth

Campylosteira pilicornis Horváth 1906a, p. 19 [Israel].

TYPE: Sex unknown; Jerusalem, Syria; Hungarian Mus.

DISTRIBUTION: Israel.

HOST PLANT: Unrecorded.

*Campylosteira pilifera Reuter

Campylostira pilifera Reuter 1880a, p. 12 [Greece]; 1891a, p. 25.—Puton 1887, p. 100.—Horváth 1892a, pp. 309, 311.

Serenthia pilifera: Lethierry and Severin 1896, p. 5.

Campylosteira pilifera: Reuter 1902, p. 151.—Horváth 1906a, p. 23.— Stichel 1960a, p. 272.

TYPE: Sex unknown; Olympus, Greece; Helsin. Mus.

DISTRIBUTION: Greece.

HOST PLANT: Unrecorded.

Campylosteira pilifera var. diminuta Horváth

Campylosteira pilifera var. *diminuta* Horváth 1905b, p. 561 [Greece]; 1906a, p. 23.—Stichel 1960a, p. 272.

TYPE: Sex unknown; Attica, Greece; Hungarian Mus.

DISTRIBUTION: Greece.

HOST PLANT: Unrecorded.

*Campylosteira pilifera var. humilis Horváth

Campylosteira pilifera var. *humilis* Horváth 1905b, p. 560 [Greece]; 1906a, p. 23.—Stichel 1960a, p. 272.

TYPE: Holotype ♀; Greece; Hungarian Mus.

DISTRIBUTION: Greece.

HOST PLANT: Unrecorded.

*Campylosteira rotundata Takeya

Campyrostira [sic] *rotundata* Takeya 1933, p. 34, pl. 3, fig. 2, text fig. 2 [Japan].

Campylostira rotundata: Takeya 1951a, p. 6.—Esaki 1954, p. 235, fig. 607.

TYPE: Holotype ♀; Kyoto, Honshu, Japan; Kyushu Univ.

DISTRIBUTION: Japan; China (Hunan).

HOST PLANT: Unrecorded.

Campylosteira serena Horváth

Campylosteira serena Horváth 1902a, p. 593 [Spain]; 1906a, p. 22.— Gomez-Menor 1955b, p. 249.—Stichel 1960a, p. 272 [Sardinia].

TYPE: Holotype ♀; Ciudad Real, Spain; Hungarian Mus.
DISTRIBUTION: Spain; Sardinia.
HOST PLANT: Unrecorded.

Campylosteira sinuata Fieber

Campylostira sinuata Fieber 1861, p. 132 [Germany].—Puton 1879c, p. 93.—Horváth 1892a, p. 311 [Transcaucasus].—Hüeber 1893, p. 303.—Börner 1935, p. 75.
Campylosteira sinuata: Horváth 1906a, p. 22, pl. 1, fig. 3.—Stichel 1926, p. 106, fig. 294; 1960a, p. 272.—Kiritshenko 1951, p. 243.
Monanthia sinuata: Walker 1873a, p. 190.
Serenthia sinuata: Lethierry and Severin 1896, p. 5.
TYPE: Sex unknown; Germany; Vienna Mus.
DISTRIBUTION: Germany; U.S.S.R. (Transcaucasus).
HOST PLANT: Unrecorded.

Campylosteira sororcula Horváth

Campylosteira sororcula Horváth 1905b, p. 560 [Algeria]; 1906a, p. 23.
TYPE: Holotype ♂; St. Charles, Algeria; Hungarian Mus.
DISTRIBUTION: Algeria.
HOST PLANT: Unrecorded.

*Campylosteira verna (Fallén)

Tingis verna Fallén 1826, p. 16 [Sweden]; 1829, p. 147.
Monanthia verna: Herrich-Schaeffer 1838, pp. 53, 64, pl. 127, fig. 398 [Germany; Czechoslovakia].
Campylosteira brachycera Fieber 1844, p. 43, pl. 3, figs. 27–32 [moss].—Herrich-Schaeffer 1850, p. 160.—Mayr 1858, p. 569 [Austria; Hungary].
Campylosteira verna: Fieber 1844, p. 45, pl. 3, fig. 38.—Kolenati 1856, p. 429 [Transcaucasus; Onosma echioides].—Reuter 1874, p. 565.—Horváth 1898b, p. 279; 1906a, pp. 17, 21, pl. 1, fig. 2 [Denmark; Belgium; Italy; Rumania].—Jensen-Haarup 1912, p. 150, fig. 94.—Reichensperger 1920, p. 61.—Butler 1923, p. 200.—Stichel 1926, p. 106, fig. 293; 1960a, p. 271, fig. 36 [Poland; Albania].—Gulde 1938, p. 247, fig.—Hoberlandt 1942, p. 124; 1943b, p. 122.—Kiritshenko 1951, p. 243.—Bator 1953, p. 323, pl. 4, fig. 2.—Mancini 1953c, p. 22.—Štusak 1958, p. 367, figs. 8–11.—Southwood and Leston 1959, p. 141, pl. 18, fig. 2, pl. 21, fig. 1.
Campylostira brachycera: Fieber 1861, p. 132.—Douglas and Scott 1865, p. 259.—Frey-Gessner 1865, p. 233 [Switzerland].—Horváth 1874b, p. 432.—Saunders 1875, p. 246.
Campylostira verna: Fieber 1861, p. 132.—Douglas and Scott 1865, p. 258.—Reiber and Puton 1876, p. 67 [France].—Vollenhoven 1878, p. 282, pl. 10, fig. 3 [Netherlands].—Puton 1879c, p. 92.—Jakovlev 1880b, p. 100 [Caucasus].—Reuter 1882b, p. 113.—Saun-

ders 1892, p. 124, pl. 11, fig. 6.—Horváth 1892a, p. 310.—Hüeber 1893, p. 300.—Oshanin 1908, p. 403 [Spain].—Schumacher 1914, p. 256.—Scholte 1935, p. 29, fig. 4.—Börner 1935, p. 75.—Blöte 1945, p. 82 [Greece].—Novak and Wagner 1951, p. 70 [Yugoslavia].

Serenthia verna: Lethierry and Severin 1896, p. 6.

TYPE: Sex unknown; Sweden; Lund Zool. Inst.

DISTRIBUTION: England; Belgium; Netherlands; France; Spain; Italy; Switzerland; Germany; Denmark; Sweden; Poland; Austria; Czechoslovakia; Hungary; Yugoslavia; Albania; Rumania; Greece; U.S.S.R. (Caucasus; Transcaucasus).

HOST PLANTS: *Onosma echioides;* moss.

NOTE: Eggs [Štusak].

Campylosteira verna var. latipennis Horváth

Campylostira verna var. *latipennis* Horváth 1892a, pp. 310, 312 [Rumania; Hungary].

Campylosteira verna var. *latipennis:* Horváth 1906a, p. 22 [Yugoslavia; Germany; France].—Mužik 1907, p. 52 [Czechoslovakia].

Serenthia verna var. *latipennis:* Lethierry and Severin 1896, p. 6.

TYPE: Unknown.

DISTRIBUTION: France; Germany; Czechoslovakia; Hungary; Yugoslavia; Rumania.

HOST PLANT: Unrecorded.

Genus CAMPYLOTINGIS Drake and Bondar

Campylotingis Drake and Bondar 1932, p. 89.—Monte 1939b, p. 66; 1941e, p. 81.—Drake and Ruhoff 1960a, p. 43.

TYPE SPECIES: *Tigava mollicula* Drake.

*Campylotingis bondari (Drake)

Tigava bondari Drake 1930b, p. 25 [Brazil]; 1931a, p. 405.

Campylotingis bondari: Drake and Bondar 1932, p. 89.—Costa Lima 1936, p. 125.—Monte 1941e, p. 82 [*Machaerium*].—Silva 1956, p. 19, fig. 4 [*Canavalia ensiformis; Dolichos lablab; Phaseolus lunatus; Phaseolus vulgaris; Vigna sinensis*].

TYPE: Holotype ♂, macropterous; Bahia, Brazil; Drake Coll. (USNM).

DISTRIBUTION: Brazil.

HOST PLANTS: *Canavalia ensiformis; Dolichos lablab; Machaerium* sp.; *Phaseolus lunatus; Phaseolus vulgaris; Vigna sinensis.*

*Campylotingis carvalhoi Drake and Hambleton

Campylotingis carvalhoi Drake and Hambleton 1938a, p. 47 [Brazil; Papilionaceae].—Monte 1941e, p. 82 [*Ferreirea spectabilis*].

TYPE: Holotype ♂, macropterous; Curvello, Minas Gerais, Brazil; Drake Coll. (USNM).

DISTRIBUTION: Brazil.

HOST PLANTS: *Ferreirea spectabilis;* Papilionaceae.

*Campylotingis clara Drake and Hambleton

Campylotingis clara Drake and Hambleton 1942b, p. 77 [Brazil].

TYPE: Holotype ♂, macropterous; Belo Horizonte, Minas Gerais, Brazil; Drake Coll. (USNM).

DISTRIBUTION: Brazil.

HOST PLANT: Unrecorded.

*Campylotingis clavata Drake and Hambleton

Campylotingis clavata Drake and Hambleton 1939, p. 156 [Brazil].—Monte 1941e, p. 82 [Myrocarpus fastigiatus].

TYPE: Holotype ♂, macropterous; Belo Horizonte, Minas Gerais, Brazil; Drake Coll. (USNM).

DISTRIBUTION: Brazil.

HOST PLANT: Myrocarpus fastigiatus.

*Campylotingis genetica Drake and Hambleton

Campylotingis genetica Drake and Hambleton 1942b, p. 78 [Brazil].

TYPE: Holotype ♂, macropterous; Viçosa, Brazil; Drake Coll. (USNM).

DISTRIBUTION: Brazil.

HOST PLANT: Unrecorded.

*Campylotingis integra Drake and Hambleton

Campylotingis integra Drake and Hambleton 1942b, p. 79 [Brazil].

TYPE: Holotype ♂, macropterous; Belo Horizonte, Minas Gerais, Brazil; Drake Coll. (USNM).

DISTRIBUTION: Brazil.

HOST PLANT: Unrecorded.

*Campylotingis jansoni (Drake)

Tigava jansoni Drake 1922c, p. 364, pl. 39, fig. 8 [Brazil].

Campylotingis jansoni: Drake and Bondar 1932, p. 89.—Drake and Hambleton 1938a, p. 46 [Machaerium].

TYPE: Holotype ♂; Chapada, Brazil; Carnegie Mus.

DISTRIBUTION: Brazil.

HOST PLANT: Machaerium sp.

*Campylotingis lenatis Drake

Camplotingis [sic] lenatis Drake 1935, p. 14 [Paraguay].

Campylotingis lenatis: Drake and Hambleton 1938a, p. 46 [Brazil; Machaerium].—Monte 1940e, p. 290, fig. 3.

TYPE: Holotype ♂; S. Bernadino, Paraguay; Vienna Mus.

DISTRIBUTION: Paraguay; Brazil.

HOST PLANT: Machaerium sp.

*Campylotingis levis Drake and Hambleton

Campylotingis levis Drake and Hambleton 1942b, p. 80 [Brazil].

TYPE: Holotype ♂, macropterous; São Paulo, Brazil; Drake Coll. (USNM).

DISTRIBUTION: Brazil.

HOST PLANT: Unrecorded.

*Campylotingis machaerii Drake and Hambleton

Camplotingis [sic] machaerii Drake and Hambleton 1934, p. 442 [Brazil; Argentina; Machaerium].—Drake 1936b, p. 700.

Campylotingis machaerii: Costa Lima 1936, p. 125.—Bosq 1937, p. 128.—Monte 1939b, p. 66 [Ferreirea spectabilis]; 1940b, p. 375.

Campylotingis snipesi Drake and Hambleton 1944b, p. 125.

TYPE: Holotype ♂, macropterous; Viçosa, Minas Gerais, Brazil; Drake Coll. (USNM).

DISTRIBUTION: Brazil; Argentina.

HOST PLANTS: Ferreirea spectabilis; Machaerium sp.

*Campylotingis mollicula (Drake)

Tigava mollicula Drake 1922c, p. 365 [Brazil].

Campylotingis mollicula: Drake and Bondar 1932, p. 89.

TYPE: Holotype ♀; Chapada, Brazil; Carnegie Mus.

DISTRIBUTION: Brazil.

HOST PLANT: Unrecorded.

*Campylotingis mollis Drake and Bondar

Campylotingis mollis Drake and Bondar 1932, p. 90 [Brazil; Cassia].—Costa Lima 1936, p. 125.—Silva 1956, p. 21.

TYPE: Holotype ♂, macropterous; Bahia, Brazil; Drake Coll. (USNM).

DISTRIBUTION: Brazil.

HOST PLANT: Cassia sp.

*Campylotingis prudens Drake and Hambleton

Campylotingis prudens Drake and Hambleton 1938a, p. 47 [Brazil; Machaerium].—Monte 1939b, p. 66 [Machaerium villosum]; 1940e, p. 290, fig. 4.

TYPE: Holotype ♂, macropterous; São Paulo, Brazil; Drake Coll. (USNM).

DISTRIBUTION: Brazil; Argentina.

HOST PLANTS: Machaerium villosum; Machaerium sp.

*Campylotingis tantilla Drake

Camplotingis [sic] tantilla Drake 1935, p. 14, fig. 2 [Paraguay].

Campylotingis tantilla: Drake and Hambleton 1938a, p. 46 [Brazil; Machaerium].

TYPE: Holotype ♂; S. Bernardino, Paraguay; Vienna Mus.

DISTRIBUTION: Paraguay; Brazil.

HOST PLANT: Machaerium sp.

Genus CANTINONA Distant

Cantinona Distant 1913, p. 158.—Drake and Ruhoff 1960a, p. 43.

TYPE SPECIES: Cantinona praecellens Distant.

Cantinona praecellens Distant

Cantinona praecellens Distant 1913, p. 159, pl. 11, fig. 15 [Seychelles].—
Drake and Ruhoff 1961b, p. 168, fig. 14.

TYPE: Sex unknown; Seychelles; British Mus.

DISTRIBUTION: Seychelles Island.

HOST PLANT: Unrecorded.

Genus CATOPLATUS Spinola

Catoplatus Spinola 1837, p. 137.—Stål 1873, pp. 121, 128; 1874, p. 57.—
Lethierry and Severin 1896, p. 20.—Horváth 1906a, pp. 14, 85
(key).—Oshanin 1908, p. 442; 1912, p. 45.—Kiritshenko 1918, p.
109; 1951, pp. 242, 251 (key).—Stichel 1926, pp. 104, 113 (key);
1935, p. 349; 1938a, p. 408; 1960a, p. 323 (key); 1960b, p. 398;
1960c, p. 137.—Börner 1935, pp. 74, 77 (key).—Gulde 1938, pp. 244,
300 (key).—Hoberlandt 1942, p. 125; 1943, p. 119; 1955, p. 92.—
China 1943, p. 247.—Blöte 1945, p. 88.—Singer 1952, p. 53.—Drake
and Ruhoff 1960a, p. 43.

Catoplatus (Coscinopoea) Stål 1873, p. 128; 1874, p. 58.—Drake and Ruhoff 1960a, p. 48.

Monanthia (Catoplatus): Puton 1879c, p. 117.—Saunders 1892, p.
134.

TYPE SPECIES: *Tingis fabricii* Stål.

*Catoplatus anticus (Reuter)

Monanthia (Catoplatus) antica Reuter 1880, p. 11 [Greece].

Catoplatus anticus: Lethierry and Severin 1896, p. 20.—Horváth 1906a,
p. 88 [Turkey]; 1916, p. 9 [Albania]; 1918, p. 334.—Kiritshenko
1951, p. 251 [Russia].—Mancini 1953b, p. 186.—Hoberlandt 1955,
p. 92 [Israel].—Stichel 1960a, p. 324.

TYPE: Sex unknown; Greece; Helsin. Mus.

DISTRIBUTION: Albania; Greece; Turkey; Israel; U.S.S.R.

HOST PLANT: Unrecorded.

Catoplatus anticus var. syriacus Horváth

Catoplatus anticus var. *syriacus* Horváth 1906a, p. 88 [Israel].—Hoberlandt 1955, p. 92 [Turkey; Russia].

TYPE: Sex unknown; Syria; Hungarian Mus.

DISTRIBUTION: Israel; Turkey; U.S.S.R. (Crimea).

HOST PLANT: Unrecorded.

Catoplatus bletoni Vidal

Catoplatus bletoni Vidal 1937, p. 197, fig. 2 [Morocco].

TYPE: Sex unknown; Morocco; Vidal Coll.

DISTRIBUTION: Morocco.

HOST PLANT: Unrecorded.

*Catoplatus carthusianus (Goeze)

Cimex carthusianus Goeze 1778, p. 268.—Fourcroy 1785, p. 212 [Eryngium].

Tingis eryngii Latrielle 1804, p. 253.—Vallot 1829, pp. 99, 113 [Eryngium campestre].

Tingis melanocephala Panzer 1806, heft 100, tab. 21 [Germany].— Herrich-Schaeffer 1835, p. 58.

Monanthia melanocephala: Le Peletier and Serville 1828, p. 653.— Herrich-Schaeffer 1838, p. 54 [Hungary; Czechoslovakia].—Mayr 1858, p. 570 [Caucasus; Austria].

Piesma melanocephalum: Burmeister 1835, p. 258 [Portugal].

Dictyonota eryngii: Westwood 1840b, p. 121 [England].

Monanthia (Tropidocheila) melanocephala: Herrich-Schaeffer 1850, p. 151.

Monanthia albida (not Herrich-Schaeffer): Fieber 1861, p. 124 [Seseli glaucum].

Monanthia nigripes Motschulsky 1863, p. 91 [Algeria].—Kiritshenko 1915, p. 300.

Monanthia eryngii: Garbiglietti 1869, p. 273 [Italy].—Jakovlev 1880b, p. 109 [Onopordon].—Chicote 1880, p. 189 [Spain].—Hüeber 1893, p. 343.

Catoplatus (Coscinopoea) eryngii: Stål 1873, p. 128; 1874a, p. 58.

Catoplatus (Coscinopoea) albidus: Stål 1874, p. 58.

Monanthia (Catoplatus) eryngii: Puton 1879c, p. 117 [France; Eryngium maritimum].

Catoplatus carthusianus: Reuter 1891a, p. 26 [Greece].—Lambertie 1906, p. 25.—Horváth 1906a, pp. 86, 89 [Turkey].—Oshanin 1908, p. 443 [Morocco; Rumania; Iran].—Moroder Sala 1920, p. 12.— Reichensperger 1920, p. 62.—de Seabra 1924, p. 16, fig. 28; 1931, p. 429, figs. 500 (2–4), 501.—Stichel 1926, p. 113; 1960a, p. 324, fig. 127 [Sardinia; Bulgaria].—Lindberg 1932a, p. 43.—Scholte 1935, p. 77, fig. 20 [Netherlands].—Hoberlandt 1942, p. 125; 1955, p. 92 [Transcaucasus].—Kiritshenko 1951, p. 251.—Novak and Wagner 1951, p. 71 [Yugoslavia; Eryngium amethystinum].—Mancini 1953b, p. 186 [Albania]; 1953c, p. 22.—Seidenstücker 1954, p. 236.— Gomez-Menor 1955b, p. 249.—Štusak 1957a, p. 21, figs. 4, 5; 1957b, p. 136, fig. 4; 1959a, p. 52, figs. 1–8.

Catoplatus melanocephalus: Lethierry and Severin 1896, p. 20.

Cantacader nigripes: Oshanin 1908, p. 401.—Drake 1950a, p. 164.

TYPE: Unknown.

DISTRIBUTION: England; France; Netherlands; Spain; Portugal; Italy; Sardinia; Austria; Czechoslovakia; Germany; Albania; Hungary; Yugoslavia; Bulgaria; Greece; Rumania; Turkey; Iran; U.S.S.R. (Caucasus; Transcaucasus); Algeria; Morocco.

HOST PLANTS: *Eryngium amethystinum; Eryngium campestre; Eryngium maritimum; Eryngium* sp.; *Onopordon* sp.; *Seseli glaucum.*

NOTE: Life history study [Štusak 1959a]; eggs [Štusak 1957a]; nymphs and immature stages [Štusak 1957b; 1959a].

*Catoplatus carthusianus var. albidus (Herrich-Schaeffer)

Monanthia albida Herrich-Schaeffer 1838, p. 54, pl. 125, fig. b; pl. 126, fig. 396 [Hungary].—Ferrari 1874, p. 171 [Italy]; 1878, p. 66.—Reiber and Puton 1876, p. 69.—Bolivar and Chicote 1879, p. 166 [Spain].— Jakovlev 1880b, p. 109 [Caucasus].

Monanthia (Tropidocheila) schaefferi Fieber 1844, p. 78, pl. 6, figs. 31–35 [Czechoslovakia; Austria; *Seseli glaucum*].

Monanthia (Tropidocheila) albida: Herrich-Schaeffer 1850, p. 151.

Monanthia schaefferi: Mayr 1858, p. 570 [Lichtenstein; Greece; Yugoslavia; Germany; *Eryngium*].

Catoplatus (Coscinopoea) albida: Stål 1873, p. 128.

Catoplatus dacicus Montandon 1895, p. 160 [Rumania].

Catoplatus carthusianus var. *albidus:* Horváth 1906a, p. 89.—Stichel 1926, p. 114; 1960a, p. 324 [Sardinia].—Novak and Wagner 1951, p. 71.—Kiritshenko 1951, p. 251.—Hoberlandt 1955, p. 92 [Transcaucasus].—Stušak 1959a, p. 52.

TYPE: Unknown.

DISTRIBUTION: Italy; Sardinia; Austria; Germany; Czechoslovakia; Hungary; Yugoslavia; Rumania; Lichtenstein; Spain; Greece; U.S.S.R. (Caucasus; Transcaucasus).

HOST PLANTS: *Seseli glaucum; Eryngium* sp.

Catoplatus carthusianus var. intermedius Vidal

Catoplatus carthusianus var. *intermedius* Vidal 1937, p. 198 [Morocco].—Stichel 1960a, p. 324.

TYPE: Sex unknown; Oujda, Morocco; Vidal Coll.

DISTRIBUTION: Morocco.

HOST PLANT: Unrecorded.

*Catoplatus citrinus Horváth

Catoplatus citrinus Horváth 1897a, p. 89 [Turkestan]; 1906a, p. 91.—Kiritshenko 1959, p. 105.

TYPE: Sex unknown; Samarkand, Turkestan; Hungarian Mus.

DISTRIBUTION: U.S.S.R. (Turkestan).

HOST PLANT: Unrecorded.

*Catoplatus crassipes (Fieber)

Monanthia crassipes Fieber 1861, p. 123 [Yugoslavia].

Catoplatus crassipes: Lethierry and Severin 1896, p. 20.—Horváth 1906a, p. 88, fig. 4.—Stichel 1960a, p. 323.

TYPE: Sex unknown; Serbia; Vienna Mus.

DISTRIBUTION: Yugoslavia.

HOST PLANT: Unrecorded.

*Catoplatus dilatatus (Jakovlev)

Monanthia (Catoplatus) dilatata Jakovlev 1880a, p. 140 [Caucasus].
Monanthia dilatata: Jakovlev 1880b, p. 109.
Monanthia (Catoplatus) krueperi Reuter 1880a, p. 11 [Turkey].
Catoplatus krueperi: Lethierry and Severin 1896, p. 20.
Catoplatus dilatatus: Lethierry and Severin 1896, p. 20.—Horváth
1906a, p. 87 [Armenia; Syria].—Lindberg 1948a, p. 59 [Olea; Cyprus;
Tunisia; Greece].—Kiritshenko 1951, p. 251.—Seidenstücker 1954,
p. 235.—Hoberlandt 1955, p. 92 [Transcaucasus].—Stichel 1960,
p. 323.

TYPE: Sex unknown; Derbent, Caucasus, Russia; Leningrad Inst.
DISTRIBUTION: U.S.S.R. (Armenia; Caucasus; Transcaucasus); Turkey;
Syria; Cyprus; Greece; Tunisia.
HOST PLANT: Olea sp.

Catoplatus dispar Drake and Maa (emendation)

Catoplatus disparis Drake and Maa 1954, p. 114 [China].
TYPE: Holotype ♂; Suisapa, Western Hupeh, China; Cal. Acad.
DISTRIBUTION: China.
HOST PLANT: Unrecorded.

*Catoplatus distinctus Montandon

Catoplatus distinctus Montandon 1895, p. 160 [Rumania].—Horváth
1906a, p. 91.—Stichel 1938a, p. 408 [Russia]; 1960a, p. 326.—Kiritshenko 1951, p. 251.—Seidenstücker 1954, p. 236 [Turkey].—Hoberlandt 1955, p. 93.

TYPE: Comana, District de Vlaşca, Rumania; sex and deposition of
type unknown.
DISTRIBUTION: Rumania; Turkey; U.S.S.R.
HOST PLANT: Unrecorded.

*Catoplatus fabricii (Stål)

Tingis costata (not Fabricius): Fallén 1807, p. 36; 1829, p. 143.—Zetter-
stedt 1828, p. 480 [Lapland]; 1840, p. 269.—Herrich-Schaeffer 1835,
p. 58.—Germar 1836, fasc. 18, tab. 25 [Germany; Sweden].
Catoplatus costatus: Spinola 1837, p. 167.—Stål 1874, p. 58.
Monanthia costata: Herrich-Schaeffer 1838, p. 55, pl. 123, fig. 390.—
Fieber 1861, p. 123.—Douglas and Scott 1865, p. 248.—Thomson
1871, p. 398.—Saunders 1875, p. 248.—Vollenhoven 1878, pp. 270,
272, pl. 22, fig. 10 [Netherlands].—Chicote 1880, p. 189 [Spain].—
Hüeber 1893, p. 341 [Switzerland].
Monanthia (Tropidocheila) costata: Fieber 1844, p. 72, pl. 6, figs. 10–12
[Italy; Hungary; England].—Sahlberg 1848, p. 132 [Finland].—
Herrich-Schaeffer 1850, p. 152.—Flor 1860, p. 347 [France].
Tingis fabricii Stål 1868, p. 93.
Monanthia oblonga Garbiglietti 1869, p. 274.

Catoplatus fabricii: Stål 1873, p. 128.—Reuter 1882b, p. 119.—Horváth 1906a, p. 87 [*Chrysanthemum leucanthemum*].—Muzik 1907, p. 60 [Czechoslovakia].—Oshanin 1908, p. 442 [Belgium; Russia; Rumania; Austria].—Schumacher 1914, p. 258.—Lindberg 1919, p. 42.—Reichensperger 1920, p. 62.—Sahlberg 1920, p. 84.—Stichel 1926, p. 113; 1938a, p. 408 [Norway; Albania]; 1960a, p. 323 [Poland; Bulgaria; Yugoslavia; *Genista tinctoria*].—Scholte 1935, p. 76, fig. 19 [*Medicago lupulina*].—Gulde 1938, p. 302, fig.—Blöte 1945, p. 88 [Tunisia; Algeria; Egypt].—Mancini 1949b, p. 37; 1949c, p. 137; 1954b, p. 11.—Southwood and Leston 1959, p. 150, pl. 19, fig. 4.— Štusak 1961a, p. 84, fig. 9; pl. 1, fig. d.

Monanthia fabricii: Horváth 1874b, p. 432.—Butler 1923, p. 212 [*Hypericum; Spartium*].

Monanthia (Catoplatus) costata: Puton 1879c, p. 117 [*Chrysanthemum*].— Saunders 1892, p. 134, pl. 12, fig. 8.

Catoplatus fabrici [sic]: Gomez-Menor 1955b, p. 249.

TYPE: Unknown.

DISTRIBUTION: England; Belgium; Netherlands; France; Spain; Germany; Switzerland; Italy; Hungary; Austria; Czechoslovakia; Rumania; Albania; Yugoslavia; Bulgaria; Poland; Sweden; Norway; Finland; (Lapland); U.S.S.R.; Algeria; Egypt; Tunisia.

HOST PLANTS: *Chrysanthemum leucanthemum; Chrysanthemum* sp.; *Genista tinctoria; Genista* sp.; *Hypericum* sp.; *Medicago lupulina; Spartium* sp.

NOTE: Eggs [Štusak].

*Catoplatus fulvicornis (Jakovlev)

Monanthia (Catoplatus) fulvicornis Jakovlev 1890, p. 334 [Russia].

Catoplatus fulvicornis: Horváth 1906a, p. 91 [Caucasus; Turkmen; Turkistan; Afghanistan; Turkey].—Hoberlandt 1955a, p. 92 [Transcaucasus].—Stichel 1960a, p. 325.

TYPE: Sex unknown; Russia; Leningrad Inst.

DISTRIBUTION: U.S.S.R. (Turkmen; Caucasus; Transcaucasus; Turkistan); Afghanistan; Turkey.

HOST PLANT: Unrecorded.

*Catoplatus hilaris Horváth

Catoplatus hilaris Horváth 1906a, p. 90 [Israel].—Seidenstücker 1954, p. 236 [Turkey].—Hoberlandt 1955, p. 92 [Syria].—Stichel 1960a, p. 326.

TYPE: Sex unknown; Syria; Hungarian Mus.

DISTRIBUTION: Israel; Syria; Lebanon; Turkey.

HOST PLANT: Unrecorded.

*Catoplatus horvathi (Puton)

Monanthia flavipes Horváth 1874a, p. 334 [Hungary]; 1874b, p. 432.
Monanthia (*Catoplatus*) *horvathi* Puton 1879c, p. 119 [France].
Monanthia horvathi: Horváth 1889, p. 329 [Austria; *Eryngium campestre*].—
d'Antessanty 1890, p. 33 [*Eryngium*].—Hüeber 1893, p. 343
[Bulgaria].
Catoplatus flavipes: Lethierry and Severin 1896, p. 20 [Yugoslavia].—
Horváth 1906a, p. 90 [Rumania].—Oshanin 1908, p. 444 [Crimea;
Tauria].—Stichel 1926, p. 114; 1938a, p. 408 [Belgium; Albania;
Turkey]; 1960a, p. 325.—Scholte 1935, p. 77 [Netherlands].—
Hoberlandt 1943b, pp. 121, 124 [Czechoslovakia].—Kiritshenko
1951, p. 251.
Catoplatus horvathi: Drake and Ruhoff 1961b, p. 167; 1961c, p. 149.

TYPE: Sex unknown; France; Paris Mus.

DISTRIBUTION: France; Belgium; Netherlands; Austria; Czechoslovakia;
Hungary; Bulgaria; Rumania; Yugoslavia; Albania; U.S.S.R. (Crimea;
Tauria); Turkey.

HOST PLANTS: *Eryngium campestre; Eryngium* sp.

Catoplatus horvathi var. pallens Dobšik

Catoplatus flavipes var. *pallens* Dobšik 1951, p. 40 [Czechoslovakia].

TYPE: Holotype ♀; Lazánecký, Czechoslovakia; deposition unknown.

DISTRIBUTION: Czechoslovakia.

HOST PLANT: Unrecorded.

*Catoplatus leucus Kiritshenko

Catoplatus leucus Kiritshenko 1914, p. 195 [Turkestan].

TYPE: Sex unknown; Iskender, Turkestan, Russia; Leningrad Inst.

DISTRIBUTION: U.S.S.R. (Turkestan).

HOST PLANT: Unrecorded.

Catoplatus mamorensis Bergevin

Catoplatus mamorensis Bergevin 1922, p. 108, figs. 1, 2 [Morocco; *Quercus
suber*].

TYPE: Sex unknown; Rabat, Morocco; Bergevin Coll. (Paris Mus.).

DISTRIBUTION: Morocco.

HOST PLANT: *Quercus suber*.

*Catoplatus mamorensis var. biseriatus Lindberg

Catoplatus mamorensis var. *biseriatus* Lindberg 1936a, p. 85, fig. 3 [Mo-
rocco].

TYPE: Holotype ♀; Morocco; Thérys Coll.

DISTRIBUTION: Morocco.

HOST PLANT: Unrecorded.

*Catoplatus nigriceps Horváth

Monanthia (*Tropidocheila*) *melanocephala* (not Panzer): Fieber 1844, p.
77, pl. 6, figs. 26–30 [Germany; Austria].

Tingis melanocephala: Kolenati 1856, p. 425 [Transcaucasus].
Monanthia eryngii (not Latrielle): Fieber 1861, p. 124.
Monanthia (Catoplatus) melanocephala: Puton 1879c, p. 118 [*Eryngium campestre*].
Monanthia melanocephala: Hüeber 1893, p. 344.
Catoplatus nigriceps Horváth 1905b, p. 569; 1906a, p. 89 [Hungary; Caucasus; *Potentilla*].—Stichel 1926, p. 114; 1960a, p. 325.—Hoberlandt 1943, p. 119 [Czechoslovakia].—Blöte 1945, p. 88 [Tunisia].—Drake 1948a, p. 7 [Japan].—Takeya 1951a, p. 18.—Kiritshenko 1951, p. 251.
TYPE: Unknown.
DISTRIBUTION: Czechoslovakia; Austria; Hungary; Germany; U.S.S.R. (Caucasus; Transcaucasus); Japan; Tunisia.
HOST PLANTS: *Eryngium campestre; Potentilla* sp.
NOTE: The record of *C. nigriceps* in Japan is based upon a ♀ specimen labeled "Sappora-Matsum." kindly sent by the late Prof. Matsumura.

*Catoplatus olivieri (Puton)
Monanthia (Tropidochila) olivieri Puton 1873, p. 18 [Algeria].
Monanthia (Catoplatus) olivieri: Puton 1879c, p. 117 [Sardenia].
Catoplatus (Coscinopoea) olivieri: Stål 1874, p. 58.
Catoplatus olivieri: Lethierry and Severin 1896, p. 21.—Horváth 1906a, p. 90 [Tunisia].—Lindberg 1932a, p. 43 [Morocco].—Stichel 1960a, p. 325.
TYPE: Sex unknown; Bône, Algeria; Paris Mus.
DISTRIBUTION: Algeria; Tunisia; Morocco; Sardenia.
HOST PLANT: Unrecorded.

Genus CELANTIA Distant

Celantia Distant 1903b, p. 137.—Drake and Ruhoff 1960a, p. 43.
TYPE SPECIES: *Leptodictya vagans* Distant.

Celantia creta Drake
Celantia creta Drake 1960, p. 366, fig. 17 [New Britain].
TYPE: Holotype ♂; Kerawat, New Britain; Bishop Mus.
DISTRIBUTION: New Britain Island, Bismarck Archipelago.
HOST PLANT: Unrecorded.

*Celantia nitidula (Stål)
Tingis (Tingis) nitidula Stål 1873, p. 130 [Australia].
Phyllontochila nitidula: Lethierry and Severin 1896, p. 17.
Celantia nitidula: Drake and Ruhoff 1961b, p. 167.
TYPE: Sex unknown; Australia; Stockholm Mus.
DISTRIBUTION: Australia.
HOST PLANT: Unrecorded.

†Celantia seposita Cockerell

Celantia (?) seposita Cockerell 1921, p. 542, fig. 1 [fossil; Oligocene; Isle of Wight].—Drake and Ruhoff 1960a, p. 11.

TYPE: Sex undeterminable; Isle of Wight; British Mus.

DISTRIBUTION: Fossil.

*Celantia teres Drake (emendation)

Celantia teretis Drake 1951, p. 174 [India].

TYPE: Holotype ♀; Trichinopoly, India; Hungarian Mus.

DISTRIBUTION: India.

HOST PLANT: Unrecorded.

Celantia vagans (Distant)

Leptodictya vagans Distant 1903a, p. 48 [Ceylon].

Celantia vagans: Distant 1903b, p. 137, fig. 101.—Drake and Ruhoff 1961b, p. 168, fig. 13.

TYPE: Sex unknown; Ceylon; British Mus.

DISTRIBUTION: Ceylon.

HOST PLANT: Unrecorded.

Genus CERATINODERMA Stål

Ceratinoderma Stål 1873, p. 117.—Lethierry and Severin 1896, p. 9.— Drake and Ruhoff 1960a, p. 23.

TYPE SPECIES: Ceratinoderma fornicata Stål.

Ceratinoderma fornicata Stål

Ceratinoderma fornicata Stål 1873, p. 117 [Caffraria].—Distant 1902a, p. 240, pl. 15, fig. 4.—Drake 1954f, p. 1.

TYPE: Holotype ♀; Caffraria, South Africa; Stockholm Mus.

DISTRIBUTION: South Africa.

HOST PLANT: Unrecorded.

Ceratinoderma kivuensis Schouteden

Ceratinoderma kivuensis Schouteden 1955a, p. 27 [Congo].

TYPE: Sex unknown; Burunga, Kivu, Belgian Congo; Cent. Afr. Mus.

DISTRIBUTION: Congo.

HOST PLANT: Unrecorded.

Genus COCHLOCHILA Stål

Monanthia (Cochlochila) Stål 1873, p. 133.

Cochlochila: Horváth 1910, p. 67.—Drake 1948i, pp. 179–181.—Drake and Ruhoff 1960a, p. 44.

Physodictyon Lindberg 1927, p. 16.—Drake and Ruhoff 1960a, p. 77.

TYPE SPECIES: Monanthia (Cochlochila) bullita Stål.

Cochlochila adenana Drake

Cochlochila adenana Drake 1957a, p. 419, fig. 3 [Aden].

TYPE: Holotype ♂; Jebel Jihaf, Western Aden Protectorate, Arabia; British Mus.

DISTRIBUTION: Aden Protectorate.

HOST PLANT: Unrecorded.

*****Cochlochila aemula** Drake

Cochlochila aemula Drake 1958b, p. 27 [Congo].

TYPE: Holotype ♂; Lusinga, Belgian Congo; Parcs Nat. Inst.

DISTRIBUTION: Congo.

HOST PLANT: Unrecorded.

*****Cochlochila bequaerti** Schouteden

Cochlochila bequaerti Schouteden 1916b, p. 294 [Congo].

TYPE: Sex unknown; Mufungwa-Sampwe, Belgian Congo; Cent. Afr. Mus.

DISTRIBUTION: Congo; South Africa (Cape Province).

HOST PLANT: Unrecorded.

*****Cochlochila bullita** (Stål)

Monanthia (Cochlochila) bullita Stål 1873, p. 133.

Tingis globulifera Walker 1873a, p. 182 [India; heliotrope].—Kirby 1891, p. 110, pl. 4, fig. 11 [Ceylon].

Monanthia globulifera: Distant 1902b, p. 356; 1903b, p. 144, fig. 107; 1910a, p. 123 [Coleus; sage].—Maxwell-Lefroy 1909, p. 692, fig. 460 [Ocimum basilicum].—Fletcher 1918, p. 267 [Ocimum sanctum]; 1920, p. 264 [mint; safflower].—Iyengar 1924, p. 296, pls. 27, 28.—Singh 1953, p. 118.—Sharga 1953, p. 885, figs. 1–5 [Ocimum canum; Ocimum kilimandscharicum; Salvia officinalis; Carthamus tinctorius; Mentha]; 1955, p. 284, figs. 1–7.—Thontadarya and Channa Basavanna 1959, p. 289.

Monanthia mitrata Distant 1904, p. 433, pl. 8, figs. 14, 14a [Cape Province].—Hesse 1925, p. 90.—Blöte 1945, p. 91.—Drake 1948i, pp. 179, 181.

Cochlochila bullita: Horváth 1909b, p. 632; 1910, p. 67.—Drake 1948i, p. 179; 1956a, p. 4 [China]; 1956f, p. 422 [Uganda; Kenya; Java].—Drake and Maa 1953, p. 91.

Cochlochila mitrata: Horváth 1910, p. 67 [Tanganyika].—Schouteden 1923, p. 109 [Congo].

Monanthia bullita: Drake 1937a, p. 386 [Philippines].

TYPE: Unknown.

DISTRIBUTION: South Africa (Cape Province); Kenya; Uganda; Tanganyika; Congo; India; Ceylon; Greater Sunda Islands (Java); Philippine Islands; China.

HOST PLANTS: *Carthamus tinctorius; Coleus* sp.; *Mentha* sp; *Ocimum basilicum; Ocimum canum; Ocimum kilimandscharicum; Ocimum sanctum; Salvia officinalis;* heliotrope.

NOTE: Life history studies [Iyengar; Sharga 1953]; genitalia and reproductive organs [Sharga 1955]; predators [Sharga 1953].

*Cochlochila capeneri Drake and Slater

Cochlochila capeneri Drake and Slater 1955, p. 49 [Transvaal].—Drake 1961c, p. 129 [Natal; Cape Province].

TYPE: Holotype ♀, macropterous; Kaalfontein, Pretoria, South Africa; Drake Coll. (USNM).

DISTRIBUTION: South Africa (Transvaal; Natal; Cape Province).

HOST PLANT: Unrecorded.

NOTE: Type locality incorrectly given as "Rustenburg, South Africa" [Drake].

Cochlochila exolenta Drake

Cochlochila exolenta Drake 1957a, p. 416, fig. [Aden; jasmine].

TYPE: Holotype ♀; Jebel Jihaf, Western Aden Protectorate, Arabia; British Mus.

DISTRIBUTION: Aden Protectorate.

HOST PLANT: Wild jasmine.

*Cochlochila ituriensis Schouteden

Cochlochila ituriensis Schouteden 1953d, p. 167 [Congo].—Drake 1958b, p. 29.

TYPE: Sex unknown; Yebo Moto, Belgian Congo; Cent. Afr. Mus.

DISTRIBUTION: Congo.

HOST PLANT: Unrecorded.

*Cochlochila kilimensis Horváth

Cochlochila kilimensis Horváth 1910, p. 67 [Tanganyika].—Drake 1948i, p. 181 [Kenya; Rhodesia]; 1954e, p. 3 [Congo]; 1958b, p. 29.

TYPE: Sex unknown; Kibongoto, Kilimandjaro; Stockholm Mus.

DISTRIBUTION: Tanganyika; Kenya; Congo; Northern Rhodesia.

HOST PLANT: Unrecorded.

*Cochlochila lewisi (Scott)

Leptodictya? lewisi Scott 1880, p. 314 [Japan].—Oshanin 1908, p. 450.—Takeya 1951a, p. 20.

Monanthia conchata Matsumura 1913, p. 151, pl. 14, fig. 16; 1931, p. 1202.

Physodictyon vesicarius Lindberg 1927, p. 17, pl. 1, fig. 1 [Siberia].

Cochlochila conchata: Esaki 1932, p. 1636, fig.; 1954, p. 236, fig. 611.—Saito 1934, p. 69 [Korea].—Drake 1948i, p. 179 [China].—Takeya 1951a, p. 22 [*Petasites japonica; Ligularia sibirica; Phytolacca acinosa; Cacalia thunbergii*]; 1953a, p. 2.

Cochlochila lewisi: Drake and Ruhoff 1961c, p. 150.

TYPE: Japan; sex and deposition of type unknown, presumably lost.
DISTRIBUTION: Japan; China; U.S.S.R. (Siberia); Korea.
HOST PLANTS: *Cacalia thunbergii; Ligularia sibirica; Petasites japonica; Phytolacca acinosa.*
NOTE: Accredited wrongly to Horváth by Matsumura (1913).

*Cochlochila naivashae Drake
   Cochlochila naivashae Drake 1948i, p. 180 [Kenya].
TYPE: Holotype ♂; Naivasha, Kenya; Coryndon Mus.
DISTRIBUTION: Kenya.
HOST PLANT: Unrecorded.

*Cochlochila nilgiriensis (Distant)
   Monanthia nilgiriensis Distant 1903a, p. 50 [India]; 1903b, p. 144.—
   Drake 1933, p. 1015.—Singh 1953, p. 118.
   Cochlochila nilgiriensis: Drake 1948i, p. 181.—Gomez-Menor 1956a,
   fig. 4 (fig. only).
TYPE: Sex unknown; Nilgiri Hills, India; British Mus.
DISTRIBUTION: India; Ceylon.
HOST PLANT: *Tectona grandis.*

Cochlochila yemenana Drake
   Cochlochila yemenana Drake 1957a, p. 417, fig. 2 [Yemen].
TYPE: Holotype ♂; Jebel Sumara, Yemen, Arabia; British Mus.
DISTRIBUTION: Yemen.
HOST PLANT: Unrecorded.

*Cochlochila zetana Drake
   Cochlochila zetana Drake 1954c, p. 70 [Orange Free State].
TYPE: Holotype ♀, macropterous; Bloemfontein, Orange Free State;
Drake Coll. (USNM).
DISTRIBUTION: South Africa (Orange Free State).
HOST PLANT: Unrecorded.

Genus CODOTINGIS Drake

   Codotingis Drake 1942b, p. 360.—Drake and Ruhoff 1960a, p. 44.
TYPE SPECIES: *Codotingis recurva* Drake.

*Codotingis evansi Drake   PLATE 27
   Codotingis evansi Drake 1961b, p. 108, pl. 4 [Queensland].
TYPE: Holotype ♂; Moruen District, Queensland, Australia; Austr. Mus.
DISTRIBUTION: Australia (Queensland).
HOST PLANT: Unrecorded.

*Codotingis recurva Drake
   Codotingis recurva Drake 1942b, p. 361 [Queensland].
TYPE: Holotype ♀, macropterous; Nanango District, Queensland,
Australia; Drake Coll. (USNM).
DISTRIBUTION: Australia (Queensland).
HOST PLANT: Unrecorded.

Genus COLEOPTERODES Philippi

Solenostoma Signoret 1863, p. 575.—Stål 1873, p. 117.—Lethierry and
Severin 1896, p. 9.—Reed 1900, p. 178 (p. 85, separate).—Drake
and Ruhoff 1960a, p. 25.

Coleopterodes Philippi 1864, p. 306.—Kirkaldy 1900, p. 241.—Bergroth
1922, p. 152.—Drake and Ruhoff 1960a, p. 24.

TYPE SPECIES: *Solenostoma liliputiana* Signoret = *Coleopterodes fuscescens*
Philippi.

*Coleopterodes brunnea Drake and Poor

Coleopterodes liliputiana var. *brunnea* Drake and Poor 1938b, p. 104
[Argentina; *Baccharis pingraea*].
Coleopterodes brunnea: Drake 1944a, p. 67.

TYPE: Holotype ♀; Argentina; La Plata Mus.
DISTRIBUTION: Argentina.
HOST PLANT: *Baccharis pingraea.*

*Coleopterodes liliputiana (Signoret)

Solenostoma liliputiana Signoret 1863, p. 575, pl. 13, fig. 27 [Chile].—
Stål 1873, p. 117.—Berg 1884, p. 100 [Argentina; *Baccharis pingraea*].—
Reed 1900, p. 178 (p. 85, separate).—Pennington 1921, p. 20.—
Bosq 1937, p. 131.
Coleopterodes fuscescens Philippi 1864, p. 308.—Walker 1873b, p. 4.
Monanthia liliputiana: Walker 1873a, p. 194.
Solenostoma lipiputianum [sic]: Champion 1898b, p. 56.
Coleopterodes liliputianum: Drake 1922b, p. 50.
Coleopterodes liliputiana: Drake 1922c, p. 353, pl. 39, fig. 13; 1939c, p.
332; 1948h, p. 76 [*Acacia cavenia*].

TYPE: Chile; sex and deposition of type unknown.
DISTRIBUTION: Chile; Argentina.
HOST PLANTS: *Acacia cavenia; Baccharis pingraea.*

Genus COLLINUTIUS Distant

Collinutius Distant 1903b, p. 134.—Drake and Ruhoff 1960a, p. 44.
TYPE SPECIES: *Tingis alicollis* Walker.

*Collinutius alicollis (Walker)

Tingis alicollis Walker 1873a, p. 182 [India].
Phyllontochila alicollis: Distant 1902b, p. 354.
Collinutius alicollis: Distant 1903b, p. 135, fig. 98.—Drake and Maa
1954, p. 115 [China].

TYPE: Sex unknown; Hindostan; British Mus.
DISTRIBUTION: India; China.
HOST PLANT: Unrecorded.

Genus COMPSEUTA Stål

Monanthia (Compseuta) Stål 1873, p. 133.
Compseuta: Distant 1904, p. 433; 1910, p. 105.—Horváth 1910, p. 70.—
Drake 1948f, pp. 197–204.—Drake and Ruhoff 1960a, p. 44.
TYPE SPECIES: Tropidocheila ornatella Stål.

*Compseuta bioculata Drake

Compseuta bioculata Drake 1948f, pp. 202, 203, fig. 1 [Nigeria].
TYPE: Holotype ♀, macropterous; Cameroon Mts., Nigeria; Drake
Coll. (USNM).
DISTRIBUTION: Nigeria; South Africa.
HOST PLANT: Unrecorded.

*Compseuta bispinosa Drake

Compseuta bispinosa Drake 1951, p. 173 [Tanganyika].—Drake and
Ruhoff 1961c, p. 145.
Compseuta kittenbergeri Drake 1951, p. 173.
TYPE: Holotype ♂; Arusha, Africa orientalis; Hungarian Mus.
DISTRIBUTION: Tanganyika; Egypt.
HOST PLANT: Unrecorded.

*Compseuta capensis (Walker)

Piesma capensis Walker 1873b, p. 6 [Natal].
Monanthia capensis: Distant 1902a, p. 243; 1902b, p. 356.
Compseuta capensis: Drake 1948f, p. 202.
TYPE: Sex unknown; Natal, South Africa; British Mus.
DISTRIBUTION: South Africa (Natal); Uganda.
HOST PLANT: Unrecorded.

*Compseuta comes Drake

Compseuta comes Drake 1951, p. 172 [Tanganyika].
TYPE: Holotype ♂; Arusha, Africa orientalis; Hungarian Mus.
DISTRIBUTION: Tanganyika.
HOST PLANT: Unrecorded.

*Compseuta cordiae Drake

Compseuta cordiae Drake 1948f, pp. 200, 203 [Uganda; Cordia]; 1954g,
p. 665 [Ethiopia; Cordia abyssinica].—Schouteden 1957c, p. 318
[Congo].
TYPE: Holotype ♀, macropterous; Kampola, Uganda; Drake Coll.
(USNM).
DISTRIBUTION: Uganda; Congo; South Africa; Ethiopia; Tanganyika.
HOST PLANTS: Cordia abyssinica; Cordia sp.

*Compseuta dispar Schouteden

Compseuta dispar Schouteden 1923, p. 109 [Congo].
TYPE: Sex unknown; Madyu, Belgian Congo; Cent. Afr. Mus.
DISTRIBUTION: Congo; Uganda.
HOST PLANT: Unrecorded.

Compseuta expleta Drake

Compseuta expleta Drake 1955b, p. 85 [Angola].

TYPE: Holotype ♂; Serra do Moco, Luimbale, Angola; Cent. Afr. Mus.

DISTRIBUTION: Angola.

HOST PLANT: Unrecorded.

*Compseuta holana Drake

Compseuta holana Drake 1948f, pp. 199, 203 [Zanzibar; Ethiopia; Tanganyika].

TYPE: Holotype ♂, macropterous; Zanzibar; Drake Coll. (USNM).

DISTRIBUTION: Zanzibar; Tanganyika; Ethiopia; Uganda; Congo; South Africa.

HOST PLANT: Unrecorded.

*Compseuta lamellata Drake

Compseuta lamellata Drake 1958a, p. 105 [Transvaal].

TYPE: Holotype ♂, macropterous; El Andshoek, Eastern Transvaal, South Africa; Drake Coll. (USNM).

DISTRIBUTION: South Africa (Transvaal).

HOST PLANT: Unrecorded.

*Compseuta latipennis Horváth

Compseuta latipennis Horváth 1910, p. 70 [Tanganyika].

TYPE: Sex unknown; Kibonota, Kilimandjaro; Stockholm Mus.

DISTRIBUTION: Tanganyika.

HOST PLANT: Unrecorded.

*Compseuta lefroyi Distant

Compseuta lefroyi Distant 1909a, p. 113 [India]; 1910a, p. 106, fig. 52.— Drake 1948a, p. 4 [Java; *Lantana*].—Drake and Ruhoff 1962a, p. 156; 1962b, p. 250.

Compseuta tropica Hacker 1928, p. 184, fig. 1 [Queensland].—Drake 1948a, p. 4.

Compseuta tessellata Drake and Poor 1936a, p. 441 [Hainan Island].— Drake 1948a, p. 4 [China].

Compseuta lefroyi var. *tropica:* Drake 1948f, pp. 197, 203.

Compseuta lefroyi var. *tessellata:* Drake 1948f, pp. 197, 203.

TYPE: Sex unknown; Pusa, Bengal, India; British Mus.

DISTRIBUTION: India; Australia (Queensland); China (Hainan Island); Greater Sunda Islands (Java).

HOST PLANTS: *Lantana* sp.; *Cordia myxa*.

*Compseuta montandoni Distant

Compseuta montandoni Distant 1904, p. 434, pl. 8, fig. 15 [South Africa].— Horváth 1910, p. 71 [Tanganyika].—Drake 1948f, p. 201.—Priessner and Alfieri 1953, p. 65 [Egypt; *Triumfetta flavescens*].—Drake and Slater 1955, p. 49 [Natal].

TYPE: Sex unknown; Rikatla, South Africa; British Mus.
DISTRIBUTION: South Africa (Natal); Tanganyika; Kenya; Egypt.
HOST PLANT: *Triumfetta flavescens*.

Compseuta montandoni var. simulans Horváth

Compseuta montandoni var. *simulans* Horváth 1910, p. 71 [Tanganyika].
TYPE: Sex unknown; Kilimandjaro; Stockholm Mus.
DISTRIBUTION: Tanganyika.
HOST PLANT: Unrecorded.

Compseuta motoensis Schouteden

Compseuta motoensis Schouteden 1955a, p. 30 [Congo].
TYPE: Sex unknown; Moto, Belgium Congo; Cent. Afr. Mus.
DISTRIBUTION: Congo.
HOST PLANT: Unrecorded.

*Compseuta notialis Drake

Compseuta notialis Drake 1948f, pp. 199, 204 [Uganda].
TYPE: Holotype ♀, macropterous; Masaka, Uganda; Drake Coll.
(USNM).
DISTRIBUTION: Uganda; Egypt; South Africa.
HOST PLANT: Unrecorded.

*Compseuta ornatella (Stål)

Tropidocheila ornatella Stål 1855a, p. 37 [Caffraria].
Monanthia (Physatochila) ornatella: Stål 1865, p. 28.
Monanthia (Compseuta) ornatella: Stål 1873, p. 133.
Monanthia ornatella: Walker 1873a, p. 195.—Distant 1902a, p. 242, pl. 15, fig. 9.
Compseuta ornatella: Distant 1904, p. 433.—Schouteden 1916b, p. 292 [Congo]; 1923, p. 108; 1957c, p. 318 [Ruanda].—Drake 1948f, p. 198; 1954e, p. 3; 1955b, p. 86 [Uganda; Kenya; Angola]; 1958b, p. 28 [Rhodesia].—Drake and Gomez-Menor 1954, p. 91 [Spanish Guinea].
Monanthia nigristernum Horváth 1910, p. 69 [Tanganyika].
TYPE: Sex unknown; Caffraria, South Africa; Stockholm Mus.
DISTRIBUTION: South Africa; Northern Rhodesia; Congo; Kenya; Tanganyika; Angola; Uganda; Ruanda-Urundi; Spanish Guinea.
HOST PLANT: Unrecorded.

*Compseuta ornatella var. biseriata Drake

Compseuta ornatella var. *biseriata* Drake 1948f, pp. 198, 204 [Uganda].
TYPE: Holotype ♀, macropterous; Entebbe, Uganda; Drake Coll.
(USNM).
DISTRIBUTION: Uganda; South Africa.
HOST PLANT: Unrecorded.

*Compseuta ornatella var. carinata Drake

Compseuta tenella [sic] subsp. *carinata* Drake 1958b, p. 28 [Congo].

TYPE: Holotype ♀; Lusinga, Belgian Congo; Parcs Nat. Inst.

DISTRIBUTION: Congo.

HOST PLANT: Unrecorded.

*Compseuta ornatella var. teres Drake (emendation)

Compseuta ornatella var. *teretis* Drake 1948f, pp. 199, 204 [Uganda]; 1954a, p. 232 [Guinea].

TYPE: Holotype ♀, macropterous; W. Nile, Uganda; Drake Coll. (USNM).

DISTRIBUTION: Uganda; Guinea; South Africa.

HOST PLANT: Unrecorded.

*Compseuta picta Schouteden

Compseuta picta Schouteden 1923, p. 108 [Congo].—Drake 1954e, p. 3; 1955b, p. 86 [Angola].—Drake and Gomez-Menor 1954, p. 91 [Spanish Guinea; Cameroons].—Gomez-Menor 1956a, p. 112 [Malvaceae].

TYPE: Sex unknown; Belgian Congo; Cent. Afr. Mus.

DISTRIBUTION: Congo; Angola; Cameroons; Spanish Guinea.

HOST PLANT: Malvaceae.

Compseuta picta var. brevicarinata Schouteden

Compseuta picta var. *brevicarinata* Schouteden 1923, p. 108 [Congo].

TYPE: Sex unknown; Kamaiembi, Kasai, Belgian Congo; Cent. Afr. Mus.

DISTRIBUTION: Congo.

HOST PLANT: Unrecorded.

*Compseuta picta var. funebris Schouteden

Compseuta picta var. *funebris* Schouteden 1923, p. 109 [Congo].

TYPE: Sex unknown; Kamaiembi, Belgian Congo; Cent. Afr. Mus.

DISTRIBUTION: Congo.

HOST PLANT: Unrecorded.

*Compseuta sejuncta Drake

Compseuta sejuncta Drake 1948f, pp. 201, 204 [Egypt].

TYPE: Holotype ♂, macropterous; Shenki, Egypt; Drake Coll. (USNM).

DISTRIBUTION: Egypt.

HOST PLANT: Unrecorded.

Genus **CONCHOTINGIS** Drake

Conchotingis Drake 1954c, p. 71.—Drake and Ruhoff 1960a, p. 45.

Conchochila Drake 1958c, p. 329.—Drake and Ruhoff 1960a, p. 45.

TYPE SPECIES: *Xenotingis trepidantis* Drake.

*Conchotingis borneoana Drake and Ruhoff

Conchotingis borneoana Drake and Ruhoff 1961b, p. 172, fig. 17a [Borneo].
TYPE: Holotype ♀, macropterous; Sandakan, Borneo; Drake Coll. (USNM).
DISTRIBUTION: Greater Sunda Islands (Borneo).
HOST PLANT: Unrecorded.

Conchotingis insulana (Drake)

Conchochila insulana Drake 1958c, p. 331 [Malagasy].
Conchotingis insulana: Drake and Ruhoff 1960a, p. 45.
TYPE: Holotype ♂; Périnet, Madagascar; Madagascar Sci. Inst.
DISTRIBUTION: Malagasy Republic.
HOST PLANT: Unrecorded.

*Conchotingis sundra (Drake)

Conchochila sundra Drake 1958c, p. 329, fig. 1 [Malagasy].
Conchotingis sundra: Drake and Ruhoff 1960a, p. 45.
TYPE: Holotype ♂; Périnet, Madagascar; Madagascar Sci. Inst.
DISTRIBUTION: Malagasy Republic.
HOST PLANT: Unrecorded.

*Conchotingis trepidans (Drake) emendation

Xenotingis trepidantis Drake 1927d, p. 310 [Malagasy].
Conchotingis trepidantis: Drake 1954c, p. 71; 1958c, p. 332.
TYPE: Holotype ♀, macropterous; Madagascar; Drake Coll. (USNM).
DISTRIBUTION: Malagasy Republic.
HOST PLANT: Unrecorded.

Genus CONGOCHILA Drake

Congochila Drake 1954e, p. 8.—Drake and Ruhoff 1960a, p. 45.
TYPE SPECIES: *Congochila congoana* Drake.

*Congochila congoana Drake

Congochila congoana Drake 1954e, p. 9 [Congo].
TYPE: Holotype ♂; Libenge, Savane, Liki-Bembe, Belgian Congo; Brussels Mus.
DISTRIBUTION: Congo.
HOST PLANT: Unrecorded.

Genus COPIUM Thunberg

Copium Thunberg 1822, p. 8.—Lethierry and Severin 1896, p. 15.—
Horváth 1906a, pp. 14, 91 (key).—Oshanin 1908, p. 445; 1912,
p. 45.—Stichel 1926, pp. 104, 114 (key); 1935, p. 349; 1938a, p. 408;
1960a, p. 326; 1960b, p. 399.—de Seabra 1931, p. 430.—Gulde
1938, pp. 244, 304 (key).—Kiritshenko 1951, pp. 242, 251.—Takeya
1951a, p. 18.—Singer 1952, p. 53.—Wagner 1954, p. 200 (key);

1956, p. 86 (key).—Hoberlandt 1955, p. 93.—Monod and Carayon 1958, pp. 1–30.—Drake and Ruhoff 1960a, p. 45.

Monanthia Le Peletier and Serville 1828, p. 653.—Drake and Ruhoff 1960a, p. 68.

Eurycera Laporte 1833, p. 49.—Stål 1874, p. 57.—Rey 1888, p. 190.— Drake and Ruhoff 1960a, p. 56.

Laccometopus Fieber 1844, pp. 30, 96; 1861, p. 119.—Drake and Ruhoff 1960a, p. 63.

TYPE SPECIES: *Copium cornutum* Thunberg = *Cimex clavicornis* Linnaeus.

*Copium adumbratum (Horváth)

Eurycera adumbrata Horváth 1891, p. 79 [Armenia].

Copium adumbratum: Lethierry and Severin 1896, p. 15.—Horváth 1906a, p. 93 [Syria].—Oshanin 1908, p. 446 [Transcaucasus].— Seidenstücker 1954, p. 236 [Turkey].—Wagner 1954, pp. 202, 209, figs. 1, 8, 15, 22; 1956, p. 86.—Hoberlandt 1955, p. 93.—Stichel 1960a, p. 326.

Paracopium adumbratum: Horváth 1929, p. 322.

TYPE: Holotype ♀; Armenia; Hungarian Mus.

DISTRIBUTION: U.S.S.R. (Armenia; Transcaucasus); Syria; Turkey.

HOST PLANT: Unrecorded.

*Copium bernardi Wagner

Copium bernardi Wagner 1954, pp. 203, 209, figs. 5, 13, 20, 27 [Algeria; *Teucrium polium*]; 1956, p. 86.—Monod and Carayon 1958, p. 5.— Stichel 1960a, p. 329.

TYPE: Holotype ♂; T'in Taradjeli, Tassili–Plateau, Sahara; Wagner Coll.

DISTRIBUTION: Algeria.

HOST PLANT: *Teucrium polium.*

*Copium brevicorne (Jakovlev)

Eurycera brevicornis Jakovlev 1880b, p. 103 [Caucasus].—Rey 1888, p. 191.

Copium brevicorne: Lethierry and Severin 1896, p. 15.—Wagner 1954, pp. 200, 203, 206, 209, figs. 6, 12, 19, 26 [Greece; Yugoslavia]; 1956, p. 86.—Monod and Carayon 1958, p. 5.—Stichel 1960a, p. 331 [Cyprus].

Copium teucrii var. *brevicorne:* Horváth 1906a, p. 93 [Tunisia; Armenia; Turkey; Syria].—Oshanin 1908, p. 446 [Rumania].—Kiritshenko 1951, p. 252.—Hoberlandt 1955, p. 93 [Transcaucasus; Israel].

TYPE: Sex unknown; Derbent, Dagestan, Russia; Leningrad Inst.

DISTRIBUTION: U.S.S.R. (Dagestan; Caucasus; Transcaucasus; Armenia); Turkey; Syria; Israel; Rumania; Yugoslavia; Greece; Cyprus; Tunisia.

HOST PLANT: Unrecorded.

*Copium clavicorne (Linnaeus) PLATES 18, 19, 20

Cimex clavicornis Linnaeus 1758, p. 442, (no. 12); 1761, p. 246 (no. 911); 1767, p. 717 (no. 16).—Houttuyn 1765, p. 339.—Müller 1774, p. 482.—Fourcroy 1785, p. 212 [*Teucrium chameadrys*].—Gmelin 1790, p. 2125.

Acanthia clavicornis: Fabricius 1775, p. 694; 1781, p. 336; 1787, p. 278; 1794, p. 70.—Roemer 1789, p. 79, fig. 4.—Rossi 1790, p. 223 [Italy].—Panzer 1794, heft 23, tab. 23.—Walckenaer 1802, p. 337 [France].

Tingis clavicornis: Fabricius 1803, p. 124.—Latreille 1804, p. 251.—Vallot 1829, p. 99 [*Teucrium montanum*].—Herrich-Schaeffer 1835, p. 57.

Tingis punctata Lamarck 1816, p. 504.

Copium cornutum Thunberg 1822, p. 8; 1825, p. 9.—Horváth 1906a, p. 92 [Greece; Rumania; Turkey]; 1916, p. 9 [Albania].—Mužik 1907, p. 61, fig. 5.—Stichel 1926, p. 114; 1938a, p. 408 [Poland].—de Seabra 1931, pp. 431, 444, figs. 502(1–4), 503 [Portugal].—Börner 1935, p. 78, fig. 115.—Scholte 1935, p. 77, fig. 21 [Netherlands].—Gulde 1938, p. 305, fig.—Hoberlandt 1942, p. 126; 1943a, p. 119; 1943b, p. 124; 1955, p. 93 [Israel].—Blöte 1945, p. 85.—Kiritshenko 1951, p. 252.—Behr 1952, p. 326, figs. 1–6.—Bator 1953, p. 326, pl. 3, fig. 2.—Mancini 1953a, p. 186.—Seidenstücker 1954, p. 236.—Wagner 1954, pp. 200, 202, 209, figs. 3, 10, 17, 24; 1956a, p. 86.—Gomez-Menor 1955b, p. 249 [Spain].—Monod and Carayon 1958, pp. 5, 8, figs. 1–7 [*Teucrium flavum; Teucrium marum*].

Monanthia clavicornis: Le Peletier and Serville 1828, p. 653.—Westwood 1840a, p. 478; 1840b, p. 121 [England].

Eurycera nigricornis Laporte 1833, p. 49.—Burmeister 1835, p. 258.—Spinola 1837, p. 167.—Amyot and Serville 1843, p. 296.

Eurycera clavicornis: Brullé 1835, p. 341, pl. 26, fig. 2.—Herrich-Schaeffer 1838, p. 65, pl. 129, fig. 400a.—Blanchard 1840, p. 113.—Jakovlev 1875b, p. 262; 1880b, p. 103.—Reiber and Puton 1876, p. 69.—Andre 1876, p. 34; 1878a, p. 25.—Ferrari 1878, p. 66.—Puton 1879c, p. 106 [*Teucrium scorodonium*].—Rey 1888, p. 190, fig.—Dubois 1888, p. 120.—d'Antessanty 1890, p. 31.—Hüeber 1893, p. 326.

Laccometopus clavicornis: Fieber 1844, p. 97, pl. 8, figs. 10–16 [Czechoslovakia]; 1861, p. 119.—Frauenfeld 1853, p. 160.—Mayr 1858, p. 571 [Austria].—Garbiglietti 1869, p. 272.—Gredler 1870, p. 75 [Germany].—Horváth 1874b, p. 432 [Hungary].—Douglas 1877, p. 236.—Buchanan-White 1877, p. 283.—Rübsaamen 1896, p. 428, pl. 15, fig. 8.—Drake and Ruhoff 1960a, p. 63.

Tingis (Laccometopus) clavicornis: Kolenati 1856, p. 426 [Caucasus; Transcaucasus; *Teucrium canum; Teucrium scordium*].

Laccometohus [sic] *clavicornis:* Frey-Gessner 1865, p. 231 [Switzerland]

Dictyonota nigricornis: Walker 1873a, p. 176.

Eurycera cornuta: Reuter 1881, p. 170.

Copium clavicorne: Lethierry and Severin 1896, p. 15.—Reichensperger 1920, p. 61.—Ross and Hedicke 1927, p. 281.—Stichel 1960a, p. 328, fig. 137 [Belgium; Sardinia; Yugoslavia; Bulgaria].

Copium clavicornis: Wagner 1954, pp. 200, 209.—Drake and Davis 1960, fig. 2.—Drake and Ruhoff 1960a, pp. 45–47, pl. 4.

TYPE: "Europa"; Stockholm Mus.; sex unknown.

DISTRIBUTION: England; Belgium; Netherlands; France; Spain; Portugal; Sardinia; Italy; Switzerland; Germany; Austria; Czechoslovakia; Hungary; Rumania; Greece; Albania; Poland; Bulgaria; Yugoslavia; Turkey; U.S.S.R. (Caucasus; Transcaucasus); Israel.

HOST PLANTS: *Teucrium chamaedrys; Teucrium canum; Teucrium flavum; Teucrium marum; Teucrium montanum; Teucrium scordium; Teucrium scorodonium; Teucrium* sp.

NOTE: 1. The following references concern *Cimex clavicornis: Cimex sp. 687* Linnaeus 1746, p. 212; *Cimex sp. 56* Geoffroy 1762, p. 461 (cited Linnaean references and that specimens were feeding on flowers of chamaedry); (unnamed insect) Reaumur 1737, p. 427a, pl. 34, fig. 3, 4 (contains a good discussion of gall-making insect and figure of galls on "Fluer du camedry"). 2. Host plant damage [Douglas; Behr]. 3. Discussion on nomenclature and history [Drake and Ruhoff].

*Copium horvathi Wagner

Copium horvathi Wagner 1957, p. 28, figs. 1–5 [Turkey; Greece].—Stichel 1960a, p. 331 [Yugoslavia; Bulgaria; *Teucrium*].

TYPE: Unknown.

DISTRIBUTION: Turkey; Greece; Yugoslavia; Bulgaria.

HOST PLANT: *Teucrium* sp.

*Copium intermedium (Rey)

Eurycera intermedia Rey 1888, p. 191, fig. [Corsica; Sardinia].

Copium intermedium: Lethierry and Severin 1896, p. 16.—Wagner 1954, pp. 200, 207, 209, figs. 7, 14, 21; 1956, pp. 84, 86, figs. 1–6.—Stichel 1960a, p. 330.

Copium teucrii var. *intermedium:* Horváth 1906a, p. 93 [Bulgaria].— Mancini 1935, p. 9 [Capraia].—Novak and Wagner 1951, p. 71 [Yugoslavia; *Juniperus phoenicea; Helichrysum italicum*].—Gomez-Menor 1955b, p. 249 [Spain].

TYPE: Unknown.

DISTRIBUTION: Spain; Italy (Capraia Island); Corsica; Sardinia; Bulgaria; Yugoslavia.

HOST PLANTS: *Helichrysum italicum; Juniperus phoenicea.*

*Copium japonicum Esaki

Laccometopus clavicornis (not Linnaeus): Scott 1874, p. 291 [Japan; Keiskea japonica].

Copium japonicum Esaki 1931, pp. 244, 251, fig. 2; 1932, p. 1637, fig.; 1954, p. 237, fig. 614.—Takeya 1931, p. 81; 1951a, p. 19 [Taiwan; Mosla punctata].—Monod and Carayon 1958, p. 5.

Paracopium japonicum: Drake 1937b, p. 591 [China].

TYPE: Holotype ♂; Mino, Honshu, Japan; Kyushu Univ.

DISTRIBUTION: Japan; China; Taiwan.

HOST PLANTS: Keiskea japonica; Mosla punctata.

*Copium magnicorne (Rey)

Eurycera magnicornis Rey 1888, p. 191, fig. [France].

Copium magnicorne: Lethierry and Severin 1896, p. 16.—Wagner 1954, p. 208; 1955, p. 182, figs. 1–6; 1956, p. 86; 1958, p. 241 [Teucrium montanum; Teucrium chamaedrys].—Monod and Carayon 1958, p. 5.— Stichel 1960a, p. 330.

TYPE: Sex unknown; Rouen, France; Lyon Mus.

DISTRIBUTION: France.

HOST PLANTS: Teucrium chamaedrys; Teucrium montanum.

*Copium reyi Wagner

Copium reyi Wagner 1954, pp. 203, 205, 209, figs. 2, 9, 16, 23 [France; Teucrium scorodonium]; 1956, p. 86.—Monod and Carayon 1958, p. 5.—Stichel 1960a, p. 327.

TYPE: Holotype ♂; Madeloc, France; Wagner Coll.

DISTRIBUTION: France.

HOST PLANT: Teucrium scorodonium.

*Copium teucrii (Host)   PLATES 21, 22

Cimex teucrii Host 1788, p. 255, fig. [Teucrium supinum].

Tingis teucrii: Westwood 1840a, p. 478.

Laccometopus teucrii: Frauenfeld 1853, p. 160 [Teucrium montanum].— Mayr 1858, p. 571 [Austria; Russia].—Fieber 1861, p. 119 [Italy].— Garbiglietti 1869, p. 272.—Gredler 1870, p. 75 [Germany; Teucrium chamaedrys].—Horváth 1874b, p. 432 [Hungary].—Rübsaamen 1896, p. 429, pl. 16, figs. 1, 4, 37, 38 [Teucrium polium].

Monanthia teucrii: Walker 1873a, p. 188.

Eurycera teucrii: Puton 1879c, p. 106 [Corsica; France].—Jakovlev 1880b, p. 103.—Rey 1888, p. 190, fig.; 1893, p. 97.—Dubois 1888, p. 121.—d'Antessanty 1890, p. 31.—Hüeber 1893, p. 328.

Copium teucrii: Lethierry and Severin 1896, p. 16.—Lambertie 1906, p. 25.—Horváth 1906a, p. 93 [Teucrium capitatum; Switzerland; Yugoslavia].—Oshanin 1908, p. 445 [Spain; Caucasus; Crimea].— Reuter 1908, p. 89.—Moroder Sala 1920, p. 12.—Stichel 1926, p. 114; 1938a, p. 408 [Albania]; 1960a, p. 329 [Helichrysum angustifolium;

Belgium; Sardinia; Greece; Bulgaria].—Lindberg 1932a, p. 43
[Morocco]; 1948, p. 59 [Cyprus].—Scholte 1935, p. 77 [Nether-
lands].—Börner 1935, p. 78.—Ross and Hedicke 1927, p. 281.—
Vidal 1937, p. 199.—Blöte 1945, p. 85.—González 1948, p. 51.—
Kiritshenko 1951, p. 252.—Bator 1953, p. 326.—Priesner and Alfieri
1953, p. 65 [Egypt].—Seidenstücker 1954, p. 236 [Turkey].—
Wagner 1954, pp. 203, 209, figs. 4, 11, 18, 25; 1956, p. 86.—Hober-
landt 1955, p. 93 [Transcaucasus; Israel].—Monod and Carayon
1958, p. 5, figs. 8–16.
  Copium lusitanicum de Seabra 1924, p. 17, figs. 29, 30 [Portugal].—
Wagner 1954, p. 209.
  Copium teucri [sic]: Gomez-Menor 1956a, p. 115, fig. 11 (fig. only).
  TYPE: Unknown.
  DISTRIBUTION: Portugal; Spain; France; Netherlands; Belgium; Ger-
many; Austria; Italy; Corsica; Sardinia; Switzerland; Hungary; Yugo-
slavia; Greece; Cyprus; Albania; Bulgaria; Turkey; U.S.S.R. (Caucasus;
Transcaucasus; Crimea); Israel; Morocco; Alberia; Egypt.
  HOST PLANTS: *Helichrysum angustifolium; Teucrium capitatum; Teucrium
chamaedrys; Teucrium montanum; Teucrium polium; Teucrium supinum; Teucrium
sp.*

Genus CORINTHUS Distant

Corinthus Distant 1920, p. 155.—Drake and Ruhoff 1960a, p. 47.
  TYPE SPECIES: *Corinthus typicus* Distant.

Corinthus typicus Distant

  Corinthus typicus Distant 1920, p. 156 [New Caledonia].—Drake and
Davis 1960, fig. 42.
  TYPE: Sex unknown; Houadou, New Caledonia; British Mus.
  DISTRIBUTION: New Caledonia.
  HOST PLANT: Unrecorded.

Genus CORYCERA Drake

Corycera Drake 1922c, p. 368.—Monte 1939b, p. 66; 1941e, p. 84.—
Hurd 1946, p. 457.—Drake and Ruhoff 1960a, p. 47.
  TYPE SPECIES: *Corycera comptula* Drake.

*Corycera alboater Drake and Hambleton

  Corycera alboater Drake and Hambleton 1935, p. 143 [Brazil; *Dahlstedtia
pinnata*].
  TYPE: Holotype ♂, macropterous; Estação Biologica, Alta da Serra,
São Paulo, Brazil; Drake Coll. (USNM).
  DISTRIBUTION: Brazil.
  HOST PLANT: *Dahlstedtia pinnata.*

*Corycera albocosta (Drake)

Gelchossa albocosta Drake 1922c, p. 372, pl. 39, fig. 2 [Brazil].
Leptopharsa albocosta: Monte 1941e, p. 109.
Corycera albocosta: Drake and Ruhoff 1961c, p. 145.
TYPE: Holotype ♂; Chapada, Brazil; Carnegie Mus.
DISTRIBUTION: Brazil.
HOST PLANT: Unrecorded.

*Corycera comptula Drake

Corycera comptula Drake 1922c, p. 369, pl. 39, fig. 3 [Brazil]; 1930a, p. 1; 1935, p. 12 [Paraguay].—Drake and Hambleton 1944b, p. 124.
TYPE: Holotype ♂; Chapada, Brazil; Carnegie Mus.
DISTRIBUTION: Brazil; Paraguay.
HOST PLANT: Unrecorded.

Corycera fallax Monte

Corycera fallax Monte 1942a, p. 92 [Brazil].
TYPE: Holotype ♂; Palmeiras, Ipaussú, São Paulo, Brazil; Monte Coll. (Mus. Nacional).
DISTRIBUTION: Brazil.
HOST PLANT: Unrecorded.

*Corycera fortis Drake

Corycera fortis Drake 1942a, p. 18 [Paraguay].
TYPE: Holotype ♂, macropterous; Chaco, Paraguay; Drake Coll. (USNM).
DISTRIBUTION: Paraguay.
HOST PLANT: Unrecorded.

*Corycera gibbosa Monte

Corycera gibbosa Monte 1938c, p. 64, fig. [Brazil; *Roupala*]; 1940c, p. 191, fig. 25; 1940e, p. 296.
Corycera rhopalae Drake and Poor 1938a, p. 29.
TYPE: Holotype ♂; Belo Horizonte, Brazil; Monte Coll. (Mus. Nacional).
DISTRIBUTION: Brazil.
HOST PLANT: *Roupala* sp.

*Corycera juncta Drake and Hambleton

Corycera juncta Drake and Hambleton 1944b, p. 124 [Brazil].
TYPE: Holotype ♀, macropterous; São Paulo, Brazil; Drake Coll. (USNM).
DISTRIBUTION: Brazil.
HOST PLANT: Unrecorded.

*Corycera machaerii Drake and Hambleton

Corycera machaerii Drake and Hambleton 1935, p. 142 [Brazil; *Machaerium*].

TYPE: Holotype ♂, macropterous; Ponte Nova, Minas Gerais, Brazil; Drake Coll. (USNM).

DISTRIBUTION: Brazil.

HOST PLANT: *Machaerium* sp.

*Corycera panamensis Drake and Poor

Corycera panamensis Drake and Poor 1938a, p. 30 [Canal Zone].

TYPE: Holotype ♀, macropterous; Panama Canal Zone; Drake Coll. (USNM).

DISTRIBUTION: Panama (Canal Zone).

HOST PLANT: Unrecorded.

*Corycera pusilla Monte

Corycera pusilla Monte 1942a, p. 92 [Brazil].

TYPE: Holotype ♂; Bocaina, São Paulo, Brazil; Monte Coll. (Mus. Nacional).

DISTRIBUTION: Brazil.

HOST PLANT: Unrecorded.

Corycera rochalimai Monte

Corycera rocha-limai Monte 1940e, p. 296, fig. 6 [Brazil].

TYPE: Holotype ♂; Belo Horizonte, Minas Gerais, Brazil; Monte Coll. (Mus. Nacional).

DISTRIBUTION: Brazil.

HOST PLANT: Unrecorded.

*Corycera rugulosa Drake

Corycera rugulosa Drake 1922c, p. 369 [Brazil].—Monte 1939b, p. 67 [*Erythroxylon*].

TYPE: Holotype ♀; Chapada, Brazil; Carnegie Mus.

DISTRIBUTION: Brazil.

HOST PLANT: *Erythroxylon* sp.

Corycera schubarti Monte

Corycera schubarti Monte 1946b, p. 282 [Brazil].

TYPE: Holotype ♂; Pirassununga, São Paulo, Brazil; Monte Coll. (Mus. Nacional).

DISTRIBUTION: Brazil.

HOST PLANT: Unrecorded.

*Corycera separata (Drake and Hambleton)

Amblystira separata Drake and Hambleton 1935, p. 142 [Brazil; *Erythroxylon*].—Monte 1938b, p. 128.

Corycera separata: Monte 1941e, p. 86.

TYPE: Holotype♂, macropterous; Itararé, São Paulo, Brazil; Drake Coll. (USNM).

DISTRIBUTION: Brazil; British Guiana.

HOST PLANT: *Erythroxylon* sp.

*Corycera spissa Drake

Corycera spissa Drake 1935, p. 12, fig. 1 [Paraguay].—Monte 1939b, p. 67 [Brazil; *Croton antisyphiliticus*]; 1940c, p. 193.

TYPE: Holotype ♂; S. Bernardino, Paraguay; Vienna Mus.

DISTRIBUTION: Paraguay; Brazil.

HOST PLANT: *Croton antisyphiliticus.*

*Corycera vallaris Drake

Corycera vallaris Drake 1942, p. 18 [Paraguay].

TYPE: Holotype ♂, macropterous; Horqueta, Paraguay; Drake Coll. (USNM).

DISTRIBUTION: Paraguay.

HOST PLANT: Unrecorded.

Genus CORYTHAICA Stål

Corythaica Stål 1873, pp. 120, 128.—Champion 1897, p. 9; 1898b, p. 58.—Van Duzee 1917b, p. 817.—Gibson 1919c, p. 98 (key).—Blatchley 1926, p. 470 (key).—Monte 1939b, p. 67; 1941e, p. 86; 1942d, p. 104.—Hurd 1945, pp. 79–99 (monograph); 1946, p. 480.—Bailey 1951, p. 47.—Drake and Ruhoff 1960a, p. 47.

Typonotus Uhler 1893a, p. 716.—Drake and Ruhoff 1960a, p. 87.

Dolichocysta Champion 1898b, p. 56.—Van Duzee 1916, p. 25; 1917b, p. 215.—Drake 1917a, p. 214 (key).—Gibson 1919c, p. 101 (key).—Drake and Ruhoff 1960a, p. 54.

Leptotingis Monte 1938b, p. 128; 1939b, p. 75; 1941e, p. 121.—Drake and Ruhoff 1960a, p. 65.

TYPE SPECIES: *Tingis monacha* Stål.

*Corythaica acuta (Drake)

Dolichocysta acuta Drake 1917a, p. 214 [Colo.; Mont.].

Corythaica acuta: Gibson 1919c, p. 100.—Hurd 1945, pp. 81, 93, pl. 1, fig. 3.

TYPE: Holotype ♂, macropterous; Fort Collins, Colorado, U.S.; Drake Coll. (USNM).

DISTRIBUTION: U.S. (Colo.; Mont.; Nev.).

HOST PLANT: Unrecorded.

*Corythaica bellula Torre-Bueno

Corythaica bellula Torre-Bueno 1917, p. 19 [N.Y.].—Gibson 1919c, p. 100.—Blatchley 1926, p. 471.—Drake 1928b, p. 102; 1930d, p. 268.—Hurd 1945, pp. 81, 93, pl. 1, fig. 2.—Bailey 1951, p. 48, fig. 2 [Conn.; R.I.; Mass.; N.H.; *Panicum lindheimeri*]; 1959, p. 64 [Maine].—Byers 1959, p. 193.

Corythaica floridana Blatchley 1926, p. 472 [Fla.]; 1928, p. 5.

TYPE: Lectotype ♀; White Plains, New York, U.S.; Snow Mus.
DISTRIBUTION: U.S. (N.H.; Mass.; Maine; Conn.; R.I.; N.Y.; Fla.;
Nebr.).
HOST PLANT: *Panicum lindheimeri.*
NOTE: Life history study [Bailey]; notes on type specimen [Byers].

*Corythaica bosqi Monte

Corythaica bosqi Monte 1938d, p. 391 [Argentina].—Hurd 1945, pp. 82,
98, fig. 5.

TYPE: Holotype ♂; Santiago del Estero, Fortín Inca, Argentina; Monte
Coll. (Mus. Nacional).
DISTRIBUTION: Argentina.
HOST PLANT: Unrecorded.

*Corythaica caestri (Reed)

Tingis caestri Reed 1900, p. 181 (reprint, p. 88) [Chile].
Corythaica cucullata (not Berg): Drake and Poor 1938b, p. 108 (in part).
Corythaica caestri: Drake 1939c, p. 333.—Hurd 1945, pp. 82, 91, fig. 3.

TYPE: Holotype ♀, macropterous; Chile; Drake Coll. (USNM).
DISTRIBUTION: Chile.
HOST PLANT: Unrecorded.

*Corythaica carinata Uhler

Corythaica carinata Uhler 1886, p. 22 (nov. nud.); 1894a, p. 203 [Gre-
nada].—Champion 1897, p. 9, pl. 1, figs. 11, 11a [Guatemala];
1898b, p. 59 [St. Vincent].—Van Duzee 1907, p. 19 [Jamaica].—
Gibson 1919c, p. 100 [Tex.; eggplant].—Wolcott 1923, p. 246
[Puerto Rico].—Drake and Bruner 1924a, p. 151 [Cuba; Haiti].—
Gowdy 1926, p. 35.—Barber 1939, p. 369.—Monte 1943c, p. 114
[*Solanum melongena*].—Hurd 1945, pp. 82, 88, pl. 1, fig. 1 [Honduras;
Dominican Republic].—Bruner, Scaramuzza and Otero 1945, p. 11
[*Althaea rosea*].—Drake and Cobben 1960, p. 87, fig. 87 [Fla.; Mexico;
Aruba; Curaçao; St. Eustatius; St. Martin; Saba; *Passiflora foetida;
Corchorus hirsutus; Achyranthes aspera; Piriqueta ovata; Sida procumbens*].
Corythaica constricta Osborn and Drake 1917b, p. 304 [Colo.].
Dolichocysta constricta: Gibson 1919c, p. 103.

TYPE: Sex unknown; Mount Gay Estate, Grenada, British West Indies;
British Mus.
DISTRIBUTION: Windward Islands (Grenada; St. Vincent); Haiti;
Dominican Republic; Jamaica; Puerto Rico; Trinidad; Cuba; Netherlands
Antilles (Aruba; Curaçao); Leeward Islands (St. Eustatius; Saba; St.
Martin); Honduras; Guatemala; Mexico; U.S. (Tex.; Colo.; Fla.).
HOST PLANTS: *Achyranthes aspera; Althaea rosea; Corchorus hirsutus; Passiflora
foetida; Piriqueta ovata; Sida procumbens; Solanum melongena.*

*Corythaica costata Gibson

Corythaica costata Gibson 1919c, p. 99 [Peru; cotton].—Fenton 1934, p. 199.—Monte 1940e, p. 284 [Ecuador; Lycopersicum esculentum]; 1943c, p. 114 [Gossypium].—Drake and Hambleton 1942a, p. 330; 1945, p. 366 [Colombia].—Hurd 1945, pp. 82, 94, pl. 1, fig. 4.

TYPE: Holotype ♂, macropterous; Santa Clara, Peru; USNM.

DISTRIBUTION: Peru; Ecuador; Colombia.

HOST PLANTS: Gossypium sp.; Lycopersicum esculentum.

*Corythaica cucullata (Berg)

Leptobyrsa cucullata Berg 1879a, p. 41 [Argentina]; 1879b, p. 135.— Pennington 1921, p. 20.

Corythaica cucullata: Drake and Poor 1938b, p. 108, fig. 2.—Monte 1940e, p. 284 [Sphaeralcea miniata]; 1943c, p. 114.—Hurd 1945, pp. 82, 87, fig. 1.

TYPE: Sex unknown; Buenos Aires Province, Argentina; La Plata Mus.

DISTRIBUTION: Argentina.

HOST PLANT: Sphaeralcea miniata.

*Corythaica cyathicollis (Costa)

Tingis cyathicollis Costa 1864, p. 146, pl. 2, fig. 4.

Corythaica monacha (not Stål 1858): Stål 1873, p. 128 (in part).—Jones 1915, p. 4 [Puerto Rico; eggplant; Solanum torvum].—Cotton 1917, p. 170.—Gibson 1919c, p. 99 [Solanum melongena; Ricinus communis] (in part).—Wolcott 1923, p. 246.—Townsend 1928, p. 19, fig. 20.— Bosq 1937, p. 128.

Leptobyrsa passiflorae Berg 1884, p. 102 [Argentina; Passiflora caerulea].— Pennington 1921, p. 20.

Typonotus planaris Uhler 1893a, p. 716 [St. Vincent]; 1894a, p. 203 [Grenada].—Champion 1897, p. 9.

Corythaica planaris: Drake and Bruner 1924a, p. 151.—Drake 1932, p. 100 [Canal Zone].—Drake and Hambleton 1934, p. 451 [Brazil; Solanum tuberosum; Solanum sisymbrifolium; Lycopersicum esculentum; Solanum racemiflorum].—Costa Lima 1936, p. 126.—Monte 1937a, p. 31, fig. 9 [Solanum balbisii]; 1937b, p. 79, fig. [Solanum lycopersicum; Solanum gilo]; 1937c, p. 72; 1938d, p. 391.—Drake and Poor 1937d, p. 311.—Bosq 1937, p. 128 [Solanum bonariense; Solanum elaeagnifolium].— Barber 1939, p. 369 [St. Thomas].—Soares 1941, p. 262, figs. 2, 5, 6, 7.—Gomez-Menor 1956a, p. 112.

Corythaica planaria [sic]: Drake 1935, p. 20.

Corythaica cyathicollis: Drake and Poor 1938b, p. 108.—Monte 1939b, p. 67 [Solanum juripeba]; 1940d, p. 105 [Solanum quitoense]; 1941e, p. 86 [Solanum variabile].—Drake and Hambleton 1945, p. 366 [Colombia].—Hurd 1945, pp. 82, 84, pl. 1, fig. 5 [Martinique; tobacco; cabbage].—Silva 1956, p. 21, fig. 5 [Solanum paniculatum; Solanum

pulverulentum].—Drake and Cobben 1960, p. 89 [Aruba; Curaçao; St. Eustatius; Saba; St. Martin; *Solanum racemonsum; Solanum argillicolum; Solanum nigrum americanum*].
Corythaica passiflorae: Monte 1942d, p. 110; 1943c, pp. 113–120, fig. [Cuba; *Solanum hirtum; Solanum grandiflorum*]; 1945b, p. 36, fig. [*Solanum tabacifolium*]; 1947a, p. 233, fig.—Bruner, Scaramuzza and Otero 1945, p. 168.
TYPE: Presumably lost.
DISTRIBUTION: Windward Islands (Martinique; St. Vincent; Grenada); Cuba; Puerto Rico; Virgin Islands (St. Thomas); Netherlands Antilles (Aruba; Curaçao); Leeward Islands (Saba; St. Martin; St. Eustatius); Panama (Canal Zone); Colombia; Venezuela; Brazil; Peru; Argentina.
HOST PLANTS: *Lycopersicum esculentum; Passiflora caerulea; Ricinus communis; Solanum argillicolum; Solanum balbisii; Solanum bonariense; Solanum elaeagnifolium; Solanum gilo; Solanum grandiflorum; Solanum hirtum; Solanum juripeba; Solanum lycopersicum; Solanum melongena; Solanum nigrum* v. *americanum; Solanum paniculatum; Solanum pulverulentum; Solanum quitoense; Solanum racemiflorum; Solanum racemosum; Solanum sisymbrifolium; Solanum tabacifolium; Solanum torvum; Solanum tuberosum; Solanum variabile;* cabbage; tobacco.
NOTE: Life history studies [Cotton; Monte 1943c, 1945b]; predators and parasites [Cotton; Soares].

*Corythaica cytharina (Butler)
Monanthia cytharina Butler 1877, p. 90 [James Island].
Leptostyla cytharina: Distant 1902b, p. 354.—Champion 1924, p. 260.
Corythaica renormata Barber 1925, p. 251 [Daphne Major].
Corythaica cytharina: Barber 1934, p. 286.—Hurd 1945, pp. 82, 86, figs. 2a, b.
TYPE: Sex unknown; James Island, Galapagos Islands; British Mus.
DISTRIBUTION: Galapagos Islands (James; Daphne Major).
HOST PLANT: Unrecorded.

*Corythaica monacha (Stål)
Tingis monacha Stål 1858, p. 64 [Brazil].
Corythaica monacha: Stål 1873, p. 128 (in part).—Gibson 1919c, p. 99 (in part).—Drake and Bruner 1924a, p. 151.—Drake 1926b, p. 378; 1936b, p. 700 [Argentina].—Costa Lima 1930, p. 84; 1936, p. 126.— Drake and Hambleton 1934, p. 450 [*Sida glomerata*].—Drake and Poor 1937d, p. 311 [Chile].—Monte 1937a, p. 30, fig. 8 [*Sida cordifolia; Gossypium*]; 1943c, p. 115 [*Sida rhombifolia; Richardia brasiliensis*].—Soares 1941, p. 263, figs. 1, 3, 4.—Hurd 1945, p. 82, pl. 1, fig. 6 [Venezuela].—Blöte 1945, p. 85.—Silva 1956, p. 24, fig. 6 [*Sida ulmifolia*].
Corythaica monancha [sic]: Drake 1930a, p. 1; 1935, p. 20 [Paraguay].
TYPE: Sex unknown; Brazil; Stockholm Mus.

DISTRIBUTION: Brazil; Paraguay; Venezuela; Argentina; Chile; Peru.

HOST PLANTS: *Gossypium* sp.; *Richardia brasiliensis; Sida cordifolia; Sida glomerata; Sida rhombifolia; Sida ulmifolia;* tomato.

NOTE: Parasites [Soares].

*Corythaica smithi Drake

Corythaica smithi Drake 1921b, p. 50, pl. 1, figs. a, a' [Colombia].—Hurd 1945, pp. 81, 95, pl. 1, figs. 7, 7a.

TYPE: Sex unknown; Bonda, Colombia; Carnegie Mus.

DISTRIBUTION: Colombia.

HOST PLANT: Unrecorded.

*Corythaica umbrosa (Monte)

Leptotingis umbrosa Monte 1938b, p. 128 [Brazil; *Richardia brasiliensis*]; 1939b, p. 76 [*Diodia conferta*]; 1940c, p. 193.

Corythaica umbrosa: Monte 1942d, p. 105, fig. 1; 1943c, p. 115.—Drake and Hambleton 1942a, p. 330.—Hurd 1945, pp. 81, 95, fig. 4 [Paraguay].

TYPE: Holotype ♂; Belo Horizonte, Minas Gerais, Brazil; Monte Coll. (Mus. Nacional).

DISTRIBUTION: Brazil; Paraguay.

HOST PLANTS: *Diodia conferta; Richardia brasiliensis.*

*Corythaica venusta (Champion)

Dolichocysta venusta Champion 1898b, p. 57, pl. 2, figs. 1, 1a [Mexico].—Heidemann 1899a, p. 339 [Mont.; Tex.].—Drake 1917a, p. 214 [Colo.].—Gibson 1919c, p. 102 [Calif.].—Monte 1942d, p. 112.—Perkins and Swezey 1924, p. 52 [*Lantana*].

Dolichocysta magna Gibson 1919c, p. 102 [S. Dak.; Nebr.].

Dolichocysta densata Gibson 1919c, p. 102.—Monte 1942d, p. 112, fig. 3.

Dolichocysta obscura Van Duzee 1923, p. 140.

Corythaica venusta: Hurd 1945, pp. 81, 90, pl. 1, figs. 8, 8a [Ariz.; N. Mex.; Kans.; *Eriogonum; Salsola pestifer*].

TYPE: Sex unknown; Guadelupe, Lower California, Mexico; Vienna Mus.

DISTRIBUTION: Mexico; U.S. (Ariz.; N. Mex.; Tex.; Calif.; Colo.; S. Dak.; Kans.; Nebr.; Mont.); Canada (B.C.).

HOST PLANTS: *Eriogonum* sp.; *Lantana* sp.; *Salsola pestifer.*

Genus CORYTHAUMA Drake and Poor

Corythauma Drake and Poor 1939c, p. 206.—Drake and Ruhoff 1960a, p. 48.

TYPE SPECIES: *Leptopharsa ayyari* Drake.

*Corythauma ayyari (Drake)

Leptopharsa ayyari Drake 1933, p. 1016 [India; jasmine].
Corythauma ayyari: Drake and Poor 1939c, p. 206 [Lantana].
TYPE: Holotype ♀, macropterous; S. Arcot, Cuddalore, Madras Presidency, India; Drake Coll. (USNM).
DISTRIBUTION: India; Penang Island.
HOST PLANTS: Jasminum pubescens; Lantana sp.; chamela leaves.

*Corythauma varia Drake and Maa

Corythauma ayyari var. varia Drake and Maa 1953, p. 95 [India].
Corythauma varia: Drake and Ruhoff 1962a, p. 156.
TYPE: Holotype ♀, macropterous; Trichinopoly, Madras, India; Drake Coll. (USNM).
DISTRIBUTION: India.
HOST PLANT: Unrecorded.

Genus CORYTHOTINGIS Drake and Poor

Corythotingis Drake and Poor 1943, p. 195.—Drake and Ruhoff 1960a, p. 48.
TYPE SPECIES: Corythotingis zimmermani Drake and Poor.

Corythotingis zimmermani Drake and Poor

Corythotingis zimmermani Drake and Poor 1943, p. 196, fig. 3 [Fiji].
TYPE: Holotype ♂; Mt. Korobamba, Viti Levu, Fiji; Bishop Mus.
DISTRIBUTION: Fiji Islands (Viti Levu).
HOST PLANT: Unrecorded.

Genus CORYTHUCHA Stål

Corythucha Stål 1873, pp. 119, 122.—Champion 1897, p. 6 (key).— Osborn and Drake 1916a, p. 224 (key).—Van Duzee 1916, p. 25; 1917b, p. 212.—Gibson 1918, pp. 64–104 (key).—Parshley 1919b, p. 70; 1923b, p. 699.—Britton 1920, p. 77.—Barber 1922a, p. 16; 1922b, p. 19.—Drake 1922d, p. 64; 1928b, p. 100.—McAtee 1923, p. 147.—Downes 1925, p. 14; 1927a, p. 10.—Torre-Bueno 1929, p. 311.—Knowlton 1933, p. 262.—Monte 1941e, p. 88.—Froeschner 1944, pp. 646, 667.—Hurd 1946, p. 482.—Bailey 1951, p. 62.— Ash 1954, p. 185.—Gibson and Carrello 1959, p. 19.—Drake and Ruhoff 1960a, p. 48.
Corythuca [sic]: Uhler 1886, p. 22.—Lethierry and Severin 1896, p. 10.— Torre-Bueno 1908, p. 232; 1910, p. 30.—Banks 1910, p. 55.—Smith 1910, p. 148.—Blatchley 1926, p. 453 (key).—Blöte 1945, p. 82.
TYPE SPECIES: Tingis fuscigera Stål.

*Corythucha abdita Drake

Corythucha abdita Drake 1948j, p. 435 [Guatemala].

TYPE: Holotype ♂, macropterous; S. Geronimo, Guatemala; Drake Coll. (USNM).

DISTRIBUTION: Guatemala.

HOST PLANT: Unrecorded.

*Corythucha acculta Drake and Poor

Corythucha acculta Drake and Poor 1942, p. 302 [Argentina].

TYPE: Holotype ♂; Tucumán, Argentina; Argentina Mus.

DISTRIBUTION: Argentina.

HOST PLANT: Unrecorded.

*Corythucha aesculi Osborn and Drake

Corythucha aesculi Osborn and Drake 1916a, p. 232, pl. 8, fig. g [Aesculus glabra; Ohio]; 1917b, p. 304 [Ill.; Ky.].—Gibson 1918, pp. 71, 76, 78 [Aesculus hippocastanum].—Drake 1928b, p. 101 [N.Y.].—Stehr 1938, p. 13, figs. 1–3, tables 1–10 [Aesculus octandra].—Froeschner 1944, p. 668 [Mo.].

Corythucha fuscigera (not Stål): Gibson 1918, p. 78 (in part).

Corythuca aesculi: Blatchley 1926, p. 465 [Ind.; Fla.].

TYPE: Holotype ♀, macropterous; Columbus, Ohio, U.S.; Drake Coll. (USNM).

DISTRIBUTION: U.S. (Ohio; Ind.; Ill.; Iowa; Mo.; Ky.; Ark.; W. Va.; Va.; D.C.; Md.; N.C.; Fla.; N.Y.; Conn.).

HOST PLANTS: Aesculus glabra; Aesculus hippocastanum; Aesculus octandra.

NOTE: Life history study [Stehr]; predators [Stehr].

*Corythucha agalma Drake and Cobben

Corythucha decens (not Stål): Champion 1897, p. 7 (in part).

Corythucha agalma Drake and Cobben 1960, pp. 68, 96, fig. 88b [Saba; Guatemala; Vernonia].

TYPE: Holotype ♀, macropterous; Hellsgate, Saba; Drake Coll. (USNM).

DISTRIBUTION: Leeward Islands (Saba); Guatemala.

HOST PLANT: Vernonia sp.

*Corythucha arcuata (Say)

Tingis arcuata Say 1832, p. 27.—Fitch 1858, p. 794.—Le Conte 1859, p. 350.—Walker 1873a, p. 180.—Uhler 1878a, p. 415 (in part).

Corythucha arcuata: Stål 1873, p. 123 [Tex.; Ill.].—Osborn and Drake 1916a, p. 227, pl. 9 [Ohio]; 1917b, p. 297 [Wis.; Iowa; Quercus macrocarpa].—Parshley 1917b, p. 54 [N.H.; Mass.; R.I.; Conn.]; 1922b, p. 11 [S. Dak.].—Van Duzee 1917b, p. 212 [Que.; Ont.; N.J.; D.C.; Ala.; N.C.].—Gibson 1918, pp. 72, 75, 101.—Barber and Weiss 1922, p. 5, fig. 1.—Hussey 1922a, p. 11 [N. Dak.]; 1922b, p. 23 [Quercus muehlenbergii; Mich.].—Knowlton 1933, p. 262

[Utah].—Froeschner 1944, p. 667 [Mo.].—Bailey 1951, p. 63 [Va.; Vt.; *Quercus prinoides*].—Feldman and Bailey 1952, pp. 98, 99, 102, 103, fig. 6.

Corythuca arcuata: Uhler 1884, p. 284, fig. 327 [Canada; oaks].— Summers 1891, p. 90, fig. 11 (fig. only).—Gillette and Baker 1895, p. 57 [Colo.].—Morrill 1903, p. 127, pl. 3 [*Quercus alba; Quercus acuminata; Quercus prinus; Quercus rubra*].—Parshley 1914, p. 145 [Maine].—Blatchley 1926, p. 464, fig. 103 [Ind.].

Corythuca ciliata (not Say): Provancher 1886, p. 158.—Van Duzee 1912, p. 323.

Corythuca juglandis (not Fitch): Provancher 1886, p. 158.—Van Duzee 1912, p. 323.

Corythucha polygrapha Lintner 1888, p. 109 [N.Y.; Md.; *Castanea americana*].

Corythuca arquata [sic]: Van Duzee 1889, p. 5; 1894, p. 181.

Corythuca polygraphia [sic]: Banks 1910, p. 56.

Corythucha mali Gibson 1918, pp. 71, 77, 98.

Corythucha piercei Gibson 1918, pp. 72, 77, 85 [Ariz.; *Quercus*].

Corythucha arcuata var. *mali:* Drake 1921b, p. 54 [apple; maple].— Parshley 1922b, p. 11.

Corythuca arcuata var. *mali:* Blatchley 1926, p. 465 [rose].

TYPE: Apparently lost.

DISTRIBUTION: U.S. (Maine; N.H.; Mass.; Vt.; R.I.; Conn.; N.Y.; N.J.; Pa.; Md.; D.C.; Va.; N.C.; S.C.; Ga.; Ala.; Miss.; Ohio; Ill.; Ind.; Mo.; Mich.; Wis.; Nebr.; Minn.; Iowa; N. Dak.; S. Dak.; Colo.; Utah; Ariz.; N. Mex.; Tex.); Canada (Que.; Ont.).

HOST PLANTS: Primary host plants—*Quercus acuminata; Quercus alba; Quercus macrocarpa; Quercus muehlenbergii; Quercus prinoides; Quercus prinus; Quercus rubra; Quercus* sp.; *Castanea americana;* occasionally found feeding and breeding on *Pyrus malus;* maple; wild rose.

NOTE: Life history studies [Morrill; Bailey]; nymphs [Barber and Weiss]; ovipositors [Feldman and Bailey].

Corythucha argentinensis Monte

Corythucha argentinensis Monte 1940e, p. 297 [Argentina].

TYPE: Holotype ♂; Resistencia, Argentina; Monte Coll. (Mus. Nacional).

DISTRIBUTION: Argentina.

HOST PLANT: Unrecorded.

*Corythucha associata Osborn and Drake

Corythucha associata Osborn and Drake 1916b, p. 14 [Tenn.; *Prunus serotina*]; 1917b, p. 304 [Ga.; N.Y.; D.C.].—Gibson 1918, pp. 71, 74, 79 [peach].—Drake 1921b, p. 54 [Ohio; Md.]; 1925c, p. 36 [Miss.].—

Barber and Weiss 1922, p. 9.—McAtee 1923, p. 147 [Va.].—Bailey 1951, p. 66 [Conn.].
Corythucha spinulosa Gibson 1918, pp. 71, 75, 79 [N.J.].—Dickerson and Weiss 1918, p. 121, pl. 7.
Corythucha fuscigera (not Stål): Gibson 1918, p. 78 (in part).
Corythuca associata: Blatchley 1926, p. 456 [Ind.; Pa.].
TYPE: Holotype ♂, macropterous; Clarksville, Tennessee, U.S.; Drake Coll. (USNM).
DISTRIBUTION: U.S. (R.I.; Conn.; N.Y.; N.J.; Md.; D.C.; Va.; Ga.; Ala.; S.C.; Miss.; Tenn.; Ohio; Pa.; Ind.; Ill.; Iowa).
HOST PLANTS: *Prunus serotina; Prunus persica.*
NOTE: Life history studies [Bailey; Dickerson and Weiss; Barber and Weiss].

*Corythucha baccharidis Drake

Corythucha baccharidis Drake 1922b, p. 37 [Fla.; *Baccharis*].
Corythuca baccharidis: Blatchley 1926, p. 463 [*Baccharis halimifolia*].
TYPE: Holotype ♂, macropterous; Paradise Keys, Florida, U.S.; USNM.
DISTRIBUTION: U.S. (Fla.; Miss.; Tex.).
HOST PLANTS: *Baccharis halimifolia; Baccharis* sp.

*Corythucha bellula Gibson

Corythucha bellula Gibson 1918, pp. 72, 75, 93 [Ohio; *Crataegus*].—Wellhouse 1919, p. 441, figs. 24, 25 [N.Y.; *Crataegus neofluvialis; Crataegus albicans; Crataegus punctata*].—Drake 1922d, p. 64 [alder]; 1928b, p. 101 [*Crataegus pruinosa; Alnus incana; Ribes oxyacanthoides*].—Bailey 1951, p. 67 [Vt.; Maine; *Corylus*]; 1959, p. 65 [N.H.].
Corythuca bellula: Blatchley 1926, p. 458.
TYPE: Holotype ♀, macropterous; Tiffin, Ohio, U.S.; USNM.
DISTRIBUTION: U.S. (Maine; N.H.; Vt.; N.Y.; Ohio).
HOST PLANTS: *Alnus incana; Corylus* sp.; *Crataegus albicans; Crataegus neofluvialis; Crataegus pruinosa; Crataegus punctata; Crataegus* sp.; *Ribes oxyacanthoides.*
NOTE: Life history study [Wellhouse].

Corythucha boliviana Monte

Corythucha boliviana Monte 1946c, p. 27 [Bolivia].
TYPE: Holotype ♂; La Paz, Bolivia; Monte Coll. (Mus. Nacional).
DISTRIBUTION: Bolivia.
HOST PLANT: Unrecorded.

*Corythucha brunnea Gibson

Corythucha brunnea Gibson 1918, pp. 72, 75, 93 [La.; Tex.; *Crataegus*].
TYPE: Holotype ♀, macropterous; Alexandria, Louisiana, U.S.; USNM.
DISTRIBUTION: U.S. (La.; Tex.; Miss.; Ill.).
HOST PLANT: *Crataegus* sp.

*Corythucha bulbosa Osborn and Drake

Corythucha bulbosa Osborn and Drake 1916a, p. 232, pl. 8, fig. e [Ohio; Md.]; 1917b, p. 304 [*Staphylea trifolia*].—McAtee 1917b, p. 79; 1923a, p. 147 [D.C.].—Gibson 1918, pp. 71, 74, 77 [Va.].—Barber and Weiss 1922, p. 9.—Barber 1922a, p. 16 [N.J.].

Corythuca bulbosa: Weiss 1919a, p. 17 [Pa.].—Blatchley 1926, p. 455 [Ind.].

TYPE: Holotype ♀, macropterous; Sugar Grove, Ohio, U.S.; Drake Coll. (USNM).

DISTRIBUTION: U.S. (Ohio; Mo.; Ind.; Ill.; Pa.; N.J.; Md.; D.C.; Va.).

HOST PLANT: *Staphylea trifolia*.

NOTE: Life history study [Weiss].

*Corythucha caelata Uhler

Corythuca caelata Uhler 1894b, p. 279 [Mexico].—Banks 1910, p. 55 [Calif.].

Corythucha caelata: Gibson 1918, pp. 71, 77, 101 (in part).

Corythucha compta Drake and Hambleton 1944a, p. 96.

TYPE: Lectotype ♂, macropterous; "S. Cal."; Cal. Acad.

DISTRIBUTION: Mexico (San Esteban, Baja California); U.S. (Calif.).

HOST PLANT: Taken on pods of *Yucca arborescens*.

*Corythucha caryae Bailey

Corythucha caryae Bailey 1951, p. 68, fig. 3 [Mass.; N.H.; *Carya ovata*]; 1959, p. 65 [R.I.; *Carya*].—Feldman and Bailey 1952, pp. 98, 100, 102, 103, fig. 12.

TYPE: Holotype ♂; Newbury, Massachusetts, U.S.; MCZ.

DISTRIBUTION: U.S. (Mass.; N.H.; R.I.).

HOST PLANTS: *Carya ovata; Carya* sp.

NOTE: Parasites [Bailey 1951]; ovipositors [Feldman and Bailey].

*Corythucha celtidis Osborn and Drake

Corythucha celtidis Osborn and Drake 1916a, p. 227 [Ohio; hackberry].— Gibson 1918, pp. 72, 77, 84.—Drake 1919a, p. 418 [Ky.; Tenn.; S.C.]; 1925c, p. 37 [*Celtis occidentalis*].—Weiss 1921, p. 104 [N.J.].— Barber and Weiss 1922, p. 8.—McAtee 1923, p. 148 [Md.].

Corythuca celtidis: Blatchley 1926, p. 468 [Ind.].

TYPE: Sex unknown; Columbus, Ohio, U.S.; Ohio State Univ.

DISTRIBUTION: U.S. (Ohio; Iowa; Ill.; Ind.; Ky.; Tenn.; Ga.; N.C.; S.C.; Md.; N.J.).

HOST PLANT: *Celtis occidentalis*.

NOTE: Life history study [Weiss].

*Corythucha celtidis var. **mississippiensis** Drake

Corythucha celtidis var. *mississippiensis* Drake 1925c, p. 36 [Miss.; Ga.; S.C.; Tenn.; *Celtis mississippiensis*].

Corythuca celtidis var. *mississippiensis:* Blatchley 1926, p. 468.

TYPE: Holotype ♂, macropterous; Columbus, Mississippi, U.S.; Drake Coll. (USNM).
DISTRIBUTION: U.S. (Miss.; Ga.; Tenn.; S.C.).
HOST PLANT: *Celtis mississippiensis.*

*Corythucha cerasi Drake
Corythucha cerasi Drake 1948j, p. 435 [Wash.; Ind.; cherry; oak].
TYPE: Holotype ♂, macropterous; Wenatchee, Washington, U.S.; Drake Coll. (USNM).
DISTRIBUTION: U.S. (Wash.; Ind.).
HOST PLANTS: Cherry; oak.

*Corythucha championi Drake and Cobben FRONTISPIECE
Corythucha decens (not Stål): Champion 1897, p. 7, pl. 1, figs. 7, 7a (in part) [Guatemala].—Gibson 1918, pp. 74, 96 [Panama].—Drake 1926b, p. 379.—Drake and Hambleton 1945, p. 366; 1946b, p. 123.
Corythucha championi Drake and Cobben 1960, pp. 68, 93, figs. 88a, 89 [Curaçao; *Abutilon umbellatum; Ayenia magna*].
TYPE: Holotype ♂, macropterous; Groot St. Jeris, Curaçao, Netherlands Antilles; Drake Coll. (USNM).
DISTRIBUTION: Netherlands Antilles (Curaçao); Mexico; Guatemala; Colombia; El Salvador; U.S. (Pa.).
HOST PLANTS: *Abutilon umbellatum; Ayenia magna.*

*Corythucha ciliata (Say)
Tingis ciliata Say 1832, p. 27.—Fitch 1858, p. 793.—Le Conte 1859, p. 348.—Walker 1873a, p. 180.—Uhler 1878, p. 414 [Ala.; Md.; sycamore].
Tingis hyalina Herrich-Schaeffer 1840, p. 84, pl. 173, fig. 532 [Carolina]; 1850, p. 161.—Fieber 1844, p. 103, pl. 9, figs. 1–4.—Walker 1873a, p. 180.
Corythucha ciliata: Stål 1873, p. 123 [Ill.; N.J.].—Osborn and Drake 1916a, p. 225, pl. 8, fig. h [Ohio]; 1917b, p. 297 [Iowa; Tex.].—Parshley 1917b, p. 53 [Conn.; R.I.]; 1923b, p. 702.—Van Duzee 1917b, p. 212 [Que.; Ont.; D.C.].—Wade 1917, p. 3, figs. 3–7 [Okla.].—Gibson 1918, pp. 75, 102.—Drake 1919a, p. 418 [Mo.; *Fraxinus; Carya ovata; Broussonetia papyrifera*].—Kotinsky 1921, p. 74, fig. 53.—Barber and Weiss 1922, p. 4.—Hussey 1922b, p. 23 [Mich.].—Felt 1933, p. 49.—Froeschner 1944, p. 667.—Bailey 1951, p. 72 [Vt.; *Chamaedaphne*].—Feldman and Bailey 1952, pp. 98, 100, 102, 103, fig. 13.
Corythucha hyalina: Stål 1873, p. 123.
Corythuca ciliata: Lintner 1888, p. 107 [N.Y.; *Platanus occidentalis*].—Cockerell 1893, p. 364 [Colo.].—Van Duzee 1894, p. 181.—Gillette and Baker 1895, p. 57.—Morrill 1903, p. 133 [Mass.].—Wirtner 1904, p. 202 [Pa.].—Smith 1910, p. 148.—Weiss 1913, p. 407.—

Parshley 1914, p. 145 [Maine].—Blatchley 1926, p. 458 [Ind.].—
Blöte 1945, p. 82 [Va.].
Corythuca ciliati [sic]: Summers 1891, p. 90 [Tenn.].
TYPE: Unknown.
DISTRIBUTION: U.S. (Colo.; Okla.; Tex.; Iowa; Mo.; Mich.; Ill.; Ohio;
Ind.; Pa.; N.Y.; N.J.; Md.; D.C.; Va.; N.C.; Ala.; Ga.; Fla.; Tenn.;
Mass.; R.I.; Conn.; Vt.; Maine); Canada (Ont.; Que.).
HOST PLANTS: Primary host *Platanus occidentalis;* also found on *Brous-
sonetia papyrifera; Carya ovata; Chamaedaphne* sp.; *Fraxinus* sp.
NOTE: Life history studies [Morrill; Wade; Bailey]; ovipositor [Feldman
and Bailey].

*Corythucha clara Drake and Hambleton
Corythucha clara Drake and Hambleton 1938a, p. 66 [Brazil].—Monte
1941e, p. 88 [Urticaceae].
TYPE: Holotype ♂, macropterous; Rio Claro, São Paulo, Brazil;
Drake Coll. (USNM).
DISTRIBUTION: Brazil.
HOST PLANT: Urticaceae.

*Corythucha confraterna Gibson
Corythucha confraterna Gibson 1918, pp. 72, 75, 102 [Calif.; Mexico;
Platanus].
TYPE: Holotype ♀, macropterous; Los Angeles, California, U.S.;
USNM.
DISTRIBUTION: U.S. (Calif.; Ariz.); Mexico.
HOST PLANT: *Platanus* sp.

*Corythucha coryli Osborn and Drake
Corythucha coryli Osborn and Drake 1917b, p. 299 [Md.; *Corylus ameri-
cana*].—Gibson 1918, pp. 72, 74, 92.—McAtee 1923, p. 148 [Va.].—
Bailey 1951, p. 73 [Mass.; *Ostrya virginiana*]; 1959, p. 66 [Conn.;
N.H.; R.I.; *Corylus*].—Feldman and Bailey 1952, pp. 98, 100, 102,
fig. 15.
Corythuca coryli: Blatchley 1926, p. 455 [N.J.; Ind.].
TYPE: Holotype ♀, macropterous; Plummer's Island, Maryland, U.S.;
Drake Coll. (USNM).
DISTRIBUTION: U.S. (Md.; D.C.; Va.; Iowa; Ill.; Kans.; Nebr.; Ind.;
N.J.; Mass.; Conn.; R.I.; N.H.).
HOST PLANTS: *Corylus americana; Corylus* sp.; *Ostrya virginiana.*

*Corythucha cydoniae (Fitch)
Tingis cydoniae Fitch 1861, p. 114, fig. [Mass.; quince].
Corythuca arcuata (not Say): Comstock 1880, p. 221 [D.C.; *Crataegus
cordata; Crataegus coccinea; Crataegus tomentosa; Crataegus crusgalli;
Crataegus parvifolia*].—Lintner 1888, p. 108, figs. 42, 43.—Wirtner
1904, p. 202 [Pa.].

Corythuca arcuata var. *crataegi* Morrill 1903, p. 132.

Corythuca cydoniae: Banks 1910, p. 56 [N.Y.].—Blatchley 1926, p. 455, fig. 99 [Ind.; Ont.].

Corythucha crataegi: Osborn and Drake 1916a, p. 229, pl. 8, fig. f [Ohio]; 1917b, p. 300 [Tex.; Colo.; Md.; Va.; S.C.; Ga.; S. Dak.; Iowa; Nebr.; Wis.].—Parshley 1917b, p. 54 [Conn.]; 1917c, p. 47.—McAtee 1917b, p. 78 [*Amelanchier; Cephalanthus*].

Corythucha cydoniae: Gibson 1918, pp. 72, 75, 87 [Canada; *Amelanchier intermedia; Cydonia vulgaris*].—Barber 1922a, p. 16 [N.J.].—Hussey 1922a, p. 11 [N. Dak.; Mich.; *Amelanchier canadensis*].—McAtee 1923, p. 148 [*Cephalanthus occidentalis*].—Torre-Bueno 1926a, p. 54; 1933, p. 228 [*Quercus;* Ark.].—Froeschner 1944, p. 667 [Mo.].—Sailer 1945, p. 81.—Bailey 1951, p. 74, graphs 1, 2 [*Chaenomeles; Pyrus americana; Pyrus melanocarpa; Pyrus aucuparia; Pyracantha coccinea; Malus;* loquat; pear]; 1959, p. 66 [R.I.; *Cotoneaster hupehensis*].—Feldman and Bailey 1952, pp. 96, 98, 100, 102, 103, figs. 3, 7.—Ash 1954, p. 185.

Corythucha occidentalis Drake (*in* Gibson 1918, pp. 74, 91) [Calif.].

TYPE: Leominster, Massachusetts, U.S.; sex and deposition of type unknown.

DISTRIBUTION: U.S. (Maine; R.I.; Mass.; Conn.; Vt.; N.Y.; N.J.; Pa.; Md.; D.C.; Va.; S.C.; Ala.; Ga.; Ark.; Tex.; Nebr.; Mich.; Wis.; Ohio; Ind.; Mo.; Idaho; Iowa; Colo.; S. Dak.; N. Dak.; Utah; Wash.; Calif.); Canada (Ont.); Mexico.

HOST PLANTS: *Amelanchier canadensis; Amelanchier intermedia; Amelanchier* sp.; *Cephalanthus occidentalis; Cephalanthus* sp.; *Chaenomeles* sp.; *Cotoneaster hupehensis; Crataegus coccinea; Crataegus cordata; Crataegus crusgalli; Crataegus parvifolia; Crataegus tomentosa; Crataegus* sp.; *Cydonia vulgaris; Pyracantha coccinea; Pyrus americana; Pyrus aucuparia; Pyrus melanocarpa; Malus* sp.; *Quercus* sp.; loquat; pear.

NOTE: Life history studies [Comstock; Bailey]; bite to man [Sailer].

*Corythucha decepta Drake

Corythucha decepta Drake 1932, p. 100 [Mexico]; 1938a, p. 70 [*Alnus acuminata*].—Monte 1947a, p. 237.

Corythucha deceptiva [sic]: Drake and Hambleton 1945, p. 366 [Guatemala].

TYPE: Holotype ♂; San Miguel, Hidalgo, Mexico; MCZ.

DISTRIBUTION: Mexico; Guatemala.

HOST PLANT: *Alnus acuminata.*

*Corythucha distincta Osborn and Drake

Corythucha sp. Cockerell 1893, p. 364 [Colo.; *Cnicus*].

Corythuca fuscigera (not Stål): Gillette and Baker 1895, p. 57.

Corythucha distincta Osborn and Drake 1916b, p. 13; 1917b, p. 301

[Wash.; Mont.; Wyo.; Utah; Calif.; *Carduus lanceolatus*].—Gibson 1918, pp. 72, 75, 81.—Parshley 1919a, p. 18 [B.C.; hollyhock]; 1922b, p. 11 [S. Dak.].—Downes 1925, p. 15, fig. 5; 1927a, p. 10 [*Lathyrus nuttallii*].

TYPE: Sex unknown; Colorado, U.S.; Ohio State Univ.

DISTRIBUTION: U.S. (Calif.; Wash.; S. Dak.; Wyo.; Mont.; Utah; Colo.); Canada (B.C.).

HOST PLANTS: *Carduus lanceolatus; Cnicus* sp.; *Lathyrus nuttallii;* hollyhock.

*Corythucha distincta var. spinata Osborn and Drake

Corythucha distincta var. *spinata* Osborn and Drake 1917b, p. 301, figs. 1 a, b [Mont.; *Carduus*].

TYPE: Holotype ♀, macropterous; Florence, Montana, U.S.; Drake Coll. (USNM).

DISTRIBUTION: U.S. (Mont.).

HOST PLANT: *Carduus* sp.

NOTE: This may not be a good variety.

*Corythucha elegans Drake

Corythucha elegans Drake (*in* Gibson 1918, pp. 73, 75, 89) [Colo.; N.Y.; *Salix*]; 1919b, p. 159 [Ont.; Mich.; *Populus balsamifera*]; 1922d, p. 65, figs. 25 a, b, 26 [*Populus tremuloides; Populus grandidentata*].—Torre-Bueno 1929, p. 311 [Mass.].—Hurd 1946, p. 483 [Wis.].

Corythuca elegans: Blatchley 1926, p. 456, fig. 102a.

TYPE: Holotype ♀, macropterous; Poudre Canyon, Colorado, U.S.; Drake Coll. (USNM).

DISTRIBUTION: U.S. (Colo.; Wis.; Mich.; N.Y.; Mass.); Canada (Ont.; B.C.; Sask.; Man.).

HOST PLANTS: Primary host *Salix* sp.; also breeds to some extent on *Populus balsamifera; Populus grandidentata; Populus tremuloides.*

NOTE: Eggs and instars [Drake 1919b]; predators [Drake 1919b].

*Corythucha eriodictyonae Osborn and Drake

Corythucha eriodictyonae Osborn and Drake 1917b, p. 302 [Calif.; *Eriodictyon californicum*].—Van Duzee 1917a, p. 258.—Gibson 1918, pp. 77, 99.

Corythucha erydictyonae [sic]: Drake and Davis 1960, fig. 71.

TYPE: Holotype ♂, macropterous; San Francisquito Cr., San Mateo Co., California, U.S.; Drake Coll. (USNM).

DISTRIBUTION: U.S. (Calif.).

HOST PLANT: *Eriodictyon californicum.*

*Corythucha floridana Heidemann

Corythuca floridana Heidemann 1909, p. 236, fig. [Fla.; *Cephalanthus*].—Van Duzee 1909, p. 173.—Blatchley 1926, p. 459, fig. 101.

Corythucha floridana: Osborn and Drake 1917b, p. 300 [oak].—Gibson 1918, pp. 76, 101.

TYPE: Holotype ♂, macropterous; Biscayne Bay, Florida, U.S.; USNM.

DISTRIBUTION: U.S. (Fla).

HOST PLANTS: *Cephalanthus occidentalis*; *Cephalanthus* sp.; oak.

*Corythucha fuscigera (Stål)

Tingis fuscigera Stål 1862, p. 323 [Mexico].

Monanthia lucida Walker 1873a, p. 191.

Corythucha fuscigera: Stål 1873, p. 122.—Champion 1897, p. 7, pl. 1, figs. 6, 6a [Calif.; Guatemala]; 1898b, p. 57.—Van Duzee 1914, p. 11 [chaparral]; 1917a, p. 258 [*Hosackia crassifolia*].—Osborn and Drake 1917b, p. 303.—Gibson 1918, p. 78 (in part).—Drake 1919a, p. 419 [Ariz.]; 1926b, p. 378.

Leptostyla ? lucida: Uhler 1886, p. 22.

Corythuca fuscigera: Uhler 1894b, p. 278.—Distant 1902b, p. 357.

TYPE: Holotype ♀; Mexico; Stockholm Mus.

DISTRIBUTION: Mexico; Guatemala; U.S. (Calif.; Ariz.).

HOST PLANTS: *Hosackia crassifolia*; chaparral.

NOTE: Most records of *C. fuscigera* in the United States are referable to other species.

*Corythucha fuscomaculata (Stål)

Tingis fusco-maculata Stål 1858, p. 63 [Brazil].

Corythucha fuscomaculata: Stål 1873, p. 123.—Distant 1888, p. lxxxiii.—Champion 1898b, p. 57, pl. 2, fig. 2.—Gibson 1918, pp. 76, 89.—Drake and Hambleton 1934, p. 451 [*Triumfetta semitriloba*].—Drake and Poor 1937d, p. 312 [Peru].—Monte 1939b, p. 68 [Colombia]; 1941e, p. 88 [Mexico; Argentina].—Kormilev 1955a, p. 67 [Paraguay; Bolivia].

Corythuca fuscomaculata: Costa Lima 1936, p. 126.—Monte 1937a, p. 31 [*Triumfetta rhomboidea*].—Silva 1956, p. 25, fig. 7.

TYPE: Sex unknown; Brazil; Stockholm Mus.

DISTRIBUTION: Brazil; Peru; Colombia; Bolivia; Argentina; Paraguay; Mexico.

HOST PLANTS: *Triumfetta rhomboidea; Triumfetta semitriloba; Solanum* sp.

*Corythucha globigera Breddin

Corythucha globigera Breddin 1901, p. 82 [Ecuador].—Drake and Hambleton 1944b, p. 129 [Peru].—Drake and Ruhoff 1961c, p. 145.

Corythucha globulifera Monte 1940d, p. 102, fig. 14 [Venezuela; *Solanum*].

TYPE: Holotype ♂; Santa Inez, Ecuador; Berlin Mus.

DISTRIBUTION: Ecuador; Peru; Venezuela.

HOST PLANT: *Solanum* sp.

*Corythucha gossypii (Fabricius)

Acanthia gossypii Fabricius 1794, p. 78.

Tingis gossypii: Fabricius 1803, p. 126.—Le Peletier and Serville 1828, p. 653.—Burmeister 1835, p. 259 [Mexico].—Herrich-Schaeffer

1840, p. 85, pl. 173, fig. 534 [St. Thomas]; 1850, p. 162.—Fieber 1844, p. 104, pl. 9, fig. 5.—Guérin-Méneville 1857, p. 409 [Cuba; cotton].—Walker 1873a, p. 180.

Tingis decens Stål 1862, p. 324.

Galeatus gossypii: Stål 1868, p. 93.

Corythucha decens: Stål 1873, p. 123.—Champion 1897, p. 7 (in part).— Lutz 1929, p. 233 [Pa.].

Corythucha gossypii: Stål 1873, p. 123.—Barber 1914, p. 507 [Fla.]; 1939, p. 368.—Osborn and Drake 1917b, p. 300 [Grenada; *Ichthyo-methia piscipula*].—Gibson 1918, pp. 72, 77, 96.—Drake 1919a, p. 418; 1926a, p. 87; 1928e, p. 5 [Honduras; soursop].—Van Duzee 1923, p. 140 [Coronados Islands; *Atamisquea emarginata*].—Wilson 1923, p. 9 [St. Croix].—Gowdy 1925, p. 19 [congo pea; *Hibiscus*]; 1926, p. 35.—Leonard and Mills 1931, pp. 309–321 [Trinidad; N. Mex.; Tex.; Venezuela; Antigua; Guatemala; Costa Rica; Panama; Haiti; Montserrat; Dominican Republic; St. Vincent; lemon; orange; grapefruit; *Jatropha; Dahlia; Prunus persicus; Citrus medica; Cassia emarginata; Annona diversifolia*].—Fenton 1934, p. 198 [mango; *Cajanus indicus; Solanum torvum*].—Monte 1940d, p. 102 [Colombia].—Drake and Hambleton 1945, p. 366 [Salvador; Ecuador; Nicaragua; eggplant]; 1946b, p. 123.—Bruner, Scaramuzza and Otero 1945, pp. 14, 15, 29, 45, 72, 84, 114, 132, 152, 155, 188 [*Annona squamosa; Arachis hypogaea; Erythrina berteroana; Gossypium; Musa paradisiaca; Phaseolus limensis; Roystonea regia; Zanthoxylum martini-cense*].—Ramos 1946, p. 25 [Mona Island; *Capparis flexuosa*].—Gomez-Menor 1956a, p. 112.—Drake and Cobben 1960, p. 91, fig. 88d [Aruba; Curaçao; Bonaire; St. Eustatius; Saba; St. Martin; *Jatropha gossypifolia; Jatropha multifida; Capparis cynophallophora; Hibiscus rosa-sinensis; Hibiscus esculentus; Solanum lycopersicum; Solanum melongena; Lagenaria leucantha*].

Corythuca gossypii: Van Duzee 1907, p. 18 [Jamaica].—Jones 1915, p. 4 [yautia; *Canavalia ensiformis; Ricinus communis*].—Wolcott 1923, p. 246 [Puerto Rico; *Carica papaya; Annona muricata*].—Blatchley 1926, p. 460.

TYPE: Holotype ♀, macropterous; "Americae meridionalis, Insulis Dom."; Kiel Coll. (Copenhagen Mus.).

DISTRIBUTION: Jamaica; Haiti; Dominican Republic; Trinidad; Leeward Islands (Antigua; St. Eustatius; Saba; St. Martin; Montserrat); Windward Islands (St. Vincent; Grenada); Virgin Islands (St. Croix; St. Thomas; St. John); Cuba; Puerto Rico; Netherlands Antilles (Bonaire; Aruba; Curaçao); Ecuador; Colombia; Venezuela; Panama; Costa Rica; Nicaragua; El Salvador; Honduras; Guatemala; Mexico (Coronados, San Esteban Islands); Mona Island; U.S. (Tex.; N. Mex.; Fla.; Pa.).

HOST PLANTS: *Annona diversifolia; Annona muricata; Annona squamosa; Arachis hypogaea; Atamisquea emarginata; Cajanus indicus; Canavalia ensiformis; Capparis cynophallophora; Capparis flexuosa; Carica papaya; Cassia emarginata; Citrus medica; Dahlia* sp.; *Erythrina berteroana; Gossypium* sp.; *Hibiscus esculentus; Hibiscus rosa-sinensis; Hibiscus* sp.; *Ichthyomethia piscipula; Jatropha gossypifolia; Jatropha multifida; Jatropha* sp.; *Lagenaria leucantha; Musa paradisiaca; Phaseolus limensis; Prunus persicus; Ricinus communis; Roystonea regia; Solanum lycopersicum; Solanum melongena; Solanum torvum; Zanthoxylum martinicense;* mango; lemon; grapefruit; orange; yautia; soursop.

NOTE: Life history studies [Leonard and Mills]; predators [Leonard and Mills].

*Corythucha heidemanni Drake

Corythucha heidemanni Drake (*in* Gibson 1918, pp. 75, 87) [N.Y.]; 1919b, p. 159 [Ont.; birch]; 1928b, p. 101 [*Ulmus americana; Ulmus fulva*].—Parshley 1920b, p. 142 [Vt.; alder]; 1922a, p. 236; 1923b, p. 701.—Proctor 1946, p. 74.—Bailey 1951, p. 82 [Mass.; N.H.; Conn.; N.B.; *Sorbus; Alnus*].—Feldman and Bailey 1952, pp. 97–100, 102, 103, figs. 16, 18.—Lindberg 1958b, p. 14 [Nfld.; N.S.; *Alnus crispa*].
Corythucha borealis Parshley (*in* Gibson 1918, pp. 75, 92) [Maine].
Corythuca heidemanni: Blatchley 1926, p. 457.

TYPE: Holotype ♀, macropterous; Cranberry Lake, New York, U.S.; Drake Coll. (USNM).

DISTRIBUTION: U.S. (N.Y.; Conn.; Mass.; Maine; N.H.; Vt.); Canada (N.S.; Nfld.; Ont.; N.B.).

HOST PLANTS: *Alnus crispa; Alnus* sp.; *Betula lutea; Sorbus* sp.; *Ulmus americana; Ulmus fulva.*

*Corythucha hewitti Drake

Corythucha hewitti Drake 1919b, p. 159 [Manitoba; *Corylus americana*].—Parshley 1921, p. 17.—Downes 1925, p. 15, fig. 4 [*Corylus californica*].—Hurd 1946, p. 483 [Pa.; Iowa; Colo.].—Bailey 1951, p. 84 [Conn.].
Corythucha hesperia Parshley 1919a, p. 23 [B.C.].

TYPE: Sex unknown; Aweme, Manitoba, Canada; Canada. Coll.

DISTRIBUTION: Canada (Man.; Ont.; B.C.); U.S. (Minn.; Wis.; Iowa; Colo.; Pa.; Conn.).

HOST PLANTS: *Corylus americana; Corylus californica.*

*Corythucha hispida Uhler

Corythuca hispida Uhler 1894b, p. 279 [Mexico].—Banks 1910, p. 56 [Calif.].
Corythucha hispida: Gibson 1918, pp. 77, 104 (in part).—Van Duzee 1923, p. 140 [*Abutilon*].

TYPE: Holotype ♂, macropterous; San Esteban, Lower California, Mexico; Cal. Acad.

DISTRIBUTION: Mexico (Baja Calif.); U.S. (Calif.).

HOST PLANT: *Abutilon* sp.

*Corythucha immaculata Osborn and Drake

Corythucha immaculata Osborn and Drake 1916b, p. 11 [Calif.]; 1917b, p. 301 [Oreg.; Colo.].—Drake 1918d, p. 86 [Idaho; Mont.]; 1919a, p. 419; 1919b, p. 159 [B.C.].—Gibson 1918, pp. 76, 103.—Parshley 1921, p. 17.—Downes 1925, p. 16, fig. 7.—Knowlton 1933, p. 263 [Utah].

Corythuca pura Gibson 1917, p. 258 [Wash.; *Balsamorhiza sagittata*].

Corythucha pura: Gibson 1918, pp. 72, 77, 103.—Parshley 1919a, p. 24.

TYPE: Sex unknown; Alameda, California, U.S.; Ohio State Univ.

DISTRIBUTION: U.S. (Calif.; Oreg.; Wash.; Idaho; Mont.; Utah; Colo.); Canada (B.C.).

HOST PLANT: *Balsamorhiza sagittata*.

*Corythucha incurvata Uhler

Corythuca incurvata Uhler 1894b, p. 280 [Mexico; Ariz.].

Corythuca arcuata (not Say): Pemberton 1911, p. 339, pls.12–14 [*Heteromeles arbutifolia;* Calif.].

Corythucha bullata Van Duzee 1917a, p. 258.

Corythucha incurvata: Van Duzee 1917b, p. 213 [Oreg.].—McAtee 1917b, p. 78.—Gibson 1918, pp. 72, 74, 92.—Drake and Ruhoff 1962a, p. 156.

Corythucha heteromelecola Drake 1920, p. 50.

TYPE: Sex unknown; "Cal. 7"; Cal. Acad.

DISTRIBUTION: U.S. (Calif.; Ariz.; Oreg.); Mexico.

HOST PLANT: *Heteromeles arbutifolia*.

NOTE: Life history study [Pemberton].

*Corythucha juglandis (Fitch)

Tingis juglandis Fitch 1857, p. 466, item 193 [N.Y.; basswood].

Corythucha juglandis: Stål 1873, p. 123 [Ill.; N.J.].—Osborn and Drake 1916a, p. 226 [walnut; Ohio]; 1917b, p. 297 [Ga.; Tenn.; Iowa; Wis.].—Gibson 1918, pp. 71, 75, 80 [Kans.; Tex.; *Tilia americana*].—Myers 1926, p. 111.—Proctor 1946, p. 74.—Bailey 1951, p. 84 [Vt.; N.B.; *Carya illinoensis; Rubus; Sorbus*].—Feldman and Bailey 1952, pp. 98, 101, 102, fig. 10.

Tingis arcuata (not Say): Uhler 1878, p. 415 (in part).

Corythuca juglandis: Uhler 1884, p. 285 [butternut].—Van Duzee 1905, p. 549.—Blatchley 1926, p. 466.

Corythuca arcuata: Smith 1910, p. 148.—Parshley 1914, p. 145 [Maine]; 1917b, p. 55 [N.H.; Mass.; R.I.; Conn.].

Corythucha contracta Osborn and Drake 1916a, p. 230.—Gibson 1918, p. 104.—Drake 1921b, p. 51 [Ind.].—Barber and Weiss 1922, p. 8.—Proctor 1946, p. 74 [*Sorbus americana*].

Corythucha parshleyi Gibson 1918, pp. 72, 76, 83 [*Carya olivaeformis; Amelanchier intermedia*].—Weiss and Dickerson 1918b, p. 401 [*Juglans cinerea; Juglans sieboldiana; Juglans nigra*].—Drake 1919b, p. 159 [N.C.].
Corythuca contracta: Blatchley 1926, p. 467.—Blöte 1945, p. 83 [Md.; Va.].

TYPE: Holotype ♂, macropterous; New York State, U.S.; USNM.
DISTRIBUTION: U.S. (Maine; N.H.; Vt.; Mass.; R.I.; Conn.; N.Y.; N.J.; Md.; Va.; N.C.; S.C.; Ga.; Tenn.; Ohio; Ind.; Ill.; Wis.; Iowa; Kans.; Tex.; Miss.); Canada (N.B.).
HOST PLANTS: *Amelanchier intermedia; Carya illinoensis; Carya olivaeformis; Juglans cinerea; Juglans nigra; Juglans sieboldiana; Rubus* sp.; *Sorbus* sp.; *Sorbus americana; Tilia americana.*
NOTE: Life history studies [Barber and Weiss; Weiss and Dickerson]; ovipositors [Feldman and Bailey].

*Corythucha lowryi Drake
Corythucha lowryi Drake 1948j, p. 434 [Wis.; *Carpinus caroliniana*].
TYPE: Holotype ♂, macropterous; Frederic, Wisconsin, U.S.; Drake Coll. (USNM).
DISTRIBUTION: U.S. (Wis.).
HOST PLANT: *Carpinus caroliniana.*

*Corythucha marmorata (Uhler)
Tingis marmorata Uhler 1878, p. 415 [N.C.].
Corythuca marmorata: Van Duzee 1889, p. 5 [Canada]; 1894, p. 181 [N.Y.]; 1907, p. 19 [Jamaica]; 1909, p. 173 [Fla.].—Howard 1904, p. 89.—Felt 1904, p. 125 [ragweed].—Smith 1910, p. 148 [N.J.].—Osborn and Drake 1915a, p. 506 [Ohio].—Blatchley 1926, p. 462, pl. 4, fig. 6.—Blöte 1945, p. 83 [Va.].
Corythuca irrorata Howard 1898, p. 99 [Ala.; *Chrysanthemum*].
Corythuca gossypii (not Fabricius): Torre-Bueno 1908, p. 232.
Corythucha marmorata: Van Duzee 1914, p. 11 [Calif.; sunflower]; 1917b, p. 214 [Ont.; N. Mex.].—Barber 1914, p. 507.—Osborn and Drake 1916a, p. 226; 1917b, p. 298 [Nebr.; Ind.; Mich.; Pa.; Maine; Mass.; Ga.; Tenn.; La.; Iowa; Colo.].—Parshley 1917b, p. 54 [N.H.; Vt.; R.I.; Conn.]; 1917c, p. 47; 1919a, p. 20 [B.C.]; 1922b, p. 11 [S. Dak.]; 1923a, p. 103; 1923b, p. 702, pl. 17, fig. 6.—McAtee 1917b, p. 78 [D.C.; *Aster*]; 1923, p. 148 [*Solidago; Ambrosa trifida*].—Gibson 1918, pp. 76, 94.—Barber and Weiss 1922, p. 7, fig. 3.—Hussey 1922a, p. 11 [N. Dak.]; 1922b, p. 23 [goldenrod].—Weiss 1924, p. 367 [*Solidago sempervirens*].—Weiss and Lott 1924, p. 68.—Downes 1925, p. 16, fig. 6.—Torre-Bueno 1925, p. 179.—Drake 1926b, p. 379.—Knowlton 1933, p. 263.—Abbott 1935, p. 13.—Froeschner 1944, p. 667 [Mo.; *Helianthus*].—Proctor 1946, p. 74.—Bailey 1951, p. 86

[*Tanacetum*]; 1959, p. 67 [*Rudbeckia serotina; Echinops sphaerocephalus*].—
Feldman and Bailey 1952, pp. 96, 98, 101–103, figs. 2, 8.
Corythucha decens (not Stål): Van Duzee 1917b, p. 214 (in part).
Corythucha lactea Drake (*in* Gibson 1918, pp. 74, 94) [Utah].
Corythucha marmorata var. *informis* Parshley 1919a, p. 20 [N.S.]; 1922b,
p. 11.—Downes 1925, p. 16.—Bailey 1951, p. 86.
Corythucha marmorata var. *minutissima* Drake 1920, p. 50.
TYPE: North Carolina, U.S.; sex and deposition of type unknown.
DISTRIBUTION: U.S. (Maine; N.H.; Vt.; Mass.; R.I.; Conn.; N.Y.; N.J.;
Pa.; Md.; D.C.; Va.; N.C.; Ga.; Miss.; Fla.; Ala.; La.; Tenn.; W. Va.;
Ohio; Ind.; Ill.; Iowa; Kans.; Mo.; Mich.; Wis.; Nebr.; N. Dak.; S. Dak.;
Colo.; Utah; Idaho; Oreg.; N. Mex.; Ariz.; Tex.; Calif.); Canada (Ont.;
B.C.; N.S.); Jamaica; Mexico.

HOST PLANTS: *Ambrosia trifida; Aster* sp.; *Chrysanthemum* sp.; *Echinops
sphaerocephalus; Helianthus tuberosus; Helianthus* sp.; *Rudbeckia serotina; Solidago
sempervirens; Solidago* sp.; *Tanacetum* sp.

NOTE: Life history studies [Felt; Barber and Weiss; Bailey]; eggs
[Abbott]; causes damage in greenhouses [Osborn and Drake.].

*Corythucha mcelfreshi Drake

Corythucha mcelfreshi Drake 1921b, p. 50, pl. 1, figs. b, b′ [Mexico].
TYPE: Holotype ♂, macropterous; Mexico; Drake Coll. (USNM).
DISTRIBUTION: Mexico.
HOST PLANT: Unrecorded.

*Corythucha mollicula Osborn and Drake

Corythucha mollicula Osborn and Drake 1916b, p. 12, fig. 2 [Mich.].—
Drake 1921b, p. 53 [S.C.; poplar]; 1922d, p. 64, figs. 25c,d.—Hussey
1922b, p. 23.—Parshley 1922a, p. 236; 1923b, p. 701 [Conn.].—
McAtee 1923, p. 148 [Md.; Va.].—Froeschner 1944, p. 667 [Mo.].—
Proctor 1946, p. 74 [Maine].—Bailey 1951, p. 90 [R.I.; *Populus*];
1959a, p. 67.—Feldman and Bailey 1952, pp. 98, 101–103, fig. 5.
Corythucha salicis Osborn and Drake 1917b, p. 298 [Mass.; Wis.; Mont.;
currant].—Gibson 1918, pp. 73, 76, 85 [Fla.; *Ribes*].—Drake 1919b,
p. 159 [N.J.; N.Y.; Ont.; Man.; *Salix discolor*].—Parshley 1920a,
p. 273 [*Salix*]; 1921, p. 17 [*Salix hookeriana*].—Downes 1925, p. 15,
fig. 1.
Corythucha molliculata [sic]: Gibson 1918, pp. 85, 90.
Corythucha canadensis Parshley 1919a, p. 18 [B.C.].
Corythuca mollicula: Blatchley 1926, p. 461, fig. 102c.

TYPE: Holotype ♀, macropterous; East Lansing, Michigan, U.S.; Drake
Coll. (USNM).

DISTRIBUTION: U.S. (Maine; N.H.; Mass.; R.I.; Conn.; N.Y.; N.J.;
Pa.; Md.; Va.; S.C.; Ga.; Fla.; Mich.; Mo.; Ill.; Ind.; Wis.; Kans.; N. Dak.;

S. Dak.; Nebr.; Idaho.; Mont.; Oreg.; Wash.); Canada (Man.; B.C.; Ont.).
HOST PLANTS: *Populus* sp.; *Ribes* sp.; *Salix discolor; Salix hookeriana; Salix* sp.
*Corythucha montivaga Drake
   Corythucha montivaga Drake 1919a, p. 417 [Mont.].—Hurd 1946, p. 484
   [Wyo.].
   TYPE: Holotype ♀, macropterous; Bear Pw. Mt., Montana, U.S.; Drake
Coll. (USNM).
   DISTRIBUTION: U.S. (Mont.; Wyo.; Utah).
   HOST PLANT: Unrecorded.
   NOTE: The holotype was erroneouly recorded as a ♂ in the original
description.
*Corythucha morrilli Osborn and Drake
   Corythucha morrilli Osborn and Drake 1917b, p. 298 [Colo; Ariz.].—
   Gibson 1918, pp. 74, 95.—Drake 1919a, p. 419 [N. Mex.; Tex.;
   Calif.; *Helianthus*]; 1921b, p. 51 [ebony]; 1926b, p. 379; 1938a, p. 70.—
   Drake and Bruner 1924a, p. 154 [Jamaica; Cuba].—Downes 1925,
   p. 16 [B.C.; *Artemisia dracunculoides*].—Blatchley 1928, p. 4 [Fla.].—
   Tilden 1950, p. 135 [*Baccharis pilularis*].—Drake and Cobben 1960,
   p. 93, fig. 88c [Aruba; Curaçao; Bonaire; St. Eustatius; *Egletes
   prostrata; Ipomoea batatas; Helianthus annuus; Lagascea mollis; Synedrella
   nodiflora; Wedelia jacquini*].
   Corythucha decens (not Stål): Van Duzee 1917b, p. 214 (in part).
   Corythucha mexicana Gibson 1918, pp. 76, 95 [Mexico].
   Corythucha morrillii [sic]: Gowdy 1926, p. 35.
   Corythucha morelli [sic]: Knowlton 1933, p. 263 [Utah].
   Corythuca morrilli: Hardy 1954, p. 282 [Hawaii; *Xanthium; Ambrosia
   artemisiifolia; Verbesina encelioides*].—Bianchi 1955a, p. 378 [*Pluchea
   indica*]; 1955b, p. 383 [*Xanthium canadense*].
   TYPE: Holotype ♂, macropterous; Fort Collins, Colorado, U.S.; Drake
Coll. (USNM).
   DISTRIBUTION: U.S. (Colo.; Utah; Calif.; Ariz.; N. Mex.; Tex.; Fla.;
Hawaii); Canada (B.C.); Mexico; Guatemala; Cuba; Jamaica; Nether-
lands Antilles (Aruba; Curaçao; Bonaire); Leeward Islands (St. Eustatius).
   HOST PLANTS: *Ambrosia artemisiifolia; Artemisia dracunculoides; Baccharis
pilularis; Erigeron canadensis; Egletes prostrata; Helianthus annuus; Helianthus*
sp.; *Ipomoea batatas; Lagascea mollis; Pluchea indica; Synedrella nodiflora; Ver-
besina encelioides; Wedelia jacquini; Xanthium canadense; Xanthium* sp.; ebony.
   NOTE: Biological notes [Tilden]. Introduced into Hawaii.
*Corythucha nicholi Drake
   Corythucha nicholi Drake 1928f, p. 3 [Ariz.].
   TYPE: Holotype ♂, macropterous; Santa Rita Mountains, Arizona,
U.S.; Drake Coll. (USNM).
   DISTRIBUTION: U.S. (Ariz.).
   HOST PLANT: Unrecorded.

*Corythucha nobilis Drake and Bondar

Corythucha nobilis Drake and Bondar 1932, p. 92 [Brazil; *Solanum*].—
Costa Lima 1936, p. 126.

Corythuca nobilis: Silva 1956, p. 27.

TYPE: Holotype ♂, macropterous; Bahia, Brazil; Drake Coll. (USNM).

DISTRIBUTION: Brazil; Paraguay.

HOST PLANT: *Solanum* sp.

*Corythucha nocens Drake and Hambleton (emendation)

Corythucha nocentis Drake and Hambleton 1942a, p. 330 [Peru]; 1945,
p. 366 [Ecuador].

TYPE: Holotype ♂, macropterous; Canete, Peru; Drake Coll. (USNM).

DISTRIBUTION: Peru; Ecuador.

HOST PLANT: Unrecorded.

*Corythucha obliqua Osborn and Drake

Corythucha obliqua Osborn and Drake 1916b, p. 11 [Calif.]; 1917b, p.
301 [Oreg.; Idaho].—Gibson 1918, pp. 72, 76, 84 [*Ceanothus*].—
Drake 1919a, p. 418.

Corythucha maculata Van Duzee 1917a, p. 257 [Utah; Colo.].

Corythucha coelata [sic] (not Uhler): Van Duzee 1917a, p. 259.

Corythucha fuscigera (not Stål): Van Duzee 1917b, p. 213 (in part).

Corythucha contaminata Gibson 1918, pp. 72, 76, 82 [*Ceanothus cardulatus*].

TYPE: Holotype ♀, macropterous; Dutch Flats, California, U.S.; Drake
Coll. (USNM).

DISTRIBUTION: U.S. (Calif.; Oreg.; Idaho; Wash.; Utah.; Colo.).

HOST PLANTS: *Ceanothus cardulatus; Ceanothus sanguineus; Ceanothus* sp.

*Corythucha omani Drake

Corythucha omani Drake 1941a, p. 144 [Ariz.].

TYPE: Holotype ♂, macropterous; Nogales, Arizona, U.S.; USNM.

DISTRIBUTION: U.S. (Ariz.).

HOST PLANT: Unrecorded.

*Corythucha padi Drake

Corythucha padi Drake 1917a, p. 215 [Mont.; Oreg.; choke cherry];
1919b, p. 159 [Idaho]; 1932, p. 100.—Osborn and Drake 1917b,
p. 303 [Wash.; B.C.; *Prunus demissa*].—Gibson 1918, pp. 71, 75, 88.—
Parshley 1919a, p. 19 [alder; hazel].—Downes 1925, p. 15, fig. 3
[walnut].—Knowlton 1933, p. 262 [Utah].

Corythucha coloradensis Gibson 1918, pp. 72, 76, 89 [Colo.; Nebr.; *Rhus
toxicodendron*].

Corythucha fuscigera (not Stål): Gibson 1918, p. 78 (in part).

TYPE: Holotype ♀, macropterous; Missoula, Montana, U.S.; Drake
Coll. (USNM).

DISTRIBUTION: U.S. (Mont.; Colo.; Utah; Oreg.; Wash.; Idaho; Nebr.);
Canada (B.C.).

HOST PLANTS: Primary host *Prunus demissa;* also recorded from *Rhus toxicodendron;* hazel; alder; walnut.

*Corythucha pallida Osborn and Drake

Corythucha pallida Osborn and Drake 1916a, p. 230 [Ohio; linden]; 1917b, p. 300 [Md.; Tenn.; Va.; Ariz.; *Tilia americana; Morus rubra*].—McAtee 1917b, p. 78 [D.C.]; 1923a, p. 148.—Gibson 1918, pp. 76, 100.—Drake 1925c, p. 36 [Miss.].—Froeschner 1944, p. 667 [Mo.].—Proctor 1946, p. 74 [Maine].—Bailey 1951, p. 91 [*Podophyllum peltatum*].

Corythuca pallida: Blatchley 1926, p. 459 [Ind.].—Blöte 1945, p. 83 [N.C.].

TYPE: Sex unknown; Columbus, Ohio, U.S.; Ohio State Univ.

DISTRIBUTION: U.S. (Maine; Md.; D.C.; Va.; W. Va.; Ohio; Ill.; Tenn.; Miss.; Mo.; Ind.; Ga.; N.C.; S.C.; Ala.; Ariz.).

HOST PLANTS: *Morus rubra; Podophyllum peltatum; Tilia americana.*

*Corythucha pallipes Parshley

Corythucha juglandis (not Fitch): Van Duzee 1917b, p. 215 (in part).

Corythucha pallipes Parshley (*in* Gibson 1918, pp. 73, 77, 82) [Conn.; *Salix sieboldiana*]; 1919b, p. 70; 1923b, p. 701 [*Salix*].—Drake 1922d, p. 65; 1922f, pp. 111–116, pl. 4, fig. 44 [Mich.; Wis.; Oreg.; Wash.; Man.; *Betula alba; Fagus grandiflora; Ostrya virginiana; Pyrus americana; Acer spicatum; Acer saccharinum; Acer saccharum; Acer pennsylvanicum*].— Bailey 1951, p. 91 [Vt.; Que.; N.B.; *Betula papyrifera*].—Feldman and Bailey 1952, pp. 98, 101–103, fig. 17.—Lindberg 1958b, p. 14 [Nfld.].

Corythucha betulae Drake (*in* Gibson 1918, pp. 71, 75, 86) [N.Y.; *Betula lutea*]; 1919b, p. 159 [Ont.; *Betula lenta*].—Parshley 1919b, p. 70.

Corythucha cyrta Parshley (*in* Gibson 1918, pp. 75, 86) [Maine; Mass.: N.H.]; 1919b, p. 70; 1920a, p. 272.

Corythucha paleipes [sic]: Barber 1922a, p. 16 [N.J.].

Corythuca pallipes: Blatchley 1926, p. 457, fig. 100.—Drake and Davis 1960, fig. 18.

TYPE: Holotype ♀; Stamford, Connecticut, U.S.; Cal. Acad.

DISTRIBUTION: U.S. (Maine; Mass.; Vt.; N.H.; Conn.; N.Y.; N.J.; Oreg.; Wis.; Mich.; Wash.); Canada (Que.; Man.; N.B.; Ont.; Nfld.).

HOST PLANTS: *Acer pennsylvanicum; Acer saccharinum; Acer saccharum; Acer spicatum; Betula alba; Betula lenta; Betula lutea; Betula papyrifera; Fagus grandifolia; Ostrya virginiana; Pyrus americana; Salix sieboldiana; Salix* sp.

NOTE: Life history studies [Drake 1922b; Bailey]; predaceous insects [Bailey; Drake].

*Corythucha palmatis Drake

Corythucha palmatis Drake 1929, p. 37 [Costa Rica].

TYPE: Holotype ♂; San José, Costa Rica; Hamburg Mus.

DISTRIBUTION: Costa Rica.

HOST PLANT: Unrecorded.

*Corythucha pellucida Drake and Hambleton

Corythucha pellucida Drake and Hambleton 1938a, p. 67 [Brazil; *Celtis ferruginea*].—Monte 1939b, p. 68 [*Celtis brasiliensis*].

TYPE: Holotype ♂, macropterous; Campinas, São Paulo, Brazil; Drake Coll. (USNM).

DISTRIBUTION: Brazil.

HOST PLANTS: *Celtis brasiliensis; Celtis ferruginea.*

*Corythucha pergandei Heidemann

Corythuca pergandei Heidemann 1906, p. 10, figs. 2, 3 [D.C.; Pa.; Va.; Mass.; Ill.; Kans.; elms; crab apple; hazel; *Alnus*].—Smith 1910, p. 148 [N.J.; N.Y.].—Parshley 1914, p. 145 [Maine].—Blatchley 1926, p. 466, fig. 104 [Ga.].

Corythucha pergandei: Osborn and Drake 1916a, p. 228, figs. 4, 5 [Ohio]; 1917b, p. 300 [Wis.; Md.; Tenn.].—Parshley 1917b, p. 54 [N.H.; Conn.]; 1923a, p. 102 [N.S.].—Van Duzee 1917b, p. 213 [Ont.].— Gibson 1918, pp. 71, 75, 91 [Calif.; Tex.; *Betula nigra; Betula lenta; Alnus rugosa; Pyrus prunifolia; Ulmus*].—Weiss and Dickerson 1918a, p. 205, fig. [*Alnus glutinosa; Betula lutea; Betula populifolia*].—Barber and Weiss 1922, p. 6, fig. 2.—Hussey 1922b, p. 23 [Mich.; *Alnus incana*].—McAtee 1923, p. 148 [*Prunus americana; Celtis crassifolia*].— Torre-Bueno 1926a, p. 54.—Drake 1928b, p. 100.—Bailey 1951, p. 94 [Vt.].—Feldman and Bailey 1952, pp. 96, 98, 101–103, figs. 1, 2.

TYPE: Holotype ♂, macropterous; Washington, D.C., U.S.; USNM.

DISTRIBUTION: U.S. (Maine; N.H.; Vt.; Mass.; Conn.; N.Y.; N.J.; Pa.; Md.; D.C.; Va.; Ga.; Tenn.; Ky.; Ohio; Ind.; Ill.; W. Va.; Mich.; Wis.; Minn.; Iowa; Mo.; Nebr.; Kans.; Okla.; Tex.; Calif.); Canada (Ont.; N.S.; B.C.).

HOST PLANTS: Primary—*Alnus glutinosa; Alnus incana; Alnus rugosa; Alnus* sp.; also recorded from: *Betula lenta; Betula lutea; Betula nigra; Betula populifolia; Celtis crassifolia; Corylus americana; Prunus americana; Pyrus prunifolia; Ulmus* sp.

NOTE: Life history studies [Weiss and Dickerson; Bailey]; taken at light [McAtee]; ovipositor [Feldman and Bailey].

*Corythucha pruni Osborn and Drake

Corythucha pruni Osborn and Drake 1916a, p. 231 [D.C.; *Prunus serotina*]; 1917b, p. 303.—McAtee 1917b, p. 79.—Gibson 1918, pp. 71, 76, 80 [N.Y.; N.C.; Ohio].—Hussey 1922b, p. 23 [Mich.].—Bailey

1951, p. 96, fig. 4, graphs 3–5 [Vt.; Mass.]; 1959, p. 67 [Conn.;
R.I.].—Feldman and Bailey 1952, pp. 96, 98, 102, 103, figs. 4, 9.
Corythucha hoodiana Osborn and Drake 1917b, p. 302 [Oreg.].—Gibson
1918, pp. 76, 82.
Corythucha exigua Drake (*in* Gibson 1918, pp. 76, 83).
Corythucha pyriformis Parshley 1920c, p. 81 [Maine; N.H.]; 1922a, p.
236.
Corythuca pruni: Blatchley 1926, p. 465.
Corythuca exigua: Blatchley 1926, p. 467.
TYPE: Sex unknown; Washington, D.C., U.S.; Ohio State Univ.
DISTRIBUTION: U.S. (Maine; N.H.; Conn.; R.I.; Mass.; Vt.; N.Y.;
Md.; D.C.; Va.; N.C.; Ga.; Ohio; Mich.; Ind.; Ill.; Mo.; Iowa; Nebr.;
Utah; Oreg.).
HOST PLANT: *Prunus serotina.*
NOTE: Life history study [Bailey]; leaf injury [Bailey]; ovipositor [Feld-
man and Bailey].

*Corythucha sagillata Drake

Corythucha sagillata Drake 1932, p. 101 [Ariz.; *Vauquelinia californica*].
TYPE: Holotype ♀, macropterous; Santa Catalina Mountains, Arizona,
U.S.; Drake Coll. (USNM).
DISTRIBUTION: U.S. (Ariz.).
HOST PLANT: *Vauquelinia californica.*

*Corythucha salicata Gibson

Corythucha salicata Gibson 1918, pp. 77, 90 [Oreg.].—Parshley 1919a,
p. 20 [B.C.]; 1921, p. 17 [*Salix lasiandra*].—Drake 1921b, p. 53 [Wash.;
Man.; poplar; alder].—Downes 1925, p. 16, fig. 2 [*Salix scouleriana*].—
Thompson and Wong 1933, pp. 1090–1095, fig. 95.
Corythucha drakei Gibson 1918, pp. 71, 77, 98 [Calif.; *Pyrus malus*].
Corythucha essigi Drake 1918c, p. 385 [maize].
Corythucha platini Drake 1920, p. 49 [sycamore].
TYPE: Holotype ♀, macropterous; Hood River, Oregon, U.S.; Drake
Coll. (USNM).
DISTRIBUTION: U.S. (Oreg.; Wash.; Calif.; Idaho; Utah); Canada
(Man.; B.C.).
HOST PLANTS: *Salix lasiandra; Salix scouleriana; Pyrus malus; Zea mays;*
poplar; alder; sycamore.
NOTE: Life history study [Thompson and Wong].

*Corythucha scitula Drake

Corythucha scitula Drake 1948c, p. 24 [Oreg.; *Corylus rostrata*].
TYPE: Holotype ♂, macropterous; Stayton, Oregon, U.S.; Drake Coll.
(USNM).
DISTRIBUTION: U.S. (Oreg.).
HOST PLANT: *Corylus rostrata.*

*Corythucha seguyi Drake

Corythucha seguyi Drake 1921b, p. 51, pl. 1, fig. c [Bolivia].—Drake and Hambleton 1945, p. 366 [Peru].

TYPE: Sex unknown; Cochabamba, Bolivia; Paris Mus.

DISTRIBUTION: Bolivia; Peru.

HOST PLANT: Unrecorded.

*Corythucha serta Drake and Hambleton

Corythucha serta Drake and Hambleton 1945, p. 366 [Guatemala].

TYPE: Holotype ♂, macropterous; Lake Atitlán, Guatemala; Drake Coll. (USNM).

DISTRIBUTION: Guatemala; Mexico.

HOST PLANT: Unrecorded.

*Corythucha setosa Champion

Corythucha setosa Champion 1897, p. 8, pl. 1, figs. 10, 10a [Guatemala].—Van Duzee 1917b, p. 215 [Calif.].—Gibson 1918, pp. 77, 100 [Mexico].—Drake and Hambleton 1946b, p. 122.

TYPE: Sex unknown; Cerro Zunil, Guatemala; British Mus.

DISTRIBUTION: Guatemala; Mexico; U.S. (Calif.).

HOST PLANT: Unrecorded.

Corythucha socia Monte

Corythucha socia Monte 1940e, p. 296 [Brazil; Euphorbiaceae].

TYPE: Holotype ♂; Lapinha, Lagôa Santa, Brazil; Monte Coll. (Mus. Nacional).

DISTRIBUTION: Brazil.

HOST PLANT: Euphorbiaceae.

*Corythucha sphaeralceae Drake

Corythucha hispida (not Uhler): Van Duzee 1917b, p. 214 (in part) [Ariz.].—Knowlton 1931, p. 43 [Utah].

Corythucha sphaeralceae Drake 1920, p. 51 [Calif.; Sphaeralcea].

Corythucha pacifica Drake 1920, p. 52 [Wash.].

TYPE: Holotype ♀, macropterous; Deep Springs Valley, Inyo County, California, U.S.; Drake Coll. (USNM).

DISTRIBUTION: U.S. (Calif.; Ariz.; Utah).

HOST PLANT: Sphaeralcea sp.

*Corythucha spinosa (Dugès)

Tingis spinosa Dugès 1889, p. 207, pl. 18 [Mexico; Ricinus communis].

Tingis hyalina (not Herrich-Schaeffer): Guérin-Méneville 1857, p. 408 [Cuba].

Corythucha spinosa: Champion 1897, p. 8, pl. 1, figs. 9, 9a; 1898b, p. 57.—Van Duzee 1917b, p. 214 [Calif.].—Gibson 1918, pp. 77, 99.—Drake and Bruner 1924a, p. 154 [Bambusa].—Perkins and Swezey 1924, p. 52 [Lantana camara].—Drake 1926a, p. 87.—Bruner, Scaramuzza and Otero 1945, pp. 97, 168, 184 [*Solanum torvum;* *Triumfetta grossulariaefolia*].

Corythucha unifasciata (not Champion): Gibson 1918, pp. 76, 97.

TYPE: Silao de la Victoria, Guanajuato, Mexico; sex and deposition of type unknown.

DISTRIBUTION: Mexico; Cuba; Trinidad; Costa Rica; U.S. (Calif.).

HOST PLANTS: *Lantana camara;* *Bambusa* sp.; *Solanum torvum;* *Ricinus communis;* *Triumfetta grossulariaefolia.*

Corythucha translucida Monte

Corythucha translucida Monte 1946c, p. 28 [Bolivia].

TYPE: Holotype ♂; La Paz, Bolivia; Monte Coll. (Mus. Nacional).

DISTRIBUTION: Bolivia.

HOST PLANT: Unrecorded.

*Corythucha tuthilli Drake

Corythucha tuthilli Drake 1940a, p. 172 [Colo.].

TYPE: Holotype ♂, macropterous; Creede, Colorado, U.S.; Drake Coll. (USNM).

DISTRIBUTION: U.S. (Colo.).

HOST PLANT: Unrecorded.

*Corythucha ulmi Osborn and Drake

Corythucha pallida var. *ulmi* ? Osborn and Drake 1916a, p. 231 [Ohio; *Ulmus americana*].

Corythucha ulmi: Gibson 1918, pp. 77, 97 [Md.; N.Y.; S.C.].—Parshley 1922a, p. 236 [N.H.]; 1922b, p. 11 [S. Dak.]; 1923b, p. 702 [Conn.].—McAtee 1923, p. 148 [Va.; *Ulmus fulva*].—Felt 1933, p. 49.—Froeschner 1944, p. 668 [Mo.].—Hurd 1946, p. 484 [Nebr.; Minn.].—Bailey 1951, p. 105 [Vt.; Mass.; *Ulmus thomasii*]; 1959, p. 69.—Feldman and Bailey 1952, pp. 98, 102, 103, fig. 11.—Ash 1954, p. 185 [Ind.; *Ulmus glabra camperdownii*].

Corythuca ulmi: Blatchley 1926, p. 464.

TYPE: Neotype ♀, macropterous; Plummer's Island, Maryland, U.S.; Drake Coll. (USNM).

DISTRIBUTION: U.S. (N.H.; Vt.; Mass.; Conn.; N.Y.; Md.; Va.; S.C.; Miss.; Ohio; Ind.; Mich.; Ill.; Wis.; Minn.; Iowa; Mo.; Nebr.; S. Dak.).

HOST PLANTS: *Ulmus americana;* *Ulmus fulva;* *Ulmus glabra camperdownii;* *Ulmus thomasii.*

*Corythucha unifasciata Champion

Corythucha unifasciata Champion 1897, p. 7, pl. 1, figs. 8, 8a [Mexico; Guatemala; Panama].

TYPE: Sex unknown; Las Mercedes, Guatemala; British Mus.

DISTRIBUTION: Mexico; Guatemala; Panama.

HOST PLANT: Unrecorded.

Genus COTTOTHUCHA Drake and Poor

Cottothucha Drake and Poor 1941, p. 162.—Drake and Ruhoff 1960a, p. 49.

TYPE SPECIES: *Cottothucha oceanae* Drake and Poor.

*Cottothucha oceanae Drake and Poor

Cottothucha oceanae Drake and Poor 1941, p. 163 [Amboina].—Drake and Ruhoff 1961b, p. 182, fig. 23 [Luzon].

TYPE: Holotype ♂; Amboina Island; Cal. Acad.

DISTRIBUTION: Moluccas (Amboina); Philippine Islands (Luzon).

HOST PLANT: *Raphidophora merrillii*.

Genus CROMERUS Distant

Cromerus Distant 1902b, p. 355.—Drake 1926e, p. 334.—Drake and Ruhoff 1960a, p. 49.

TYPE SPECIES: *Monanthia invaria* Walker.

*Cromerus bakeri Drake

Cromerus bakeri Drake 1930e, p. 166 [Samar].

TYPE: Holotype ♀, macropterous; Samar Island, Philippine Islands; Drake Coll. (USNM).

DISTRIBUTION: Phillippine Islands (Samar).

HOST PLANT: Unrecorded.

*Cromerus excelans Drake

Cromerus invarius (not Walker): Drake 1930e, p. 167 [Samar; Mindanao].

Cromerus excelans Drake 1953b, p. 91.

TYPE: Holotype ♂, macropterous; Butuan, Mindanao, Philippine Islands; Drake Coll. (USNM).

DISTRIBUTION: Philippine Islands (Samar; Mindanao).

HOST PLANT: Unrecorded.

*Cromerus gressitti Drake

Cromerus gressitti Drake 1937b, p. 591 [China].

TYPE: Holotype ♂, macropterous; Yim-na Shan, E. Kwangtung, China; Drake Coll. (USNM).

DISTRIBUTION: China.

HOST PLANT: Unrecorded.

*Cromerus hackeri Drake and Poor

Cromerus hackeri Drake and Poor 1939c, p. 203 [Australia].

TYPE: Holotype ♂, macropterous; Cedar Creek, Queensland, Australia; Drake Coll. (USNM).

DISTRIBUTION: Australia (Queensland).

HOST PLANT: Unrecorded.

*Cromerus invarius (Walker)

Monanthia invaria Walker 1873a, p. 196 [New Guinea].
Cromerus invaria: Distant 1902b, p. 356.—Drake 1960a, p. 355.
TYPE: Sex unknown; New Guinea; British Mus.
DISTRIBUTION: New Guinea.
HOST PLANT: Unrecorded.

*Cromerus kalshoveni Drake

Cromerus kalshoveni Drake 1926e, p. 334 [Java; *Vitex heterophylla*]; 1930e, p. 167 [Mindanao].
TYPE: Holotype ♀, macropterous; Kediri, Java; Drake Coll. (USNM).
DISTRIBUTION: Greater Sunda Islands (Java); Philippine Islands (Mindanao).
HOST PLANT: *Vitex heterophylla.*

*Cromerus palawanus Drake and Maa

Cromerus palawanus Drake and Maa 1955, p. 6 [Palawan].
TYPE: Holotype ♀, macropterous; Binaluan, Palawan, Philippine Islands; Drake Coll. (USNM).
DISTRIBUTION: Philippine Islands (Palawan).
HOST PLANT: Unrecorded.

*Cromerus viadoi Drake and Maa

Cromerus viadoi Drake and Maa 1955, p. 5 [Mindanao].
TYPE: Holotype ♂, macropterous; Mindanao, Philippine Islands; Drake Coll. (USNM).
DISTRIBUTION: Philippine Islands (Mindanao).
HOST PLANT: Unrecorded.

Genus CYSTEOCHILA Stål

Cysteochila Stål 1873, pp. 121, 129.—Lethierry and Severin 1896, p. 22.—Distant 1903b, p. 138.—Bergroth 1921, p. 104.—Horváth 1925a, p. 3.—Drake and Poor 1937a, p. 6.—Drake 1956b, p. 110.—Drake and Ruhoff 1960a, p. 49.—Stichel 1960b, p. 400.
Bredenbachius Distant 1903a, p. 50; 1903b, p. 139.—Drake and Ruhoff 1960a, p. 40.
TYPE SPECIES: *Monanthia?* *tingoides* Motschulsky.

*Cysteochila abetti Schouteden

Cysteochila abetti Schouteden 1919, p. 140 [Congo]; 1923, p. 103.—Drake 1956a, p. 4 [Uganda].
TYPE: Sex unknown; Kilo, Belgian Congo; Cent. Afr. Mus.
DISTRIBUTION: Congo; Uganda.
HOST PLANT: Unrecorded.

*Cysteochila ablusa Drake

Cysteochila ablusa Drake 1948a, p. 6 [India].

TYPE: Holotype ♂, macropterous; Barwai, India; Drake Coll. (USNM).

DISTRIBUTION: India.

HOST PLANT: *Bauhinia variegata*.

*Cysteochila abundans Drake and Poor (emendation)

Cysteochila abundantis Drake and Poor 1937a, p. 8 [Mindanao]; 1937b, p. 400 [Luzon].—Singh 1953, p. 118.

TYPE: Holotype ♂; Tangkulan, Bukidnon Province, Mindanao, Philippine Islands; Drake Coll. (USNM).

DISTRIBUTION: Philippine Islands (Mindanao; Luzon).

HOST PLANT: Unrecorded.

*Cysteochila aletheia Drake and Ruhoff

Cysteochila aletheia Drake and Ruhoff 1962b, p. 251 [Papua].

TYPE: Holotype ♂, macropterous; Bisiatabu, Port Moresby, Papua Territory, New Guinea; So. Austr. Mus.

DISTRIBUTION: New Guinea (Papua).

HOST PLANT: Unrecorded.

Cysteochila angulipennis Horváth

Cysteochila angulipennis Horváth 1929, p. 323 [Zanzibar].

TYPE: Holotype ♂; Zanzibar; British Mus.

DISTRIBUTION: Zanzibar.

HOST PLANT: Unrecorded.

Cysteochila annandalei (Distant)

Bredenbachius annandalei Distant 1909a, p. 119 [India]; 1910a, p. 120.

TYPE: Sex unknown; Calcutta, India; British Mus.

DISTRIBUTION: India.

HOST PLANT: Unrecorded.

Cysteochila aspera Drake and Poor

Cysteochila aspera Drake and Poor 1941, p. 160 [Amboina].

TYPE: Holotype ♂; Amboina Island; Cal. Acad.

DISTRIBUTION: Moluccas (Amboina).

HOST PLANT: Unrecorded.

*Cysteochila bakeri Drake and Poor

Cysteochila bakeri Drake and Poor 1937a, p. 9 [Mindanao; Luzon]; 1937b, p. 399.

TYPE: Holotype ♀, macropterous; Surigao, Mindanao, Philippine Islands; USNM.

DISTRIBUTION: Philippine Islands (Mindanao; Luzon).

HOST PLANT: Unrecorded.

Cysteochila basilewskyi Schouteden

Cysteochila basilewskyi Schouteden 1957c, p. 316 [Ruanda].

TYPE: Sex unknown; Ruanda; Cent. Afr. Mus.

DISTRIBUTION: Ruanda-Urundi.

HOST PLANT: Unrecorded.

*Cysteochila biseriata Schouteden

Cysteochila biseriata Schouteden 1916b, p. 295 [Congo]; 1923, p. 103.— Mayné and Ghesquière 1934, p. 20 [*Hevea*].

TYPE: Sex unknown; Congo da Lemba, Belgian Congo; Cent. Afr. Mus.

DISTRIBUTION: Congo.

HOST PLANT: *Hevea* sp.

Cysteochila bredoi Schouteden

Cysteochila bredoi Schouteden 1953b, p. 117 [Congo].

TYPE: Sex unknown; Bunia, Belgian Congo; Cent. Afr. Mus.

DISTRIBUTION: Congo.

HOST PLANT: Unrecorded.

*Cysteochila brunnea Hacker

Cysteochila brunnea Hacker 1928, p. 180, pl. 23, fig. 13 [Queensland].

TYPE: Sex unknown; Cairns District, Australia; Queensland Mus.

DISTRIBUTION: Australia (Queensland).

HOST PLANT: Unrecorded.

Cysteochila burgeoni Schouteden

Cysteochila burgeoni Schouteden 1953b, p. 115 [Congo].

TYPE: Sex unknown; Rutshuru, Belgian Congo; Cent. Afr. Mus.

DISTRIBUTION: Congo.

HOST PLANT: Unrecorded.

*Cysteochila caffra Stål

Cysteochila caffra Stål 1873, p. 129 [Caffraria].—Distant 1902a, p. 242, pl. 15, fig. 8.

TYPE: Holotype ♀; Caffraria, South Africa; Stockholm Mus.

DISTRIBUTION: South Africa; Malagasy Republic.

HOST PLANT: Unrecorded.

*Cysteochila chiniana Drake

Cysteochila chiniana Drake 1942a, p. 5 [China].

Physatochila fieberi (not Scott): Takeya 1951a, p. 20 [Japan; *Cissus japonica*].

Physatocheila fieberi: Takeya 1953d, p. 175.

TYPE: Holotype ♂, macropterous; Tien Sun Shan, China; Drake Coll. (USNM).

DISTRIBUTION: China; Japan; Taiwan.

HOST PLANT: *Cissus japonica.*

Cysteochila collarti Schouteden

Cysteochila collarti Schouteden 1953b, p. 116 [Congo].

TYPE: Sex unknown; Stanleyville, Belgian Congo; Cent. Afr. Mus.
DISTRIBUTION: Congo.
HOST PLANT: Unrecorded.

***Cysteochila consanguinea** (Distant)

Bredenbachius consanguineus Distant 1909a, p. 118 [Burma]; 1910a, p. 119.

Cysteochila consanguiensis [sic]: Drake and Poor 1936a, p. 439 [Hainan].

Cysteochila consanguineus: Drake 1937b, p. 593 [China].

TYPE: Sex unknown; Tenasserim, Burma; British Mus.
DISTRIBUTION: Burma; India; China (Hainan Island).
HOST PLANT: Unrecorded.

***Cysteochila constans** (Drake) emendation

Oncophysa constantis Drake 1927a, p. 54 [Hong Kong].—Wu 1935, p. 449.

Cysteochila constantis: Drake and Poor 1937a, p. 11.

TYPE: Holotype ♀, macropterous; Hong Kong; Drake Coll. (USNM).
DISTRIBUTION: Hong Kong.
HOST PLANT: Unrecorded.

***Cysteochila consueta** Drake

Cysteochila consueta Drake 1948a, p. 5, fig. 2 [Taiwan; Viet-Nam].—Takeya 1951a, p. 21.

TYPE: Holotype ♂; Formosa; Drake Coll. (USNM).
DISTRIBUTION: Taiwan; Viet-Nam.
HOST PLANT: Unrecorded.

Cysteochila cracens Drake (emendation)

Cysteochila cracentis Drake 1954b, p. 3 [Western Australia].

TYPE: Holotype ♂; Yancep, Western Australia, Australia; British Mus.
DISTRIBUTION: Australia (Western Australia).
HOST PLANT: Unrecorded.

***Cysteochila cremeri** Drake

Cysteochila cremeri Drake 1955d, p. 2, fig. 1 [Congo].

TYPE: Holotype ♂; Libenge, Belgian Congo; Brussels Mus.
DISTRIBUTION: Congo.
HOST PLANT: Unrecorded.

***Cysteochila delineata** (Distant)

Bredenbachius delineatus Distant 1909a, p. 119 [India]; 1910a, p. 119, fig. 61.

Cysteochila delineatus: Drake 1933, p. 1015.—Drake and Poor 1936b, p. 114 [*Bauhinia purpurea*].—Singh 1953, p. 118.

TYPE: Sex unknown; Calcutta, India; Indian Mus.
DISTRIBUTION: India.
HOST PLANT: *Bauhinia purpurea*.

*Cysteochila dikoana Drake

Cysteochila dikoana Drake 1954b, p. 4 [Nigeria].

TYPE: Holotype ♀, macropterous; Dikoa, Nigeria; Drake Coll. (USNM).

DISTRIBUTION: Nigeria; Congo.

HOST PLANT: Unrecorded.

Cysteochila emmelia Drake

Cysteochila emmelia Drake 1960, p. 347 [New Guinea].

TYPE: Holotype ♂; Mt. Wilhelm, Northeast New Guinea; Bishop Mus.

DISTRIBUTION: New Guinea (Northeast).

HOST PLANT: Unrecorded.

*Cysteochila endeca Drake

Cysteochila endeca Drake 1954b, p. 4 [Senegal; Ghana; Uganda; Cape Province].

Cysteochila endica [sic]: Lindberg 1958a, p. 79 [Cape Verde; *Tamarindus indica*].

TYPE: Holotype ♂; Bambey, Senegal; British Mus.

DISTRIBUTION: Senegal; Ghana; Uganda; South Africa (Cape Province); Cape Verde Islands.

HOST PLANT: *Tamarindus indica*.

*Cysteochila euphues Drake and Ruhoff

Cysteochila euphues Drake and Ruhoff 1962a, p. 157 [Larat].

TYPE: Holotype ♀, macropterous; Larat Island, Tanimbar Islands, E. Malay Archipelago; Cal. Acad.

DISTRIBUTION: Tanimbar Islands (Larat).

HOST PLANT: Unrecorded.

Cysteochila exigua Drake

Cysteochila exigua Drake 1957f, p. 125 [Malagasy].

TYPE: Holotype ♀; Madagascar; Madagascar Sci. Inst.

DISTRIBUTION: Malagasy Republic.

HOST PLANT: Unrecorded.

*Cysteochila expleta Drake and Maa

Cysteochila expleta Drake and Maa 1954, p. 112 [India].

TYPE: Holotype ♂; Kodai Kanal, Madras, India; British Mus.

DISTRIBUTION: India; Philippine Islands (Luzon).

HOST PLANT: Unrecorded.

Cysteochila faceta Drake

Cysteochila faceta Drake 1958c, p. 316 [Malagasy].

TYPE: Holotype ♀; Mont Tsaratanana, Madagascar; Madagascar Sci. Inst.

DISTRIBUTION: Malagasy Republic.

HOST PLANT: Unrecorded.

*Cysteochila fieberi (Scott)

Monanthia fieberi Scott 1874, pp. 291, 442 [Japan].
Physatochila fieberi: Lethierry and Severin 1896, p. 21.
Physatochila montrosa (not Scott): Takeya 1951a, p. 20.
Physatocheila monstrosa: Takeya 1953d, p. 173, pl. 6, fig. 1 [*Boehmeria spicata*].
Cysteochila fieberi: Drake and Maa 1954, p. 112 [India; China; Taiwan].
TYPE: Sex unknown; Japan; British Mus.
DISTRIBUTION: Japan; China; Taiwan; India.
HOST PLANT: *Boehmeria spicata*.

Cysteochila ghesquierei Schouteden

Cysteochila ghesquierei Schouteden 1953b, p. 117 [Congo; *Pseudospondias microcarpa*].
TYPE: Sex unknown; Bengamissa, Belgian Congo; Cent. Afr. Mus.
DISTRIBUTION: Congo.
HOST PLANT: *Pseudospondias microcarpa*.

*Cysteochila gibbula (Horváth)

Physatocheila gibbula Horváth 1912c, p. 342, fig. 2 [Java].
Cysteochila gibbula: Drake and Ruhoff 1961c, p. 145.
TYPE: Holotype ♂; Banjuwangi, Java; Hungarian Mus.
DISTRIBUTION: Greater Sunda Islands (Java).
HOST PLANT: Unrecorded.

*Cysteochila hackeri Drake

Cysteochila hackeri Drake 1939a, p. 87 [South Australia].
TYPE: Holotype ♀, macropterous; Melrose, Australia; Drake Coll. (USNM).
DISTRIBUTION: Australia (South Australia).
HOST PLANT: Unrecorded.

*Cysteochila humeralis (Distant)

Bredenbachius humeralis Distant 1909a, p. 120 [India]; 1910a, p. 121, fig. 62.
TYPE: Sex unknown; Dhikala, Naini Tal, Upper Province, India; Indian Mus.
DISTRIBUTION: India.
HOST PLANT: Unrecorded.

*Cysteochila humerella Drake

Cysteochila humerella Drake 1958c, p. 317 [Malagasy].
TYPE: Holotype ♂; Analavelona, Madagascar; Madagascar Sci. Inst.
DISTRIBUTION: Malagasy Republic.
HOST PLANT: Unrecorded.

*Cysteochila idonea Drake

　　Cysteochila idonea Drake 1956d, p. 109. fig. 4 [Kusaie; Three Sisters]; 1960, p. 345, fig. 5 [New Guinea].

TYPE: Holotype ♂, macropterous; Mt. Matante, Kusaie, Caroline Islands; USNM.

DISTRIBUTION: Caroline Islands (Kusaie); Solomon Islands (Three Sisters); New Guinea (Northeast).

HOST PLANT: Unrecorded.

*Cysteochila impressa Horváth

　　Cysteochila impressa Horváth 1910, p. 66 [Tanganyika].—Drake 1954a, p. 232 [Senegal]; 1957f, p. 127 [Malagasy].

TYPE: Holotype ♂; Kibongoto, Kilimandjaro; Stockholm Mus.

DISTRIBUTION: Tanganyika; Kenya; Senegal; Malagasy Republic.

HOST PLANT: Unrecorded.

*Cysteochila incolana Drake

　　Cysteochila incolana Drake 1956h, p. 18 [Cape Province]; 1961c, p. 129, pl. 8.

TYPE: Holotype ♂; Lion's Head, Capetown, South Africa; British Mus.

DISTRIBUTION: South Africa (Cape Province).

HOST PLANT: Unrecorded.

Cysteochila ituriensis Schouteden

　　Cysteochila ituriensis Schouteden 1953b, p. 121 [Congo].

TYPE: Sex unknown; Bondo Mabe, Belgian Congo; Cent. Afr. Mus.

DISTRIBUTION: Congo.

HOST PLANT: Unrecorded.

Cysteochila jacobsoni (Blöte)

　　Bredenbachius jacobsoni Blöte 1945, p. 89 [Java].

TYPE: Sex unknown; Gunung Gedeh, Java; Leiden Mus.

DISTRIBUTION: Greater Sunda Islands (Java).

HOST PLANT: Unrecorded.

*Cysteochila javensis Drake and Poor

　　Cysteochila javensis Drake and Poor 1937b, p. 400 [Java].

TYPE: Holotype ♀, macropterous; Pekalongan, Java; Drake Coll. (USNM).

DISTRIBUTION: Greater Sunda Islands (Java); India.

HOST PLANT: Unrecorded.

Cysteochila jimmina Drake

　　Cysteochila jimmina Drake 1960, p. 349 [New Guinea].

TYPE: Holotype ♀; Kumur, Upper Jimmi Valley, Northeast New Guinea; Bishop Mus.

DISTRIBUTION: New Guinea (Northeast).

HOST PLANT: Unrecorded.

Cysteochila josephinae (Schouteden)

Physatochila josephinae Schouteden 1923, p. 106 [Congo].
Cysteochila josephinae: Drake and Ruhoff 1961c, p. 145.
TYPE: Sex unknown; Vista, Belgian Congo; Cent. Afr. Mus.
DISTRIBUTION: Congo.
HOST PLANT: Unrecorded.

Cysteochila katangae Schouteden

Cysteochila katangae Schouteden 1953b, p. 123 [Congo].
TYPE: Sex unknown; Elizabethville, Belgian Congo; Cent. Afr. Mus.
DISTRIBUTION: Congo.
HOST PLANT: Unrecorded.

Cysteochila kintambo Schouteden

Cysteochila kintambo Schouteden 1953b, p. 118 [Congo].
TYPE: Sex unknown; Leopoldville, Belgian Congo; Cent. Afr. Mus.
DISTRIBUTION: Congo.
HOST PLANT: Unrecorded.

*Cysteochila lecta Drake and Poor

Cysteochila lecta Drake and Poor 1937a, p. 7 [Borneo].
TYPE: Holotype ♀, macropterous; Sandakan, Borneo; USNM.
DISTRIBUTION: Greater Sunda Islands (Borneo).
HOST PLANT: Unrecorded.

Cysteochila lita Drake

Cysteochila lita Drake 1960, p. 345, fig. 6 [New Guinea].
TYPE: Holotype ♂; Wisselmeren, Enarotadi, Netherlands New Guinea; Bishop Mus.
DISTRIBUTION: New Guinea (Netherlands).
HOST PLANT: Unrecorded.

Cysteochila lueboensis Schouteden

Cysteochila lueboensis Schouteden 1953b, p. 119 [Congo; Hevea].
TYPE: Sex unknown; Luebo, Belgian Congo; Cent. Afr. Mus.
DISTRIBUTION: Congo.
HOST PLANT: Hevea sp.

*Cysteochila luzona Drake and Maa

Cysteochila luzona Drake and Maa 1955, p. 4 [Luzon].
TYPE: Holotype ♀, macropterous; Mt. Makiling, Luzon, Philippine Islands; Drake Coll. (USNM).
DISTRIBUTION: Philippine Islands (Luzon).
HOST PLANT: Unrecorded.

*Cysteochila malaisaei Drake and Ruhoff

Cysteochila malaisaei Drake and Ruhoff 1962a, p. 158 [Burma].
TYPE: Holotype ♂, macropterous; Kambaiti, Burma; Stockholm Mus.
DISTRIBUTION: Burma.
HOST PLANT: Unrecorded.

*Cysteochila malayana Drake

Cysteochila malayana Drake 1956h, p. 19 [Malaya].

TYPE: Holotype ♂, macropterous; Salangor, Malaya; British Mus.

DISTRIBUTION: Federation of Malaya; Laut Island.

HOST PLANT: Unrecorded.

Cysteochila maynei Schouteden

Cysteochila maynei Schouteden 1916b, p. 296 [Congo].

TYPE: Sex unknown; Congo da Lemba, Belgian Congo; Cent. Afr. Mus.

DISTRIBUTION: Congo.

HOST PLANT: Unrecorded.

Cysteochila mokuensis Schouteden

Cysteochila mokuensis Schouteden 1953b, p. 120 [Congo].

TYPE: Sex unknown; Moku, Belgian Congo; Cent. Afr. Mus.

DISTRIBUTION: Congo.

HOST PLANT: Unrecorded.

*Cysteochila monstrosa (Scott)

Monanthia monstrosa Scott 1874, pp. 291, 441 [Japan].

Physatochila monstrosa: Lethierry and Severin 1896, p. 21.—Oshanin 1908, p. 449.

Cysteochila monostrosa [sic]: Drake and Ruhoff 1961c, p. 145.

TYPE: Sex unknown; Japan; apparently lost.

DISTRIBUTION: Japan; China (Fukien).

HOST PLANT: Unrecorded.

*Cysteochila munda Drake

Cysteochila munda Drake 1954b, p. 5 [Cape Province].

TYPE: Holotype ♂, macropterous; Pondoland, Cape Province, South Africa; British Mus.

DISTRIBUTION: South Africa (Cape Province).

HOST PLANT: Unrecorded.

*Cysteochila natalensis (Stål)

Physatocheila natalensis Stål 1855a, p. 38 [Natal].

Monanthia (Physatochila) natalensis: Stål 1865, p. 28 [Caffraria].

Monanthia (Compseuta) natalensis: Stål 1873, p. 133.

Monanthia natalensis: Walker 1873a, p. 195.—Distant 1902a, p. 242, pl. 15, fig. 10.

Physatochila sordidula Horváth 1910, p. 66 [Tanganyika].

Cysteochila humeralis (not Distant) Schouteden 1953b, p. 122 [Congo].

Cysteochila gibbosula Schouteden 1955b, p. 168.

Cysteochila natalensis: Drake 1956b, p. 109.

TYPE: Sex unknown; Natal, South Africa; Stockholm Mus.

DISTRIBUTION: South Africa (Natal); Congo; Tanganyika; Uganda; Kenya.

HOST PLANT: Unrecorded.

*Cysteochila nativa Drake

Cysteochila nativa Drake 1960, p. 347, fig. 7 [New Guinea].

TYPE: Holotype ♀, macropterous; Finchhafen, Northeast New Guinea; Drake Coll. (USNM).

DISTRIBUTION: New Guinea (Northeast)

HOST PLANT: Unrecorded.

*Cysteochila nervosana Drake

Cysteochila nervosana Drake 1956b, p. 110 [Natal; Cape Province].

TYPE: Holotype ♀; Weenan, Natal, South Africa; British Mus.

DISTRIBUTION: South Africa (Natal; Cape Province).

HOST PLANT: Unrecorded.

Cysteochila nigriceps (Signoret)

Monanthia nigriceps Signoret 1861, p. 955 [Malagasy].—Stål 1873, p. 134.

Monanthia (Physatochila) nigriceps: Stål 1865, p. 29.

Cysteochila nigriceps: Lethierry and Severin 1896, p. 22.—Drake and Ruhoff 1960c, p. 31.

TYPE: Sex unknown; Madagascar; Vienna Mus.

DISTRIBUTION: Malagasy Republic.

HOST PLANT: Unrecorded.

*Cysteochila nitens (Drake and Poor)

Oncophysa nitentis Drake and Poor 1937a, p. 11 [Luzon].

Cysteochila nitens: Drake and Ruhoff 1961c, p. 145.

TYPE: Holotype ♀, macropterous; Mount Banahao, Luzon, Philippine Islands; Drake Coll. (USNM).

DISTRIBUTION: Philippine Islands (Luzon).

HOST PLANT: Unrecorded.

*Cysteochila orta Drake and Maa

Cysteochila orta Drake and Maa 1953, p. 93 [China].

TYPE: Holotype ♀, macropterous; Foochow, Fukien, China; Drake Coll. (USNM).

DISTRIBUTION: China.

HOST PLANT: Unrecorded.

*Cysteochila oscitans Drake and Maa (emendation)

Cysteochila oscitantis Drake and Maa 1953, p. 93 [China].

TYPE: Holotype ♂, macropterous; Shaowu Hsien, Fukien, China; Drake Coll. (USNM).

DISTRIBUTION: China.

HOST PLANT: Unrecorded.

*Cysteochila otaviana Drake

Cysteochila otaviana Drake 1954b, p. 6 [South-West Africa].

TYPE: Holotype ♂, macropterous; Otavi, South-West Africa; Drake Coll. (USNM).

DISTRIBUTION: South-West Africa.

HOST PLANT: Unrecorded.

*Cysteochila pallens Horváth

Cysteochila pallens Horváth 1915, p. 331 [Eritrea].—Silvestri 1915, p. 241 [Olea chrysophylla]; 1934, p. 259, fig. 223.

TYPE: Sex unknown; Nefasit, Eritrea; Hungarian Mus.

DISTRIBUTION: Eritrea.

HOST PLANT: Olea chrysophylla.

*Cysteochila phae Drake and Ruhoff

Cysteochila phae Drake and Ruhoff 1961c, p. 148, fig. 3 [Uganda; French Somaliland].

TYPE: Holotype ♂, macropterous; Dijibouti, French Somaliland; Paris Mus.

DISTRIBUTION: Uganda; French Somaliland.

HOST PLANT: Unrecorded.

Cysteochila phiala Drake

Cysteochila phiala Drake 1957f, p. 126 [Malagasy].

TYPE: Holotype ♂; Tananarive-Tsimbazaza, Madagascar; Madagascar Sci. Inst.

DISTRIBUTION: Malagasy Republic.

HOST PLANT: Unrecorded.

*Cysteochila picta (Distant)

Bredenbachius pictus Distant 1903a, p. 50 [Burma]; 1903b, p. 140, fig. 103.

Cysteochila pictus: Drake 1930e, p. 168 [Luzon].

Cysteochila picta: Drake and Poor 1937a, p. 7 [Mindanao].

TYPE: Sex unknown; Myitta, Tenasserim, Burma; British Mus.

DISTRIBUTION: Burma; Philippine Islands (Luzon; Mindanao).

HOST PLANT: Unrecorded.

*Cysteochila poecilia Drake and Ruhoff   PLATE 9

Cysteochila poecilia Drake and Ruhoff 1961c, p. 146, fig. 2 [Chad].

TYPE: Holotype ♀; Sahara, south of Tibesti, Chad; Paris Mus.

DISTRIBUTION: Republic of Chad.

HOST PLANT: Unrecorded.

*Cysteochila ponda Drake

Cysteochila ponda Drake 1937b, p. 593, fig. 18 [China].

TYPE: Holotype ♀, macropterous; Hong Shan, Kiangsi, China; Drake Coll. (USNM).

DISTRIBUTION: China.

HOST PLANT: Unrecorded.

Cysteochila propria Drake

Cysteochila propria Drake 1958c, p. 318 [Malagasy].

TYPE: Holotype ♀; Périnet, Madagascar; Madagascar Sci. Inst.

DISTRIBUTION: Malagasy Republic.

HOST PLANT: Unrecorded.

*Cysteochila rhodesiae Drake

Cysteochila rhodesiae Drake 1954b, p. 7 [Rhodesia].
Cysteochila rhodesia [sic]: Drake 1958a, p. 103 [Angola].

TYPE: Holotype ♂, macropterous; Southern Rhodesia; Hungarian Mus.
DISTRIBUTION: Southern Rhodesia; Angola.
HOST PLANT: Unrecorded.
NOTE: Taken in light trap [Drake 1958a].

*Cysteochila rubida Horváth

Cysteochila rubida Horváth 1924, p. 193 [Malagasy].

TYPE: Sex unknown; Sinus Antongil, Madagascar; Hungarian Mus.
DISTRIBUTION: Malagasy Republic.
HOST PLANT: Unrecorded.

*Cysteochila rustica Drake

Cysteochila rustica Drake 1957e, p. 400 [Reunion].

TYPE: Holotype ♂, macropterous; Saint-Denis, La Montagne, Reunion; Madagascar Sci. Inst.
DISTRIBUTION: Mascarene Islands (Reunion).
HOST PLANT: Unrecorded.

Cysteochila seydeli Schouteden

Cysteochila seydeli Schouteden 1953b, p. 119 [Congo].

TYPE: Sex unknown; Elizabethville, Belgian Congo; Cent. Afr. Mus.
DISTRIBUTION: Congo.
HOST PLANT: Unrecorded.

*Cysteochila sordida (Stål)

Monanthia (Physatocheila) sordida Stål 1859, p. 259 [Cape Province];
1865, p. 29.
Monanthia sordida: Walker 1873a, p. 195.
Cysteochila sordida: Stål 1873, p. 129.—Distant 1902a, p. 242.—Silvestri
1915, p. 241 [Olea verrucosa]; 1934a, p. 259.—Horváth 1925a, p. 3.

TYPE: Sex unknown; Cape of Good Hope, South Africa; Stockholm
Mus.
DISTRIBUTION: South Africa (Cape Province).
HOST PLANT: Olea verrucosa.

*Cysteochila suensoni Drake

Cysteochila suensoni Drake 1942a, p. 5 [China].

TYPE: Holotype ♀, macropterous; Tien Sun Shan, China; Drake Coll.
(USNM).
DISTRIBUTION: China.
HOST PLANT: Unrecorded.

Cysteochila suspecta Schouteden

Cysteochila ? suspecta Schouteden 1953b, p. 121 [Congo].

TYPE: Sex unknown; Uvira, Belgian Congo; Cent. Afr. Mus.

DISTRIBUTION: Congo.

HOST PLANT: Unrecorded.

Cysteochila syscena Drake

Cysteochila syscena Drake 1960, p. 350 [New Britain].

TYPE: Holotype ♀; Ti, Nakanai Mts., New Britain; Bishop Mus.

DISTRIBUTION: New Britain Island, Bismarck Archipelago.

HOST PLANT: Unrecorded.

*Cysteochila taprobanes Kirkaldy

Cysteochila taphrobanes Kirkaldy 1908c, p. 12 [Ceylon].—Distant 1910a, p. 126.

TYPE: Galle, Ceylon; sex and deposition of type unknown.

DISTRIBUTION: Ceylon; India.

HOST PLANT: Unrecorded.

*Cysteochila tarda Drake

Cysteochila tarda Drake 1954a, p. 235 [Senegal; Sudan].

TYPE: Holotype ♂; Bambey, Senegal; Inst. Fr. Afr. N.

DISTRIBUTION: Senegal; Sudan.

HOST PLANT: "Kittirbush."

*Cysteochila terminalis Drake

Cysteochila terminalis Drake 1948a, p. 6 [India].

TYPE: Holotype ♀, macropterous; Samsingh, Kalimpong, India; Drake Coll. (USNM).

DISTRIBUTION: India.

HOST PLANT: Unrecorded.

*Cysteochila tingoides (Motschulsky)

Monanthia ? tingoides Motschulsky 1863, p. 92 [Ceylon].—Kirby 1891, p. 109.

Cysteochila tingoides: Stål 1873, p. 129.—Distant 1903b, p. 139.—Bergroth 1921, p. 103.—Drake 1948a, p. 4 [India].

TYPE: Sex unknown; Montagnes de Nura-Ellia, Ceylon; Leningrad Inst.

DISTRIBUTION: Ceylon; India.

HOST PLANT: Unrecorded.

*Cysteochila tombeuri Schouteden

Cysteochila tombeuri Schouteden 1923, p. 103 [Tanganyika].—Drake 1958a, p. 103 [Angola; So. Rhodesia; Mozambique; Kenya].

TYPE: Sex unknown; Kigoma, Tanganyika; Cent. Afr. Mus.

DISTRIBUTION: Tanganyika; Kenya; Angola; Mozambique; Southern Rhodesia.

HOST PLANT: Unrecorded.

*Cysteochila tricolor (Hacker)

Furcilliger tricolor Hacker 1929, p. 332, text fig. 1 [Queensland].

Cysteochila franzeni Drake 1942a, p. 4.

Cysteochila bicolor [sic]: Drake 1942a, p. 1.

Cysteochila tricolor: Drake and Maa 1953, p. 92.

TYPE: Sex unknown; Mount Glorious, Queensland, Australia; Queensland Mus.

DISTRIBUTION: Australia (Queensland).

HOST PLANT: Unrecorded.

*Cysteochila tzitzikamana Drake

Cysteochila tzitzikamana Drake 1956f, p. 422 [Cape Province].

TYPE: Holotype ♂; Tzitzikama Forest, Stormrivierpiek, Cape Province, South Africa; Lund Zool. Inst.

DISTRIBUTION: South Africa (Cape Province); Congo.

HOST PLANT: Unrecorded.

*Cysteochila undosa Drake

Cysteochila undosa Drake 1942a, p. 6 [Burma].

TYPE: Holotype ♂, macropterous; Kambaiti, Burma; Drake Coll. (USNM).

DISTRIBUTION: Burma.

HOST PLANT: Unrecorded.

*Cysteochila vadosa Drake

Cysteochila vadosa Drake 1956h, p. 18 [Natal].

TYPE: Holotype ♂, macropterous; Umkomaas, Natal, South Africa; Drake Coll. (USNM).

DISTRIBUTION: South Africa (Natal).

HOST PLANT: Unrecorded.

*Cysteochila visenda Drake and Poor

Cysteochila visenda Drake and Poor 1937a, p. 8 [Negros].

TYPE: Holotype ♂, macropterous; Cuernos Mountains, Oriental Negros Province, Negros, Philippine Islands; Drake Coll. (USNM).

DISTRIBUTION: Philippine Islands (Negros).

HOST PLANT: Unrecorded.

*Cysteochila vitilevuana Drake and Poor

Monanthia natalensis (not Stål): Kirkaldy 1908b, p. 366 [Fiji].

Cysteochila vitilevuana Drake and Poor 1943, p. 193.—Drake and Hurd 1945a, p. 287, fig. 1.

TYPE: Holotype ♂; Nandarivatu, Viti Levu, Fiji; Bishop Mus.

DISTRIBUTION: Fiji Islands (Viti Levu).

HOST PLANT: Unrecorded.

*Cysteochila vota Drake

Cysteochila vota Drake 1948a, p. 7 [Japan].—Takeya 1951a, p. 21.

TYPE: Holotype ♀, macropterous; Moji, Japan; Drake Coll. (USNM).
DISTRIBUTION: Japan.
HOST PLANT: Unrecorded.

*Cysteochila vota var. **fida** Drake and Maa

Cysteochila vota var. *fida* Drake and Maa 1953, p. 92 [China].

TYPE: Holotype ♂, macropterous; Shaowu City, Fukien, China; Drake Coll. (USNM).
DISTRIBUTION: China.
HOST PLANT: Unrecorded.

*Cysteochila wechinai Drake

Cysteochila chiniana Drake 1954b, p. 5 (not 1942) [Luzon].
Cysteochila wechinai Drake 1954f, p. 5.

TYPE: Holotype ♂; Trinidad, Luzon, Philippine Islands; British Mus.
DISTRIBUTION: Philippine Islands (Luzon).
HOST PLANT: Unrecorded.

*Cysteochila yungana Drake and Maa

Cysteochila yungana Drake and Maa 1955, p. 4 [China].

TYPE: Holotype ♀, macropterous; Yungan City, Fukien, China; Drake Coll. (USNM).
DISTRIBUTION: China.
HOST PLANT: Unrecorded.

Cysteochila zavattarii Mancini

Cysteochila zavattarii Mancini 1953a, p. 184 [Ethiopia].

TYPE: Holotype ♀; Mega, Ethiopia; Mancini Coll.
DISTRIBUTION: Ethiopia.
HOST PLANT: Unrecorded.

Genus DASYTINGIS Drake and Poor

Dasytingis Drake and Poor 1936b, p. 145.—Drake and Ruhoff 1960a, p. 49.

TYPE SPECIES: *Dasytingis rudis* Drake and Poor.

*Dasytingis rudis Drake and Poor

Dasytingis rudis Drake and Poor 1936b, p. 145, fig. 1 [India].—Drake and Ruhoff 1962c, p. 133.
Tingis bengalana Drake 1956h, p. 20.

TYPE: Holotype ♂, macropterous; Hoshangabad, Rahatgaon, India; Drake Coll. (USNM).
DISTRIBUTION: India.
HOST PLANT: *Vitex ruganda.*

*Dasytingis semota Drake and Lutz

Dasytingis semota Drake and Lutz 1953, p. 104 [India].

TYPE: Holotype ♂, macropterous; Karikal, India; Drake Coll. (USNM).
DISTRIBUTION: India.
HOST PLANT: Unrecorded.

Genus DICHOCYSTA Champion

Dichocysta Champion 1898a, p. 33.—Banks 1910, p. 56.—Van Duzee 1916, p. 26; 1917b, p. 221.—Blatchley 1926, p. 485.—Hurd 1946, p. 453.—Drake and Ruhoff 1960a, p. 50.

TYPE SPECIES: *Dichocysta pictipes* Champion.

*Dichocysta pictipes Champion

Dichocysta pictipes Champion 1898a, p. 34, pl. 3, figs. 1, 1a, b, 2 [Guatemala; Panama].—Heidemann 1899a, p. 339 [Ariz.].—Barber 1910, p. 38.—Drake 1918d, p. 88 [Fla.]; 1928e, p. 2 [Honduras; cacao]; 1938a, p. 70 [Mexico].—Blatchley 1926, p. 485 [Costa Rica].

TYPE: Sex unknown; David, Chiriqui, Panama; British Mus.
DISTRIBUTION: U.S. (Fla.; Tex.; Ariz.); Mexico; Guatemala; Honduras; Costa Rica; Panama.
HOST PLANT: Cacao.

Genus DICONOCORIS Mayr

Diconocoris Mayr 1865, p. 442.—Stål 1873, p. 134.—Lethierry and Severin 1896, p. 25.—Drake 1937a, p. 386.—Drake and Ruhoff 1960a, p. 50.

Diplogomphus Horváth 1906c, p. 296.—Drake and Poor 1937a, p. 10.—Drake and Ruhoff 1960a, p. 53.

TYPE SPECIES: *Diconocoris javanus* Mayr.

*Diconocoris capusi (Horváth)   PLATES 30, 31

Diplogomphus capusi Horváth 1906c, p. 296, fig. [Viet-Nam].—Drake and Poor 1937a, p. 10.

Diconocoris capusi: Drake 1937a, p. 386.—Drake and Davis 1960, fig. 54.

TYPE: Indochina; sex and deposition of type unknown.
DISTRIBUTION: Viet-Nam.
HOST PLANT: Unrecorded.

*Diconocoris distanti Drake

Elasmognathus greeni (not Kirby): Distant 1903b, p. 142, fig. 105 [Ceylon; *Piper nigrum*].

Diconocoris distanti Drake 1954f, p. 4.

TYPE: Holotype ♂; Peradeniya, Ceylon; British Mus.
DISTRIBUTION: Ceylon.
HOST PLANT: *Piper nigrum*.

Diconocoris greeni (Kirby)

Elasmognathus greeni Kirby 1891, p. 109, pl. 4, fig. 5. [Ceylon].—
Kirkaldy 1902, p. 297.

Elasmognathus pallida Kirby 1891, p. 110.

Diplogomphus greeni: Drake and Poor 1937a, p. 10.

Diconocoris greeni: Drake 1937a, p. 386.

TYPE: Sex unknown; Ceylon; British Mus.

DISTRIBUTION: Ceylon.

HOST PLANT: Wild pepper.

*Diconocoris hewetti (Distant)

Elasmognathus hewetti Distant 1908b, p. 127, pl. 7, figs. 2, 2a [Borneo].

Elasmognathus picturatus Distant 1909c, p. 165, pl. 10, fig. 4, 4a.

Elasmognathus hewitti [sic]: van der Vecht 1931, pp. 824, 828 [Sumatra; pepper]; 1935, pp. 484, 492, pl. 1 [Bangka Islands].

Diplogomphus hewitti [sic]: Drake and Poor 1937a, p. 10.—Blöte 1945, p. 89.

Cysteochila picturatus: Drake 1937a, p. 386.

Diconocoris hewetti: Drake 1937a, p. 386.—Drake and Ruhoff 1960c, p. 36.

TYPE: Sex unknown; Kuching, Borneo; British Mus.

DISTRIBUTION: Greater Sunda Islands (Borneo; Sumatra); Bangka Islands.

HOST PLANT: Pepper.

NOTE: Biology [van der Vecht 1935].

*Diconocoris inusitatus (Drake)

Elasmognathus inusitatus Drake 1927d, p. 309 [Luzon].

Diplogomphus inusitatus: Drake and Poor 1937a, p. 10.

Diconocoris inusitatus: Drake 1937a, p. 386.

TYPE: Holotype ♂, macropterous; Mount Maquiling, Luzon, Philippine Islands; Drake Coll. (USNM).

DISTRIBUTION: Philippine Islands (Luzon).

HOST PLANT: Unrecorded.

*Diconocoris javanus Mayr

Diconocoris javanus Mayr 1865, p. 442 [Java].—Stål 1873, p. 134.—
Drake 1937a, p. 386, figs. 1a, b.—Drake and Poor 1941, p. 160 [Amboina].

Monanthia javana: Walker 1873a, p. 196.

TYPE: Sex unknown; Java; Vienna Mus.

DISTRIBUTION: Greater Sunda Islands (Java); Moluccas (Amboina).

HOST PLANT: Unrecorded.

Diconocoris nepalensis (Distant)

Elasmognathus nepalensis Distant 1909a, p. 120 [Nepal]; 1910a, p. 122, fig. 63.

Diplogomphus nepalensis: Bergroth 1911, p. 186.

Diplogomphus napalensis [sic]: Drake and Poor 1937a, p. 10 [India].

Diconocoris nepalensis: Drake 1937a, p. 386.

TYPE: Sex unknown; Thamaspur, Nepal; Indian Mus.

DISTRIBUTION: Nepal; India.

HOST PLANT: Unrecorded.

Genus DICROTINGIS Drake and Ruhoff

Dicrotingis Drake and Ruhoff 1960c, p. 34.

TYPE SPECIES: *Leptopharsa digitalis* Drake.

*****Dicrotingis digitalis** (Drake)   PLATE 26

Leptopharsa digitalis Drake 1928d, p. 22 [Haiti; *Phyllostylon rhamnoides*].

Dicrotingis digitalis: Drake and Ruhoff 1960c, p. 35, fig. 4a, b.

TYPE: Lectotype ♂, macropterous; Crox des Missiones, Plaine Gulde Sac, Haiti; Drake Coll. (USNM).

DISTRIBUTION: Haiti.

HOST PLANT: *Phyllostylon rhamnoides*.

NOTE: Holotype apparently lost. Paratype ♂, same locality and date as holotype, here designated as lectotype.

Genus DICTYLA Stål

Dictyla Stål 1874, p. 57.—Drake and Ruhoff 1960a, p. 50.—Stichel 1960a, p. 336; 1960b, p. 400; 1960c, p. 139.

Monanthia (of most authors, but not Le Peletier and Serville; see Drake and Ruhoff 1960a, pp. 45, 50).—Mayr 1858, p. 571.—Stål 1873, pp. 122, 133.—Horváth 1874b, p. 432; 1906a, pp. 15, 97 (key).— d'Antessanty 1890, p. 32.—Lethierry and Severin 1896, p. 23.— Oshanin 1908, p. 450; 1912, p. 45.—Banks 1910, p. 57.—Jensen–Haarup 1912, p. 155 (key).—Van Duzee 1917b, pp. 223, 819.—Drake 1917c, pp. 49–52 (key); 1943a, p. 142.—Sahlberg 1920, p. 84.— Stichel 1926, pp. 105, 115 (key); 1935, p. 349; 1938a, p. 408.—de Seabra 1931, pp. 408, 434 (key).—Lindberg 1932a, p. 44.—Börner 1935, pp. 74, 78 (key).—Scholte 1935, p. 91 (key).—Drake and Poor 1936c, p. 388.—Gulde 1938, pp. 245, 311 (key).—Monte 1939b, p. 76; 1941e, p. 123.—China 1943, p. 248.—Hoberlandt 1943, p. 124.—Blöte 1945, p. 90.—Hurd 1946, p. 450.—Kiritshenko 1951, pp. 242, 253 (key).—Singer 1952, p. 54.

TYPE SPECIES: *Monanthia platyoma* Fieber.

Dictyla abyssinica (Drake)

Monanthia abyssinica Drake 1954g, p. 658, fig. 1 [Ethiopia; *Cordia abyssinica*].

Dictyla abyssinica: Drake and Ruhoff 1960a, p. 51.

TYPE: Holotype ♀; Doukam, Ethiopia; British Mus.

DISTRIBUTION: Ethiopia.

HOST PLANT: *Cordia abyssinica.*

*Dictyla aima Drake

Dictyla aima Drake 1961b, p. 107, pl. 3 [Queensland].

TYPE: Holotype ♂; Queensland, Australia; Austr. Mus.

DISTRIBUTION: Australia (Queensland).

HOST PLANT: Collected on "cuolahah box."

*Dictyla ainsliei (Drake and Poor)

Monanthia ainsliei Drake and Poor 1938a, p. 28, fig. 1 [Guatemala].

Dictyla ainsliei: Drake and Ruhoff 1960a, p. 51.

TYPE: Holotype ♀, macropterous; Concepcion, Guatemala; Drake Coll. (USNM).

DISTRIBUTION: Guatemala.

HOST PLANT: Unrecorded.

*Dictyla alia Drake and Cobben

Dictyla alia Drake and Cobben 1960, pp. 67, 69, figs. 74a, 75a, 76a, 77 [Curaçao; Aruba; Bonaire; *Cordia alba*].

TYPE: Holotype ♂, macropterous; St. Martha, Curaçao, Netherlands Antilles; Drake Coll. (USNM).

DISTRIBUTION: Netherlands Antilles (Curaçao; Aruba; Bonaire).

HOST PLANT: *Cordia alba.*

*Dictyla amitina (Horváth)

Monanthia amitina Horváth 1925a, p. 13 [Queensland].—Hacker 1927 p. 25, fig. 18; 1928a, p. 181.

Dictyla amitina: Drake and Ruhoff 1960a, p. 51.—Drake 1961b, p. 107 pl. 3.

TYPE: Sex unknown; Queensland, Australia; Stockholm Mus.

DISTRIBUTION: Australia (Queensland).

HOST PLANT: Unrecorded.

*Dictyla aurigana (Drake)

Monanthia aurigana Drake 1954b, p. 2 [Natal].

Dictyla aurigana: Drake and Ruhoff 1960a, p. 51.

TYPE: Holotype ♂; Shepstone, Natal, South Africa; British Mus.

DISTRIBUTION: South Africa (Natal).

HOST PLANT: Unrecorded.

*Dictyla aurigana subsp. discoris (Drake)

Monanthia aurigana subsp. *discoris* Drake 1954b, p. 2 [Tanganyika].

Dictyla aurigana subsp. *discoris:* Drake and Ruhoff 1960a, p. 51.

TYPE: Holotype ♀, macropterous; Lindi, Tanganyika; Drake Coll. (USNM).

DISTRIBUTION: Tanganyika.

HOST PLANT: Unrecorded.

*Dictyla balli (Drake)

Monanthia balli Drake 1922c, p. 355 [Haiti].—Drake and Bruner 1924a, p. 144.

Dictyla balli: Drake and Ruhoff 1960a, p. 51.

TYPE: Holotype ♀, macropterous; Port au Prince, Haiti; Drake Coll. (USNM).

DISTRIBUTION: Haiti; Bahama Islands (Cat and Harbor Islands).

HOST PLANT: Unrecorded.

*Dictyla berryi (Drake)

Monanthia berryi Drake 1943a, pp. 141, 142.—Drake and Hambleton 1944b, p. 121 [Peru]; 1945, p. 356 [Ecuador].

Dictyla berryi: Drake and Ruhoff 1960a, p. 51.

TYPE: Holotype ♂, macropterous; Chanchaqui, Peru; USNM.

DISTRIBUTION: Peru; Ecuador.

HOST PLANT: Unrecorded.

NOTE: Drake and Hambleton 1944b corrected the type locality to "Chanchaqui, Peru" not "Montevideo, Uruguay" as published in the original description.

*Dictyla burgeoni (Schouteden)

Monanthia burgeoni Schouteden 1923, p. 107 [Congo].

TYPE: Sex unknown; Bas Uélé, Belgian Congo; Cent. Afr. Mus.

DISTRIBUTION: Congo.

HOST PLANT: Unrecorded.

NOTE: Further study reveals this to be a valid species, not a synonym of *nodipennis* as designated in Drake 1956a, p. 4.

Dictyla burgeoni var. satanas (Schouteden)

Monanthia burgeoni var. *satanas* Schouteden 1923, p. 107 [Congo].

TYPE: Sex unknown; Bas Uélé, Belgian Congo; Cent. Afr. Mus.

DISTRIBUTION: Congo.

HOST PLANT: Unrecorded.

*Dictyla cheriani (Drake)

Monanthia cheriani Drake 1936a, p. 145 [India; *Corida*].

Dictyla cheriani: Drake and Ruhoff 1960a, p. 51; 1961b, p. 131, fig. 7.

TYPE: Holotype ♂, macropterous; Coimbatore, India; Drake Coll. (USNM).

DISTRIBUTION: India.

HOST PLANT: *Corida* sp.

*Dictyla c-nigrum (Champion)

Monanthia c-nigrum Champion 1898a, p. 47, pl. 3, fig. 25 [Mexico; Guatemala; Nicaragua].—Van Duzee 1907, p. 23 [Jamaica].—Drake 1922c, p. 355 [Haiti]; 1929, p. 35 [Costa Rica]; 1943a, p. 142 [Brazil].—Barber 1939, p. 372.—Monte 1941d, p. 100.—Drake and Hambleton 1945, p. 356.

Dictyla c-nigrum: Drake and Ruhoff 1960a, p. 51.

TYPE: Sex unknown; Atoyac, Mexico; British Mus.

DISTRIBUTION: Mexico; Guatemala; Nicaragua; Costa Rica; Haiti; Jamaica; Brazil; Guadeloupe Island.

HOST PLANT: Unrecorded.

Dictyla collarti (Schouteden)

Monanthia collarti Schouteden 1953e, p. 196 [Congo].

Dictyla collarti: Drake and Ruhoff 1960a, p. 51.

TYPE: Sex unknown; Mayumbe, Belgian Congo; Cent. Afr. Mus.

DISTRIBUTION: Congo.

HOST PLANT: Unrecorded.

*Dictyla coloradensis (Drake)

Monanthia coloradensis Drake 1917c, pp. 50, 51, fig. 1b [Colo.].

Dictyla coloradensis: Drake and Ruhoff 1960a, p. 51.

TYPE: Holotype ♀, macropterous; Colorado, U.S.; Drake Coll. (USNM).

DISTRIBUTION: U.S. (Colo.; Tex.; Oreg.).

HOST PLANT: Unrecorded.

*Dictyla comes (Drake)

Monanthia comes Drake 1948a, p. 2 [China]; 1954g, p. 658 [Ethiopia; Cape Province; Orange Free State; Natal; Uganda]; 1956a, p. 4 [Congo; India; Arabia; Egypt; Morocco; Senegal; Kenya; Nigeria; West Africa].

Dictyla comes: Drake and Ruhoff 1960a, p. 51.

TYPE: Holotype ♂, macropterous; Kumming, Tausan-fu, Yunnan Province, China; Drake Coll. (USNM).

DISTRIBUTION: China; India; Arabia; Morocco; Egypt; Ethiopia; Congo; Senegal; Kenya; Uganda; Nigeria; South Africa (Orange Free State; Cape Province; Natal); West Africa.

HOST PLANT: Unrecorded.

*Dictyla convergens (Herrich-Schaeffer)

Tingis convergens Herrich-Schaeffer 1835, p. 59.

Monanthia convergens: Burmeister 1835, p. 261 [*Myosotis palustris*].—Herrich-Schaeffer 1837, p. 15, pl. 114, p. 361; 1838, p. 58.

Monanthia (*Physatocheila*) *humuli* (not Fabricius): Fieber 1844, p. 84, pl. 7, figs. 17–18 [Austria; Germany; Czechoslovakia; England].—Herrich-Schaeffer 1850, p. 153.—Flor 1860, p. 355 [Estonia; Latvia; Sweden; France].

Monanthia humuli: Scholz 1847, p. 120.—Fieber 1861, p. 125.—Douglas and Scott 1865, p. 244.—Frey-Gessner 1865, p. 232 [Switzerland].—Jakovlev 1869, p. 111 [Russia].—Garbiglietti 1869, p. 273 [Italy].—Gredler 1870, p. 75.—Thomson 1871, p. 398.—Saunders 1875, p. 249; 1892, p. 136, pl. 13, fig. 1 [Scotland; Wales; *Myosotis*].—Reiber and Puton 1876, p. 69.—Vollenhoven 1878, p. 274, pl. 9, fig. 6 [Netherlands].—Puton 1879c, p. 122; 1886a, p. 12.—Chicote 1880, p. 189 [Spain].—Reuter 1882b, p. 163 [Finland; *Myosotis lingulata*].—Ferrari 1884, p. 475 [Tunisia].—Hüeber 1893, p. 352.—Horváth 1906a, pp. 99, 102.—Mužik 1907, p. 63.—Oshanin 1908, p. 452 [Belgium; Hungary; Rumania; Portugal].—Jensen-Haarup 1912, pp. 155, 157, fig. 98c [Denmark].—Schumacher 1914, p. 259.—Reichensperger 1920, p. 62.—Butler 1923, p. 215.—Stichel 1926, p. 116, fig. 306.—Ross and Hedicke 1927, p. 188.—de Seabra 1931, p. 436, fig. 507.—Scholte 1935, p. 91, fig. 25 [*Myosotis cespitosa*].—Gulde 1938, p. 315, fig.—Cobben 1948, p. 82; 1958a, p. 14, fig. 17.—Kiritshenko 1951, p. 253.—Leston 1954, p. 101, fig. 5.—Štusák 1957b, pp. 138, 140, figs. 8, 10b, 12b.—Southwood and Leston 1959, p. 151, pl. 21, fig. 12; pl. 25, fig. 2.

Dictyla humuli: Drake and Ruhoff 1960a, p. 51.—Stichel 1960a, p. 341, fig. 175 [Poland].

Dictyla convergens: Drake and Ruhoff 1960b, p. 74, pl. 21.

TYPE: Unknown.

DISTRIBUTION: Germany; France; England; Scotland; Wales; Switzerland; Czechoslovakia; Austria; Italy; Poland; Sweden; Denmark; Finland; Hungary; Rumania; Belgium; Portugal; Spain; Netherlands; U.S.S.R. (Estonia; Latvia); Tunisia.

HOST PLANTS: *Myosotis cespitosa; Myosotis lingulata; Myosotis palustris; Myosotis* sp.

NOTE: Study of immature stages [Leston; Štusák]. Described by Herrich-Schaeffer but wrongly accredited by him and others to Klug [Herrich-Schaeffer 1837, p. 15].

*Dictyla echii (Schrank)

Cimex clavicornis (not Linnaeus): Schrank 1781, p. 265.—Villers 1789, p. 485, pl. 3, fig.

Cimex echii Schrank 1782, p. 276.

Acanthia echii: Schrank 1801, p. 65.—Wolff 1804, p. 130, pl. 13, fig. 124 [*Echium vulgare*].

Tingis humuli (not Fabricius): Fallén 1807, p. 36; 1829, p. 144.—Brullé 1835, p. 340, pl. 26, fig. 1 [Greece].—Blanchard 1840, p. 113.

Tingis echii: Herrich-Schaeffer 1835, p. 59.—Schilling 1838, p. 105.

Monanthia humuli: Burmeister 1835, p. 261.—Costa 1847a, p. 22; 1847c, p. 162.

Monanthia echii: Herrich-Schaeffer 1837, p. 14, pl. 114, fig. 360, 124c; 1838, p. 58.—Jakovlev 1880b, p. 110 [*Echium rubrum; Echium italicum*].—Reuter 1891a, p. 26 [Crete].—Horváth 1906a, pp. 99, 103 [Armenia; Turkestan; Siberia; Turkey; Algeria]; 1918a, p. 334.— Oshanin 1908, p. 453 [Belgium; Rumania; Yugoslavia; Iran].— Jensen-Haarup 1912, pp. 155, 157 [Denmark].—Schumacher 1914, p. 259.—Moroder Sala 1920, p. 13.—Stichel 1926, p. 116; 1938a, p. 408 [Albania; Israel; Poland; Norway].—Ross and Hedicke 1927, pp. 86, 136, 181 [*Lycopsis arvensis*].—de Seabra 1931, p. 437, figs. 506 (2–5), 509.—Lindberg 1932a, p. 44 [Morocco]; 1948, p. 60 [Bulgaria].—Scholte 1935, p. 91, fig. 24.—Vidal 1937, p. 199 [*Echium creticum*].—Blöte 1945, p. 90 [Egypt; Tunisia; Corsica].—Cobben 1948, p. 82; 1958a, p. 14, fig. 18.—Kiritshenko 1951, p. 254.—Novak and Wagner 1951, p. 71 [*Echium altissimum; Echium pustulatum*].— Mancini 1953a, p. 186.—Bator 1953, p. 327, pl. 4, fig. 6.—Hoberlandt 1955, p. 95 [Cyprus].—Štusak 1957b, pp. 138, 140, fig. 7; 1958, p. 369, fig. 16.

Monanthia clavicornis: Amyot and Serville 1843, p. 298 [France; Sicily].

Monanthia (Physatocheila) wolffii Fieber 1844, p. 86, pl. 7, figs. 22–24 [Germany; Italy; Hungary; Sweden].—Herrich-Schaeffer 1850, p. 153.—Flor 1860, p. 352 [Estonia; Latvia; Caucasus; *Symphytum; Pulmonaria*].

Monanthia (Tropidocheila) wolffii: Sahlberg 1848, p. 133 [Finland].

Monanthia wolffii: Mayr 1858, p. 571 [Austria; Czechoslovakia; *Cynoglossum*].—Fieber 1861, p. 125.—Frey-Gessner 1865, p. 232 [Switzerland].—Jakovlev 1869, p. 111; 1880b, p. 109.—Gredler 1870, p. 75 [*Anchusa officinalis*].—Stål 1874, p. 59.—Ferrari 1874, p. 171; 1878, p. 66.—Vollenhoven 1878, p. 275, pl. 9, fig. 7 [Netherlands].—Puton 1879c, p. 120; 1881, p. 123 [Syria].—Bolivar and Chicote 1879, p. 166 [Spain; Portugal].—Reuter 1882b, p. 120.—d'Antessanty 1890, p. 33 [*Cynoglossum officinale*].—Hüeber 1893, p. 349.

Dictyla echii: Drake and Ruhoff 1960a, p. 51.—Stichel 1960a, p. 342, fig. 178 [Poland; Sardinia; *Anchusa arvensis*].

TYPE: Unknown.

DISTRIBUTION: Netherlands; France; Belgium; Spain; Portugal; Germany; Austria; Switzerland; Czechoslovakia; Hungary; Italy; Sicily; Sardinia; Corsica; Poland; Denmark; Sweden; Finland; Norway; Rumania; Yugoslavia; Albania; Bulgaria; Greece; Crete; Cyprus; Turkey; U.S.S.R. (Latvia; Estonia; Siberia; Turkestan; Transcaucasus; Caucasus; Armenia); Syria; Israel; Iran; Morocco; Algeria; Egypt; Tunisia.

HOST PLANTS: *Anchusa arvensis; Anchusa officinalis; Cynoglossum officinale; Cynoglossum* sp.; *Echium altissimum; Echium creticum; Echium italicum; Echium pustulatum; Echium rubrum; Echium vulgare; Echium* sp.; *Lycopsis arvensis; Pulmonaria* sp.; *Symphytum* sp.

NOTE: Study of immature stages [Štusak 1957b].

Dictyla echii var. nigricans (Hoberlandt)

Monanthia echii var. *nigricans* Hoberlandt 1943, pp. 116, 117, 119 [Czechoslovakia].

Dictyla echii var. *nigricans:* Drake and Ruhoff 1960a, p. 51.—Stichel 1960a, p. 342.

TYPE: Holotype ♂; Hodonín, Moravia, Czechoslovakia; Prague Mus.

DISTRIBUTION: Czechoslovakia.

HOST PLANT: Unrecorded.

*Dictyla echii var. rufina (Seidenstücker)

Monanthia echii subvar. *rufina* Seidenstücker 1954, pp. 230, 235 [Turkey].—Hoberlandt 1955, p. 95 [Syria].

Dictyla echii var. *rufina:* Drake and Ruhoff 1960a, p. 51.—Stichel 1960a, p. 342.

TYPE: Turkey; sex and deposition of type unknown.

DISTRIBUTION: Turkey; Syria.

HOST PLANT: Unrecorded.

*Dictyla ehrethiae (Gibson)

Monanthia ehrethiae Gibson (*in* Drake 1917c, pp. 49, 50) [Tex.; *Ehretia elliptica*].

Monanthia ehrethia [sic]: Drake 1943a, p. 142 [Mexico].

Dictyla ehrethiae: Drake and Ruhoff 1960a, p. 51.

TYPE: Holotype ♀, macropterous; Brownsville, Texas, U.S.; USNM.

DISTRIBUTION: U.S. (Tex.); Mexico.

HOST PLANT: *Ehretia elliptica.*

*Dictyla evidens (Drake) (New Status)

Monanthia formosa Drake 1923a, p. 102 [Taiwan].—Esaki 1926, p. 163.—Takeya 1951a, p. 22; 1953b, p. 4, fig. 1 [Japan; *Ehretia thyrsiflora*].—Maa 1957, pp. 119, 131 [*Ehretia taiwaniana; Ehretia dicksonii*].

Monanthia evidens Drake 1927a, p. 53 [Luzon]; 1937a, p. 385.—Drake and Poor 1937b, p. 397 [*Ehretia acuminata*].—Takeya 1951a, p. 23.

Monanthia formosana [sic]: Drake and Maa 1953, p. 90 [China].

Dictyla formosa: Drake and Ruhoff 1960a, p. 51.

TYPE: Holotype ♂; Kankau, Formosa; Horn Coll.

DISTRIBUTION: Taiwan; China; Japan; Philippine Islands (Luzon).

HOST PLANTS: *Ehretia acuminata; Ehretia dicksonii; Ehretia taiwaniana; Ehretia thyrsiflora.*

*Dictyla femoralis (Stål)

Monanthia (Compseuta) femoralis Stål 1873, p. 133 [Caffraria].

Monanthia femoralis: Lethierry and Severin 1896, p. 23.—Distant 1902a, p. 243.

Dictyla femoralis: Drake and Ruhoff 1960a, p. 51.

TYPE: Holotype ♀; Caffraria, South Africa; Stockholm Mus.

DISTRIBUTION: South Africa (Zululand).

HOST PLANT: Unrecorded.

*Dictyla figurata (Drake)

Monanthia figurata Drake 1922c, p. 354, pl. 39, fig. 12 [Brazil]; 1930a, p. 1; 1931b, p. 510.—Drake and Hambleton 1938b, p. 52 [*Cordia*].

Dictyla figurata: Drake and Ruhoff 1960a, p. 51.

TYPE: Holotype ♂; Chapada, Brazil; Carnegie Mus.

DISTRIBUTION: Brazil.

HOST PLANT: *Cordia* sp.

*Dictyla flavipes (Signoret)

Monanthia flavipes Signoret 1861, p. 956 [Malagasy].—Stål 1873, p. 134.

Dictyla flavipes: Drake and Ruhoff 1960a, p. 51; 1960c, p. 29; 1961b, p. 131, fig. 6.

TYPE: Lectotype ♂; Mayotte, Comoro Islands; Vienna Mus.

DISTRIBUTION: Malagasy Republic; Comoro Islands (Mayotte).

HOST PLANT: Unrecorded.

*Dictyla fulvescens (Kiritshenko)

Monanthia fulvescens Kiritshenko 1952, p. 179 [Russia].

Dictyla fulvescens: Drake and Ruhoff 1960a, p. 51.

TYPE: Sex unknown; Tadzhikistan, Russia; Leningrad Inst.

DISTRIBUTION: U.S.S.R.

HOST PLANT: Unrecorded.

Dictyla gerardi (Schouteden)

Monanthia gerardi Schouteden 1953e, p. 198 [Congo].

Dictyla gerardi: Drake and Ruhoff 1960a, p. 51.

TYPE: Sex unknown; Katompe, Katanga, Belgian Congo; Cent. Afr. Mus.

DISTRIBUTION: Congo.

HOST PLANT: Unrecorded.

*Dictyla haitiensis (Drake and Poor)

Monanthia haitiensis Drake and Poor 1938a, p. 28 [Haiti].—Hurd 1946, p. 451 [Puerto Rico].

Dictyla haitiensis: Drake and Ruhoff 1960a, p. 51.

TYPE: Holotype ♀, macropterous; Port au Prince, Haiti; Drake Coll. (USNM).

DISTRIBUTION: Haiti; Puerto Rico.

HOST PLANT: *Cordia serrata.*

*Dictyla humuli (Fabricius)

Acanthia humuli Fabricius 1794, p. 77 [Germany; *Humulus*].

Tingis humuli: Fabricius 1803, p. 126.—Herrich-Schaeffer 1835, p. 58.

Tingis symphyti Vallot 1829, p. 99 [*Symphytum officinale*].

Monanthia costata (not Fabricius): Burmeister 1835, p. 261.—Herrich-Schaeffer 1837, p. 15, pl. 114, fig. 362.

Monanthia (*Physatocheila*) *vesiculifera* Fieber 1844, p. 87, pl. 7, figs. 25–26 [Sicily; Italy; Austria].—Herrich-Schaeffer 1850, p. 153.

Monanthia vesiculifera: Scholz 1847, p. 121.—Mayr 1858, p. 571 [Hungary].—Fieber 1861, p. 126.—Frey-Gessner 1865, p. 232 [Switzerland].—Stål 1874, p. 59.—Jakovlev 1876b, p. 66; 1880b, p. 110 [Caucasus].—Vollenhoven 1878, p. 276, pl. 22, fig. 9 [Netherlands]. —Sahlberg 1878, p. 21.—Puton 1879c, p. 123 [France].—Dubois 1888, p. 122.—Rey 1893, p. 97.—Hüeber 1893, p. 354 [Czechoslovakia].

Monanthia symphyti: Horváth 1889, p. 326; 1906a, pp. 99, 101 [Yugoslavia; Rumania; Siberia].—Reuter 1891b, p. 184.—Mužik 1907, p. 63.—Oshanin 1908, p. 452 [Algeria].—Reichensperger 1920, p. 62.—Stichel 1926, p. 116.—Scholte 1935, p. 92, fig. 26.—Gulde 1938, p. 317 [*Symphytum*].—Blöte 1945, p. 91 [Tunisia].—Cobben 1948, p. 82; 1958, p. 14, fig. 16.—Mancini 1949b, p. 37.—Kiritshenko 1951, p. 253.—Bator 1953, p. 327, pl. 4, fig. 3.—Gomez-Menor 1955b, p. 249 [Spain].—Štusák and Stys 1959, pp. 178–187, 191, figs. 1, 2, 7, 8, 13–18, 25–28, 30, 32, 33–35, 37–39.—Štusák 1961a, p. 86, figs. 2, 3, 5d, 12, 13, 19, 21.

Dictyla symphyti: Drake and Ruhoff 1960a, p. 51.—Stichel 1960a, p. 340, fig. 174 [Poland; Bulgaria].

Dictyla humuli: Drake and Ruhoff 1960b, pp. 70–72, pl. 20.

TYPE: Holotype ♀, brachypterous; Germany; Kiel Coll. (Copenhagen Mus.).

DISTRIBUTION: Netherlands; France; Spain; Germany; Switzerland; Czechoslovakia; Austria; Hungary; Italy; Sicily; Yugoslavia; Rumania; Bulgaria; Poland; U.S.S.R. (Caucasus; Siberia); Algeria; Tunisia.

HOST PLANTS: *Humulus* sp.; *Symphytum officinale; Symphytum* sp.

NOTE: Study of morphology and nymphs [Štusák and Stys]; eggs [Štusák].

*Dictyla imparis (Drake)

Monanthia imparis Drake 1954b, p. 1 [Kenya].

Dictyla imparis: Drake and Ruhoff 1960a, p. 51.

TYPE: Holotype ♀; Ngong, Kenya; Hungarian Mus.

DISTRIBUTION: Kenya.

HOST PLANT: Unrecorded.

*Dictyla indigena (Wollaston)

Tingis indigena Wollaston 1858, p. 124 [Madeira; *Echium candicans*].
Monanthia indigena: Stål 1874, p. 58.—Horváth 1906a, p. 102 [Canary Islands]; 1909a, p. 292.—Lindberg 1936b, p. 30; 1958a, p. 79 [Cape Verde Islands; *Echium stenosiphon; Echium hypertropicum*].—China 1938, p. 21, fig. 4.—Gomez-Menor 1955b, p. 249.
Dictyla indigena: Drake and Ruhoff 1960a, p. 51.—Stichel 1960a, p. 336.
TYPE: Sex unknown; Feijãa de Córte, Madeira; British Mus.
DISTRIBUTION: Madeira Islands; Cape Verde Islands; Canary Islands
HOST PLANTS: *Echium candicans; Echium hypertropicum; Echium stenosiphon*

Dictyla indigena subsp. **bugioensis** (China)

Monanthia indigena subsp. *bugioensis* China 1938, p. 22, fig. 4 [Madeira].
Dictyla indigena subsp. *bugioensis:* Drake and Ruhoff 1960a, p. 51.
TYPE: Sex unknown; Southern Dezerta, Madeira; British Mus.
DISTRIBUTION: Madeira Islands.
HOST PLANT: Unrecorded.

*Dictyla labeculata (Uhler)

Monanthia labeculata Uhler 1893b, p. 264 [Calif.; *Pinus monophylla*].—Drake 1917c, pp. 49, 51, fig. 1a.—Hurd 1946, p. 451 [N. Mex.].
Monanthia labecula [sic]: Van Duzee 1916, p. 26; 1917a, p. 261.
Monanthia lobeculata [sic]: Drake 1943a, p. 142 [Colo.; Ariz.].
Dictyla labeculata: Drake and Ruhoff 1960a, p. 51.
TYPE: Holotype ♂, macropterous; Argus Mountains, California, U.S.; USNM.
DISTRIBUTION: U.S. (Calif.; Ariz.; Colo.; N. Mex.); Canada (B.C.).
HOST PLANT: *Pinus monophylla*.

*Dictyla leporis (Drake)

Monanthia leporis Drake 1937a, p. 385 [China].
Dictyla leporis: Drake and Ruhoff 1960a, p. 51.
TYPE: Holotype ♀; Kuling, Kiangsi Province, China; Vienna Mus.
DISTRIBUTION: China.
HOST PLANT: Unrecorded.

Dictyla leroyi (Schouteden)

Monanthia leroyi Schouteden 1953e, p. 197 [Congo; *Cordia chrysocarpa*].
Dictyla leroyi: Drake and Ruhoff 1960a, p. 51.
TYPE: Sex unknown; Kivu, Belgian Congo; Cent. Afr. Mus.
DISTRIBUTION: Congo.
HOST PLANT: *Cordia chrysocarpa*.

*Dictyla loricata (Distant)

Monanthia loricata Distant 1888, p. lxxxiii [Brazil].—Berg 1892, p. 201 [Argentina], (reprint p. 101).—Champion 1898b, p. 64, pl. 3, fig. 11.—Pennington 1921, p. 20.—Drake 1922c, p. 354; 1943a, p. 142 [Bolivia; Paraguay]; 1947a, p. 1.—Monte 1937a, p. 33, fig. 12 [*Cordia*

corymbosa]; 1939b, p. 76 [Venezuela; *Cordia*]; 1940d, p. 101.—Drake and Hambleton 1938a, p. 45 [*Tournefortia*]; 1945b, p. 356 [Colombia].—Drake and Poor 1938b, p. 106.—Silva 1956, p. 43, fig. 15.
Dictyla loricata: Drake and Ruhoff 1960a, p. 51.

TYPE: Sex unknown; Entre Rios, Brazil; Brussels Mus.

DISTRIBUTION: Brazil; Colombia; Argentina; Venezuela; Bolivia; Paraguay; Ecuador.

HOST PLANTS: *Cordia corymbosa; Cordia* sp.; *Tournefortia* sp.

*Dictyla lupata (Drake and Poor)

Monanthia lupata Drake and Poor 1936b, p. 142 [India].
Dictyla lupata: Drake and Ruhoff 1960a, p. 51.

TYPE: Holotype ♂, macropterous; Gujranwala, India; Drake Coll. (USNM).

DISTRIBUTION: India.

HOST PLANT: Unrecorded.

*Dictyla lupuli (Herrich-Schaeffer)

Monanthia lupuli Herrich-Schaeffer 1837, p. 13, pl. 114, fig. 359; 1838, p. 58.—Scholz 1847, p. 120.—Mayr 1858, p. 571 [Austria].—Fieber 1861, p. 126.—Frey-Gessner 1865, p. 232 [Switzerland].—Stål 1874, p. 59.—Puton 1879c, p. 121 [France].—Jakovlev 1880b, p. 109 [Russia]; 1893, p. 294.—Reuter 1882b, pp. 120, 121 [Finland].—Hüeber 1893, p. 351.—Horváth 1906a, pp. 99, 102 [Italy; Bulgaria; Siberia].—Mužik 1907, p. 63.—Oshanin 1908, p. 453 [Spain; Rumania; Caucasus].—Stichel 1926, p. 116 [*Myosotis*]; 1938a, p. 408 [Poland].—Scholte 1935, p. 92 [Netherlands].—Blöte 1945, p. 91 [Yugoslavia].—Kiritshenko 1951, p. 253.—Bator 1953, p. 327, pl. 4, fig. 5.—Hoberlandt 1955, p. 94 [Turkey].
Monanthia (Physatocheila) lupuli: Fieber 1844, p. 85, pl. 7, figs. 19–21 [Czechoslovakia; Hungary; Germany].—Herrich-Schaeffer 1850, p. 153.—Flor 1860, p. 354 [Estonia; Latvia; Algeria; *Myosotis palustris*].
Dictyla lupuli: Drake and Ruhoff 1960a, p. 51.—Stichel 1960a, p. 341 [Sardinia].

TYPE: Unknown.

DISTRIBUTION: Netherlands; France; Spain; Germany; Switzerland; Czechoslovakia; Italy; Sardinia; Hungary; Austria; Bulgaria; Yugoslavia; Rumania; Turkey; Poland; Finland; U.S.S.R. (Estonia; Latvia; Siberia; Caucasus); Algeria.

HOST PLANTS: *Myosotis palustris; Myosotis* sp.

NOTE: Described by Herrich-Schaeffer but wrongly accredited by him to Kunze [Herrich-Schaeffer 1837, p. 13].

*Dictyla monotropidia (Stål)

Monanthia (Physatocheila) monotropidia Stål 1858, p. 63 [Brazil].
Monanthia monotropidia: Stål 1873, p. 133 [Colombia].—Distant 1888,

p. lxxxiii.—Champion 1898a, p. 47, pl. 3, figs. 24, a, b [Guatemala; Panama]; 1898b, p. 64.—Van Duzee 1907, p. 23 [Jamaica].—Osborn and Drake 1915b, p. 536.—Drake 1922c, p. 354 [Cuba; Haiti; Mexico]; 1926a, p. 86 [*Cordia gerascanthus*]; 1926b, p. 375; 1928e, p. 1 [Honduras]; 1929, p. 35 [Costa Rica]; 1931b, p. 510; 1935, p. 9 [Paraguay]; 1943a, p. 142 [Bolivia; Venezuela]; 1947a, p. 1.— Wolcott 1923, p. 247 [Puerto Rico].—Fenton 1934, p. 199 [Argentina; cotton].—Costa Lima 1936, p. 129.—Bosq 1937, p. 130.—Drake and Poor 1937d, p. 301 [Peru; *Cordia*]; 1939b, p. 95.—Monte 1937a, p. 33; 1937c, pp. 71, 72 [*Cordia tomentosa*].—Drake and Hambleton 1938a, p. 44; 1945, p. 356 [El Salvador].—Barber 1939, p. 371.— Bruner, Scaramuzza and Otero 1945, p. 59.—Swezey 1945, p. 372.— Hurd 1946, p. 451 [Trinidad; *Cordia alliodora*].—Singh 1953, p. 118.— Gibson and Carrillo 1959, p. 19.

Dictyla monotropidia: Drake and Ruhoff 1960a, p. 51.

TYPE: Holotype ♀; Brazil; Stockholm Mus.

DISTRIBUTION: Brazil; Colombia; Peru; Bolivia; Paraguay; Venezuela; Argentina; Panama; El Salvador; Guatemala; Mexico; Honduras; Costa Rica; Haiti; Cuba; Jamaica; Puerto Rico; Trinidad.

HOST PLANTS: *Cordia alliodora; Cordia gerascanthus; Cordia tomentosa; Cordia* sp.; cotton.

NOTE: Intercepted on orchids from Mexico at port-of-entry, Texas [Swezey].

*Dictyla montandoni (Horváth)

Monanthia montandoni Horváth 1885, p. 322 [Rumania]; 1906a, p. 99 [Russia].—Kiritshenko 1951, p. 253.—Putshkov 1960, p. 304 [*Tournefortia sibirica*].

Dictyla montandoni: Drake and Ruhoff 1960a, p. 51.—Stichel 1960a, p. 337.

TYPE: Holotype ♀; Canstantia, Rumania; Hungarian Mus.

DISTRIBUTION: Rumania; U.S.S.R.

HOST PLANT: *Tournefortia sibirica.*

NOTE: Life history study [Putshkov].

Dictyla montandoni var. rivalis (Horváth)

Monanthia montandoni var. *rivalis* Horváth 1905b, p. 570 [Russia]; 1906a, p. 99.

Dictyla montandoni var. *rivalis:* Drake and Ruhoff 1960a, p. 51.

TYPE: Holotype ♀; Sarepta, Russia; Hungarian Mus.

DISTRIBUTION: U.S.S.R.

HOST PLANT: Unrecorded.

*Dictyla nassata (Puton)

Monanthia reticulata Rambur 1839, p. 166 [Spain].
Monanthia convergens (not Herrich-Schaeffer): Costa 1847b, p. 19; 1847d, p. 255.
Monanthia (*Physatocheila*) *reticulata:* Fieber 1844, p. 90.
Monanthia nassata Puton 1874b, p. 436 [Algeria; France; Corsica]; 1876, p. 279; 1879c, p. 122; 1886a, p. 5 [Tunisia].—Bolivar and Chicote 1879, p. 166 [Portugal].—Horváth 1906a, p. 101 [Eritrea; Turkey; Greece; Yugoslavia; Hungary; Italy; Egypt; Canary Islands]; 1906d, p. 2; 1909a, p. 292.—Stichel 1926, p. 115; 1938a, p. 408 [Albania].—de Seabra 1931, p. 436, figs. 506(1), 508.—Lindberg 1932a, p. 44; 1936b, p. 30; 1948, p. 60 [Cyprus; Sicily; *Echium sericeum*].—Mancini 1935, p. 10 [Giglio Islands].—Vidal 1937, p. 199 [Morocco].—Kiritshenko 1951, p. 253 [Russia].—Hoberlandt 1952, p. 112; 1955a, p. 94 [Israel; Caucasus].—Bator 1953, p. 327, pl. 2, fig. 8.—Priesner and Alfieri 1953, p. 65.—Štusak and Stys 1959, pp. 178–184, 186, 197, figs. 3–6, 9–12, 19–24, 29, 31, 40.
Dictyla nassata: Drake and Ruhoff 1960a, p. 51.—Stichel 1960a, p. 339 [Malta; Sardinia; Lybia; Turkestan; *Cynoglossum; Onosma*].

TYPE: Unknown.

DISTRIBUTION: Spain; Portugal; Corsica; Sardinia; France; Sicily; Malta; Italy; Hungary; Albania; Yugoslavia; Greece; Cyprus; Turkey; Israel; U.S.S.R. (Turkestan; Caucasus); Morocco; Algeria; Tunisia; Egypt; Lybia; Eritrea; Giglio Islands; Canary Islands.

HOST PLANTS: *Cynoglossum* sp.; *Echium sericeum; Halogeton sativus; Echium plantagineum; Onosma* sp.

NOTE: Study of immature forms [Štusak and Stys].

*Dictyla nodipennis (Horváth)

Monanthia nodipennis Horváth 1910, p. 68 [Tanganyika].—Drake 1956a, p. 4 [Congo; Kenya; Uganda].
Monanthia zavattarii Mancini 1953a, p. 185, fig. 2 [Ethiopia].
Dictyla nodipennis: Drake and Ruhoff 1960a, p. 51; 1961c, p. 145.
Dictyla zavattarii: Drake and Ruhoff 1960a, p. 51.

TYPE: Holotype ♀; Kibongoto, Kilimandjaro; Stockholm Mus.
DISTRIBUTION: Tanganyika; Kenya; Uganda; Congo; Ethiopia.
HOST PLANT: Unrecorded.

†Dictyla novaki Drake and Ruhoff

Monanthia flexuosa Novák 1877a, p. 79, pl. 2, figs. 8–11 [Bohemia]; 1877b, p. 9, pl. 2, figs. 8–11.—Scudder 1890, p. 357 [Horizon: Aquitanian]; 1891a, p. 421.
Dictyla flexuosa: Drake and Ruhoff 1960a, pp. 11, 51.
Dictyla novaki Drake and Ruhoff 1962a, p. 156.

TYPE: Sex undeterminable; fossil; Krottensee, Bohemia; Tertiary; Prague Mus.

DISTRIBUTION: Fossil.

*Dictyla parilis (Drake)

Monanthia parilis Drake 1936b, p. 700 [Argentina].—Drake and Poor 1939b, p. 95.

Monanthia paritis [sic]: Drake 1943a, p. 142 [Paraguay; Brazil].

Dictyla parilis: Drake and Ruhoff 1960a, p. 51.

TYPE: Holotype ♀, macropterous; Loreto, Argentina; Leningrad Inst.

DISTRIBUTION: Argentina; Paraguay; Brazil.

HOST PLANT: Unrecorded.

*Dictyla parmata (Distant)

Monanthia parmata Distant 1888, p. lxxxiii [Brazil].—Champion 1898b, p. 64, pl. 3, fig. 12.—Drake 1922c, p. 355; 1930a, p. 1; 1931b, p. 510 [Argentina]; 1935, p. 9 [Paraguay]; 1943a, p. 142 [Peru].— Drake and Hambleton 1934, p. 437 [Cordia corymbosa].—Costa Lima 1936, p. 130.—Monte 1937a, p. 33 [Cordia; Cordia verbenacea]; 1938d, p. 387; 1940d, p. 101 [Venezuela]; 1941e, p. 125 [Cochranea auchusae-folia].—Silva 1956, p. 43, fig. 16 [Cordia curassavica].

Dictyla parmata: Drake and Ruhoff 1960a, p. 51.—Drake and Cobben 1960, p. 69, figs. 74b, 75b, 76b [Aruba; Curaçao; Bonaire; Cordia cylindristachya].

TYPE: Sex unknown; Botafogo, Brazil; Brussels Mus.

DISTRIBUTION: Brazil; Argentina; Paraguay; Peru; Venezuela; Bolivia; Netherlands Antilles (Aruba; Bonaire; Curaçao).

HOST PLANTS: Cochranea auchusaefolia; Cordia corymbosa; Cordia curassavica; Cordia verbenacea; Cordia cylindristachya; Cordia sp.

*Dictyla patquiana (Drake)

Monanthia patquiana Drake 1955a, p. 79 [Argentina].

Dictyla patquiana: Drake and Ruhoff 1960a, p. 51.

TYPE: Holotype ♂; Patquia, Argentina; British Mus.

DISTRIBUTION: Argentina.

HOST PLANT: Unrecorded.

*Dictyla picturata (Distant)   PLATE 34

Monanthia picturata Distant 1902a, p. 243, pl. 15, fig. 11 [Cape Province].—Drake 1961c, p. 129, pl. 7.

Dictyla picturata: Drake and Ruhoff 1960a, p. 51.

TYPE: Sex unknown; Cape Colony, South Africa; So. Afr. Mus.

DISTRIBUTION: South Africa (Cape Province).

HOST PLANT: Unrecorded.

*Dictyla platyoma (Fieber)

Monanthia platyoma Fieber 1861, p. 125 [Czechoslovakia; Austria; *Myosotis palustris; Symphytum*].—Jakovlev 1869, p. 111 [Russia]; 1871, p. 24; 1880b, p. 108 [Caucasus]; 1893, p. 294.—Horváth 1874b, p. 432 [Hungary]; 1906a, p. 100 [Turkey; Siberia; Turkestan; Greece; Rumania; *Echinospermum lappula*].—Reuter 1890a, p. 250; 1891b, p. 184; 1902, p. 151.—Hüeber 1893, p. 349 [Germany].—Lethierry and Severin 1896, p. 24 [Turkomania].—Mužik 1907, p. 63.—Stichel 1926, p. 115.—Lindberg 1934, p. 29 [China].—Gulde 1938, p. 314 [*Myosotis*].—Kiritshenko 1951, p. 253.—Hoberlandt 1952, p. 112 [Cyprus]; 1955, p. 94.

Dictyla platyomia [sic]: Stål 1874, p. 57.

Dictyla platyoma: Drake and Ruhoff 1960a, p. 51, pl. 5.—Stichel 1960a, p. 338 [Bulgaria].

TYPE: Unknown.

DISTRIBUTION: Germany; Austria; Czechoslovakia; Hungary; Rumania; Bulgaria; Greece; Turkey; Cyprus; U.S.S.R. (Turkestan; Tukmen; Siberia; Caucasus); China.

HOST PLANTS: *Echinospermum lappula; Myosotis palustris; Myosotis* sp.; *Symphytum* sp.

*Dictyla pongana (Drake)

Monanthia pongana Drake 1953d, p. 211 [South-West Africa].

Dictyla pongana: Drake and Ruhoff 1960a, p. 51.

TYPE: Holotype ♂; Okahandja, South-West Africa; British Mus.

DISTRIBUTION: South-West Africa.

HOST PLANT: Unrecorded.

*Dictyla pucallpana (Drake and Hambleton)

Monanthia pucallpana Drake and Hambleton 1945, p. 356 [Peru].

Dictyla pucallpana: Drake and Ruhoff 1960a, p. 51.

TYPE: Holotype ♂, macropterous; Pucallpa, Peru; Drake Coll. (USNM).

DISTRIBUTION: Peru.

HOST PLANT: Unrecorded.

*Dictyla putoni (Montandon)

Monanthia putoni Montandon 1895, p. 161 [Rumania; *Echium*].—Horváth 1906a, p. 101 [Hungary; Russia; Turkey].—Stichel 1938a, p. 408 [Albania; Bulgaria].—Kiritshenko 1951, p. 253.—Seidenstücker 1954, p. 236.—Hoberlandt 1955, p. 94 [Caucasus].—Štusák and Stys 1959, p. 185.

Dictyla putoni: Drake and Ruhoff 1960a, p. 51.—Stichel 1960a, p. 339 [France; Egypt].

TYPE: Zorleni, Moldavie, Rumania; sex and deposition of type unknown.

DISTRIBUTION: France; Hungary; Rumania; Bulgaria; Turkey; Albania; U.S.S.R. (Caucasus); Egypt.
HOST PLANT: *Echium* sp.

*Dictyla putoni var. pulla (Horváth)
Monanthia putoni var. *pulla* Horváth 1905b, p. 572 [Hungary]; 1906a, p. 101 [Rumania; Greece; Sardinia; Tunisia].—Novak and Wagner 1951, p. 71 [*Echium altissimum; Cynoglossum creticum; Onosma visianii*].—Priesner and Alfieri 1953, p. 65 [Egypt].
Dictyla putoni var. *pulla:* Drake and Ruhoff 1960a, p. 51.
TYPE: Sex unknown; Hungary; Hungarian Mus.
DISTRIBUTION: Hungary; Rumania; Yugoslavia; Greece; Sardinia; Egypt; Tunisia.
HOST PLANTS: *Cynoglossum creticum; Echium altissimum; Onosma visianii.*

*Dictyla rasilis (Drake and Maa)
Monanthia rasilis Drake and Maa 1955, p. 3 [Taiwan; *Solanum verbascifolium*].
Dictyla rasilis: Drake and Ruhoff 1960a, p. 51.
TYPE: Holotype ♂, macropterous; Koshun, Formosa; Drake Coll. (USNM).
DISTRIBUTION: Taiwan.
HOST PLANT: *Solanum verbascifolium.*

Dictyla ruandae (Schouteden)
Monanthia ruandae Schouteden 1953e, p. 199 [Ruanda].
Dictyla ruandae: Drake and Ruhoff 1960a, p. 51.
TYPE: Sex unknown; Bugarama, Ruanda; Cent. Afr. Mus.
DISTRIBUTION: Ruanda-Urundi.
HOST PLANT: Unrecorded.

*Dictyla ruficeps (Horváth)
Monanthia ruficeps Horváth 1905b, p. 571 [Tunisia]; 1906a, p. 99.
Dictyla ruficeps: Drake and Ruhoff 1960a, p. 51.—Stichel 1960a, p. 337.
TYPE: Holotype ♀; Cherichera, Tunisia; Hungarian Mus.
DISTRIBUTION: Tunisia.
HOST PLANT: Unrecorded.

*Dictyla sahlbergi (Horváth)
Monanthia sahlbergi Horváth 1906a, p. 100 [Turkestan].
Dictyla sahlbergi: Drake and Ruhoff 1960a, p. 51.
TYPE: Sex unknown; Bekljar-bek, Turkestan, Russia; Hungarian Mus.
DISTRIBUTION: U.S.S.R. (Turkestan).
HOST PLANT: Unrecorded.

*Dictyla salicorum (Baba)
Stephanitis salicorum Baba 1925, p. 3.
Monanthia salicorum: Takeya 1930a, pp. 67–72, 1 pl. (8 figs.) [Japan; *Salix pupurea*]; 1951a, p. 22.—Maa 1957, p. 132.

Dictyla salicorum: Drake and Ruhoff 1960a, p. 51.
TYPE: Sex unknown; Shenano Province, Honshu, Japan; Nagano Agricultural Experiment Station, Japan.
DISTRIBUTION: Japan.
HOST PLANT: *Salix purpurea.*
NOTE: Redescription of type specimen [Takeya 1930].

*Dictyla sauteri (Drake)
Monanthia sauteri Drake 1923a, p. 103 [Taiwan]; 1927a, p. 53 [Philippines].—Esaki 1926, p. 163.—Drake and Poor 1937b, p. 397 [Luzon; *Cordia myxa*].—Takeya 1951a, p. 22.
Dictyla sauteri: Drake and Ruhoff 1960a, p. 51.
TYPE: Holotype ♀; Kankau, Formosa; Horn Coll.
DISTRIBUTION: Taiwan; Philippine Islands (Luzon).
HOST PLANT: *Cordia myxa.*

*Dictyla seorsa (Drake and Poor)
Monanthia seorsa Drake and Poor 1937b, p. 398 [Taiwan].—Drake 1938b, p. 195 [China].—Takeya 1951a, p. 23.—Maa 1957, pp. 124, 132 [India].
Dictyla seorsa: Drake and Ruhoff 1960a, p. 51.
TYPE: Holotype ♂, macropterous; Formosa; Drake Coll. (USNM).
DISTRIBUTION: Taiwan; China; India.
HOST PLANT: Unrecorded.

*Dictyla seorsa var. inflata (Drake and Poor)
Monanthia seorsa var. *inflata* Drake and Poor 1937b, p. 398 [Luzon].
Dictyla seorsa var. *inflata:* Drake and Ruhoff 1960a, p. 51.
TYPE: Holotype ♀, macropterous; Los Banos, Luzon, Philippine Islands; Drake Coll. (USNM).
DISTRIBUTION: Philippine Islands (Luzon).
HOST PLANT: Unrecorded.

*Dictyla sessoris (Drake and Poor)
Monanthia sessoris Drake and Poor 1937b, p. 398 [Luzon].
Dictyla sessoris: Drake and Ruhoff 1960a, p. 51.
TYPE: Holotype ♀, macropterous; Mt. Makiling, Luzon, Philippine Islands; Drake Coll. (USNM).
DISTRIBUTION: Philippine Islands (Luzon; Mindanao).
HOST PLANT: Unrecorded.

*Dictyla sjostedti (Horváth)
Monanthia sjöstedti Horváth 1910, p. 69 [Tanganyika].—Drake 1956a, p. 3 [Congo; Kenya; Uganda]; 1956f, p. 422 [Rhodesia; *Hoslundia*].
Dictyla sjostedti: Drake and Ruhoff 1960a, p. 51.
TYPE: Holotype ♀; Kibongoto, Kilimandjaro; Stockholm Mus.
DISTRIBUTION: Tanganyika; Congo; Uganda; Kenya; Southern Rhodesia.
HOST PLANT: *Hoslundia* sp.

*Dictyla subdola (Horváth)

Monanthia subdola Horváth 1905b, p. 571 [Armenia]; 1906a, p. 100 [Turkestan].—Oshanin 1908, p. 451 [Transcaucasus].

Dictyla subdola: Drake and Ruhoff 1960a, p. 51.—Stichel 1960a, p. 338.

TYPE: Holotype ♀; Vallis Araxis, Armenia; Hungarian Mus.

DISTRIBUTION: U.S.S.R. (Armenia; Turkestan; Transcaucasus).

HOST PLANT: Unrecorded.

*Dictyla triconula (Seidenstücker)

Monanthia triconula Seidenstücker 1954, pp. 230, 233, 236, figs. 1b, 2 [Turkey; *Cynoglossum officinale*].—Hoberlandt 1955, p. 95 [*Cynoglossum*].

Dictyla triconula: Drake and Ruhoff 1960a, p. 51.—Stichel 1960a, p. 342, fig. 180.

TYPE: Holotype ♂; Namrun, Turkey; Seidenstücker Coll.

DISTRIBUTION: Turkey.

HOST PLANTS: *Cynoglossum officinale; Cynoglossum* sp.

*Dictyla tuberosa (Horváth)

Monanthia tuberosa Horváth 1929, p. 324 [Natal].

Dictyla tuberosa: Drake and Ruhoff 1960a, p. 51.

TYPE: Sex unknown; Weenen, Natal, South Africa; British Mus.

DISTRIBUTION: South Africa (Natal).

HOST PLANT: Unrecorded.

*Dictyla uichancoi (Drake and Poor)

Monanthia uichancoi Drake and Poor 1937b, p. 399 [Luzon].

Dictyla uichancoi: Drake and Ruhoff 1960a, p. 51.

TYPE: Holotype ♂, macropterous; Calamba, Luzon, Philippine Islands; Drake Coll. (USNM).

DISTRIBUTION: Philippine Islands (Luzon); Taiwan.

HOST PLANT: Unrecorded.

†Dictyla veterna (Scudder)   PLATE 35

Monanthia veterna Scudder 1890, p. 359, pl. 23, figs. 5, 9 [Colo.]; 1891, p. 422 [Horizon: Oliogocene].

Dictyla veterna: Drake and Ruhoff 1960a, pp. 11, 51.

TYPE: Sex undeterminable; fossil; Florissant, Colorado, U.S.; MCZ.

DISTRIBUTION: Fossil.

*Dictyla vulcanorum (Schouteden)

Monanthia vulcanorum Schouteden 1953e, p. 200 [Ruanda]; 1957c, p. 318.—Drake 1958b, p. 26 [Kenya].

Dictyla vulcanorum: Drake and Ruhoff 1960a, p. 51.

TYPE: Sex unknown; Ruanda; Cent. Afr. Mus.

DISTRIBUTION: Ruanda-Urundi; Kenya.

HOST PLANT: Unrecorded.

Genus DICYSTA Champion

Dicysta Champion 1897a, p. 5.—Drake 1922a, pp. 269–273 (key).—
Monte 1939b, p. 68; 1941e, p. 92.—Hurd 1946, p. 477.—Drake and
Ruhoff 1960a, p. 53.

TYPE SPECIES: *Dicysta vitrea* Champion.

*Dicysta amica Drake and Hambleton

Dicysta amica Drake and Hambleton 1939, p. 162 [Brazil].—Monte
1941e, p. 92 [Bignoniaceae].

TYPE: Holotype ♀, macropterous; Belo Horizonte, Minas Gerais, Brazil;
Drake Coll. (USNM).

DISTRIBUTION: Brazil.

HOST PLANT: Bignoniaceae.

*Dicysta braziliensis Drake

Dicysta braziliensis Drake 1922a, p. 272 [Brazil]; 1931b, p. 512 [Peru].

TYPE: Holotype ♂; Santarem, Brazil; Carnegie Mus.

DISTRIBUTION: Brazil; Peru.

HOST PLANT: Unrecorded.

*Dicysta cara Drake

Dicysta cara Drake 1939a, p. 87 [Queensland].

TYPE: Holotype ♀, macropterous; Maleny, Queensland, Australia;
Drake Coll. (USNM).

DISTRIBUTION: Australia (Queensland).

HOST PLANT: Unrecorded.

*Dicysta fonsecai Monte

Dicysta fonsecai Monte 1940e, p. 299 [Brazil].

TYPE: Holotype ♂; Guarujá, Santos, São Paulo, Brazil; Monte Coll.
(Mus. Nacional).

DISTRIBUTION: Brazil.

HOST PLANT: Unrecorded.

*Dicysta hollandi Drake

Dicysta hollandi Drake 1922a, p. 271, fig. 1 [Brazil].—Drake and Hambleton 1945, p. 365 [Peru].

TYPE: Holotype ♀, macropterous; Chapada, Brazil; Carnegie Mus.

DISTRIBUTION: Brazil; Peru.

HOST PLANT: Unrecorded.

*Dicysta lauta Drake and Hambleton

Dicysta lauta Drake and Hambleton 1935, p. 152, fig. 6 [Brazil; *Adenocalymna*].

TYPE: Holotype ♂, macropterous; Ponte Nova, Minas Gerais, Brazil;
Drake Coll. (USNM).

DISTRIBUTION: Brazil.

HOST PLANT: *Adenocalymna* sp.

*Dicysta limata Drake and Hambleton

Dicysta limata Drake and Hambleton 1939, p. 162 [Brazil].

TYPE: Holotype ♂, macropterous; Belém, Pará, Brazil; Drake Coll. (USNM).

DISTRIBUTION: Brazil.

HOST PLANT: Unrecorded.

*Dicysta parilis Drake

Dicysta parilis Drake 1939, p. 88 [Queensland].

TYPE: Holotype ♀, macropterous; Mackay, Queensland, Australia; Drake Coll. (USNM).

DISTRIBUTION: Australia (Queensland).

HOST PLANT: Unrecorded.

*Dicysta peruviana Drake and Poor

Dicysta peruviana Drake and Poor 1940, p. 231 [Peru].

TYPE: Holotype ♀, macropterous; Lima, Peru; Drake Coll. (USNM).

DISTRIBUTION: Peru.

HOST PLANT: Unrecorded.

*Dicysta sagillata Drake

Dicysta sagillata Drake 1922c, p. 376 [Panama].—Monte 1939b, p. 68 [Brazil; Bignoniaceae].

TYPE: Holotype ♀, macropterous; Porto Bello, Panama; USNM.

DISTRIBUTION: Panama; Brazil.

HOST PLANT: Bignoniaceae.

*Dicysta smithi Drake

Dicysta smithi Drake 1922a, p. 273 [Brazil].—Drake and Hambleton 1938b, p. 57.—Monte 1940c, p. 193 [*Adenocalymna*].

TYPE: Holotype ♀, macropterous; Chapada, Brazil; Carnegie Mus.

DISTRIBUTION: Brazil.

HOST PLANT: *Adenocalymna* sp.

*Dicysta vitrea Champion

Dicysta vitrea Champion 1897, p. 5, pl. 1, figs. 4, 4a [Panama].—Drake 1922a, p. 270 [Brazil]; 1935, p. 20 [Paraguay].—Drake and Bondar 1932, p. 93 [*Mansoa glaziovii*].—Drake and Hambleton 1935, p. 152 [*Adenocalymna*]; 1945, p. 365 [Peru].—Costa Lima 1936, p. 126.—Monte 1937a, p. 34 [*Petastoma formosum; Petastoma samydoides*]; 1937c, p. 71.—Singh 1953, p. 118.—Kormilev 1955a, p. 67.— Silva 1956, p. 27.

TYPE: Holotype ♂; Volcan de Chiriqui, Panama; British Mus.

DISTRIBUTION: Panama; Brazil; Peru; Paraguay.

HOST PLANTS: *Adenocalymna* sp.; *Mansoa glaziovii; Petastoma formosum; Petastoma samydoides.*

Genus DIPLOCYSTA Horváth

Diplocysta Horváth 1925a, p. 11.—Drake and Ruhoff 1960a, p. 53.
TYPE SPECIES: *Diplocysta bilobata* Horváth.

*Diplocysta bilobata Horváth

Diplocysta bilobata Horváth 1925a, p. 12, fig. 7 [Australia].—Hacker 1928, p. 179.

TYPE: Sex unknown; Geraldton, Australia; Stockholm Mus.

DISTRIBUTION: Australia (Western Australia).

HOST PLANT: Unrecorded.

*Diplocysta globuliformis Hacker

Diplocysta globuliformis Hacker 1928, p. 179, pl. 22, figs. 9, 10 [Thursday Island; Queensland].

TYPE: Sex unknown; Thursday Island; Queensland Mus.

DISTRIBUTION: Thursday Island; Magnetic Island; Australia (Queensland).

HOST PLANT: Unrecorded.

Diplocysta papuana Drake

Diplocysta papuana Drake 1960, p. 379 [New Guinea].

TYPE: Holotype ♂; Bisianumu, E. of Port Moresby, New Guinea (Papua); Bishop Mus.

DISTRIBUTION: New Guinea (Papua).

HOST PLANT: Unrecorded.

*Diplocysta rustica Drake

Diplocysta rustica Drake 1960, p. 380 [New Guinea].

TYPE: Holotype ♂, macropterous; Eubenangee, New Guinea; Drake Coll. (USNM).

DISTRIBUTION: New Guinea.

HOST PLANT: Unrecorded.

*Diplocysta trilobata Drake and Poor   PLATE 28

Diplocysta trilobata Drake and Poor 1939c, p. 205 [Australia].—Drake and Davis 1960, figs. 43, 44.—Drake 1961b, p. 108 [Tasmania, South Australia].—Drake and Ruhoff 1962b, p. 250.

TYPE: Holotype ♀, brachypterous; Kiata, Victoria, Australia; Drake Coll. (USNM).

DISTRIBUTION: Australia (Victoria; South Australia; Tasmania).

HOST PLANT: Unrecorded.

Genus DULINIUS Distant

Dulinius Distant 1903a, p. 48; 1903b, p. 133.—Drake 1953b, p. 95.—Drake and Ruhoff 1960a, p. 54.

Sankisia Schouteden 1916b, p. 293.—Drake and Ruhoff 1960a, p. 81.

TYPE SPECIES: *Dulinius conchatus* Distant.

*Dulinius bellus Drake

Dulinus [sic] *bellus* Drake 1948g, p. 175 [Mozambique].

TYPE: Holotype ♀, macropterous; Delagga Bay, Mozambique; Drake Coll. (USNM).

DISTRIBUTION: Mozambique.

HOST PLANT: Unrecorded.

Dulinius burgeoni Schouteden

Dulinius burgeoni Schouteden 1953d, p. 170 [Congo].

TYPE: Sex unknown; Albertville, Belgian Congo; Cent. Afr. Mus.

DISTRIBUTION: Congo.

HOST PLANT: Unrecorded.

*Dulinius conchatus Distant

Dulinius conchatus Distant 1903a, p. 48 [Ceylon]; 1903b, p. 133, fig.96; 1910a, p. 110 [India; *Morinda*].—Drake and Poor 1937a, p. 18 [Java; Negros; Luzon].—Drake 1937a, p. 387 [Malaya].—Maa 1957, pp. 130, 132 [China].

TYPE: Sex unknown; Batticaloa, Ceylon; British Mus.

DISTRIBUTION: Ceylon; India; China; Federation of Malaya; Greater Sunda Islands (Java); Philippine Islands (Luzon; Negros).

HOST PLANT: *Morinda* sp.

*Dulinius congruus Drake

Dulinius congruus Drake 1953b, p. 96 [Cape Province].

TYPE: Holotype ♀, macropterous; Grahamstown, South Africa; Drake Coll. (USNM).

DISTRIBUTION: South Africa (Cape Province).

HOST PLANT: Unrecorded.

*Dulinius kraussi Drake

Dulinius kraussi Drake 1953b, p. 95 (nom. nud.); 1954c, p. 72 [Kenya].

TYPE: Holotype ♂, macropterous; Diani Beach, Kenya; Drake Coll. (USNM).

DISTRIBUTION: Kenya.

HOST PLANT: Unrecorded.

*Dulinius pulchrus (Schouteden)

Sankisia pulchra Schouteden 1916b, p. 294 [Congo].

Dulinius pulchrus: Drake 1953b, p. 95.

TYPE: Sex unknown; Sankisia, Belgian Congo; Cent. Afr. Mus.

DISTRIBUTION: Congo; Southern Rhodesia.

HOST PLANT: Unrecorded.

Dulinius unicolor (Signoret)

Tingis unicolor Signoret 1861, p. 956 [Malagasy].—Stål 1873, p. 134.

Dulinius nigrolineatus Distant 1913, p. 158, pl. 11, fig. 16 [Seychelles].

Galeatus involutus Drake 1925b, p. 108.

Dulinius unicolor: Drake and Ruhoff 1960c, p. 32, figs. 2, 3; 1960e, p. 80.—Carayon 1960, p. 110.

TYPE: Sex unknown; Madagascar; Vienna Mus.
DISTRIBUTION: Malagasy Republic; Seychelles; Uganda.
HOST PLANT: Taken on "musenosa."
NOTE: Predators [Carayon].

Genus DYSPHARSA Drake and Hambleton

Dyspharsa Drake and Hambleton 1944b, p. 127.—Hurd 1946a, p. 466.— Drake and Ruhoff 1960a, p. 54.
TYPE SPECIES: *Leptopharsa myersi* Drake.

*Dyspharsa myersi (Drake)

Leptopharsa myersi Drake 1926a, p. 87 [Trinidad].
Dyspharsa myersi: Drake and Hambleton 1944b, p. 128.—Hurd 1946, p. 467 [Cuba].

TYPE: Holotype ♀, macropterous; Mina Carlotta, Trinidad; Drake Coll. (USNM).
DISTRIBUTION: Trinidad; Cuba.
HOST PLANT: Unrecorded.

Genus ELASMOGNATHUS Fieber

Elasmognathus Fieber 1844, p. 90.—Stål 1873, pp. 121, 129.—Lethierry and Severin 1896, p. 22.—Distant 1903b, p. 141.—Drake and Poor 1937a, p. 10.—Drake and Ruhoff 1960a, p. 54.
TYPE SPECIES: *Elasmognathus helferi* Fieber.

Elasmognathus fieberi Stål

Elasmognathus fieberi Stål 1855a, p. 38 [Natal]; 1873, p. 129.—Distant 1902a, p. 242, pl. 15, fig. 7.
Monanthia (Elasmognathus) fieberi: Stål 1865, p. 29.
Monanthia fieberi: Walker 1873a, p. 195.

TYPE: Holotype ♂; Natal, South Africa; Stockholm Mus.
DISTRIBUTION: South Africa (Natal).
HOST PLANT: Unrecorded.

*Elasmognathus helferi Fieber

Elasmognathus helferi Fieber 1844, p. 91, pl. 7, figs. 33–41 [Ostindien].— Herrich-Schaeffer 1850, p. 156.—Stål 1873, p. 129 [India orientalis].—Distant 1903b, p. 142.—Drake and Davis 1960, figs. 55, 56.
Monanthia helferi: Walker 1873a, p. 195.
Elasmognathus helfneri [sic]: Drake 1927d, p. 309 [Luzon].

TYPE: "Ostindien"; sex and deposition of type unknown.
DISTRIBUTION: India; Philippine Islands (Luzon).
HOST PLANT: Unrecorded.

Genus ELASMOTROPIS Stål

Elasmotropis Stål 1874, p. 54.—Horváth 1906a, pp. 14, 56 (key).—
Mužik 1907, pp. 50, 57.—Oshanin 1908, p. 426; 1912, p. 44.—Stichel
1926, pp. 104, 110 (key); 1935, p. 349; 1938a, p. 406; 1960a, p. 304;
1960b, p. 395; 1960c, p. 134.—Kiritshenko 1951, pp. 242, 248
(key).—Drake and Ruhoff 1960a, p. 55.

Phyllontochila [sic] (*Elasmotropis*): Lethierry and Severin 1896, p. 16.

Type Species: *Monanthia* (*Phyllontocheila*) *echinopsis* Fieber = *Tingis testacea*
Herrich-Schaeffer.

Elasmotropis abimva (Schouteden)

Elasmognathus abimva Schouteden 1953d, p. 169 [Congo].

Type: Sex unknown; Abimva, Belgian Congo; Cent. Afr. Mus.

Distribution: Congo.

Host Plant: Unrecorded.

Note: From the description, the species seems to belong to *Elasmotropis*
rather than *Elasmognathus* and is here so transferred.

Elasmotropis burgeoni (Schouteden)

Elasmognathus burgeoni Schouteden 1953d, p. 167 [Congo].

Type: Sex unknown; Yebo Moto, Belgian Congo; Cent. Afr. Mus.

Distribution: Congo.

Host Plant: Unrecorded.

Note: From the description, the species seems to belong to *Elasmotropis*
rather than *Elasmognathus* and is here so transferred.

Elasmotropis distans (Jakovlev)

Monanthia (*Platychila*) *distans* Jakovlev 1903a, p. 2 [Mongolia].

Elasmotropis distans: Horváth 1906a, p. 59.—Wu 1935, p. 449.

Type: Holotype ♀, macropterous; Khangai, Mongolia; Leningrad Inst.

Distribution: Mongolia Republic.

Host Plant: Unrecorded.

Elasmotropis motoensis (Schouteden)

Elasmognathus motoensis Schouteden 1953d, p. 168 [Congo].

Type: Sex unknown; Yebo Moto, Belgian Congo; Cent. Afr. Mus.

Distribution: Congo.

Host Plant: Unrecorded.

Note: From the description, the species seems to belong to *Elasmotropis*
rather than *Elasmognathus* and is here so transferred.

*Elasmotropis selecta (Horváth)

Phyllontocheila testacea var. *selecta* Horváth 1891, p. 79.

Elasmotropis selecta: Horváth 1906a, p. 58 [Russia; Armenia].—Oshanin
1908, p. 426 [Transcaucasus].—Kiritshenko 1951, p. 248.—Stichel
1960a, p. 304.

Type: Unknown.

Distribution: U.S.S.R. (Armenia; Transcaucasus).

Host Plant: Unrecorded.

*Elasmotropis testacea (Herrich-Schaeffer)

Tingis testacea Herrich-Schaeffer 1830, heft 118, tab. 23 [Germany]; 1835, p. 58.

Monanthia testacea: Herrich-Schaeffer 1838, pp. 52, 60, pl. 125, figs. h,i. [Czechoslovakia].—Puton 1879c, p. 111 [France, Algeria].— Hüeber 1893, p. 333.

Monanthia (Phyllontocheila) echinopsis Fieber 1844, p. 62, pl. 5, figs. 19–22 [*Echinops sphaerocephala*].

Monanthia (Phyllontocheila) testacea: Herrich-Schaeffer 1850, p. 155.

Monanthia echinopsis: Mayr 1858, p. 570 [Austria].

Monanthia echinopsidis [sic]: Fieber 1861, p. 122.—Horváth 1874b, p. 432 [Hungary].—Jakovlev 1876b, p. 67 [Russia]; 1880b, p. 104 [Caucasus].

Elasmotropis echinopsidis: Stål 1874, p. 54.

Phyllontochila testacea: Reuter 1891a, p. 26 [Greece].—Lethierry and Severin 1896, p. 17 [Armenia].

Elasmotropis testacea: Horváth 1906a, p. 58.—Stichel 1926, p. 110; 1960a, p. 304, fig. 108a [Yugoslavia].—Vidal 1937, p. 197 [Morocco].—Gulde 1938, p. 282, fig.—Lindberg 1948, p. 58 [Cyprus; *Pistacia; Ceratonia siliqua*].—Hoberlandt 1951, p. 22 [Poland; Bulgaria; Syria; Egypt; Tunisia; Israel].—Priesner and Alfieri 1953, p. 64 [*Echinops*].—Štušak 1961a, p. 82, figs. 5f, 8; pl. 1, fig. B.

TYPE: Sex unknown; Regensburg, Germany; Munich Mus.

DISTRIBUTION: France; Germany; Czechoslovakia; Austria; Poland; Hungary; Bulgaria; Yugoslavia; Greece; Cyprus; Syria; Israel; U.S.S.R. (Armenia; Caucasus); Egypt; Algeria; Morocco; Tunisia.

HOST PLANTS: *Ceratonia siliqua; Echinops sphaerocephala; Echinops* sp.; *Pistacia* sp.

NOTE: Eggs (Štušak).

*Elasmotropis testacea var. egena (Puton)

Monanthia testacea var. *egena* Puton 1879c, p. 111 [Algeria].

Elasmotropis testacea var. *egena:* Horváth 1906a, p. 58 [Tunisia].— Lindberg 1932a, p. 41 [Morocco].—Vidal 1937, p. 197.—Blöte 1945, p. 86.—Priesner and Alfieri 1953, p. 64.

TYPE: Sex unknown; Oran, Algeria; Paris Mus.

DISTRIBUTION: Algeria; Tunisia; Morocco; Egypt.

HOST PLANT: Unrecorded.

*Elasmotropis testacea var. platydera Horváth

Elasmotropis testacea var. *platydera* Horváth 1906a, p. 58 [Hungary; Bulgaria].—Stichel 1926, p. 110; 1960a, p. 305 [*Echinops*].

TYPE: Unknown.

DISTRIBUTION: Hungary; Bulgaria.

HOST PLANT: *Echinops* sp.

*Elasmotropis testacea var. vicina Horváth

Elasmotropis testacea var. *vicina* Horváth 1906a, p. 58 [Russia; Syria; Egypt].—Stichel 1926, p. 110; 1960a, p. 305 [*Pistacia; Ceratonia; Cupressus*].—Vidal 1937, p. 197 [Morocco].—Lindberg 1948, p. 58 [Cyprus; Caucasus].—Priesner and Alfieri 1953, p. 64.—Seidenstücker 1954, p. 235 [Turkey].—Hoberlandt 1955, p. 88.

TYPE: Unknown.

DISTRIBUTION: Syria; Cyprus; Turkey; U.S.S.R. (Caucasus); Egypt; Morocco.

HOST PLANTS: *Ceratonia* sp.; *Cupressus* sp.; *Pistacia* sp.

Genus ENGYNOMA Drake

Engynoma Drake 1942b, p. 362.—Drake and Ruhoff 1960a, p. 55.

TYPE SPECIES: *Perissonemia tasmaniae* Drake and Poor.

*Engynoma angulata (Hacker)

Tingis (*Tingis*) *angulata* Hacker 1929, p. 329, pl. 34, fig. 9 [Queensland]. *Engynoma angulata:* Drake 1942b, p. 362.

TYPE: Sex unknown; Upper Brookfield, Queensland, Australia; Queensland Mus.

DISTRIBUTION: Australia (Queensland).

HOST PLANT: Unrecorded.

*Engynoma deaba Drake

Engynoma deaba Drake 1942b, p. 363 [Queensland].

TYPE: Holotype ♀, macropterous; National Park, Queensland, Australia; Drake Coll. (USNM).

DISTRIBUTION: Australia (Queensland).

HOST PLANT: Unrecorded.

*Engynoma immaculata Drake

Engynoma immaculata Drake 1942b, p. 362 [Queensland].

TYPE: Holotype ♂, macropterous; Cedar Creek, Queensland, Australia; Drake Coll. (USNM).

DISTRIBUTION: Australia (Queensland).

HOST PLANT: Unrecorded.

Engynoma isolata Drake and Ruhoff

Tingis insularis Hacker 1929, p. 330, pl. 34, fig. 10 [Queensland]. *Engynoma insularis:* Drake 1942b, p. 362. *Engynoma isolata* Drake and Ruhoff 1962c, p. 134.

TYPE: Sex unknown; Dunk Island, North Queensland, Australia; Queensland Mus.

DISTRIBUTION: Australia (Queensland).

HOST PLANT: Unrecorded.

*Engynoma spinicollis (Horváth)

Tingis (*Tingis*) *spinicollis* Horváth 1925a, p. 6, fig. 3 [Queensland].
Tingis spinicollis: Hacker 1928, p. 183.
Engynoma spinicollis: Drake 1942b, p. 362.

TYPE: Sex unknown; Malanda, Queensland, Australia; Stockholm Mus.
DISTRIBUTION: Australia (Queensland).
HOST PLANT: Unrecorded.

*Engynoma tasmaniae (Drake and Poor)

Perissonemia tasmaniae Drake and Poor 1937b, p. 402 [Tasmania].
Engynoma tasmaniae: Drake 1942b, p. 362.

TYPE: Holotype ♂, macropterous; Launceston, Tasmania, Australia;
Drake Coll. (USNM).
DISTRIBUTION: Australia (Tasmania).
HOST PLANT: Unrecorded.

Genus ENGYOTINGIS Drake and Ruhoff

Engyotingis Drake and Ruhoff 1961b, p. 175.
TYPE SPECIES: *Engyotingis cybele* Drake and Ruhoff.

*Engyotingis cybele Drake and Ruhoff

Engyotingis cybele Drake and Ruhoff 1961b, p. 176 [Basilan].

TYPE: Holotype ♂, macropterous; Basilan Island; Drake Coll. (USNM).
DISTRIBUTION: Basilan Islands (Basilan).
HOST PLANT: Unrecorded.

*Engyotingis tonkinana (Drake and Maa)

Ypsotingis tonkinana Drake and Maa 1955, p. 7 [Viet-Nam].—Drake
1958d, p. 153.
Engyotingis tonkinana: Drake and Ruhoff 1961b, p. 177.

TYPE: Holotype ♂, macropterous; Tonkin, Hoa-Binh, Indochina;
Drake Coll. (USNM).
DISTRIBUTION: Viet-Nam.
HOST PLANT: Unrecorded.

Genus EOTINGIS Scudder

Eotingis Scudder 1890, p. 359.—Hurd 1946, p. 455.—Drake and
Ruhoff 1960a, pp. 10, 55.
TYPE SPECIES: *Eotingis antennata* Scudder.

†Eotingis antennata Scudder

Eotingis antennata Scudder 1890, p. 360, pl. 23, figs. 1, 3 [Colo.]; 1891,
p. 406 [Horizon: Oligocene].—Drake and Ruhoff 1960a, pp. 10, 11.

TYPE: Sex undeterminable; fossil; Florissant, Colorado, U.S.; MCZ.
DISTRIBUTION: Fossil.

Genus EPIMIXIA Kirkaldy

Epimixia Kirkaldy 1908a, p. 779.—Horváth 1925a, p. 15.—Drake and Ruhoff 1960a, p. 55; 1961a, pp. 1–6 (key).

TYPE SPECIES: *Epimixia alitophrosyne* Kirkaldy.

*Epimixia alitophrosyne Kirkaldy

Epimixia alitophrosyne Kirkaldy 1908a, p. 780 [New South Wales].— Drake and Ruhoff 1961a, p. 3, fig. 1 a, b [Western Australia].

TYPE: Holotype ♀, macropterous; Sydney, New South Wales, Australia; Hawaii. Sugar Plant. Assn.

DISTRIBUTION: Australia (New South Wales; Western Australia).

HOST PLANT: Unrecorded.

Epimixia nigriceps (Signoret)

Agramma nigriceps Signoret 1881, p. L [New Caledonia].
Serenthia nigriceps: Lethierry and Severin 1896, p. 5.
Epimixia nigriceps: Drake and Ruhoff 1960a, p. 55; 1961a, p. 5.

TYPE: Sex unknown; New Caledonia; Vienna Mus.

DISTRIBUTION: New Caledonia.

HOST PLANT: Unrecorded.

Epimixia nigripes Horváth

Epimixia alitophrosyne var. *nigripes* Horváth 1925a, p. 16 [Queensland].
Epimixia nigripes: Drake and Ruhoff 1961a, p. 3.

TYPE: Holotype ♂; Evelyne, Queensland, Australia; Stockholm Mus.

DISTRIBUTION: Australia (Queensland).

HOST PLANT: Unrecorded.

*Epimixia nigripes subsp. dysmica Drake and Ruhoff

Epimixia alitophrosyne (not Kirkaldy): Horváth 1925a, p. 16 [Queensland].—Hacker 1927, p. 20, fig. 16; 1928, p. 186 [South Australia; New South Wales].
Epimixia nigripes subsp. *dysmica* Drake and Ruhoff 1961a, p. 4.

TYPE: Holotype ♂; Colosseum, Queensland, Australia; Stockholm Mus.

DISTRIBUTION: Australia (Queensland; New South Wales; South Australia).

HOST PLANT: Unrecorded.

*Epimixia veteris Drake

Epimixia veteris Drake 1944a, p. 71 [Queensland]; 1961b, p. 112 [*Casuarina*].—Drake and Ruhoff 1961a, p. 4, fig. 2 [South Australia; Western Australia].

TYPE: Holotype ♂, macropterous; Samsonvale, Queensland, Australia; Drake Coll. (USNM).

DISTRIBUTION: Australia (Queensland; South Australia; Western Australia).

HOST PLANT: *Casuarina* sp.

*Epimixia vittata Horváth   PLATE 13

  Epimixia vittata Horváth 1925a, p. 16 [Queensland].—Hacker 1928, p. 186 [Tasmania; South Australia; New South Wales].—Drake and Ruhoff 1961a, p. 4, fig. 3.
  TYPE: Holotype ♀; Colosseum, Queensland, Australia; Stockholm Mus.
  DISTRIBUTION: Australia (Queensland; Tasmania; New South Wales; South Australia).
  HOST PLANT: Unrecorded.

*Epimixia vulturna (Kirkaldy)

  Teleonemia vulturna Kirkaldy 1908a, p. 781 [Queensland].—Hacker 1927, p. 22.
  Epimixia vulturna: Drake 1944a, p. 67.—Drake and Ruhoff 1961a, p. 5, fig. 4 [New South Wales; South Australia].
  Epimixia tenuatis Drake 1944a, p. 71; 1961b, p. 112.
  Epimixia evansi Drake 1944a, p. 72 [Tasmania].
  TYPE: Holotype ♀, macropterous; Kuranda, Queensland, Australia; Hawaii. Sugar Plant. Assn.
  DISTRIBUTION: Australia (Queensland; New South Wales; South Australia; Tasmania).
  HOST PLANT: Unrecorded.

Genus ERITINGIS Drake and Ruhoff

  Eritingis Drake and Ruhoff 1962d, p. 497.
  TYPE SPECIES: *Teleonemia pacifica* Kirkaldy.

*Eritingis agyiates Drake and Ruhoff

  Eritingis agyiates Drake and Ruhoff 1962d, p. 498 [Queensland].
  TYPE: Holotype ♂, macropterous; North Pine, Queensland, Australia; Drake Coll. (USNM).
  DISTRIBUTION: Australia (Queensland).
  HOST PLANT: Unrecorded.

*Eritingis amoena Drake and Ruhoff

  Eritingis amoena Drake and Ruhoff 1962d, p. 504 [New South Wales; Tasmania; South Australia].
  TYPE: Holotype ♀, macropterous; Mittagong, New South Wales, Australia; Drake Coll. (USNM).
  DISTRIBUTION: Australia (New South Wales; South Australia; Tasmania).
  HOST PLANT: Unrecorded.

*Eritingis aporema Drake and Ruhoff

  Eritingis aporema Drake and Ruhoff 1962b, p. 250 (nom. nud.) [South Australia; Flinders Island]; 1962d, p. 503 [Queensland].
  TYPE: Holotype ♂, macropterous; Stanthorpe, Queensland, Australia; Drake Coll. (USNM).
  DISTRIBUTION: Australia (Queensland; South Australia; Flinders Island).
  HOST PLANT: Unrecorded.

*Eritingis exalla (Drake)

    Tingis exalla Drake 1961b, p. 110 [New South Wales].

    Eritingis exalla: Drake and Ruhoff 1962d, p. 497.

TYPE: Holotype ♂; Kosciusko, New South Wales, Australia; Austr. Mus.

DISTRIBUTION: Australia (New South Wales).

HOST PLANT: Unrecorded.

*Eritingis hylaea Drake and Ruhoff

    Eritingis hylaea Drake and Ruhoff 1962d, p. 502 [Queensland].

TYPE: Holotype ♂, macropterous; Roma, Queensland, Australia; Drake Coll. (USNM).

DISTRIBUTION: Australia (Queensland).

HOST PLANT: Unrecorded.

*Eritingis koebeli (Drake)

    Nethersia koebeli Drake 1944a, p. 74 [Australia].

    Eritingis (nom. nud.) *koebeli:* Drake and Ruhoff 1962b, p. 250 [South Australia].

    Eritingis koebeli: Drake and Ruhoff 1962d, p. 497.

TYPE: Holotype ♀, macropterous; Australia; Drake Coll. (USNM).

DISTRIBUTION: Australia (South Australia).

HOST PLANT: Unrecorded.

*Eritingis nostratis (Drake)

    Nethersia nostratis Drake 1944a, p. 74 [Queensland].

    Eritingis nostratis: Drake and Ruhoff 1962d, p. 497.

TYPE: Holotype ♀, macropterous; Cedar Creek, Queensland, Australia; Drake Coll. (USNM).

DISTRIBUTION: Australia (Queensland).

HOST PLANT: Unrecorded.

*Eritingis pacifica (Kirkaldy)

    Teleonemia pacifica Kirkaldy 1908a, p. 780 [Viti Levu] (in part, specimen from Rewa only).

    Ulonemia pacifica: Drake and Poor 1943, p. 193 (in part).—Drake and Hurd 1945a, p. 288 (in part).

    Eritingis pacifica: Drake and Ruhoff 1962d, pp. 497, 498.

TYPE: Lectotype ♀; Rewa, Viti Levu, Fiji Islands; Hawaii. Sugar Plant. Assn.

DISTRIBUTION: Fiji Islands (Viti Levu).

HOST PLANT: Unrecorded.

NOTE: Lectotype [Drake and Ruhoff].

*Eritingis recens (Drake and Poor)

    Perissonemia (*Ulonemia*) *recentis* Drake and Poor 1937a, p. 5 [Singapore].

    Perissonemia recentis: Drake and Poor 1937b, p. 400.

Ulonemia recens: Drake 1947d, p. 229 [Viet-Nam].

Eritingis recens: Drake and Ruhoff 1962d, p. 497, fig. 3.

TYPE: Holotype ♂, macropterous; Singapore, Straits Settlements; USNM.

DISTRIBUTION: Singapore; Viet-Nam.

HOST PLANT: Unrecorded.

Eritingis trivirgata (Horváth)

Teleonemia pacifica Kirkaldy 1908a, p. 780 [Queensland] (in part, specimen from Kuranda, Queensland only).

Tingis (Tropidocheila) trivirgata Horváth 1925a, p. 6.—Hacker 1927, p. 24.

Ulonemia pacifica: Drake and Poor 1943, p. 193 (in part).—Drake and Hurd 1945a, p. 288 (in part).—Drake 1961b, p. 112.

Tingis virgata [sic]: Drake 1947c, p. 113 (fig. only).

Eritingis (nom. nud.) *trivirgata:* Drake and Ruhoff 1962b, p. 250.

Eritingis trivirgata: Drake and Ruhoff 1962d, p. 497.

TYPE: Lectotype ♀; Mt. Tambourine, Australia; Stockholm Mus.

DISTRIBUTION: Australia (Queensland).

HOST PLANT: Unrecorded.

NOTE: Lectotype [Drake and Ruhoff 1962d].

Eritingis violina Drake and Ruhoff

Eritingis violina Drake and Ruhoff 1962d, p. 500 [New South Wales].

TYPE: Holotype ♂, macropterous; Glouchester, New South Wales, Australia; Drake Coll. (USNM).

DISTRIBUTION: Australia (New South Wales).

HOST PLANT: Unrecorded.

Genus ESOCAMPYLIA Hacker

Esocampylia Hacker 1929, p. 326.—Drake and Ruhoff 1960a, p. 56.

TYPE SPECIES: *Esocampylia incarinata* Hacker.

Esocampylia hackeri Drake

Esocampylia hackeri Drake 1942a, p. 14 [Australia; moss; lichens].

TYPE: Holotype ♀; Mt. Lofty Ridge, Australia; Drake Coll. (USNM).

DISTRIBUTION: Australia.

HOST PLANTS: Moss; lichens.

Esocampylia incarinata Hacker

Esocampylia incarinata Hacker 1929, p. 326, pl. 32, fig. 4 [Queensland].

TYPE: Sex unknown; Blackbutt Range, Queensland, Australia; Queensland Mus.

DISTRIBUTION: Australia (Queensland).

HOST PLANT: Unrecorded.

Genus ETEONEUS Distant

Eteoneus Distant 1903b, p. 129.—Drake 1946, p. 28.—Drake and Ruhoff 1960a, p. 56.

TYPE SPECIES: *Serenthia dilatata* Distant.

Eteoneus angolensis Drake

Eteoneus congolensis (not Schouteden): Drake 1955b, p. 87, fig. 1 [Angola].
Eteoneus angolensis Drake 1956b, p. 113.

TYPE: Sex unknown; Dundo, Angola; Cent. Afr. Mus.
DISTRIBUTION: Angola.
HOST PLANT: Unrecorded.

*Eteoneus angulatus Drake and Maa

Eteoneus angulatus Drake and Maa 1953, p. 89 [China].

TYPE: Holotype ♀, macropterous; Siyingpan, Yungan Hsien, Fukien, China; Drake Coll. (USNM).
DISTRIBUTION: China.
HOST PLANT: Unknown.
NOTE: Found "resting on leaf of *Ulmus* sp." [Drake and Maa].

*Eteoneus boops (Blöte)

Compseuta boops Blöte 1945, p. 89 [Sumatra].
Eteoneus boops: Drake 1948h, p. 75.

TYPE: Sex unknown; Lubuk Sikaping, Sumatra; Leiden Mus.
DISTRIBUTION: Greater Sunda Islands (Sumatra); Philippine Islands (Mindanao).
HOST PLANT: Unrecorded.

*Eteoneus confectus Drake

Eteoneus confectus Drake 1942a, p. 7 [Malaya].

TYPE: Holotype ♀, macropterous; "Malacca, Perak"; Drake Coll. (USNM).
DISTRIBUTION: Federation of Malaya; Greater Sunda Islands (Java).
HOST PLANT: Unrecorded.
NOTE: Type locality taken from label on type specimen.

Eteoneus congolensis Schouteden

Eteoneus congolensis Schouteden 1923, p. 85 [Congo].

TYPE: Sex unknown; Watsa, Haut-Uélé, Belgian Congo; Cent. Afr. Mus.
DISTRIBUTION: Congo.
HOST PLANT: Unrecorded.

*Eteoneus dilatatus (Distant)

Serenthia dilatata Distant 1903a, p. 46 [Burma].
Eteoneus dilatatus: Distant 1903b, p. 129, fig. 93.—Takeya 1931, p. 82, pl. 9, figs. 11–14 [Taiwan]; 1951a, p. 17.

TYPE: Sex unknown; Tenasserim, Burma; British Mus.
DISTRIBUTION: Burma; Taiwan.
HOST PLANT: Unrecorded.

*Eteoneus esakii Drake

Eteoneus esakii Drake 1939e, p. 102 [Peleliu; *Premna*]; 1956d, p. 110, fig. 5 [Koror].—Takeya 1951a, p. 17.

TYPE: Holotype ♂; Akarokuru-Shiasu, Peliliou, Palau Islands; Kyushu Univ.

DISTRIBUTION: Palau Islands (Peleliu; Koror).

HOST PLANT: *Premna* sp.

NOTE: Taken at light [Drake 1939f].

Eteoneus homelys Drake and Ruhoff

Eteoneus homelys Drake and Ruhoff 1962a, p. 159, pl. 41 [Amboina].

TYPE: Holotype ♂, macropterous; Amboina, Malay Archipelago; Cal. Acad.

DISTRIBUTION: Moluccas (Amboina Island).

HOST PLANT: Unrecorded.

*Eteoneus inopinus Drake

Eteoneus inopinus Drake 1945, p. 99 [Rhodesia]; 1958b, p. 29 [Congo].

TYPE: Holotype ♂, macropterous; Bulamayo, Southern Rhodesia; Drake Coll. (USNM).

DISTRIBUTION: Southern Rhodesia; Congo.

HOST PLANT: Unrecorded.

*Eteoneus lectus Drake

Eteoneus lectus Drake 1960, p. 353, fig. 9 [New Britain].

TYPE: Holotype ♂; Kerawat, Gazelle Peninsula, New Britain; Bishop Mus.

DISTRIBUTION: New Britain Island, Bismarck Archipelago.

HOST PLANT: Unrecorded.

Eteoneus minor Schouteden

Eteonus [sic] *minor* Schouteden 1955a, p. 29 [Congo].

TYPE: Sex unknown; Moto, Ituri, Belgian Congo; Cent. Afr. Mus.

DISTRIBUTION: Congo.

HOST PLANT: Unrecorded.

*Eteoneus peroronus Drake   PLATE 11

Eteoneus peroronus Drake 1942a, p. 7 [Malaya]; 1960, p. 353 [New Guinea].—Drake and Ruhoff 1962a, p. 160, pl. 42 (fig. only).

TYPE: Holotype ♀, macropterous; Parit Buntar, Malaya; Drake Coll. (USNM).

DISTRIBUTION: Federation of Malaya; New Guinea (Papua; Northeast Netherlands).

HOST PLANT: Unrecorded.

*Eteoneus sarptus Drake and Poor

Eteonus [sic] *sarptus* Drake and Poor 1937a, p. 12 [Mindanao].

TYPE: Holotype ♀, macropterous; Surigao, Mindanao, Philippine Islands; Drake Coll. (USNM).

DISTRIBUTION: Philippine Islands (Mindanao).

HOST PLANT: Unrecorded.

*Eteoneus sigillatus Drake and Poor

Eteoneus sigillatus Drake and Poor 1936b, p. 144 [India].—Singh 1953, p. 118.

Eteoneus sagillatus [sic]: Drake 1946, p. 28.

TYPE: Holotype ♀, macropterous; Haldgaddi, Kalagarh Division, United Provinces; Drake Coll. (USNM).

DISTRIBUTION: India.

HOST PLANT: Unrecorded.

*Eteoneus virtutis Drake and Poor

Eteonus [sic] *virtutis* Drake and Poor 1937a, p. 13 [Luzon].

Eteoneus virtutis: Drake and Poor 1937b, p. 402.

TYPE: Holotype ♂, macropterous; Mount Maquiling, Laguna Province, Luzon, Philippine Islands; USNM.

DISTRIBUTION: Philippine Islands (Luzon).

HOST PLANT: Unrecorded.

*Eteoneus visendus Drake and Poor

Eteoneus visendus Drake and Poor 1937a, p. 14 [Luzon].

TYPE: Holotype ♂, macropterous; Imugan, Nueva Vizcaya Province, Luzon, Philippine Islands; Drake Coll. (USNM).

DISTRIBUTION: Philippine Islands (Luzon).

HOST PLANT: Unrecorded.

Genus EUAHANES Distant

Euahanes Distant 1911a, p. 42.—Drake and Ruhoff 1960a, p. 56.

TYPE SPECIES: *Euahanes inflatus* Distant.

*Euahanes inflatus Distant

Euahanes inflatus Distant 1911a, p. 43, fig. [Cape Province].—Blöte 1945, p. 84.

TYPE: Sex unknown; Grahamstown, Cape Colony, South Africa; So. Afr. Mus.

DISTRIBUTION: South Africa (Cape Province).

HOST PLANT: Unrecorded.

Genus EURYPHARSA Stål

Eurypharsa Stål 1873, pp. 122, 133.—Monte 1939b, p. 69; 1941e. p. 94.—Hurd 1946, p. 468.—Drake and Ruhoff 1960a, p. 56.

TYPE SPECIES: *Tingis nobilis* Guérin-Méneville.

*Eurypharsa championi Bergroth

Eurypharsa championi Bergroth 1922, p. 151 [Brazil].—Drake and Hambleton 1938b, p. 53.—Monte 1940b, p. 375.—Silva 1956, p. 27.

TYPE: Sex unknown; Minas Gerais, Brazil; Helsin. Mus.

DISTRIBUTION: Brazil.

HOST PLANT: Unrecorded.

Eurypharsa farouki Silva

Eurypharsa farouki Silva 1956, p. 27, fig. 8 [Brazil].

TYPE: Holotype ♀, macropterous; Correntina, Estado da Bahia, Brazil; Instituto Biologico da Bahia.

DISTRIBUTION: Brazil.

HOST PLANT: Found "sucking the foliage of 'cipó' (Malpighiaceae?)."

Eurypharsa fenestrata Champion

Eurypharsa fenestrata Champion 1898a, p. 44, pl. 3, figs. 17, 17a [Panama].

TYPE: Sex unknown; Bugaba, Panama; British Mus.

DISTRIBUTION: Panama.

HOST PLANT: Unrecorded.

*Eurypharsa nobilis (Guérin-Méneville)

Tingis nobilis Guérin-Méneville 1844, p. 349 [Colombia; Bolivia].

Tingis circumdata Blanchard 1846, p. 219, pl. 29, fig. 7.—Stål 1873, p. 134.—Lethierry and Severin 1896, p. 26.

Eurypharsa nobilis: Stål 1873, p. 133 [Brazil].—Lethierry and Severin 1896, p. 23.—Champion 1898a, p. 44; 1898b, p. 63.—Horváth 1925b, p. 220 [Peru].—Drake 1931c, p. 226.—Drake and Hambleton 1938b, p. 53.

TYPE: Unknown.

DISTRIBUTION: Brazil; Colombia; Bolivia; Peru.

HOST PLANT: Unrecorded.

*Eurypharsa phyllophila Drake

Eurypharsa phyllophila Drake 1922c, p. 359 [Brazil].

TYPE: Holotype ♂, macropterous; Rio Guaporé, Brazil; Carnegie Mus.

DISTRIBUTION: Brazil.

HOST PLANT: Unrecorded.

*Eurypharsa quadrifenestrata Bergroth

Eurypharsa quadrifenestrata Bergroth 1898, p. 9 [Brazil]; 1922, p. 151.—Drake and Hambleton 1938b, p. 53, pl. 9, fig. c.—Silva 1956, p. 30.

TYPE: Sex unknown; Brazil; Helsin. Mus.

DISTRIBUTION: Brazil.

HOST PLANT: Unrecorded.

Genus FROGGATTIA Froggatt

Froggattia Froggatt 1901, p. 1601.—Horváth 1902b, p. 605.—Drake and Ruhoff 1960a, p. 57.

TYPE SPECIES: *Froggattia olivinia* Froggatt.

*Froggattia disticha Drake

Froggattia disticha Drake 1947c, p. 120 [Queensland].

TYPE: Holotype ♀, macropterous; Cedar Creek, Queensland, Australia; Drake Coll. (USNM).

DISTRIBUTION: Australia (Queensland).

HOST PLANT: Unrecorded.

*Froggattia hargreavesi Drake

Froggattia hargreavesi Drake 1945, p. 100 [Uganda; *Jasminum dichotomum*].

TYPE: Holotype ♂; Kampala, Uganda; British Mus.

DISTRIBUTION: Uganda.

HOST PLANT: *Jasminum dichotomum*.

*Froggattia olivinia Froggatt

Froggattia olivinia Froggatt 1901, p. 1601, fig. 14 [New South Wales; olive; *Notelaea longifolia*]. —Drake and Ruhoff 1960a, p. 57.—Drake 1961b, p. 108.

Froggattia olivina Horváth 1902b, p. 605.—Hacker 1927, p. 25 [Queensland]; 1928, p. 181 [Tasmania].—Silvestri 1934, p. 259 [*Olea europaea*].

TYPE: Sex unknown; Camden Park, New South Wales, Australia; Hungarian Mus.

DISTRIBUTION: Australia (New South Wales; Tasmania; Queensland).

HOST PLANTS: *Notelaea longifolia; Olea europaea*.

NOTE: See Drake and Ruhoff re authorship priority.

Genus FURCILLIGER Horváth

Furcilliger Horváth 1925a, p. 3.—Drake and Ruhoff 1960a, p. 57.

TYPE SPECIES: *Furcilliger asperulus* Horváth.

Furcilliger asperulus Horváth

Furcilliger asperulus Horváth 1925a, p. 4, fig. 2 [Queensland].

TYPE: Sex unknown; Herberton, Queensland, Australia; Stockholm Mus.

DISTRIBUTION: Australia (Queensland).

HOST PLANT: Unrecorded.

Furcilliger cheesmanae Drake

Furcilliger cheesmanae Drake 1954b, p. 10 [Papua].—Drake and Davis 1960, fig. 45.—Drake 1960, p. 368, fig. 20.

TYPE: Holotype ♂; Kokoda, Papua; British Mus.

DISTRIBUTION: New Guinea (Papua).

HOST PLANT: Unrecorded.

*Furcilliger orestes Drake and Ruhoff

Furcilliger orestes Drake and Ruhoff 1962d, p. 492 [New Guinea].

TYPE: Holotype ♀, macropterous; Medang, New Guinea; Drake Coll. (USNM).

DISTRIBUTION: New Guinea.

HOST PLANT: Unrecorded.

Genus GABIROBIUS Schouteden

Gabirobius Schouteden 1955b, p. 166.—Drake and Ruhoff 1960a, p. 58.

TYPE SPECIES: *Gabirobius basilewskyi* Schouteden.

Gabirobius basilewskyi Schouteden

Gabirobius basilewskyi Schouteden 1955b, p. 167 [Ruanda]; 1957c, p. 313.

TYPE: Sex unknown; Gabiro, Ruanda; Cent. Afr. Mus.

DISTRIBUTION: Ruanda-Urundi.

HOST PLANT: Unrecorded.

Genus GALEATUS Curtis

Galeatus Curtis 1833, p. 196.—Stål 1874, p. 48.—Jakovlev 1880a, p. 129.—Horváth 1897b, pp. 455–460 (key); 1906a, pp. 13, 49 (key).— Puton 1899, p. 40.—Lethierry and Severin 1896, p. 11.—Oshanin 1908, p. 421; 1912, p. 43.—Osborn and Drake 1916a, p. 236.— Stichel 1926, pp. 104, 109 (key); 1935, p. 349; 1938a, p. 406; 1960a, p. 295 (key); 1960b, p. 393; 1960c, p. 132.—Börner 1935, pp. 73, 76 (key).—Gulde 1938, pp. 243, 271 (key).—Hurd 1946, p. 478.— Kiritshenko 1951, pp. 241, 246 (key).—Singer 1952, p. 50.—Drake and Ruhoff 1960a, p. 58.

Cadmilos Distant 1909a, p. 113; 1910a, p. 107.—Drake and Ruhoff 1960a, p. 41.

TYPE SPECIES: *Tingis spinifrons* Fallén.

Galeatus armatus Takeya

Galeatus armatus Takeya 1931, p. 68, pl. 8, figs. 4, 5 [Japan]; 1951a, p. 7.

TYPE: Holotype ♂; Fukuoka, Kyushu, Japan; Kyushu Univ.

DISTRIBUTION: Japan.

HOST PLANT: Unrecorded.

*Galeatus cellularis Jakovlev

Galeatus cellularis Jakovlev 1884, p. 121 [Turkestan].—Horváth 1897b, pp. 455, 458; 1906a, p. 52.—Kiritshenko 1951, p. 247.

TYPE: Holotype ♀, macropterous; Turkestan, Russia; Leningrad Inst.

DISTRIBUTION: U.S.S.R. (Turkestan).

HOST PLANT: Unrecorded.

*Galeatus clara Drake

Galeatus clara Drake 1948e, p. 155 [China].

TYPE: Holotype ♂, macropterous; Shanghai; China; Drake Coll. (USNM).

DISTRIBUTION: China.

HOST PLANT: Unrecorded.

*Galeatus decorus Jakovlev

Galeatus decorus Jakovlev 1880a, pp. 131, 134 [Russia].—Horváth 1905b, p. 566 [Hungary; Rumania]; 1906a, p. 54.—Lindberg 1934, p. 29 [China].—Kiritshenko 1951, p. 247.—Stichel 1960a, p. 298 [Bulgaria].

TYPE: Holotype ♀, brachypterous; Chvalynsk, Saratovskaja, Russia; Leningrad Inst.

DISTRIBUTION: U.S.S.R.; Rumania; Hungary; Bulgaria; China.

HOST PLANT: Unrecorded.

*Galeatus inermis (Jakovlev)

Tingis inermis Jakovlev 1876b, p. 68, pl. 2, fig. 8 [Russia].

Galeatus inermis: Jakovlev 1880a, p. 130.—Horváth 1897b, pp. 455, 457 [Turkestan]; 1906a, p. 51.—Oshanin 1908, p. 421 [Caucasus].— Blöte 1945, p. 83.—Kiritshenko 1951, p. 246; 1959a, p. 105.—Stichel 1960a, p. 295.

TYPE: Sex unknown; Astrakhan, Russia; Leningrad Inst.

DISTRIBUTION: U.S.S.R. (Turkestan; Caucasus).

HOST PLANT: Unrecorded.

*Galeatus maculatus (Herrich-Schaeffer) PLATE 46

Tingis pyri (not Fabricius): Herrich-Schaeffer 1835, p. 58; 1836, p. 74, fig. 291.—Schilling 1838, p. 105.

Tingis cristata (not Panzer): Schilling 1838, p. 106.

Tingis maculata Herrich-Schaeffer 1838, p. 68.—Fieber 1844, p. 107, pl. 9, fig. 21; 1861, p. 130.—Mayr 1858, p. 572 [Hungary].—Frey-Gessner 1865, p. 233 [Switzerland].—Jakovlev 1869, p. 112 [Russia].

Tingis subglobosa Herrich-Schaeffer 1838, p. 68.—Fieber 1844, p. 106, pl. 9, figs. 17–20 [Czechoslovakia; Austria].—Scholz 1847, p. 122.

Campylosteira (*Dictyonota*) *subglobosa:* Kolenati 1856, p. 435 [Caucasus].

Galeatus maculatus: Stål 1874, p. 48.—Puton 1879c, p. 105 [France; *Hieracium pilosella*].—Bolivar and Chicote 1879, p. 166 [Portugal; Spain].—Jakovlev 1880a, p. 131; 1880b, p. 101.—Reuter 1885, p. 44.—Lethierry and Severin 1896, p. 11 [Algeria; Tunisia].—d'Antessanty 1890, p. 31.—Hüeber 1893, p. 322.—Horváth 1897b, pp. 457, 460 [Belgium; Netherlands; Germany; Transcaucasus]; 1906a, p. 53 [*Potentilla*]; 1923b, p. 190.—Mužik 1907, p. 57.—Reichensperger 1920, p. 61.—Moroder Sala 1920, p. 12.—Stichel 1926, p. 109 [*Hieracium*]; 1960a, p. 297, fig. 92 [Poland].—Jordan 1933, p. 229, figs. 25–30 [*Statice armeria; Herniaria glabra; Erica vulgaris*].—Scholte 1935, p. 31, fig. 6.—Gulde 1938, p. 275, fig.—Hoberlandt 1942, p. 125; 1943a, p. 118; 1943b, p. 123.—Blöte 1945, p. 83.—González 1948, p. 50.—Kiritshenko 1951, p. 247.—Gomez-Menor 1955b, p. 249.—Drake and Ruhoff 1962c, p. 135.

TYPE: Unknown.

DISTRIBUTION: Spain; Portugal; France; Netherlands; Belgium; Switzerland; Germany; Czechoslovakia; Austria; Poland; Hungary; U.S.S.R. (Transcaucasus; Caucasus); Algeria; Tunisia.

HOST PLANTS: *Erica vulgaris; Herniaria glabra; Hieracium pilosella; Hieracium* sp.; *Potentilla* sp.; *Statice armeria*.

NOTE: Life history study [Jordan].

*Galeatus major Puton

Galeatus maculatus var. *major* Puton 1886a, p. 5 [Tunisia].

Galeatus major: Horváth 1897b, pp. 457, 460 [Algeria]; 1906a, p. 53.— Gomez-Menor 1955b, p. 249 [Spain].—Stichel 1960a, p. 298 [Sicily; Italy].—Drake and Ruhoff 1962d, p. 489.

Galeatus maroccanus Lindberg 1936a, p. 81, fig. 1 [Morocco].

TYPE: Sex unknown; Tunisia; Paris Mus.

DISTRIBUTION: Tunisia; Morocco; Algeria; Spain; Sicily; Italy.

HOST PLANT: Unrecorded.

*Galeatus scitulus Drake and Maa

Galeatus scitulus Drake and Maa 1953, p. 90 [China; *Chrysanthemum*].

TYPE: Holotype ♂, macropterous; Siyingpan, Yungan Hsien, Fukien, China; Drake Coll. (USNM).

DISTRIBUTION: China.

HOST PLANT: Wild *Chrysanthemum*.

*Galeatus scrophicus Saunders

Galeatus scrophicus Saunders 1876, p. 103 [Greece].—Lethierry and Severin 1896, p. 12 [Egypt].—Horváth 1897b, pp. 455, 457 [Armenia]; 1906a, p. 52 [Crete; Algeria]; 1911c, p. 108.—Oshanin 1908, p. 422 [Caucasus].—Lindberg 1948, p. 58 [Cyprus]; 1958a, p. 78 [Cape Verde].—Priesner and Alfieri 1953, p. 63 [*Echinops spinosa*].—Drake 1954f, p. 7 [Sudan; Transvaal; Senegal; South-West Africa; sunflower].—Gomez-Menor 1955b, p. 249 [Spain]; 1956a, p. 109, fig. 3 (fig. only).—Hoberlandt 1955, p. 87 [Turkey; Iraq; Israel; Tadzhik; Transcaucasus; *Artemisia; Astragalus; Plantago*].—Stichel 1960a, p. 295 [Morocco; Canary Islands; Syria; *Launaea spinosa*].

Galeatus semilucidus Jakovlev 1884, p. 121 [Turkestan].

Galeathus [sic] *semilucidus:* Reuter 1891a, p. 26.

Cadmilos retiarius Distant 1909a, p. 114 [India; *Chrysanthemum*]; 1910a, p. 107, fig. 53.

Galeatus retiarius: Fletcher 1920, p. 263.

Galeatus serophicus [sic]: González 1948, p. 50.

Type: Sex unknown; Point Scophia, Greece; British Mus.

Distribution: Spain; Greece; Crete; Cyprus; Israel; Iraq; Turkey; Syria; U.S.S.R. (Armenia; Transcaucasus; Caucasus; Turkestan; Tadzhik); India; Algeria; Egypt; Sudan; Senegal; South Africa (Transvaal; South-West Africa); Morocco; Cape Verde Islands; Canary Islands.

Host Plants: *Artemisia* sp.; *Astragalus* sp.; *Chrysanthemum* sp.; *Echinops spinosa; Launaea spinosa; Plantago* sp.; sunflower.

*Galeatus sinuatus (Herrich-Schaeffer) PLATE 45

Tingis sinuata Herrich-Schaeffer 1838, p. 68, pl. 126, fig. 394 [Hungary]; 1850, p. 162.—Fieber 1844, p. 108, pl. 9, fig. 22; 1861, p. 129.— Scholz 1847, p. 122.—Mayr 1858, p. 572 [Austria].—Walker 1873a, p. 179.

Galeatus sinuatus: Stål 1874, p. 48.—Hüeber 1893, p. 324 [*Hieracium pilosella*].—Horváth 1897b, pp. 455, 457; 1906a, p. 52.—Oshanin 1908, p. 422 [Germany].—Stichel 1926, p. 109; 1960a, p. 295, fig. 85 [Bulgaria].—Kiritshenko 1951, p. 247.—Putshkov 1960, p. 302 [*Phlomis tuberosa*].

Tingis perspicuus Jakovlev 1875a, p. 162 [Russia].

Galeatus bvevispinus [sic] Jakovlev 1880a, p. 130.—Puton 1886b, p. 33.

Galeatus brevispinus Jakovlev 1880a, p. 131.—Reuter 1890a, p. 249.— Horváth 1897b, pp. 455, 457; 1906a, p. 52.—Puton 1899, p. 40.— Kiritshenko 1951, p. 246.

Galeatus perspicuus: Jakovlev 1880a, p. 130.

Type: Hungary; sex and deposition of type unknown.

Distribution: Hungary; Germany; Austria; Poland; Bulgaria; U.S.S.R.

Host Plants: *Hieracium pilosella; Phlomis tuberosa.*

Note: Life history study [Putshkov]. Synonymy of *brevispinus* Jakovlev fide I. M. Kerzhner.

*Galeatus spinifrons (Fallén) PLATE 44

Tingis spinifrons Fallén 1807, p. 38 [Sweden; *Solanum dulcamara*]; 1829, p. 148.—Germar 1817, fasc. 13, tab. 18.—Herrich-Schaeffer 1835, p. 58; 1838, p. 67, pl. 130, figs. a–c, g–h.—Schilling 1838, p. 106.— Amyot and Serville 1843, p. 297.—Fieber 1844, p. 104, pl. 9, figs. 6–12 [England; Czechoslovakia; Austria; Italy; *Artemisia campestris*]; 1861, p. 129.—Scholz 1847, p. 121.—Mayr 1858, p. 572.—Frey-Gessner 1865, p. 233 [Switzerland].—Garbiglietti 1869, p. 275.— Horváth 1874b, p. 432 [Hungary].

Galeatus spinifrons: Curtis 1833, p. 196.—Spinola 1837, p. 164.—Stål 1874, p. 48.—Jakovlev 1880a, p. 131; 1893, p. 294.—Reuter 1882b, p. 118 [*Calluna; Hieracium*].—Hüeber 1893, p. 320.—Horváth 1897b, pp. 456, 459 [Turkestan]; 1906a, p. 53 [Siberia; *Medicago*].—Mužik 1907, p. 57, fig. 4.—Oshanin 1908, p. 423 [Japan].—Lindberg 1919, p. 42 [*Antennaria dioica*].—Reichensperger 1920, p. 61.—Sahlberg

1920, p. 82 [*Calluna vulgaris*].—Drake 1923, p. 104.—Stichel 1926, p. 109; 1960a, p. 297, fig. 89 [Denmark].—Esaki 1932, p. 1634, fig.; 1954, p. 235, fig. 608.—Kato 1933, pl. 31, fig. 5.—Scholte 1935, p. 31 [Netherlands].—Fukui 1938, pl. 50, fig. 34.—Kiritshenko 1951, p. 247, fig. 328.—Takeya 1951a, p. 6 [Taiwan; *Artemisia vulgaris indica; Chrysanthemum indicum*]; 1953d, p. 168.— Putshkov 1960, p. 303 [*Helichrysum arenarium*].—Drake and Ruhoff 1962c, p. 135; 1962d, p. 490, fig. 2.

Tingis affinis Herrich-Schaeffer 1835, p. 58; 1836, p. 73, pl. 290 [Germany]; 1838, p. 67; 1850, p. 162.—Fieber 1844, p. 106, pl. 9, figs. 13–16; 1861, p. 129.—Sahlberg 1848, p. 136 [Finland].—Flor 1860, p. 366 [Estonia; Latvia].—Garbiglietti 1869, p. 275.—Gredler 1870, p. 76.

Galeathus [sic] *angusticollis* Reuter 1874, p. 563.

Galeatus affinis: Stål 1874, p. 48.

Galeathus [sic] *spinifrons:* Reuter 1874, p. 562.

Galeatus angusticollis: Jakovlev 1880a, p. 130 [Russia].—Hüeber 1893, p. 321.—Horváth 1897b, pp. 456, 459; 1906a, pp. 50, 52.—Mužik 1907, p. 56.—Oshanin 1908, p. 423 [Belgium].—Stichel 1926, p. 109; 1938a, p. 406 [Poland]; 1960a, p. 296.—Hoberlandt 1942, p. 125.—Kiritshenko 1951, p. 247.—Drake and Ruhoff 1962a, p. 163, pl. 43.

Sphaerocysta peckhami Ashmead 1887, p. 156 [Wis.].

Galeatus peckhami: Van Duzee 1889, p. 5 [Canada]; 1917b, p. 216 [Ont.; Man.].—Uhler 1904, p. 362.—Parshley 1916b, p. 105 [N.H.]; 1917a, p. 15 [Maine]; 1917b, p. 55; 1923b, p. 703.—Osborn and Drake 1916a, p. 236, pl. 10, fig. c [Mass.].—Drake 1918d, p. 86; 1922d, p. 66 [N.Y.; *Aster macrophyllus; Eupatorium*]; 1922e, pp. 105– 110, pl. 5 [Minn.; Mich.]; 1923a, p. 102; 1928b, p. 101.—Blatchley 1926, p. 453, fig. 98.—Proctor 1946, p. 74.—Bailey 1951, p. 39; 1959, p. 64.

Galeatus uhleri Horváth 1923a, p. 108 [N. Mex.].—Hurd 1946, p. 478 [Colo.; Alta.].

Copium artemisifolium Shinji 1938, p. 316 [*Artemisia vulgaris*].—Takeya 1951a, p. 19.

Galeatus angusticollis subsp. *uhleri:* Drake and Ruhoff 1962a, p. 163.

TYPE: Unknown.

DISTRIBUTION: England; Netherlands; Belgium; Germany; Switzerland; Czechoslovakia; Hungary; Austria; Italy; Poland; Sweden; Finland; Norway; Denmark; U.S.S.R. (Latvia; Estonia; Turkestan; Siberia); Japan; Taiwan; U.S. (Maine; Wis.; N.H.; N.Y.; Mass.; Minn.; Mich.; Colo.; Utah; N. Mex.); Canada (Ont.; Man.; Alta.).

HOST PLANTS: *Antennaria dioica; Artemisia campestris; Artemisia vulgaris; Artemisia vulgaris indica; Aster macrophyllus; Calluna vulgaris; Calluna* sp.;

Chrysanthemum indicum; Eupatorium sp.; *Helichrysum arenarium; Hieracium* sp.; *Medicago* sp.; *Solanum dulcamara.*

NOTE: Life history studies [Putshkov; Drake 1922e; Bailey].

Genus GARGAPHIA Stål

Monanthia (Gargaphia) Stål 1862, p. 324.

Gargaphia: Stål 1873, pp. 119, 124.—Uhler 1886, p. 22.—Lethierry and
Severin 1896, p. 13.—Champion 1897, p. 9 (key).—Banks 1910,
p. 56.—Van Duzee 1916, p. 25; 1917b, p. 217.—Osborn and Drake
1916a, p. 233 (key).—Drake 1917b, pp. 227–228 (key).—Gibson
1919b, pp. 187–201 (key).—Blatchley 1926, p. 472 (key).—Costa
Lima 1936, p. 126.—Monte 1939b, p. 69; 1941e, p. 95.—Hurd 1946,
p. 479.—Drake and Ruhoff 1960a, p. 58.

TYPE SPECIES: *Monanthia (Phyllontochila) patricia* Stål.

*Gargaphia acmonis Drake and Hambleton

Gargaphia acmonis Drake and Hambleton 1945, p. 366 [Peru; Colombia].

TYPE: Holotype ♂, macropterous; Tingo María, Peru; Drake Coll.
(USNM).

DISTRIBUTION: Peru; Colombia; Surinam.

HOST PLANT: *Hibiscus esculentus.*

*Gargaphia albescens Drake

Gargaphia albescens Drake 1917b, p. 228 [Calif.].—Gibson 1919b, p. 197.

TYPE: Holotype ♀, macropterous; Sacramento, California, U.S.; Drake
Coll. (USNM).

DISTRIBUTION: U.S. (Calif.).

HOST PLANT: Unrecorded.

*Gargaphia amorphae (Walsh)

Tingis amorphae Walsh 1864, p. 409 [*Amorpha fruticosa*].—Walker 1873a,
p. 180 [Ill.].

Gargaphia amorphae: Uhler 1886, p. 22.—Bergroth 1892, p. 264.—
Smith 1910, p. 149 [N.J.].—Osborn and Drake 1916a, p. 235.—McAtee
1917b, p. 79.—Gibson 1919b, p. 195 [N.C.; W. Va.].—Drake 1925c,
p. 37 [Miss.]; 1928b, p. 102 [N.Y.].—Blatchley 1926, p. 474 [Ind.].—
Froeschner 1944, p. 668 [Mo.].—Hurd 1946, p. 480 [Iowa].

Gargaphia tiliae var. *amorphae:* Van Duzee 1917b, p. 217.

TYPE: Lectotype ♀, macropterous; U.S.; USNM.

DISTRIBUTION: U.S. (N.Y.; Pa.; N.J.; Va.; N.C.; Miss.; Ohio; Mo.;
Ind.; W. Va.; Ill.; Iowa).

HOST PLANT: *Amorpha fruticosa.*

NOTE: Walsh failed to state the type locality for this species, and the
type specimen bears only the label "Collection C. V. Reiley." We believe
that the type locality is Illinois.

*Gargaphia angulata Heidemann

Gargaphia angulata Heidemann 1899b, p. 301 [Ala.; D.C.; Mo.; bean].—
Chittenden 1900, p. 32, fig. 8.—Smith 1910, p. 149, fig. 63 (fig.
only).—Osborn and Drake 1916a, p. 233, fig. 6 [Tenn.; Mass.; Pa.;
N.C.].—Van Duzee 1917b, p. 218 [Ohio].—Parshley 1917b, p. 56
[Conn.]; 1923b, p. 704, pl. 17, fig. 7.—McAtee 1917b, p. 79 [*Ceanothus
americanus*]; 1923, p. 147 [Va.].—Gibson 1919b, pp. 189, 191 [Ariz.;
N.J.].—Barber 1922a, p. 17.—Blatchley 1926, p. 474, fig. 106; pl. 4,
fig. 7 [N.Y.].—Drake 1928b, p. 102 [*Solanum*].—Froeschner 1944,
p. 669.—Hurd 1946, p. 480 [Colo.; Minn.].—Bailey 1951, p. 42.—
Drake and Ruhoff 1962a, p. 161.

Gargaphia undulata Heidemann 1901, p. 493 (nom. nud).—Van Duzee
1917b, p. 218.

TYPE: Holotype ♂, macropterous; Auburn, Alabama, U.S.; USNM.

DISTRIBUTION: U.S. (Mass.; Conn.; N.Y.; Pa.; N.J.; Md.; D.C.; Va.;
N.C.; S.C.; Ala.; Miss.; Tenn.; Ohio; Mich.; Mo.; Kans.; Minn.; Colo.;
Ariz.).

HOST PLANTS: *Ceanothus americanus; Solanum* sp.; bean.

*Gargaphia argillacea Monte

Gargaphia argillacea Monte 1943d, p. 263, fig. 1 [Brazil].

TYPE: Holotype ♂; Guarapuava, Paraná, Brazil; Monte Coll. (Mus.
Nacional).

DISTRIBUTION: Brazil.

HOST PLANT: Unrecorded.

*Gargaphia arizonica Drake and Carvalho

Gargaphia arizonica Drake and Carvalho 1944, p. 43 [Tex.; Ariz.;
N. Mex.; Mexico].

TYPE: Holotype ♂, macropterous; Huachuca Mountains, Arizona,
U.S.; Drake Coll. (USNM).

DISTRIBUTION: U.S. (Ariz.; N. Mex.; Tex.); Mexico.

HOST PLANT: Unrecorded.

*Gargaphia balli Drake and Carvalho

Gargaphia balli Drake and Carvalho 1944, p. 42 [Ariz.; N. Mex.].

TYPE: Holotype ♂, macropterous; Naco, Arizona, U.S.; Drake Coll.
(USNM).

DISTRIBUTION: U.S. (Ariz.; N. Mex.).

HOST PLANT: Unrecorded.

*Gargaphia bimaculata Parshley

Gargaphia bimaculata Parshley 1920a, p. 271 [Fla.].—Blatchley 1926, p.
475 [thistle].

Gargaphia binotata [sic]: Drake 1925c, p. 37.

TYPE: Holotype ♀, macropterous; Biscayne Bay, Florida, U.S.; Drake Coll. (USNM).
DISTRIBUTION: U.S. (Fla.).
HOST PLANT: Thistle.

Gargaphia boliviana Monte

Gargaphia boliviana Monte 1947b, p. 431 [Bolivia].
TYPE: Holotype ♂; Cochabamba, Bolivia; Monte Coll. (Mus. Nacional).
DISTRIBUTION: Bolivia.
HOST PLANT: Unrecorded.

*Gargaphia brunfelsiae Monte

Gargaphia brunfelsiae Monte 1938c, p. 64, fig. [Brazil; *Brunfelsia*]; 1938d, p. 389 [Argentina; *Brunfelsia hopeana*]; 1940c, p. 193, fig. 26; 1940e, p. 295.—Singh 1953, p. 118.
TYPE: Holotype ♂; Belo Horizonte, Brazil; Monte Coll. (Mus. Nacional).
DISTRIBUTION: Brazil; Argentina.
HOST PLANTS: *Brunfelsia hopeana; Brunfelsia* sp.

*Gargaphia comosa Monte

Gargaphia comosa Monte 1941a, p. 374, fig. 2 [Brazil].
TYPE: Holotype ♂; Catanduva, São Paulo, Brazil; Monte Coll. (Mus. Nacional).
DISTRIBUTION: Brazil.
HOST PLANT: Unrecorded.

*Gargaphia concursa Drake

Gargaphia concursa Drake 1930b, p. 25 [Brazil].—Monte 1939b, p. 69 [*Croton;* Annonaceae].—Silva 1956, p. 30.
Gargaphia concusa [sic]: Drake 1947a, p. 2.
TYPE: Holotype ♂, macropterous; Bahia, Brazil; Drake Coll. (USNM).
DISTRIBUTION: Brazil.
HOST PLANTS: *Croton* sp.; Annonaceae.

*Gargaphia condensa Gibson

Gargaphia condensa Gibson 1919b, pp. 189, 197 [Ariz.; *Dahlia parryi*].—Drake 1922b, p. 41.
Gargaphia carinata Gibson 1919b, p. 199.
TYPE: Holotype ♀, macropterous; Santa Rita Mountains, Arizona, U.S.; USNM.
DISTRIBUTION: U.S. (Ariz.).
HOST PLANT: *Dahlia parryi*.

*Gargaphia costalimai Monte

Gargaphia costa-limai Monte 1938b, p. 130, fig. 1 [Brazil; *Croton*].
TYPE: Holotype ♂; Belo Horizonte, Brazil; Monte Coll. (Mus. Nacional).
DISTRIBUTION: Brazil.
HOST PLANT: *Croton* sp.

*Gargaphia crotonae Drake and Hambleton

> *Gargaphia crotonae* Drake and Hambleton 1938a, p. 66 [Brazil; *Croton urucurana*].—Monte 1939b, p. 69 [*Solanum*]; 1940c, p. 193.

TYPE: Holotype ♂, macropterous; Atibaia, São Paulo, Brazil; Drake Coll. (USNM).

DISTRIBUTION: Brazil.

HOST PLANT: *Croton urucurana*; *Solanum* sp.

*Gargaphia deceptiva (Drake and Bruner)

> *Gelchossa deceptiva* Drake and Bruner 1924a, p. 150 [British Guiana; Trinidad].
>
> *Leptopharsa deceptiva:* Monte 1942a, p. 95 [*Ipomoea*].
>
> *Gargaphia deceptiva:* Hurd 1946, p. 480.

TYPE: Holotype ♀, macropterous; Demarara R., British Guiana; Drake Coll. (USNM).

DISTRIBUTION: British Guiana; Trinidad; Venezuela; Colombia.

HOST PLANT: *Ipomoea* sp.

*Gargaphia decoris Drake

> *Gargaphia decoris* Drake 1931b, p. 514 [Brazil]; 1935, p. 20.—Drake and Poor 1939b, p. 98 [*Solanum*].—Monte 1939b, p. 69 [*Croton urucurana*]; 1940b, p. 376.
>
> *Gargaphia decorie* [sic]: Monte 1938b, p. 131 [Argentina].

TYPE: Holotype ♂, macropterous; Belo Horizonte, Minas Gerais, Brazil; Cornell Univ.

DISTRIBUTION: Brazil; Argentina.

HOST PLANTS: *Croton urucurana; Solanum* sp. ("probably *auricalatum*").

*Gargaphia differitas Drake (emendation)

> *Gargaphia differatis* Drake 1935, p. 19 [Paraguay].—Monte 1939b, p. 70 [Brazil].—Silva 1956, p. 30 [*Dalechampia ficifolia*].

TYPE: Holotype ♂; S. Bernardina, Paraguay; Vienna Mus.

DISTRIBUTION: Paraguay; Brazil.

HOST PLANT: *Dalechampia ficifolia*.

*Gargaphia dissortis Drake

> *Gargaphia dissortis* Drake 1930a, p. 3 [Brazil].—Monte 1942a, p. 94 [Argentina].

TYPE: Holotype ♂; Chapada, Brazil; Amer. Mus.

DISTRIBUTION: Brazil; Argentina.

HOST PLANT: Unrecorded.

*Gargaphia flexuosa (Stål)

> *Monanthia (Phyllontocheila) flexuosa* Stål 1858, p. 61 [Brazil].
>
> *Monanthia (Gargaphia) flexuosa:* Stål 1862, p. 324.
>
> *Monanthia flexuosa:* Walker 1873a, p. 192.

Gargaphia flexuosa: Stål 1873, p. 124.—Drake and Hambleton 1934, p. 450 [*Cissampelos glaberrima; Cissampelos tamoides*].—Drake and Poor 1937d, p. 309, pl. 36, fig. 10.—Silva 1956, p. 30, fig. 9 [*Aristolochia* sp.].

TYPE: Holotype ♀; Brazil; Stockholm Mus.

DISTRIBUTION: Brazil.

HOST PLANTS: *Aristolochia* sp.; *Cissampelos glaberrima; Cissampelos tamoides* (?).

*Gargaphia formosa (Stål)

Monanthia (Phyllontocheila) formosa Stål 1858, p. 61 [Brazil].
Monanthia (Gargaphia) formosa: Stål 1862, p. 324.
Monanthia formosa: Walker 1873a, p. 192.
Gargaphia formosa: Stål 1873, p. 125.—Drake and Poor 1937d, p. 310.—Monte 1940e, p. 294, fig. 8 [*Solanum concinnum*].
Tingis formosa (not Stål) Göldi 1886, pp. 234–241, figs.

TYPE: Holotype ♀; Brazil; Stockholm Mus.

DISTRIBUTION: Brazil.

HOST PLANT: *Solanum concinnum.*

NOTE: Morphology and life study [Göldi].

*Gargaphia gentilis Van Duzee

Gargaphia gentilis Van Duzee 1923, p. 141 [Carmen Island; *Solanum hindsianum*].

TYPE: Holotype ♂; Carmen Island, Gulf of California, Mexico; Cal. Acad.

DISTRIBUTION: Mexico (Carmen Island).

HOST PLANT: *Solanum hindsianum.*

*Gargaphia gracilenta Drake

Gargaphia gracilenta Drake 1928i, p. 74 [Argentina].—Monte 1940e, p. 296.

TYPE: Holotype ♂, macropterous; Córdoba, Alta Gracia, Argentina; Drake Coll. (USNM).

DISTRIBUTION: Argentina.

HOST PLANT: Unrecorded.

Gargaphia holoxantha Monte

Gargaphia holoxantha Monte 1942a, p. 93, fig. 1 [Brazil].

TYPE: Holotype ♂; Campos, Estado do Rio, Brazil; Monte Coll. (Mus. Nacional).

DISTRIBUTION: Brazil.

HOST PLANT: Unrecorded.

*Gargaphia implicata Drake and Hambleton

Gargaphia concursa var. *implicata* Drake and Hambleton 1940, p. 535 [Brazil].

Gargaphia implicata: Drake and Hambleton 1944b, p. 127 [Argentina; Paraguay].

TYPE: Holotype ♂, macropterous; Viçosa, Est. de Minas Gerais, Brazil; Drake Coll. (USNM).

DISTRIBUTION: Brazil; Argentina; Paraguay.

HOST PLANT: Unrecorded.

*Gargaphia insularis Van Duzee

Gargaphia insularis Van Duzee 1923, p. 141 [Angel de la Guardia Island; *Parosela emoryi*].

TYPE: Holotype ♂; Angel de la Guardia Island, Gulf of California, Mexico; Cal. Acad.

DISTRIBUTION: Mexico (Angel de la Guardia Island).

HOST PLANT: *Parosela emoryi.*

Gargaphia interrogationis Monte

Gargaphia interrogationis Monte 1941d, p. 99, fig. 4 [Costa Rica].

TYPE: Holotype ♂; Pacora, Costa Rica; Monte Coll. (Mus. Nacional).

DISTRIBUTION: Costa Rica.

HOST PLANT: Unrecorded.

*Gargaphia iridescens Champion

Gargaphia iridescens Champion 1897, p. 10, pl. 2, figs. 1, 1a [Mexico].—Banks 1910, p. 56 [Tex.].—Van Duzee 1917b, p. 217 [Colo.]; 1923, p. 141 [San Marcos Island].—Gibson 1919b, pp. 189, 197 [Calif.; Ariz.; N. Mex.; *Ambrosia; Solanum; Malva;* sand nettle].—Torre-Bueno 1942, p. 131 [hollyhock].—Gibson and Carrillo 1959, p. 19.

TYPE: Sex unknown; Juarez, Mexico; British Mus.

DISTRIBUTION: Mexico (San Marcos Island); U.S. (Tex.; N. Mex.; Ariz.; Calif.; Colo.).

HOST PLANTS: *Ambrosia* sp.; *Malva* sp.; *Solanum* sp.; sand nettle; hollyhock.

NOTE: "Maternal solicitude" [Torre-Bueno].

*Gargaphia jucunda Drake and Hambleton

Gargaphia jucunda Drake and Hambleton 1942b, p. 80 [Panama].

TYPE: Holotype ♂, macropterous; Panama City, Panama; Drake Coll. (USNM).

DISTRIBUTION: Panama.

HOST PLANT: Unrecorded.

*Gargaphia lanei Monte

Gargaphia lanei Monte 1940b, p. 376 [Brazil].—Drake and Hambleton 1944b, p. 127.

Gargaphia limata Drake and Poor 1940, p. 228.

Gargaphia limitata [sic]: Monte 1941e, pp. 98, 171.

TYPE: Holotype ♂; Belo Horizonte, Minas Gerais, Brazil; Monte Coll. (Mus. Nacional).

DISTRIBUTION: Brazil.

HOST PLANT: Unrecorded.

*Gargaphia lunulata (Mayr)

Monanthia lunulata Mayr 1865, p. 441 [Brazil]; 1866, p. 163.—Walker 1873a, p. 193.

Gargaphia lunulata: Stål 1873, p. 124.—Berg 1884, p. 190 [Argentina; *Passiflora caerulea*].—Pennington 1921, p. 20.—Drake and Hambleton 1934, p. 450 [*Canavalia ensiformis; Phaseolus vulgaris; Hibiscus esculentus; Glycine max; Passiflora violacea; Ricinus communis; Pyrus communis; Gossypium arboreum; Stigmaphyllon; Cassia fistula; Urena lobata; Manihot utilissima; Chorisia speciosa*].—Drake 1935, p. 19 [Paraguay].—Costa Lima 1936, p. 127 [*Dolichos lablab; Phaseolus lunatus; Cassia imperialis*].— Bosq 1937, p. 128 [*Psidium;* Uruguay].—Monte 1937a, p. 36, fig. 6; 1938b, p. 131; 1938d, p. 388.—Drake and Poor 1938b, p. 109.— Araújo Mendonça 1949, pp. 183–187, figs.—Silva 1956, p. 32, fig. [*Rosa; Abelmoschus esculentus; Euphorbia heterophylla; Zornia diphylla; Cnidoscolus; Meibomia adscendens*].

Gargaphia lasciva Gibson 1919b, p. 198.—Fiuza 1946, pp. 338, 340, 341, 343.

TYPE: Rio de Janeiro, Brazil; sex and deposition of type unknown.

DISTRIBUTION: Argentina; Colombia; Brazil; Paraguay; Uruguay.

HOST PLANTS: *Abelmoschus esculentus; Canavalia ensiformis; Cassia fistula; Cassia imperialis; Chorisia speciosa; Cnidoscolus* sp.; *Dolichos lablab; Euphorbia heterophylla; Glycine max; Gossypium arboreum; Hibiscus esculentus; Manihot utilissima; Meibomia adscendens; Passiflora caerulea; Passiflora violacea; Phaseolus lunatus; Phaseolus vulgaris; Psidium* sp.; *Pyrus communis; Ricinus communis; Rosa* sp.; *Stigmaphyllon* sp.; *Urena lobata; Zornia diphylla.*

*Gargaphia manni Drake and Hurd

Gargaphia manni Drake and Hurd 1945b, p. 130 [Bolivia].

TYPE: Holotype ♂, macropterous; Waschi, Bolivia; USNM.

DISTRIBUTION: Bolivia.

HOST PLANT: Unrecorded.

*Gargaphia mexicana Drake

Gargaphia mexicana Drake 1922b, p. 40 [Mexico].—Hurd 1946, p. 480 [Tex.].

TYPE: Holotype ♀, macropterous; Tampico, Mexico; USNM.

DISTRIBUTION: Mexico; U.S. (Tex.).

HOST PLANT: Unrecorded.

*Gargaphia mirabilis Monte

Gargaphia mirabilis Monte 1938a, p. 292, fig. 32 [Venezuela; *Croton pungens*].

TYPE: Holotype ♂; Antimano, districto Federal, Venezuela; Monte Coll. (Mus. Nacional).

DISTRIBUTION: Venezuela.

HOST PLANT: *Croton pungens.*

*Gargaphia munda (Stål)

Monanthia (*Phyllontocheila*) *munda* Stål 1858, p. 60 [Brazil].
Monanthia (*Gargaphia*) *munda:* Stål 1862, p. 324.
Monanthia munda: Walker 1873a, p. 192.
Gargaphia munda: Stål 1873, p. 124.—Distant 1888, p. lxxxiii.—Pennington 1921, p. 20 [Argentina].—Drake 1922b, p. 41; 1935a, p. 20.—
Drake and Hambleton 1934, p. 450 [*Brunfelsia; Solanum*]; 1944b, p.
127.—Araujo Silva 1936, p. 7.—Bosq 1937, p. 129 [*Brunfelsia hopeana*].—Drake and Poor 1937d, p. 310, pl. 36, fig. 12 [Peru]; 1938b,
p. 109.—Monte 1944b, p. 466.
Monanthia lineifera Walker 1873a, p. 194.
Leptostyla lineifera: Champion 1898b, p. 60.—Distant 1902b, p. 356.
Gargaphia magna Gibson 1919b, p. 194 [Paraguay].
TYPE: Holotype ♀; Brazil; Stockholm Mus.
DISTRIBUTION: Brazil; Argentina; Paraguay; Peru.
HOST PLANTS: *Brunfelsia hopeana; Brunfelsia* sp.; *Solanum* sp.

*Gargaphia neivai Drake and Poor

Gargaphia neivai Drake and Poor 1940, p. 227 [Paraguay; Ecuador].—
Drake and Hambleton 1945, p. 365.
TYPE: Holotype ♂, macropterous; Horqueta, Paraguay; Drake Coll.
(USNM).
DISTRIBUTION: Ecuador; Paraguay.
HOST PLANT: Unrecorded.

*Gargaphia nexilis Drake and Hambleton

Gargaphia nexilis Drake and Hambleton 1940, p. 537 [Brazil].
TYPE: Holotype ♀, macropterous; Campinas, São Paulo, Brazil; Drake
Coll. (USNM).
DISTRIBUTION: Brazil.
HOST PLANT: Unrecorded.

*Gargaphia nigrinervis Stål

Gargaphia nigrinervis Stål 1873, p. 125 [Colombia].—Champion 1897,
p. 10, pl. 1, figs. 13, 13a [Panama].—Osborn and Drake 1915b, p.
536 [Guatemala].—Gibson 1919b, p. 192.—Drake 1926b, p. 378;
1932, p. 100; 1935, p. 20 [Venezuela].—Drake and Poor 1937d, p.
311.—Monte 1940d, p. 104 [*Solanum*].—Drake and Hambleton 1945,
p. 365 [Peru].—Drake and Cobben 1960, p. 87, fig. 86 [Aruba; Curaçao; Bonaire; *Jatropha urens*].
TYPE: Holotype ♂; Bogota, Colombia; Stockholm Mus.
DISTRIBUTION: Colombia; Venezuela; Peru; Panama; Guatemala;
Netherlands Antilles (Aruba; Curaçao; Bonaire).
HOST PLANTS: *Jatropha urens, Solanum* sp.

*Gargaphia nigrinervis var. impedita Drake and Hambleton

Gargaphia nigrinervis var. *impedita* Drake and Hambleton 1944b, p. 127 [Colombia].

TYPE: Holotype ♂, macropterous; Río Frío, Colombia; Drake Coll. (USNM).

DISTRIBUTION: Colombia.

HOST PLANT: Unrecorded.

*Gargaphia nociva Drake and Hambleton

Gargaphia nociva Drake and Hambleton 1940, p. 536 [Brazil].

TYPE: Holotype ♂, macropterous; Viçosa, Minas Gerais, Brazil; Drake Coll. (USNM).

DISTRIBUTION: Brazil.

HOST PLANT: Unrecorded.

*Gargaphia obliqua Stål

Gargaphia obliqua Stål 1873, p. 124 [Brazil].—Drake and Hambleton 1934, p. 450 [*Serjania*].—Drake 1936b, p. 700 [Argentina].—Drake and Poor 1937d, p. 310, pl. 36, fig. 9.—Monte 1947a, p. 236.— Drake and Davis 1960, fig. 33.

Gargaphia stigma Monte 1946b, p. 284.

TYPE: Holotype ♂; Rio de Janeiro, Brazil; Stockholm Mus.

DISTRIBUTION: Brazil; Argentina.

HOST PLANT: *Serjania* sp.

*Gargaphia opacula Uhler

Gargaphia opacula Uhler 1893b, p. 263 [Calif.]; 1894b, p. 278 [Magdalena].—Townsend 1894, p. 313 (N. Mex.; eggplant].—Van Duzee 1914, p. 11 [willow].—Gibson 1919b, pp. 189, 199 [Utah; Kans.; *Dahlia spinosa; Solanum melongena*].

TYPE: Holotype ♀, macropterous; Argus Mountains, California, U.S.; USNM.

DISTRIBUTION: U.S. (Calif.; N. Mex.; Utah; Kans.); Mexico (Magdalena Island).

HOST PLANTS: *Dahlia spinosa; Solanum melongena;* willow.

*Gargaphia opima Drake

Gargaphia opima Drake 1931b, p. 513 [Peru].—Drake and Hambleton 1945, p. 365 [Colombia; *Canavalia ensiformis*].

Gargaphia inca Monte 1943, p. 105, fig. 1; 1947a, p. 232, fig.

TYPE: Holotype ♂, macropterous; Miriatiriani, Cam. del Pichis, Peru; Cornell Univ.

DISTRIBUTION: Peru; Colombia; Bolivia.

HOST PLANT: *Canavalia ensiformis.*

*Gargaphia oreades Drake

    Gargaphia oreades Drake 1928i, p. 75 [Argentina]; 1935, p. 20 [Brazil]; 1936b, p. 700.—Bosq 1937, p. 129 [*Solanum nigrum; Solanum capsicastrum*].—Monte 1938d, p. 388.

    TYPE: Holotype ♂, macropterous; Buenos Aires, Argentina; Drake Coll. (USNM).

    DISTRIBUTION: Argentina; Brazil.

    HOST PLANTS: *Solanum capsicastrum; Solanum nigrum.*

*Gargaphia oregona Drake and Hurd

    Gargaphia oregona Drake and Hurd 1945b, p. 131 [Oreg.].

    TYPE: Holotype ♂, macropterous; Corvallis, Oregon, U.S.; Drake Coll. (USNM).

    DISTRIBUTION: U.S. (Oreg.).

    HOST PLANT: Unrecorded.

Gargaphia panamensis Champion

    Gargaphia panamensis Champion 1897, p. 10, pl. 1, figs. 14, 14a [Panama].—Gibson 1919b, pp. 190, 193.

    TYPE: Sex unknown; Caldera, Chiriqui, Panama; British Mus.

    DISTRIBUTION: Panama.

    HOST PLANT: Unrecorded.

*Gargaphia paraguayensis Drake and Poor

    Gargaphia paraguayensis Drake and Poor 1940, p. 229 [Paraguay].

    TYPE: Holotype ♂, macropterous; Horqueta, Paraguay; Drake Coll. (USNM).

    DISTRIBUTION: Paraguay.

    HOST PLANT: Unrecorded.

*Gargaphia patria (Drake and Hambleton)

    Leptopharsa patria Drake and Hambleton 1938a, p. 58 [Brazil; *Bathysa stipulata*].

    Gargaphia patria: Drake 1942a, p. 1.—Silva 1956, p. 34 [*Sickingia tinctoria*].

    TYPE: Holotype ♂, macropterous; São Paulo, Brazil; Drake Coll. (USNM).

    DISTRIBUTION: Brazil.

    HOST PLANTS: *Bathysa stipulata; Sickingia tinctoria.*

*Gargaphia patricia (Stål)

    Monanthia (Phyllontochila) patricia Stål 1862, p. 324 [Mexico].

    Monanthia (Gargaphia) patricia: Stål 1862, p. 324.

    Monanthia patricia: Walker 1873a, p. 191.

    Gargaphia patricia: Stål 1873, p. 125.—Champion 1897, p. 9, pl. 1, figs. 12, 12a [Panama; Guatemala].—Gibson 1919b, p. 196.—Drake 1926b, p. 377; 1936b, p. 700 [Argentina]; 1948h, p. 76.—Drake and

Poor 1937d, p. 309 [Colombia].—Monte 1940d, p. 104 [Venezuela; Euphorbiaceae]; 1941d, p. 98 [Costa Rica].

Gargaphia biolleyi Blöte 1945, p. 85 (nom. nud. of Montandon).

TYPE: Sex unknown; Mexico; Stockholm Mus.

DISTRIBUTION: Mexico; Costa Rica; Guatemala; Panama; Colombia; Venezuela; Argentina.

HOST PLANT: Euphorbiaceae.

*Gargaphia paula Drake

Gargaphia paula Drake 1939f, p. 68 [Canal Zone].—Drake and Hambleton 1945, p. 366 [Peru].

TYPE: Holotype ♂, macropterous; Barro Colorado Island, Panama Canal Zone; Drake Coll. (USNM).

DISTRIBUTION: Panama (Canal Zone); Brazil; Peru.

HOST PLANT: Unrecorded.

*Gargaphia penningtoni Drake

Gargaphia penningtoni Drake 1928i, p. 75 [Argentina]; 1935, p. 20 [Paraguay].—Drake and Hambleton 1934, p. 450 [*Sida acuta; Abutilum; Acalypha*].—Bosq 1937, p. 129.—Monte 1938d, p. 388 [*Cajanus indicus;* Brazil]; 1939b, p. 70 [*Sida; Phaseolus*]; 1940c, p. 193 [*Wissadula; Croton lobatus*].—Drake and Poor 1939b, p. 98.

Gargaphia subpilosa (not Berg): Monte 1943d, p. 264, fig. 2.

TYPE: Holotype ♂, macropterous; Buenos Aires, Argentina; Drake Coll. (USNM).

DISTRIBUTION: Argentina; Paraguay; Brazil.

HOST PLANTS: *Abutilum* sp.; *Acalypha* sp.; *Cajanus indicus; Croton lobatus; Phaseolus* sp.; *Sida acuta; Sida* sp.; *Wissadula* sp.

*Gargaphia schulzei Drake

Gargaphia schulzei Drake 1954d, p. 76 [Paraguay].

TYPE: Holotype ♂, macropterous; Asuncion, Paraguay; Drake Coll. (USNM).

DISTRIBUTION: Paraguay.

HOST PLANT: Unrecorded.

*Gargaphia seorsa Drake and Hambleton

Gargaphia seorsa Drake and Hambleton 1945, p. 365 [Peru].

TYPE: Holotype ♂, macropterous; Aguaytia, Peru; Drake Coll. (USNM).

DISTRIBUTION: Peru.

HOST PLANT: Unrecorded.

*Gargaphia serjaniae Drake and Hambleton

Gargaphia serjaniae Drake and Hambleton 1938b, p. 57, pl. 10, fig. G [Brazil; *Serjania*].

TYPE: Holotype ♂, macropterous; Pedro Leopoldo, Minas Gerais, Brazil; Drake Coll. (USNM).

DISTRIBUTION: Brazil.

HOST PLANT: *Serjania* sp.

*Gargaphia shelfordi Drake and Hambleton

Gargaphia shelfordi Drake and Hambleton 1944a, p. 95 [Mexico].

TYPE: Holotype ♂, macropterous; Victoria, Mexico; Drake Coll. (USNM).

DISTRIBUTION: Mexico.

HOST PLANT: Unrecorded.

*Gargaphia socorrona Drake

Gargaphia socorrona Drake 1954d, p. 77 [Revilla Gigedo].

TYPE: Holotype ♂, macropterous; Socorro Island, Revilla Gigedo Islands, Mexico; Drake Coll. (USNM).

DISTRIBUTION: Mexico (Revilla Gigedo Islands).

HOST PLANT: Unrecorded.

*Gargaphia solani Heidemann

Gargaphia solani Heidemann 1914, p. 136, fig. 1 [Mo.; Tex.; Okla.; Va.; *Solanum carolinense; Solanum elaeagnifolium;* eggplant; potato; coffee weed].—Fink 1915, p. 1, figs. 1, 2 [D.C.; Md.; *Cassia*].—Osborn and Drake 1916a, p. 235, fig. 7 [Ohio].—Somes 1916, p. 42.—Gibson 1919b, pp. 189, 192 [Ariz.; *Solanum tuberosum; Solanum melongena;* cotton; *Amphiachyris; Salvia pitcheri*].—Parshley 1923b, p. 704.— McAtee 1923, p. 147.—Blatchley 1926, p. 474 [N.C.].—Fenton 1934, p. 199 [S.C.; Mexico; *Salvia azurea;* hollyhock].—Froeschner 1944, p. 668.—Hurd 1946, p. 480 [Canada].—Bailey 1951, p. 43 [Conn.; *Lycopersicum esculentum; Gossypium herbaceum*].—Ash 1954, p. 185 [Ind.].

TYPE: Holotype ♀, macropterous; Lavaca County, Texas, U.S.; USNM.

DISTRIBUTION: U.S. (Conn.; N.J.; Pa.; Md.; D.C.; Va.; N.C.; S.C.; Ala.; Tenn.; Miss.; Mo.; Ark.; Ohio; Ind.; Ill.; Kans.; Iowa; Okla.; Tex.; Ariz.); Canada (B.C.); Mexico.

HOST PLANTS: *Amphiachyris* sp.; *Cassia* sp.; *Gossypium herbaceum; Lycopersicum esculentum; Salvia azurea; Salvia pitcheri; Solanum carolinense; Solanum elaeagnifolium; Solanum melongena; Solanum tuberosum; Solanum* sp.; hollyhock.

NOTE: Life history studies [Fink; Bailey]; predators [Fink; Bailey].

Gargaphia sororia Hussey   PLATE 50

Gargaphia sororia Hussey 1957, p. 175 [Fla.].

TYPE: Holotype ♂; Gadsden County, Florida, U.S.; Florida Univ.

DISTRIBUTION: U.S. (Fla.).

HOST PLANT: Unrecorded.

*Gargaphia subpilosa Berg

Gargaphia subpilosa Berg 1879a, p. 42 [Argentina; *Mikania auricularis*]; 1879b, p. 136.—Pennington 1921, p. 20.—Drake 1931b, p. 512 [Brazil]; 1948j, p. 432.—Fenton 1934, p. 199 [Bolivia; cotton; peas].— Bosq 1937, p. 129 [*Helianthus annus; Ipomoea bonariensis; Phaseolus vulgaris; Prunus cerasus; Prunus persica; Pyrus communis; Solanum tube-*

rosum].—Monte 1937a, p. 36 [*Wissadula*]; 1938d, p. 387; 1940f, pp. 301–306.—Drake and Poor 1938b, p. 109.

Gargaphia iridescens (not Champion): Bergroth 1922, p. 149.—Monte 1938d, p. 389 [*Ambrosia tenuifolia*].

Gargaphia bergi Monte 1940f, p. 306, fig. 1.

TYPE: Sex unknown; Argentina; La Plata Mus.

DISTRIBUTION: Argentina; Bolivia; Brazil.

HOST PLANTS: *Ambrosia tenuifolia; Gossypium* sp.; *Helianthus annus; Ipomoea bonariensis; Mikania auricularis; Phaseolus vulgaris; Prunus cerasus; Prunus persica; Pyrus communis; Solanum tuberosum; Wissadula* sp.; peas.

*Gargaphia tiliae (Walsh)   FIGURE 4a

Tingis tiliae Walsh 1864, p. 408 [basswood; cherry].—Walker 1873a, p. 180.

Gargaphia fasciata Stål 1873, p. 125 [Ill.].—Uhler 1886, p. 22 [Mexico].—Wirtner 1904, p. 202 [Pa.].—Gibson 1919b, p. 195 [Ala.].

Gargaphia tiliae: Uhler 1886, p. 22.—Provancher 1886, p. 159 [Canada].—Bergroth 1892, p. 264.—Van Duzee 1894, p. 181 [N.Y.]; 1912, p. 323.—Gillette and Baker 1895, p. 57 [Colo.].—Torre-Bueno 1910, p. 31.—Smith 1910, p. 149 [N.J.].—Osborn and Drake 1915a, p. 506 [Ohio]; 1916a, p. 234.—Parshley 1917b, p. 56 [N.H.; Conn.; Mass.]; 1922b, p. 11 [S. Dak.]; 1923b, p. 704.—Weiss 1919b, p. 165 [Va.; Kans.].—Gibson 1919b, pp. 189, 194 [N.C.; Md.; Tenn.; Mo.; Wis.; *Tilia pubescens; Prunus serotina*].—Hussey 1922a, p. 22 [Mich.; *Tilia americana*].—Barber and Weiss 1922, p. 13.—Barber 1922a, p. 17.—Drake 1922b, p. 41; 1926b, p. 378; 1928b, p. 102.—McAtee 1923, p. 147.—Blatchley 1926, p. 473 [Ind.; *Cercis canadensis;* sycamore].—Felt 1933, p. 49.—Froeschner 1944, p. 668.—Hurd 1946, p. 480 [Fla.; Ont.; Nebr.].—Bailey 1951, p. 45 [Maine; Vt.; N.B.; Que.; Ariz.; *Tilia*]; 1959, p. 64.—Ash 1954, p. 185.

TYPE: Holotype ♂, macropterous; Rock Island [assumed Illinois], U.S.; USNM.

DISTRIBUTION: U.S. (Maine; Vt.; N.H.; Mass.; Conn.; N.Y.; Pa.; N.J.; Md ; Va.; W. Va. N.C.; S.C.; Ga.; Fla.; Ala.; Miss.; Ky.; Tenn.; Mo.; Ohio; Ind.; Ill.; Mich.; Wis.; Nebr.; Kans.; Minn.; Iowa; S. Dak.; Colo.; Ariz.); Mexico; Canada (Ont.; N.B.; Que.).

HOST PLANTS: *Cercis canadensis; Prunus serotina; Tilia americana; Tilia pubescens; Tilia* sp.

NOTES: Life history studies [Weiss; Barber and Weiss; Bailey]; taken at light [McAtee].

There is no locality label on type specimen, only the label reading "Collection C. V. Reiley" and in his article Walsh gives only the following information "Very abundant near Rock Island and on the basswood."

*Gargaphia torresi Costa Lima

   Gargaphia torresi Costa Lima 1922, p. 112 [Brazil]; 1930, p. 84 [*Croton;*
      Triumfetta; Ipomoea]; 1936, p. 127.—Bondar   8, p. 244, figs.
      [*Phaseolus*].—Drake 1931b, p. 512 [cotton]; 1935, p. 20.—Drake and
      Hambleton 1934, p. 450 [maize; sweet potato].—Fenton 1934, p. 199
      [Argentina].—Bosq 1937, p. 130.—Monte 1937a, p. 35, fig. 7; 1939b,
      p. 70 [Paraguay].—Fiuza 1946, pp. 338, 341 [*Phaseolus vulgaris;*
      Phaseolus lunatus].—Silva 1956, p. 34, fig. 11 [*Gossypium; Canavalia*
      obtusifolia; Zinnia elegans; Hibiscus syriacus].

   TYPE: Sex unknown; Brazil; Ent. Agr. Brazil.

   DISTRIBUTION: Brazil; Argentina; Paraguay; Bolivia.

   HOST PLANTS: *Canavalia obtusifolia; Croton* sp.; *Gossypium* sp.; *Hibiscus*
syriacus; Ipomoea sp.; *Phaseolus lunatus; Phaseolus vulgaris; Phaseolus* sp.; *Sida*
sp.; *Triumfetta* sp.; *Zinnia elegans;* sweet potato; maize.

*Gargaphia trichoptera Stål

   Gargaphia trichoptera Stål 1873, p. 125 [Colombia].—Champion 1898b,
      p. 58, pl. 2, fig. 5.—Drake and Poor 1937d, p. 311.—Monte 1947b,
      p. 432 [Peru].

   TYPE: Sex unknown; Bogota, Colombia; Stockholm Mus.

   DISTRIBUTION: Colombia; Peru; Brazil.

   HOST PLANT: Unrecorded.

*Gargaphia tuthilli Drake and Carvalho

   Gargaphia tuthilli Drake and Carvalho 1944, p. 42 [Colo.].

   TYPE: Holotype ♂, macropterous; Mesa Verde, Colorado, U.S.; Drake
Coll. (USNM).

   DISTRIBUTION: U.S. (Colo.).

   HOST PLANT: Unrecorded.

*Gargaphia valerioi Drake

   Gargaphia valerioi Drake 1941a, p. 144 [Costa Rica].

   TYPE: Holotype ♂, macropterous; La Gloria, Costa Rica; USNM.

   DISTRIBUTION: Costa Rica.

   HOST PLANT: Unrecorded.

*Gargaphia vanduzeei Gibson

   Gargaphia vanduzeei Gibson 1919b, p. 198 [Costa Rica].—Hurd 1946, p.
      480 [Cuba].

   TYPE: Holotype ♂; Costa Rica; deposition of type unknown.

   DISTRIBUTION: Costa Rica; Cuba.

   HOST PLANT: Unrecorded.

   NOTE: Type damaged [Gibson].

*Gargaphia venosa Drake and Poor

   Gargaphia venosa Drake and Poor 1942, p. 301 [Argentina].

   TYPE: Holotype ♂; Resistencia, Chaco, Argentina; Argentina Mus.

   DISTRIBUTION: Argentina.

   HOST PLANT: Unrecorded.

Genus GITAVA Drake

Gitava Drake 1948e, p. 149.—Drake and Ruhoff 1960a, p. 59.
TYPE SPECIES: *Tigava ugandana* Drake.

Gitava basilewskyi Schouteden

Gitava basilewskyi Schouteden 1953c, p. 130 [Congo].
TYPE: Sex unknown; Bondo Mabe, Belgian Congo; Cent. Afr. Mus.
DISTRIBUTION: Congo.
HOST PLANT: Unrecorded.

Gitava benoiti Schouteden

Gitava benoiti Schouteden 1953c, p. 131 [Congo].
TYPE: Sex unknown; Basoko, Belgian Congo; Cent. Afr. Mus.
DISTRIBUTION: Congo.
HOST PLANT: Unrecorded.

Gitava ? dispar Schouteden

Gitava ? dispar Schouteden 1957a, p. 88 [Malagasy].
TYPE: Sex unknown; Madagascar; Paris Mus.
DISTRIBUTION: Malagasy Republic.
HOST PLANT: Unrecorded.

Gitava fusca Schouteden

Gitava fusca Schouteden 1957a, p. 87 [Malagasy].
TYPE: Sex unknown; Madagascar; Paris Mus.
DISTRIBUTION: Malagasy Republic.
HOST PLANT: Unrecorded.

Gitava madagascariensis Schouteden

Gitava madagascariensis Schouteden 1957a, p. 86 [Malagasy].
TYPE: Sex unknown; Madagascar; Paris Mus.
DISTRIBUTION: Malagasy Republic.
HOST PLANT: Unrecorded.

Gitava petila Drake

Gitava petila Drake 1954g, p. 663, fig. 4 [Ethiopia].
TYPE: Sex unknown; Mulu, Ethiopia; British Mus.
DISTRIBUTION: Ethiopia.
HOST PLANT: Unrecorded.

*Gitava procera Drake

Gitava procera Drake 1958c, p. 321 [Malagasy].
TYPE: Holotype ♀; Ankazoabo, Hera, Madagascar; Madagascar Sci. Inst.
DISTRIBUTION: Malagasy Republic.
HOST PLANT: Unrecorded.

*Gitava ugandana (Drake)

Tigava ugandana Drake 1942a, p. 11 [Uganda].

Gitava uganda [sic]: Drake 1948e, p. 149.—Drake and Ruhoff 1960a, p. 59.

Gitava ugandana: Schouteden 1953c, p. 130 [Congo].—Drake 1956a, p. 5.

TYPE: Holotype ♂, macropterous; Uganda; Drake Coll. (USNM).

DISTRIBUTION: Uganda; Congo.

HOST PLANT: Unrecorded.

*Gitava ugandana subsp. **pallens** Schouteden

Gitava ugandana subsp. *pallens* Schouteden 1953c, p. 130 [Congo].

TYPE: Sex unknown; Lubero, Kivu, Belgian Congo; Cent. Afr. Mus.

DISTRIBUTION: Congo.

HOST PLANT: Unrecorded.

Genus GYALOTINGIS Drake

Gyalotingis Drake 1960, p. 376.

TYPE SPECIES: *Gyalotingis gressitti* Drake.

*Gyalotingis gressitti Drake

Gyalotingis gressitti Drake 1960, p. 377, fig. 26 [New Guinea].

TYPE: Holotype ♀; Wisselmeren, Enarotadi, Netherlands New Guinea; Bishop Mus.

DISTRIBUTION: New Guinea (Netherlands).

HOST PLANT: Unrecorded.

Genus GYMNOTINGIS Hacker

Gymnotingis Hacker 1928, p. 181.—Drake and Ruhoff 1960a, p. 59.

TYPE SPECIES: *Gymnotingis serrulata* Hacker.

Gymnotingis serrulata Hacker

Gymnotingis serrulata Hacker 1928, p. 182, pl. 23, fig. 14 [Queensland].

TYPE: Sex unknown; Cairns District, Australia; Queensland Mus.

DISTRIBUTION: Australia (Queensland).

HOST PLANT: Unrecorded.

Genus HABROCHILA Horváth

Habrochila Horváth 1912a, p. 353.—Drake and Ruhoff 1960a, p. 59.

TYPE SPECIES: *Habrochila placida* Horváth.

*Habrochila africana Drake

Habrochila africana Drake 1948e, p. 153 [Uganda; Kenya; Natal; Transvaal; Malagasy; *Lantana*].—Schouteden 1953a, p. 104 [Congo].

TYPE: Holotype ♂; Kampal, Uganda; British Mus.

DISTRIBUTION: Uganda; Kenya; Congo; South Africa (Natal; Transvaal); Malagasy Republic.

HOST PLANT: *Lantana* sp.

*Habrochila chinensis Drake

Habrochila chinensis Drake 1947d, p. 231 [China; tea].
TYPE: Holotype ♀, macropterous; Meitonhsein, China; Drake Coll. (USNM).
DISTRIBUTION: China.
HOST PLANT: Tea (?).

*Habrochila clivosa Drake

Habrochila clivosa Drake 1954b, p. 11 [Natal].
TYPE: Holotype ♂, brachypterous; Port Shepstone, Natal, South Africa; British Mus.
DISTRIBUTION: South Africa (Natal).
HOST PLANT: Unrecorded.

Habrochila darthula (Kirkaldy)

Galeatus darthula Kirkaldy 1902, p. 297 [Ceylon; *Barleria cristata*].—
Distant 1903b, p. 131, fig. 94 [*Barleria strigosa*].
Habrochila darthula: Drake and Ruhoff 1961c, p. 151 [India].
TYPE: Sex unknown; Peradeniya, Ceylon; British Mus.
DISTRIBUTION: Ceylon; India.
HOST PLANTS: *Barleria cristata; Barleria strigosa.*

*Habrochila ghesquierei Schouteden

Habrochila ghesquierei Schouteden 1953a, p. 105 [Congo; Uganda; Ruanda; coffee]; 1957c, p. 313.
TYPE: Unknown.
DISTRIBUTION: Congo; Uganda; Ruanda-Urundi.
HOST PLANT: Coffee.

Habrochila horvathi Schouteden

Habrochila horvathi Schouteden 1923, p. 92 [Congo]; 1953a, p. 105.
TYPE: Sex unknown; Watsa, Belgian Congo; Cent. Afr. Mus.
DISTRIBUTION: Congo.
HOST PLANT: Unrecorded.

*Habrochila iolana Drake

Habrochila iolana Drake 1955a, p. 81 [Malagasy].
TYPE: Holotype ♂, macropterous; Perinet, Analamasotra Province, Madagascar; Drake Coll. (USNM).
DISTRIBUTION: Malagasy Republic.
HOST PLANT: Unrecorded.

*Habrochila laeta Drake

Habrochila laeta Drake 1954b, p. 12 [India].
TYPE: Holotype ♂; Bengalore, Madras, India; British Mus.
DISTRIBUTION: India.
HOST PLANT: Unrecorded.

*Habrochila monticola Horváth

Habrochila monticola Horváth 1929, p. 319 [Natal].—Drake and Slater 1955, p. 49.—Drake 1961c, p. 129.

TYPE: Holotype ♀; Weenen, Natal, South Africa; British Mus.
DISTRIBUTION: South Africa (Natal).
HOST PLANT: Unrecorded.

*Habrochila natalana Drake

Habrochila natalana Drake 1956f, p. 426 [Natal].

TYPE: Holotype ♂; Albert Falls, Umgeni River, E. of Pietermaritzberg, Natal, South Africa; Lund Zool. Inst.
DISTRIBUTION: South Africa (Natal).
HOST PLANT: Unrecorded.

*Habrochila placida Horváth

Habrochila placida Horváth 1912a, p. 354 [Congo; cacao].—Schouteden 1923, p. 92; 1953a, p. 105 [Uganda].—Mayné and Ghesquière 1934, p. 20 [coffee].—Carayon 1960, p. 119.

TYPE: Sex unknown; Kondue, Kasai, Belgian Congo; Cent. Afr. Mus.
DISTRIBUTION: Congo; Uganda.
HOST PLANTS: Coffee; cacao.

Genus HAEDUS Distant

Haedus Distant 1904, p. 432.—Drake 1953b, p. 93.—Drake and Ruhoff 1960a, p. 59.
Hormisdas Distant 1910b, p. 59.—Drake and Ruhoff 1960a, p. 60.

TYPE SPECIES: *Haedus clypeatus* Distant.

*Haedus bellus (Drake)

Hormisdas bella Drake 1948g, p. 176 [Sierra Leone].
Haedus bellus: Drake 1953b, p. 93.—Schouteden 1953c, p. 129 [Congo].

TYPE: Holotype ♀, macropterous; Makump, Sierra Leone; Drake Coll. (USNM).
DISTRIBUTION: Sierra Leone; Congo.
HOST PLANT: Unrecorded.

*Haedus burungus Schouteden

Haedus burunga Schouteden 1953c, p. 128 [Congo].

TYPE: Sex unknown; Burunga, Belgian Congo; Cent. Afr. Mus.
DISTRIBUTION: Congo.
HOST PLANT: Unrecorded.

*Haedus clypeatus Distant

Haedus clypeatus Distant 1904, p. 432, pl. 8, fig. 12 [Cape Province].

TYPE: Sex unknown; Wynberg, Cape Colony, South Africa; So. Afr. Mus.
DISTRIBUTION: South Africa (Cape Province).
HOST PLANT: Unrecorded.

Haedus decellei Schouteden

Haedus decellei Schouteden 1957b, p. 219 [Congo; *Croton*].

TYPE: Sex unknown; Yangambi, Belgian Congo; Cent. Afr. Mus.
DISTRIBUTION: Congo.
HOST PLANT: *Croton* sp.

*Haedus diversitas (Drake) (emendation)

Harmidas [sic] *diversatis* Drake 1927d, p. 309 [Malagasy].
Haedus diversitatus [sic]: Drake 1953b, p. 93.

TYPE: Holotype ♀, macropterous; Madagascar; Drake Coll. (USNM).
DISTRIBUTION: Malagasy Republic.
HOST PLANT: Unrecorded.

*Haedus elongatus (Drake)

Hormistes [sic] *elongata* Drake 1948g, p. 177 [Tanganyika].
Haedus elongatus: Drake 1953b, p. 93.

TYPE: Sex unknown; Arusha-Ju, Africa; Hungarian Mus.
DISTRIBUTION: Tanganyika; South Africa (Natal).
HOST PLANT: Unrecorded.

*Haedus javancus Drake

Haedus javancus Drake 1953b, p. 94 [Java].

TYPE: Sex unknown; Bandoeng, Preonger, Java; British Mus.
DISTRIBUTION: Greater Sunda Islands (Java).
HOST PLANT: Unrecorded.

*Haedus lectus (Drake)

Hormisdas lectus Drake 1937a, p. 387, fig. 1c [India; "Elephantia"].
Haedus lectus: Drake 1953b, p. 93.

TYPE: Holotype ♂; Bombay, India; Vienna Mus.
DISTRIBUTION: India.
HOST PLANT: "Elephantia."

*Haedus oios Drake and Ruhoff

Haedus oios Drake and Ruhoff 1962c, p. 139, fig. 2 [Southern Rhodesia].

TYPE: Holotype ♂, macropterous; Salisbury, Southern Rhodesia; Drake Coll. (USNM).
DISTRIBUTION: Southern Rhodesia.
HOST PLANT: Unrecorded.

*Haedus otiosus Drake

Haedus otiosus Drake 1953d, p. 215 [Northern Rhodesia].

TYPE: Holotype ♀, macropterous; N'Dola, Northern Rhodesia; Drake Coll. (USNM).
DISTRIBUTION: Northern Rhodesia.
HOST PLANT: Unrecorded.

*Haedus pallens Schouteden

Haedus bellus subsp. pallens Schouteden 1953c, p. 129 [Congo; Annona chrysophylla; Annona muricata].
Haedus pallens: Drake and Ruhoff 1962a, p. 156.
TYPE: Sex unknown; Ituri, Belgian Congo; Cent. Afr. Mus.
DISTRIBUTION: Congo; Kenya.
HOST PLANTS: Annona chrysophylla; Annona muricata.

*Haedus pictus (Distant)

Hormisdas pictus Distant 1910b, p. 60, pl. 1, figs. 1 a, b [Luzon].—Drake and Poor 1937a, p. 16.
Haedus pictus: Drake 1953b, p. 93.
TYPE: Sex unknown; Manila, Philippine Islands; British Mus.
DISTRIBUTION: Philippine Islands (Luzon).
HOST PLANT: Lantana sp.

*Haedus polulus Drake

Haedus polulus Drake 1953d, p. 216 [Senegal].
TYPE: Holotype ♂; Bambey, Senegal; British Mus.
DISTRIBUTION: Senegal.
HOST PLANT: Unrecorded.

*Haedus sidae (Drake and Poor)

Hormisdas sidae Drake and Poor 1939c, p. 206 [Sida; Uganda].
Haedus sideus [sic]: Drake 1953b, p. 93; 1954e, p. 7 [Congo].
Haedus sidus [sic]: Drake 1956a, p. 5.
TYPE: Holotype ♂; Kampala, Uganda; British Mus.
DISTRIBUTION: Uganda; Congo.
HOST PLANT: Sida sp.

*Haedus vicarius (Drake)

Hormisdas vicarius Drake 1927a, p. 56 [Luzon; Larat]; 1936a, p. 145 [India; Urena lobata]; 1938b, p. 197 [China]; 1948g, p. 176.—Drake and Poor 1937a, p. 16 [Negros]; 1937b, p. 403 [Urena lobata sinuata].
Haedus vicarius: Drake 1953b, p. 93.
TYPE: Holotype ♂, macropterous; Larat Island; Drake Coll. (USNM).
DISTRIBUTION: Tanimbar Islands (Larat); Philippine Islands (Luzon; Negros); China; India.
HOST PLANTS: Urena lobata; Urena lobata sinuata.

*Haedus villiersi (Drake)

Haedus villiers [sic] Drake 1953b, p. 93 (nom. nud.).
Hormisdas villiersi Drake 1954a, p. 236 [Ivory Coast].
TYPE: Holotype ♂; Bouaké, Ivory Coast; Inst. Fr. Afr. N.
DISTRIBUTION: Ivory Coast; Congo.
HOST PLANT: Unrecorded.

Genus HEBETINGIS Drake

Hebetingis Drake 1960a, p. 360.
TYPE SPECIES: *Hebetingis adeia* Drake.

Hebetingis adeia Drake

Hebetingis adeia Drake 1960, p. 360, fig. 13 [New Guinea].
TYPE: Holotype ♂; Asaro-Chimbu Divide, E. Highlands, Northeast New Guinea; Bishop Mus.
DISTRIBUTION: New Guinea (Northeast).
HOST PLANT: Unrecorded.

Genus HEGESIDEMUS Distant

Hegesidemus Distant 1911b, p. 270.—Drake and Ruhoff 1960a, p. 59.
TYPE SPECIES: *Hegesidemus eliyanus* Distant.

*Hegesidemus elegantulus (Distant)

Teleonemia ? elegantula Distant 1909c, p. 167, pl. 10, figs. 3, 3a [Borneo].
Compseuta elegantula: Bergroth 1921, p. 105.—Drake 1948f, p. 202.
Hegesidemus elegantulus: Drake and Ruhoff 1961c, p. 145.
TYPE: Sex unknown; Kuching, Borneo; British Mus.
DISTRIBUTION: Greater Sunda Islands (Borneo).
HOST PLANT: Unrecorded.

*Hegesidemus eliyanus Distant

Hegesidemus eliyanus Distant 1911b, p. 270 [Ceylon; *Strobilanthes*].
TYPE: Sex unknown; Nuwera Eliya, Ceylon; British Mus.
DISTRIBUTION: Ceylon.
HOST PLANT: *Strobilanthes* sp.

*Hegesidemus otiosus Drake   PLATE 29

Hegesidemus otiosus Drake 1953d, p. 221 [India].
TYPE: Holotype ♂; Nilgiri Hills, India; British Mus.
DISTRIBUTION: India.
HOST PLANT: Unrecorded.

*Hegesidemus pauliani Drake

Hegesidemus pauliani Drake 1957e, p. 402 [Reunion].
TYPE: Holotype ♂; Bébour, Reunion; Madagascar Sci. Inst.
DISTRIBUTION: Mascarene Islands (Reunion).
HOST PLANT: Unrecorded.

Genus HENRIKUS Drake

Henrikus Drake 1955e, p. 280.—Drake and Ruhoff 1960a, p. 60.
TYPE SPECIES: *Henrikus schoutedeni* Drake.

*Henrikus schoutedeni Drake

Henrikus schoutedeni Drake 1955e, p. 282, fig. 1 [Congo].

TYPE: Holotype ♂; Kmango, Kimbau, Belgian Congo; Cent. Afr. Mus.
DISTRIBUTION: Congo.
HOST PLANT: Unrecorded.

Genus HESPEROTINGIS Parshley

Hesperotingis Parshley 1917a, p. 21; 1923b, p. 707.—Van Duzee 1917b,
p. 818.—Blatchley 1926, p. 493 (key).—Hurd 1946, p. 446.—Drake
and Ruhoff 1960a, p. 60.

TYPE SPECIES: *Hesperotingis antennata* Parshley.

*Hesperotingis antennata Parshley

Hesperotingis antennata Parshley 1917a, p. 21, fig. 2 [N.J.; N.Y.; Pa.;
Conn.]; 1917b, p. 57; 1923b, p. 707.—Barber 1922a, p. 17; 1922b,
p. 23.—Olsen 1923, p. 163.—McAtee 1923, p. 145 [D.C.].—Blatchley
1926, p. 493, fig. 118; 1928, p. 5 [Fla.].—Drake 1928b, p. 102.—
Froeschner 1944, p. 670 [Mo.].—Torre-Bueno 1946, p. 94.—Bailey
1951, p. 22 [N.H.; Mass.; *Andropogon*].

TYPE: Holotype ♀, macropterous; Lakehurst, New Jersey, U.S.; USNM.
DISTRIBUTION: U.S. (N.H.; Mass.; Conn.; N.Y.; N.J.; Pa.; D.C.; Fla.;
Mo.).

HOST PLANTS: *Andropogon* sp.; "beaten from Spanish moss hanging from
limbs of *Quercus rubra*" [Blatchley 1928].

*Hesperotingis antennata var. **borealis** Parshley

Hesperotingis antennata var. *borealis* Parshley 1917a, p. 24 [N.H.]; 1917b,
p. 57.—Froeschner 1944, p. 670 [Mo.].—Hurd 1946, p. 447 [D.C.].—
Bailey 1951, p. 22.

TYPE: Sex unknown; Hampton, New Hampshire, U.S.; MCZ.
DISTRIBUTION: U.S. (N.H.; Mo.; D.C.).
HOST PLANT: Unrecorded.

*Hesperotingis duryi (Osborn and Drake)

Melanorhopala duryi Osborn and Drake 1916b, p. 15, fig. 3d [Tex.];
1917a, p. 159, fig. 2; pl. 8, fig. e.—Parshley 1917a, p. 19.

Hesperotingis duryi: Hurd 1946, p. 447 [Fla.].

TYPE: Holotype ♀, brachypterous; Brownsville, Texas, U.S.; Drake
Coll. (USNM).
DISTRIBUTION: U.S. (Tex.; Fla.).
HOST PLANT: Unrecorded.

*Hesperotingis duryi var. **confusa** Drake

Hesperotingis duryi var. *confusa* Drake 1922b, p. 48 [Tex.].

TYPE: Holotype ♀, brachypterous; Marfa, Texas, U.S.; USNM.
DISTRIBUTION: U.S. (Tex.).
HOST PLANT: Unrecorded.

*Hesperotingis floridana Drake

Hesperotingis floridana Drake 1928f, p. 4 [Fla.].

TYPE: Holotype ♀, macropterous; Florida, U.S.; USNM.

DISTRIBUTION: U.S. (Fla.).

HOST PLANT: Unrecorded.

*Hesperotingis fuscata Parshley

Hesperotingis fuscata Parshley 1917a, p. 24 [Colo.].—Hurd 1946, p. 447 [Kans.].

TYPE: Holotype ♀, brachypterous; Golden, Colorado, U.S.; USNM.

DISTRIBUTION: U.S. (Colo.; Kans.).

HOST PLANT: Unrecorded.

*Hesperotingis illinoiensis Drake

Hesperotingis illinoiensis Drake 1918d, p. 88 [Ill.].—Blatchley 1926, p. 494.—Bailey 1951, p. 24 [Conn.].

TYPE: Holotype ♀, macropterous; Palos Park, Illinois, U.S.; Drake Coll. (USNM).

DISTRIBUTION: U.S. (Ill.; Ind.; Conn.).

HOST PLANT: Unrecorded.

*Hesperotingis mississippiensis Drake

Hesperotingis mississippiensis Drake 1928f, p. 4 [Miss.].

TYPE: Holotype ♂, brachypterous; Charleston, Mississippi, U.S.; Drake Coll. (USNM).

DISTRIBUTION: U.S. (Miss.; Fla.).

HOST PLANT: Unrecorded.

*Hesperotingis occidentalis Drake

Hesperotingis occidentalis Drake 1922b, p. 49 [Colo.].

TYPE: Holotype ♀, brachypterous; Colorado, U.S.; Drake Coll. (USNM).

DISTRIBUTION: U.S. (Colo.; Calif.; Idaho).

HOST PLANT: Unrecorded.

Genus HOLOPHYGDON Kirkaldy

Holophygdon Kirkaldy 1908b, p. 364.—Drake and Poor 1937a, p. 18; 1939c, p. 207.—Drake and Ruhoff 1960a, p. 60.

TYPE SPECIES: *Holophygdon melanesica* Kirkaldy.

*Holophygdon melanesica Kirkaldy   PLATE 49

Holophygdon melanesica Kirkaldy 1908b, p. 364, pl. 4, figs. 10, 11 [Fiji].—Drake and Poor 1943, p. 205 [Viti Levu].—Drake and Davis 1960, fig. 58.

TYPE: Holotype ♀; Fiji Islands; Hawaii. Sugar Plant. Assn.

DISTRIBUTION: Fiji Islands [Viti Levu].

HOST PLANT: Unrecorded.

*Holophygdon melanesica var. fusca Drake and Poor

Holophygdon melanesica var. *fusca* Drake and Poor 1943, p. 205 [Viti Levu; Ovalau; *Raphidophora merrillii*].

TYPE: Holotype ♂; Wainiloka, Ovalau, Fiji Islands; Bishop Mus.
DISTRIBUTION: Fiji Islands (Viti Levu; Ovalau).
HOST PLANT: *Raphidophora merrillii.*

Genus HORVATHULA Schouteden

Horvathula Schouteden 1957c, p. 317.
TYPE SPECIES: *Sankisia uniseriata* Horváth.

*Horvathula uniseriata (Horváth)

Sankisia uniseriata Horváth 1929, p. 319 [Nigeria; *Cordia millenii*].
Monanthia uniseriata: Drake 1954g, p. 658 [Ethiopia; *Cordia abyssinica*].
Horvathula uniseriata: Schouteden 1957c, p. 318 [Ruanda; *Cordia chrysocarpa*].

TYPE: Holotype ♂; Ibadan, Nigeria; British Mus.
DISTRIBUTION: Nigeria; Ruanda-Urundi; Ethiopia; Kenya; Congo; Uganda.
HOST PLANTS: *Cordia abyssinica; Cordia chrysocarpa; Cordia millenii.*

Genus HOVATLAS Schouteden

Hovatlas Schouteden 1957a, p. 85.—Drake and Ruhoff 1960a, p. 60.
TYPE SPECIES: *Hovatlas elegantulus* Schouteden.

Hovatlas elegantulus Schouteden

Hovatlas elegantulus Schouteden 1957a, p. 85 [Malagasy].
TYPE: Holotype ♀; Madagascar; Paris Mus.
DISTRIBUTION: Malagasy Republic.
HOST PLANT: Unrecorded.

Genus HURDCHILA Drake

Hurdchila Drake 1953b, p. 92.—Drake and Ruhoff 1960a, p. 60.
TYPE SPECIES: *Jannaeus togularis* Drake and Poor.

*Hurdchila mira (Drake and Poor)

Jannaeus mirus Drake and Poor 1936a, p. 442 [Hainan].—Drake 1937b, p. 387 [Ceylon].
Hurdchila mira: Drake 1953b, p. 93.
TYPE: Holotype ♂, macropterous; Ta Han, Hainan Island; Drake Coll. (USNM).
DISTRIBUTION: China (Hainan Island); Ceylon.
HOST PLANT: Unrecorded.

*Hurdchila togularis (Drake and Poor)

Jannaeus togularis Drake and Poor 1936a, p. 441 [Hainan].
Hurdchila torgularis [sic]: Drake 1953b, p. 93.
TYPE: Holotype ♂, macropterous; Hainan Island, China; Drake Coll. (USNM).
DISTRIBUTION: China (Hainan Island).
HOST PLANT: Unrecorded.

Genus HYALOCHITON Horváth

Galeatus (*Hyalochiton*) Horváth 1905b, p. 566.
Hyalochiton: Horváth 1906a, pp. 13, 48 (key).—Oshanin 1908, p. 420;
  1912, p. 43.—Stichel 1926, p. 109; 1935, p. 348; 1938a, p. 406;
  1960a, p. 293; 1960b, p. 393; 1960c, p. 132.—Gulde 1938, pp. 243,
  270.—Kiritshenko 1951, pp. 241, 246.—Drake and Ruhoff 1960a, p.
  60.
TYPE SPECIES: *Galeatus komaroffii* Jakovlev.

*Hyalochiton colpochilus (Horváth)   PLATE 43
Galeatus colpochilus Horváth 1897b, pp. 456, 459 [Spain].
Hyalochiton colpochilus: Horváth 1906a, p. 49.—Lindberg 1932a, p. 41
  [Morocco].—Stichel 1938a, p. 406 [France]; 1960a, p. 293 [Greece;
  Phlomis lynchitis].—Wagner 1958, p. 240 [*Betonica officinalis*].
TYPE: Sex unknown; Ciudad Real, Spain; Hungarian Mus.
DISTRIBUTION: Spain; France; Morocco.
HOST PLANTS: *Betonica officinalis; Phlomis lynchitis.*

Hyalochiton colpochilus var. **consimilis** (Horváth)
Galeatus consimilis Horváth 1905a, p. 273 [Spain].
Hyalochiton colpochilus var. *consimilis:* Horváth 1906a, p. 49.
Hyalochiton syrmiensis var. *consimilis:* Vidal 1937, p. 197 [Morocco].
TYPE: Sex unknown; Spain; Hungarian Mus.
DISTRIBUTION: Spain; Morocco.
HOST PLANT: Unrecorded.

*Hyalochiton komaroffii (Jakovlev)
Galeatus komaroffii Jakovlev 1880a, pp. 130, 133 [Caucasus].—Horváth
  1897b, pp. 456, 458 [Hungary; Austria].
Galeatus comaroffii [sic]: Jakovlev 1880b, p. 102.
Galeatus debilis Montandon 1887, p. 65 [Yugoslavia; *Teucrium*].
Galeatus (*Hyalochiton*) *komaroffii:* Horváth 1905b, p. 56.
Hyalochiton komaroffii: Horváth 1906a, p. 49 [France].—Gulde 1938,
  p. 271, fig.—Stichel 1938a, p. 406 [Turkey]; 1960a, p. 293.—Drake
  and Ruhoff 1962d, p. 489.
Hyalochiton algiricus Lindberg 1936a, p. 83, fig. 2 [Morocco].
Hyalochiton komarovii [sic]: Kiritshenko 1951, p. 246.—Gomez-Menor
  1955b, p. 249 [Spain].

TYPE: Holotype ♂, brachypterous; Derbent, Russia; Leningrad Inst.
DISTRIBUTION: U.S.S.R. (Caucasus); Yugoslavia; Hungary; Austria; France; Spain; Turkey; Morocco.
HOST PLANT: *Teucrium* sp.

*Hyalochiton multiseriatus (Reuter)

Galeathus [sic] *multiseriatus* Reuter 1888, p. 225 [Greece]; 1891a, p.26.
Galeatus multiseriatus: Horváth 1897b, pp. 456, 459.
Hyalochiton multiseriatus: Horváth 1906a, p. 49.—Stichel 1960a, p. 294 [Turkey; Iraq; Syria; *Phlomis*].
TYPE: Sex unknown; Attica, Greece; Helsin. Mus.
DISTRIBUTION: Greece; Turkey; Iraq; Syria.
HOST PLANT: *Phlomis* sp.

*Hyalochiton strumosus (Horváth)

Galeatus strumosus Horváth 1902a, p. 594 [Turkey].
Hyalochiton strumosus: Horváth 1906a, p. 49.—Seidenstücker 1954, p. 235.—Hoberlandt 1955, p. 87.—Stichel 1960a, p. 294 [Syria].
TYPE: Sex unknown; Ak-Chehir, Anatolia, Turkey; Hungarian Mus.
DISTRIBUTION: Turkey; Syria.
HOST PLANT: Unrecorded.

Hyalochiton syrmiensis (Horváth)

Galeatus syrmiensis Horváth 1897a, p. 88 [Hungary]; 1897b, pp. 456, 458.
Hyalochiton syrmiensis: Horváth 1906a, p. 49.—Vidal 1937, p. 197 [Morocco].—González 1948, p. 50 [Spain].—Stichel 1960a, p. 293.
TYPE: Holotype ♂; Hungary; Hungarian Mus.
DISTRIBUTION: Hungary; Spain; Morocco.
HOST PLANT: Unrecorded.

Genus HYBOPHARSA Hurd

Hybopharsa Hurd 1946, p. 467.—Drake and Ruhoff 1960a, p. 61.
TYPE SPECIES: *Leptostyla colubra* Van Duzee.

*Hybopharsa colubra (Van Duzee)

Leptostyla colubra Van Duzee 1907, p. 19 [Jamaica].
Gelchossa colubra: Drake and Bruner 1924a, p. 149; 1924b, p. 155 [Cuba; *Eugenia rhombea*].—Gowdey 1926, p. 35.
Leptopharsa colubra: Bruner, Scaramuzza and Otero 1945, p. 74.
Hybopharsa colubra: Hurd 1946, p. 468 [pimento].
TYPE: Sex unknown; Jamaica; Cal. Acad.
DISTRIBUTION: Jamaica; Cuba.
HOST PLANTS: *Eugenia rhombea; Pimenta pimenta.*

Genus HYPSIPYRGIAS Kirkaldy

Hypsipyrgias Kirkaldy 1908a, p. 779.—Drake and Ruhoff 1960a, p. 61.
TYPE SPECIES: *Hypsipyrgias telamonides* Kirkaldy.

*Hypsipyrgias euphues Drake and Ruhoff

Hypsipyrgias euphues Drake and Ruhoff 1962b, p. 251 [Lord Howe].
TYPE: Holotype ♂, macropterous; Lord Howe Island; So. Austr. Mus.
DISTRIBUTION: Australia (Lord Howe Island).
HOST PLANT: Unrecorded.

*Hypsipyrgias telamonides Kirkaldy

Hypsipyrgias telamonides Kirkaldy 1908a, p. 779, pl. 43, figs. 4, 5 [Queens-
land].—Hacker 1927, p. 25; 1928a, p. 179.—Drake and Ruhoff
1962b, p. 250.
TYPE: Holotype ♀; Kuranda, Queensland, Australia; Hawaii. Sugar
Plant. Assn.
DISTRIBUTION: Australia (Queensland).
HOST PLANT: Unrecorded.
NOTE: Type specimen bears: type label, identification label in Kirkaldy's
handwriting, and printed locality label for "Cairns District." Kuranda is a
small waystation about 15 miles from Cairns, the latter label probably
used for convenience.

Genus HYPSOTINGIS Drake

Hypsotingis Drake 1960, p. 362.
TYPE SPECIES: *Hypsotingis columna* Drake.

Hypsotingis columna Drake

Hypsotingis columna Drake 1960, p. 363, fig. 15 [New Guinea].
TYPE: Holotype ♀; Urapura, Kamo Valley, Wisselmeren, Netherlands
New Guinea; Bishop Mus.
DISTRIBUTION: New Guinea (Netherlands).
HOST PLANT: Unrecorded.

Genus IDIOCYSTA China

Idiocysta China 1930, p. 141.—Drake and Ruhoff 1960a, p. 61.
TYPE SPECIES: *Idiocysta hackeri* China.

Idiocysta bicolor Drake and Poor

Idiocysta bicolor Drake and Poor 1943, p. 199, fig. 4 [Viti Levu].
TYPE: Holotype ♀; Nandarivatu, Viti Levu, Fiji Islands; Bishop Mus.
DISTRIBUTION: Fiji Islands (Viti Levu).
HOST PLANT: Unrecorded.

*Idiocysta dryadis Drake and Poor

Idiocysta dryadis Drake and Poor 1943, p. 200, fig. 5 [Viti Levu].

TYPE: Holotype ♀; Nandarivatu, Viti Levu, Fiji Islands; Bishop Mus.

DISTRIBUTION: Fiji Islands (Viti Levu).

HOST PLANT: Unrecorded.

*Idiocysta fijiana Drake and Poor

Idiocysta fijiana Drake and Poor 1943, p. 198 [Viti Levu].

TYPE: Holotype ♂; Mt. Victoria, Tholo North, Viti Levu, Fiji Islands; Bishop Mus.

DISTRIBUTION: Fiji Islands (Viti Levu).

HOST PLANT: Unrecorded.

*Idiocysta floris Drake and Poor

Idiocysta floris Drake and Poor 1943, p. 198 [Viti Levu].

TYPE: Holotype ♀; Nandarivatu, Viti Levu, Fiji Islands; Bishop Mus.

DISTRIBUTION: Fiji Islands (Viti Levu).

HOST PLANT: Unrecorded.

Idiocysta hackeri China

Idiocysta hackeri China 1930, p. 142, fig. 22 [Upolu].

TYPE: Sex unknown; Malololelei, Upolu, Samoa Islands; British Mus.

DISTRIBUTION: Territory Western Samoa Islands (Upolu).

HOST PLANT: Unrecorded.

Genus IDIOSTYLA Drake

Idiostyla Drake 1945, p. 97.—Drake and Ruhoff 1960a, p. 61.

TYPE SPECIES: *Tigava anonae* Drake and Hambleton.

*Idiostyla anonae (Drake and Hambleton)

Tigava anonae Drake and Hambleton 1938a, p. 45 [Brazil; *Annona coriacea*].—Monte 1941e, p. 143.

Idiostyla anomae [sic]: Drake 1945, p. 98.

TYPE: Holotype ♂, macropterous; Cerqueira Cesar, São Paulo, Brazil; Drake Coll. (USNM).

DISTRIBUTION: Brazil.

HOST PLANT: *Annona coriacea*.

*Idiostyla rolliniae (Drake and Hambleton)

Tigava rolliniae Drake and Hambleton 1934, p. 441 [Brazil; *Rollinia silvatica*].—Monte 1939b, p. 81; 1941e, p. 145.

Idiostyla rollinae [sic]: Drake 1945, p. 98.—Drake and Davis 1960, fig. 46.

TYPE: Holotype ♂, macropterous; Viçosa, Minas Gerais, Brazil; Drake Coll. (USNM).

DISTRIBUTION: Brazil.

HOST PLANT: *Rollinia silvatica*.

Genus ILDEFONSUS Distant

Ildefonsus Distant 1910a, p. 110.—Drake and Ruhoff 1960a, p. 61.
TYPE SPECIES: *Ildefonsus provorsus* Distant.

*Ildefonsus nexus Drake and Ruhoff

Ildefonsus nexus Drake and Ruhoff 1961b, p. 180 [Burma].
TYPE: Holotype ♀, macropterous; Kambaiti, Burma; Drake Coll. (USNM).
DISTRIBUTION: Burma.
HOST PLANT: Unrecorded.

*Ildefonsus provorsus Distant

Ildefonsus provorsus Distant 1910a, p. 110, fig. 54 [India].
TYPE: Sex unknown; E. Himalayas, Ghoom, India; British Mus.
DISTRIBUTION: India.
HOST PLANT: Unrecorded.

Genus INOMA Hacker

Inoma Hacker 1927, p. 25.—Drake and Ruhoff 1960a, p. 62.
TYPE SPECIES: *Inoma multispinosa* Hacker.

*Inoma angusta Drake

Inoma angusta Drake 1942a, p. 16 [New South Wales].
TYPE: Holotype ♂, macropterous; Dorrizo, New South Wales, Australia; Drake Coll. (USNM).
DISTRIBUTION: Australia (New South Wales).
HOST PLANT: Unrecorded.

*Inoma multispinosa Hacker   PLATE 42

Inoma multispinosa Hacker 1927, p. 25, pl. 9, fig. 12 [Queensland].
TYPE: Sex unknown; Sunnybank, Queensland, Australia; Queensland Mus.
DISTRIBUTION: Australia (Queensland).
HOST PLANT: Unrecorded.

Genus INONEMIA Drake

Inonemia Drake 1942b, p. 361.—Drake and Ruhoff 1960a, p. 62.
TYPE SPECIES: *Inonemia mussiva* Drake.

*Inonemia mussiva Drake

Inonemia mussiva Drake 1942b, p. 362 [Queensland].
TYPE: Holotype ♂, macropterous; Roma, Queensland, Australia; Drake Coll. (USNM).
DISTRIBUTION: Australia (Queensland).
HOST PLANT: Unrecorded.

*Inonemia mussiva subsp. **brevis** Drake

Inonemia mussiva subsp. *brevis* Drake 1942b, p. 362 [Queensland].

TYPE: Holotype ♀, macropterous; Roma, Queensland, Australia; Drake Coll. (USNM).

DISTRIBUTION: Australia (Queensland).

HOST PLANT: Unrecorded.

Genus ISCHNOTINGIS Horváth

Ischnotingis Horváth 1925a, p. 7.—Drake and Ruhoff 1960a, p. 62.

TYPE SPECIES: *Ischnotingis prolixa* Horváth.

*Ischnotingis fasciata Horváth

Ischnotingis fasciata Horváth 1925a, p. 9, fig. 5 [Western Australia].

TYPE: Sex unknown; Geraldton, Australia occidentalis; Stockholm Mus.

DISTRIBUTION: Australia (Western Australia; New South Wales).

HOST PLANT: Unrecorded.

*Ischnotingis horvathi Drake

Ischnotingis horvathi Drake 1954c, p. 69 [New South Wales]; 1961b, p. 112.

TYPE: Holotype ♂; Mt. Victoria, New South Wales, Australia; Hungarian Mus.

DISTRIBUTION: Australia (New South Wales).

HOST PLANT: Unrecorded.

*Ischnotingis prolixa Horváth

Ischnotingis prolixa Horváth 1925a, p. 8, fig. 4 [Western Australia].— Drake and Ruhoff 1962a, p. 156.

Ischnotingis yanchepana Drake 1953d, p. 215.

TYPE: Holotype ♀; Freemantle, Australia occidentalis; Stockholm Mus.

DISTRIBUTION: Australia (Western Australia).

HOST PLANT: Unrecorded.

Genus KAPIRIELLA Schouteden

Kapiriella Schouteden 1919, p. 138.—Drake 1953b, p. 93; 1957b, pp. 205–218 (key).—Drake and Ruhoff 1960a, p. 62.

Lembella Schouteden 1919, p. 141.—Drake and Ruhoff 1960a, p. 63.

TYPE SPECIES: *Kapiriella leplaei* Schouteden.

*Kapiriella conradsi Drake

Kapiriella conradsi Drake 1957b, p. 215 [Tanganyika].

Cysteochila conradsi: Schouteden 1957c, p. 316 [Ruanda].

TYPE: Holotype ♂; Victoria-Nyanza, Ukerewe Island, Tanganyika; Cent. Afr. Mus.

DISTRIBUTION: Tanganyika; Ruanda-Urundi.

HOST PLANT: Unrecorded.

*Kapiriella denigrata Drake

Kapiriella denigrata Drake 1956a, p. 5, fig. 1 [Congo]; 1957b, p. 217.

TYPE: Holotype ♂; Ngoma, Nord du lac Kivu, Belgian Congo; Parcs Nat. Inst.

DISTRIBUTION: Congo.

HOST PLANT: Unrecorded.

*Kapiriella desaegeri Drake

Kapiriella desaegeri Drake 1957b, p. 216 [Congo].

TYPE: Holotype ♂; National Garamba Park, Belgian Congo; Parcs Nat. Inst.

DISTRIBUTION: Congo.

HOST PLANT: Unrecorded.

*Kapiriella leplaei Schouteden

Kapiriella leplaei Schouteden 1919, p. 139 [Congo]; 1923, p. 107.— Drake 1953b, p. 93; 1954e, p. 8; 1957b, p. 212.

TYPE: Sex unknown; Kapiri, Belgian Congo; Cent. Afr. Mus.

DISTRIBUTION: Congo.

HOST PLANT: Unrecorded.

*Kapiriella maynei (Schouteden)

Lembella maynei Schouteden 1919, p. 142 [Congo]; 1923, p. 110.
Lembella maculigera Horváth 1929, p. 325 [Uganda].
Kapiriella maynei: Drake 1953b, p. 93; 1955b, p. 87 [Angola]; 1957b, p. 209, fig. 1b [Cameroons].

TYPE: Sex unknown; Congo da Lemba, Belgian Congo; Cent. Afr. Mus.

DISTRIBUTION: Congo; Cameroons; Uganda; Angola.

HOST PLANT: Unrecorded.

*Kapiriella natalana Drake

Kapiriella natalana Drake 1956f, p. 423 [Natal]; 1957b, p. 214.

TYPE: Holotype ♂; Malvern, Natal, South Africa; British Mus.

DISTRIBUTION: South Africa (Natal).

HOST PLANT: Unrecorded.

*Kapiriella polita (Drake)

Lembella polita Drake 1948e, p. 150 [Sudan]; 1953b, p. 93 (in part).
Lambella [sic] *polita:* Drake 1948h, p. 76.
Lembella iturica Schouteden 1954, p. 141 [Congo].
Kapiriella polita: Drake 1957b, p. 210 [Senegal; Uganda; millet].

TYPE: Holotype ♂, macropterous; Kavlugh, Sudan; Drake Coll. (USNM).

DISTRIBUTION: Sudan; Uganda; Congo; Senegal.

HOST PLANT: Millet.

*Kapiriella saetula Drake

Kapiriella saetula Drake 1957b, p. 214, fig. 1a [Congo].

TYPE: Holotype ♂; Kaziba, P.N.U., Belgian Congo; Parcs Nat. Inst.
DISTRIBUTION: Congo.
HOST PLANT: Unrecorded.

*Kapiriella schoutedeni Drake

Kapiriella schoutedeni Drake 1957b, p. 213, fig. 1d [Malagasy].

TYPE: Holotype ♂; Madagascar; Cent. Afr. Mus.
DISTRIBUTION: Malagasy Republic.
HOST PLANT: Unrecorded.

*Kapiriella wechinai Drake

Kapiriella wechinai Drake 1957b, p. 211, fig. 1c [Northern Rhodesia;
Congo; Kenya; Tanganyika].

TYPE: Holotype ♂; Lake Bangweulu, N'Chiti Island, Northern Rhodesia; British Mus.
DISTRIBUTION: Northern Rhodesia; Congo; Kenya; Tanganyika.
HOST PLANT: Unrecorded.

Genus LAROTINGIS Drake

Larotingis Drake 1960, p. 357.
TYPE SPECIES: *Larotingis aporia* Drake.

Larotingis aporia Drake

Larotingis aporia Drake 1960, p. 357, fig. 11 [New Guinea].

TYPE: Holotype ♂; Wisselmeren, Okaitadi, Netherlands New Guinea;
Bishop Mus.
DISTRIBUTION: New Guinea (Netherlands).
HOST PLANT: Unrecorded.

*Larotingis etes Drake and Ruhoff

Larotingis etes Drake and Ruhoff 1961b, p. 165 [Mindanao].

TYPE: Holotype ♀, macropterous; Surigao, Mindanao, Philippine
Islands; Drake Coll. (USNM).
DISTRIBUTION: Philippine Islands (Mindanao).
HOST PLANT: Unrecorded.

Genus LASIACANTHA Stål

Tingis (Lasiacantha) Stål 1873, p. 130.
Lasiacantha: Stål 1874, p. 56.—Lethierry and Severin 1896, p. 18.—
Horváth 1906a, pp. 14, 59 (key).—Muzik 1907, pp. 50, 57.—Oshanin
1908, p. 427; 1912, p. 44.—Stichel 1926, pp. 104, 109 (key); 1935,
p. 349; 1938a, p. 406; 1960a, p. 306; 1960b, p. 395; 1960c, p. 134.—
Hacker 1929, p. 334.—Börner 1935, pp. 74, 76.—Gulde 1938,
pp. 244, 283 (key).—China 1943, p. 246.—Kiritshenko 1951, pp.

242, 248 (key).—Singer 1952, p. 51.—Drake 1953b, p. 92.—Drake and Ruhoff 1960a, p. 63.

Monanthia (Lasiacantha): Puton 1886b, p. 33.

Jannaeus Distant 1909a, p. 118; 1910a, p. 117.—Drake and Ruhoff 1960a, p. 62.

Myrmecotingis Hacker 1928, p. 182.—Drake and Ruhoff 1960a, p. 69.

TYPE SPECIES: *Tingis (Lasiacantha) hedenborgii* Stål.

Lasiacantha absimilis Drake

Lasiacantha absimilis Drake 1951, p. 177 [Ethiopia]; 1954a, p. 232 [Niger].

TYPE: Holotype ♂; Bubassa, Abyssinia; Hungarian Mus.

DISTRIBUTION: Ethiopia; Niger; Sudan.

HOST PLANT: Unrecorded.

Lasiacantha altimitrata (Takeya)

Jannaeus altimitratus Takeya 1933, p. 35, pl. 3, fig. 3; text fig. 3 [Taiwan]; 1951a, p. 15.—Drake and Maa 1953, p. 88 [China; Labiatae].

Lasiacantha altimitratus: Drake 1953b, p. 92.

TYPE: Holotype ♂; Taihoku, Formosa; Kyushu Univ.

DISTRIBUTION: Taiwan; China; India.

HOST PLANT: Labiatae.

Lasiacantha capucina (Germar)

Acanthia cardui (not Linnaeus): Schellenberg 1800, p. 21, pl. 6, fig. 2.

Tingis capucina Germar 1836, fasc. 18, tab. 24 [Germany].

Monanthia (Phyllontocheila) setulosa Fieber 1844, p. 68, pl. 5, figs. 34–36 [Czechoslovakia; *Thymus serpyllus*].—Herrich-Schaeffer 1850, p. 154.

Camypolsteira (Derephysia) setulosa var. *gracilis* (not Herrich-Schaeffer): Kolenati 1856, p. 431 [Caucasus; *Thymus montanus*].

Monanthia (Phyllontocheila) gracilis: Flor 1860, p. 343 [Austria; France; Estonia; Latvia].

Monanthia setulosa: Fieber 1861, p. 122.—Frey-Gessner 1865, p. 231 [Switzerland].—Garbiglietti 1869, p. 272 [Italy].—Jakovlev 1869, p. 111; 1880b, p. 106.—Horváth 1874b, p. 432 [Hungary].—Puton 1874a, p. 226.—Reiber and Puton 1876, p. 69.—Ferrari 1878, p. 66.

Lasiacantha setulosa: Stål 1874, p. 56.

Monanthia capucina: Puton 1879c, p. 113.—d'Antessanty 1890, p. 32.—Hüeber 1893, p. 337.—Rey 1893, p. 97.

Monanthia (Lasiacantha) capucina: Puton 1886b, p. 33.

Lasiacantha capucina: Lethierry and Severin 1896, p. 18.—Horváth 1906a, p. 60 [Rumania; Yugoslavia].—Butler 1923, p. 208 [England].—Stichel 1926, p. 109 [*Ajuga; Galium; Hieracium*]; 1960a, p. 307 [Poland; Bulgaria].—Scholte 1935, p. 76, fig. 18 [Netherlands].—Gulde 1938, p. 285, fig.—Hoberlandt 1942, p. 125 [Transcaucasus].—Blöte 1945, p. 87 [Tunisia].—Kiritshenko 1951, p. 248.—Novak and Wagner 1951, p. 70.—Bator 1953, p. 325, pl. 2, fig. 6.—Gomez-

Menor 1955b, p. 249 [Spain].—Štušak 1957a, p. 20, figs. 1–3; 1957b, pp. 137, 139, figs. 6, 10a, 11b; 1961a, p. 77, fig. 5e.—Southwood and Leston 1959, p. 147, pl. 21, fig. 10.—Mancini 1959, p. 260.

Phyllontocheila capucina: Reichensperger 1920, p. 62.

TYPE: "Saxonia"; sex and deposition of type unknown.

DISTRIBUTION: England; Netherlands; France; Spain; Germany; Switzerland; Czechoslovakia; Poland; Hungary; Austria; Italy; Yugoslavia; Bulgaria; Rumania; U.S.S.R. (Estonia; Latvia; Caucasus; Transcaucasus); Tunisia.

HOST PLANTS: *Ajuga* sp.; *Galium* sp.; *Hieracium* sp.; *Thymus montanus; Thymus serpyllus;* moss.

NOTE: Study of eggs and immature stages [Štušak 1957a, 1957b, 1961a].

*Lasiacantha comans Drake (emendation)

Lasiacanthia [sic] *comantis* Drake 1953d, p. 220 [Senegal].

TYPE: Holotype ♂; Bambey, Senegal; British Mus.

DISTRIBUTION: Senegal.

HOST PLANT: Unrecorded.

*Lasiacantha compta (Drake)

Furcilliger comptus Drake 1942b, p. 363 [Queensland; *Gmelina leichardtii*].

Lasiacantha comptus: Drake and Ruhoff 1961c, p. 145.

TYPE: Holotype ♂, macropterous; Imbil, Queensland, Australia; Drake Coll. (USNM).

DISTRIBUTION: Australia (Queensland).

HOST PLANT: *Gmelina leichardtii*.

*Lasiacantha crassicornis Horváth

Lasiacantha crassicornis Horváth 1929, p. 320 [Natal].

TYPE: Holotype ♀; Weenen, Natal, South Africa; British Mus.

DISTRIBUTION: South Africa (Natal).

HOST PLANT: Unrecorded.

*Lasiacantha cuneata (Distant)

Jannaeus cuneatus Distant 1909a, p. 118 [India]; 1910a, p. 118, fig. 60.—Drake and Poor 1936b, p. 146.—Drake 1937a, p. 387 [Ceylon].—Singh 1953, p. 118.

Lasiacantha cuneautus [sic]: Drake 1953b, p. 92.

TYPE: Sex unknown; North Bengal, India; British Mus.

DISTRIBUTION: India; Ceylon; China.

HOST PLANT: Unrecorded.

*Lasiacantha discors Drake (emendation)

Lasiacantha discordis Drake 1955a, p. 80 [Western Australia].

TYPE: Holotype ♀, macropterous; Kalgoorie, Western Australia, Australia; Drake Coll. (USNM).

DISTRIBUTION: Australia (Western Australia).

HOST PLANT: Unrecorded.

*Lasiacantha gambiana Drake

   Lasiacantha gambiana Drake 1954b, p. 11 [Gambia].

TYPE: Holotype ♂, brachypterous; Bathurst, Gambia, West Africa; Drake Coll. (USNM).

DISTRIBUTION: Gambia.

HOST PLANT: Unrecorded.

*Lasiacantha gracilis (Herrich-Schaeffer)

   Tingis gracilis Herrich-Schaeffer 1830, heft 118, tab. 20 [Germany]; 1835, p. 58.—Horváth 1905b, p. 569.

   Derephysia gracilis: Herrich-Schaeffer 1838, p. 72, pl. 128, figs. d–h.

   Monanthia (Phyllontocheila) setulosa var. *gracilis:* Fieber 1844, p. 69, pl. 5, figs. 37, 38 [Austria].

   Campylosteira (Derephysia) setulosa var. *capucina* (not Germar): Kolenati 1856, p. 431.

   Monanthia setulosa var. *gracilis:* Fieber 1861, p. 122.—Frey-Gessner 1865, p. 231 [Switzerland].

   Monanthia piligera Garbiglietti 1869, p. 273 [Italy].

   Monanthia cucullifera Puton 1888, p. 105.

   Lasiacantha cucullifera: Lethierry and Severin 1896, p. 19.

   Lasiacantha gracilis: Horváth 1906a, pp. **59**, 60 [Hungary; Caucasus].— Stichel 1938a, p. 406 [France; Poland]; 1960a, p. 306 [Turkey; Bulgaria; *Satureja montana; Thymus*].—Hoberlandt 1942, p. 125 [Czechoslovakia; Transcaucasus]; 1943, p. 118.—Kiritshenko 1951, p. 248.—Wagner 1958, p. 240.

   Lasiacantha cracilis [sic]: Stichel 1935, p. 349.

TYPE: Regensburg, Germany; sex and deposition of type unknown.

DISTRIBUTION: Germany; France; Austria; Hungary; Czechoslovakia; Switzerland; Italy; Poland; Bulgaria; Turkey; U.S.S.R. (Caucasus; Transcaucasus).

HOST PLANTS: *Satureja montana; Thymus* sp.

*Lasiacantha hedenborgii (Stål)

   Tingis (Lasiacantha) hedenborgii Stål 1873, p. 130 [Cyprus].

   Lasiacantha hedenborgii: Stål 1874, p. 56.—Horváth 1906a, p. 60 [Israel].—Seidenstücker 1954, p. 235 [Turkey].—Hoberlandt 1955, p. 88.

   Monanthia hedenborgi [sic]: Puton 1881, p. 123 [Lebanon].

   Monanthia (Lasiacantha) hedenborgi [sic]: Puton 1886b, p. 33.

TYPE: Holotype ♀; Cyprus; Stockholm Mus.

DISTRIBUTION: Cyprus; Lebanon; Israel; Turkey.

HOST PLANT: Unrecorded.

*Lasiacantha histricula (Puton)

Monanthia (*Lasiacantha*) *histricula* Puton 1878, p. lxvii [Spain]; 1886b, p. 33.

Monanthia histricula: Puton 1880, p. 243 [France].

Lasiacantha histricula: Lethierry and Severin 1896, p. 19.—Horváth 1906a, p. 61.—González 1948, p. 50.—Gomez-Menor 1955b, p. 249.

TYPE: Sex unknown; Madrid, Spain; Vienna Mus.

DISTRIBUTION: Spain; France.

HOST PLANT: Unrecorded.

*Lasiacantha horvathi Drake

Lasiacantha horvathi Drake 1951, p. 176 [Tanganyika].

TYPE: Holotype ♀; Meschi, Africa Orientalis; Hungarian Mus.

DISTRIBUTION: Tanganyika; Sudan; South Africa (Cape Province).

HOST PLANT: Unrecorded.

Lasiacantha insularis Schouteden

Lasiacantha insularis Schouteden 1957a, p. 84 [Malagasy].

TYPE: Sex unknown; Tananarive, Madagascar; Paris Mus.

DISTRIBUTION: Malagasy Republic.

HOST PLANT: Unrecorded.

*Lasiacantha kin Schouteden

Lasiacantha kin Schouteden 1955a, p. 28 [Congo].

TYPE: Sex unknown; Kinchassa, Bas-Congo, Belgian Congo; Cent. Afr. Mus.

DISTRIBUTION: Congo.

HOST PLANT: Unrecorded.

Lasiacantha leai (Hacker)

Myrmecotingis leai Hacker 1928, p. 182, pl. 23. fig. 15 [Western Australia].

Lasiacantha leai: Hacker 1929, p. 334.

TYPE: Sex unknown; Swan River, Western Australia, Australia; Queensland Mus.

DISTRIBUTION: Australia (Western Australia).

HOST PLANT: Unrecorded.

NOTE: Inquiline, "originally carded with specimens of the Dolichoderine ant *Iridomyrmex conifer* Forel" [Hacker 1928].

*Lasiacantha merita Drake

Lasiacantha merita Drake 1958c, p. 322 [Malagasy].

TYPE: Sex unknown; Tuléar, Anakao du Bas, Madagascar; Madagascar Sci. Inst.

DISTRIBUTION: Malagasy Republic.

HOST PLANT: Unrecorded.

Lasiacantha odontostoma (Stål)

Tingis (Lasiacantha) odontostoma Stål 1873, p. 130 [Sierra Leone].
Lasiacantha odontostoma: Lethierry and Severin 1896, p. 19 [Guinea].
Lasiacantha odontosoma [sic]: Distant 1902a, p. 242, pl. 15, fig. 6.
TYPE: Holotype ♂; Sierra Leone; Stockholm Mus.
DISTRIBUTION: Sierra Leone; Guinea.
HOST PLANT: Unrecorded.

*Lasiacantha sideris Drake

Lasiacantha sideris Drake 1951, p. 175 [Kenya].
TYPE: Holotype ♀, macropterous; Murnias, Kenya; Hungarian Mus.
DISTRIBUTION: Kenya.
HOST PLANT: Unrecorded.

*Lasiacantha turneri Drake

Lasiacanthia [sic] *turneri* Drake 1953d, p. 219 [South-West Africa].
TYPE: Holotype ♂; Okahandja, South-West Africa; British Mus.
DISTRIBUTION: South-West Africa.
HOST PLANT: Unrecorded.

*Lasiacantha yebo Schouteden

Lasiacantha yebo Schouteden 1955a, p. 28 [Congo].
TYPE: Sex unknown; Yebo, Ituri, Belgian Congo; Cent. Afr. Mus.
DISTRIBUTION: Congo; Kenya.
HOST PLANT: Unrecorded.

Genus LEPTOBYRSA Stål

Leptobyrsa Stål 1873, pp. 119, 123.—Lethierry and Severin 1896, p. 13.—Drake and Poor 1937c, pp. 163–165.—Monte 1939b, p. 71; 1941e, p. 101.—Drake and Ruhoff 1960a, p. 64.
TYPE SPECIES: *Tingis steini* Stål.

*Leptobyrsa ardua Drake

Leptobyrsa ardua Drake 1922c, p. 376 [Brazil].—Drake and Hambleton 1938b, p. 54.—Monte 1939b, p. 71 [*Symphyoppapus reticulatus*].
TYPE: Holotype ♂, macropterous; Minas Gerais, Brazil; Drake Coll. (USNM).
DISTRIBUTION: Brazil; Argentina.
HOST PLANT: *Symphyoppapus reticulatus.*

*Leptobyrsa baccharidis Drake and Hambleton

Leptobyrsa baccharidis Drake and Hambleton 1938a, p. 65 [Brazil; *Baccharis mesoneura; Eupatorium intermedium*].—Silva 1956, p. 36.
TYPE: Holotype ♂, macropterous; São Paulo, Brazil; Drake Coll. (USNM).
DISTRIBUTION: Brazil.
HOST PLANTS: *Baccharis mesoneura; Eupatorium intermedium.*

*Leptobyrsa bruchi Drake

Leptobyrsa bruchi Drake 1928i, p. 73 [Argentina].

TYPE: Holotype♂, macropterous; Córdoba, Argentina; Drake Coll. (USNM).

DISTRIBUTION: Argentina.

HOST PLANT: Unrecorded.

*Leptobyrsa decora Drake

Leptobyrsa decora Drake 1922c, p. 375 [Colombia; Ecuador].—Monte 1938b, p. 130 [*Citrus aurantium*].

TYPE: Holotype♂, macropterous; Lacumbre, Colombia; Drake Coll. (USNM).

DISTRIBUTION: Colombia; Ecuador.

HOST PLANT: *Citrus aurantium.*

*Leptobyrsa mendocina Pennington

Leptobyrsa mendocina Pennington 1919, p. 526, fig. 1 [Argentina]; 1921, p. 20.

Leptobyrsa mendecina [sic]: Drake 1931b, p. 511.

TYPE: Holotype ♀, macropterous; Mendosa, Argentina; Drake Coll. (USNM).

DISTRIBUTION: Argentina.

HOST PLANT: Unrecorded.

*Leptobyrsa pulchra Monte

Leptobyrsa pulchra Monte 1940e, p. 286 [Brazil].

TYPE: Holotype♂; Nova Teutonia, Santa Catarina, Brazil; Monte Coll. (Mus. Nacional).

DISTRIBUTION: Brazil.

HOST PLANT: Unrecorded.

*Leptobyrsa steini (Stål)

Tingis steini Stål 1858, p. 64 [Brazil].—Walker 1873a, p. 181.

Leptobyrsa steinii [sic]: Stål 1873, p. 123.—Pennington 1919, p. 527, fig.

Leptobyrsa steini: Champion 1898b, p. 58, pl. 2, fig. 4.—Drake and Hambleton 1935, p. 148 [*Eupatorium intermedium; Baccharis mesoneura*]; 1938a, p. 65 [*Symphyopappus reticulatus*]; 1944b, p. 126.—Drake 1936b, p. 700 [Argentina].—Drake and Poor 1937d, p. 309.—Monte 1941c, p. 204, fig. 1; 1942d, p. 108; 1944b, p. 461, figs. 4–8.—Singh 1953, p. 118.

Leptobyrsa nigritarsis Monte 1937a, p. 32, fig. 10; 1937c, p. 72; 1941c, p. 207, fig. 2.

TYPE: Holotype♂; Rio de Janeiro, Brazil; Stockholm Mus.

DISTRIBUTION: Brazil; Argentina.

HOST PLANTS: *Baccharis mesoneura; Eupatorium intermedium; Symphyopappus reticulatus.*

*Leptobyrsa tersa Drake and Hambleton

  Leptobyrsa tersa Drake and Hambleton 1935, p. 148 [Brazil; *Moquinia polymorpha*].—Monte 1937a, p. 32 [*Moquinia*].

TYPE: Holotype♂, macropterous; São Paulo, Brazil; Drake Coll. (USNM).

DISTRIBUTION: Brazil.

HOST PLANTS: *Moquinia polymorpha; Moquinia* sp.

Genus LEPTOCYSTA Stål

  Leptocysta Stål 1873, pp. 121, 127.—Monte 1939b, p. 71; 1941e, p. 103; 1946a, p. 325 (key).—Drake and Ruhoff 1960a, p. 64.

TYPE SPECIES: *Tingis sexnebulosa* Stål.

*Leptocysta notialis Drake

  Leptocysta notialis Drake 1948d, p. 18 [Argentina].

TYPE: Holotype♂, macropterous; Rosas, F. C. Sud, Buenos Aires, Argentina; Drake Coll. (USNM).

DISTRIBUTION: Argentina.

HOST PLANT: Unrecorded.

*Leptocysta novatis Drake

  Leptocysta sexnebulosa (not Stål): Berg 1884, p. 103.
  Leptocysta novatis Drake 1928i, p. 72 [Argentina]; 1935, p. 17 [Paraguay].—Drake and Poor 1938b, p. 107.—Monte 1938d, p. 387; 1946a, p. 328, figs. 3, 4.

TYPE: Holotype♂, macropterous; La Plata, Argentina; Drake Coll. (USNM).

DISTRIBUTION: Argentina; Paraguay.

HOST PLANT: Unrecorded.

*Leptocysta sexnebulosa (Stål)

  Tingis sex-nebulosa Stål 1858, p. 64 [Brazil].—Walker 1873, p. 181.
  Leptocysta sexnebulosa: Stål 1873, p. 127.—Lethierry and Severin 1896, p. 15 [Argentina].—Champion 1898b, p. 61, pl. 2, figs. 10, 10a.—Pennington 1921, p. 20.—Drake 1930a, p. 1; 1931b, p. 511 [Colombia]; 1935, p. 17 [Paraguay].—Drake and Hambleton 1934, p. 442 [*Antennaria; Ipomoea batatas*]; 1945, p. 359.—Costa Lima 1936, p. 128.—Bosq 1937, p. 130.—Drake and Poor 1937d, p. 306, pl. 36, fig. 13; 1939b, p. 98.—Monte 1937, p. 34, fig. 3 [*Mikania*]; 1938b, p. 131; 1939b, p. 71 [Venezuela; *Vernonia*]; 1940c, p. 193; 1940d, p. 101; 1946a, p. 326, figs. 1, 2 [Peru].
  Leptocysta sexnolata [sic]: Drake 1936b, p. 699.

TYPE: Holotype♂; Rio de Janeiro, Brazil; Stockholm Mus.

DISTRIBUTION: Brazil; Venezuela; Peru; Colombia; Argentina; Paraguay.

HOST PLANTS: *Antennaria* sp.; *Ipomoea batatas; Mikania* sp.; *Vernonia* sp.

*Leptocysta tertia Monte

Leptocysta tertia Monte 1946a, p. 330, figs. 5, 6 [Argentina].

TYPE: Holotype ♂; Puerto Tirol, Argentina; Monte Coll. (Mus. Nacional).

DISTRIBUTION: Argentina.

HOST PLANT: Unrecorded.

Genus LEPTODICTYA Stål

Leptodictya Stål 1873, pp. 121, 127.—Lethierry and Severin 1896, p. 14.—Champion 1897, p. 23 (key).—Van Duzee 1916, p. 26; 1917b, p. 219.—Blatchley 1926, p. 477 (key).—Drake 1931e, pp. 119–121.—Monte 1939b, p. 71; 1941e, p. 103.—Hurd 1946, p. 452.—Drake and Ruhoff 1960a, p. 64.

TYPE SPECIES: *Monanthia (Physatocheila) ochropa* Stål.

Subgenus LEPTODICTYA (LEPTODICTYA) Stål

TYPE SPECIES: *Monanthia (Physatocheila) ochropa* Stål.

*Leptodictya ochropa (Stål)

Monanthia (Physatocheila) ochropa Stål 1858, p. 62 [Brazil].

Monanthia ochropa: Walker 1873a, p. 192.

Leptodictya ochropa: Stål 1873a, p. 127.—Drake 1931e, pp. 119, 121; 1936b, p. 699 [Argentina].—Drake and Poor 1937d, p. 306, pl. 36, fig. 4.—Drake and Hambleton 1938b, p. 53 [bamboo].—Monte 1938b, p. 131.—Silva 1956, p. 38, fig. 13.—Drake and Davis 1960, fig. 60.

TYPE: Holotype ♂; Rio de Janeiro, Brazil; Stockholm Mus.

DISTRIBUTION: Argentina; Brazil.

HOST PLANT: Bamboo.

Subgenus LEPTODICTYA (HANUALA) Kirkaldy

Hanuala Kirkaldy 1905, p. 217.

Leptodictya (Hanuala): Drake 1931e, pp. 119–121.—Monte 1939b, p. 72; 1941e, p. 104.—Drake and Ruhoff 1960a, p. 65.

TYPE SPECIES: *Hanuala leinahoni* Kirkaldy.

*Leptodictya (Hanuala) approximata (Stål)

Monanthia (Physatocheila) approximata Stål 1858, p. 63 [Brazil].

Monanthia approximata: Walker 1873a, p. 193.

Leptodictya approximata: Stål 1873, p. 127.—Drake 1928a, p. 46.—Drake and Poor 1937d, p. 307, pl. 36, fig. 3 [British Guiana].—Drake and Hambleton 1938b, p. 53.

Leptodictya (Hanuala) approximata: Drake 1931e, p. 121.—Monte 1941e, p. 104 [*Bambusa*].

TYPE: Sex unknown; Rio de Janeiro, Brazil; Stockholm Mus.

DISTRIBUTION: Brazil; British Guiana; Bolivia.

HOST PLANT: *Bambusa* sp.

*Leptodictya (Hanuala) austrina Drake and Hambleton

Leptodictya austrina Drake and Hambleton 1939, p. 157 [Brazil; *Olyra*].

Leptodictya (Hanuala) austrina: Monte 1941e, p. 104.

TYPE: Holotype ♂, macropterous; Ribeirão Preto, São Paulo, Brazil; Drake Coll. (USNM).

DISTRIBUTION: Brazil.

HOST PLANT: *Olyra* sp.

*Leptodictya (Hanuala) bambusae Drake

Leptodictya bambusae Drake 1918a, p. 175 [Puerto Rico; *Bambusa vulgaris*]; 1926a, p. 86 [Cuba; sugar].—Wolcott 1923, p. 247.—Drake and Bruner 1924a, p. 149 [Mexico].—Barber 1939, p. 370 [Haiti].— Bruner, Scaramuzza and Otero 1945, pp. 19, 158 [*Saccharum officinarum*].—Drake and Hambleton 1945, p. 362 [El Salvador; Guatemala; Tex.; Peru; maize]; 1946b, p. 122.—Box 1953, p. 37.

Leptodictya (Hanuala) bambusae: Drake 1931e, pp. 119, 121.

TYPE: Holotype ♂, macropterous; Mayaguez, Puerto Rico; Drake Coll. (USNM).

DISTRIBUTION: U.S. (Tex.); Puerto Rico; Cuba; Haiti; Mexico; Guatemala; El Salvador; Colombia; Ecuador; Venezuela; Peru.

HOST PLANTS: *Bambusa vulgaris; Dendrocalamus strictus; Saccharum officinarum;* maize.

*Leptodictya (Hanuala) championi Drake

Leptodictya championi Drake 1928a, p. 46 [Guatemala].

Leptodictya (Hanuala) championi: Drake 1931e, p. 121.

TYPE: Holotype ♂, macropterous; Purula, Vera Paz, Guatemala; Drake Coll. (USNM).

DISTRIBUTION: Guatemala.

HOST PLANT: Unrecorded.

*Leptodictya (Hanuala) circumcincta Champion

Leptodictya circumcincta Champion 1897, p. 24, pl. 2, figs. 12, 12a [Panama].—Drake and Ruhoff 1962d, p. 489.

Leptodictya fusca Drake 1928a, p. 50 [Canal Zone].

Leptodictya (Hanuala) fusca: Drake 1931e, p. 121.

Leptodictya (Hanuala) circumcincta: Drake 1931e, p. 121.

TYPE: Sex unknown; San Felix, Chiriqui, Panama; British Mus.

DISTRIBUTION: Panama; Canal Zone; Ecuador.

HOST PLANT: Unrecorded.

*Leptodictya (Hanuala) colombiana Drake

Leptodictya colombiana Drake 1928a, p. 48 [Colombia].

Leptodictya (Hanuala) colombiana: Drake 1931e, p. 121.

TYPE: Holotype ♂, macropterous; Colombia; Drake Coll. (USNM).

DISTRIBUTION: Colombia; Peru; Ecuador.

HOST PLANT: Kidney bean.

*Leptodictya (Hanuala) comes Drake and Hambleton (emendation)

Leptodictya comitis Drake and Hambleton 1938b, p. 54, pl. 10, fig. e [Brazil; *Olyra;* bamboo].

Leptodictya (Hanuala) comitis: Monte 1939b, p. 72; 1941e, p. 105.

TYPE: Holotype ♂, macropterous; Ponte Nova, Minas Gerais, Brazil; Drake Coll. (USNM).

DISTRIBUTION: Brazil.

HOST PLANTS: *Olyra* sp.; bamboo.

*Leptodictya (Hanuala) cretata Champion

Leptodictya cretata Champion 1897, p. 23, pl. 2, figs. 11, 11a, b [Guatemala].

Leptodictya (Hanuala) cretata: Drake 1931e, pp. 120, 121 [Costa Rica; bamboo].

TYPE: Sex unknown; Panajachel, Guatemala; British Mus.

DISTRIBUTION: Guatemala; Costa Rica.

HOST PLANT: Bamboo.

*Leptodictya (Hanuala) decor Drake and Hambleton (emendation)

Leptodictya decoris Drake and Hambleton 1945, p. 364 [Peru; bamboo].

TYPE: Holotype ♂, macropterous; Tingo Maria, Peru; Drake Coll. (USNM).

DISTRIBUTION: Peru.

HOST PLANT: Bamboo.

Leptodictya (Hanuala) dilatata Monte

Leptodictya dilatata Monte 1942a, p. 97 [Brazil].

TYPE: Holotype ♀; Nova Friburgo, Estado do Rio, Brazil; Monte Coll. (Mus. Nacional).

DISTRIBUTION: Brazil.

HOST PLANT: Unrecorded.

*Leptodictya (Hanuala) dohrni (Stål)

Monanthia (Physatocheila) dohrni Stål 1858, p. 62 [Brazil].

Monanthia dohrni: Walker 1873a, p. 193.

Leptodictya dohrnii [sic]: Stål 1873, p. 127.—Drake 1931b, p. 511.

Leptodictya dohrni: Lethierry and Severin 1896, p. 14.—Drake and Poor 1937d, p. 307, pl. 36, fig. 1.—Monte 1941b, pp. 101–106, fig.

Leptodictya (Hanuala) dohrnii [sic]: Drake 1931e, p. 121.

TYPE: Holotype ♀; Rio de Janeiro, Brazil; Stockholm Mus.

DISTRIBUTION: Brazil; Peru.

HOST PLANT: Unrecorded.

*Leptodictya (Hanuala) dola Drake and Hambleton

Leptodictya dola Drake and Hambleton 1939, p. 159 [Brazil; *Panicum maximum*].

Leptodictya (Hanuala) dola: Monte 1941e, p. 105.

TYPE: Holotype ♂, macropterous; Viçosa, Minas Gerais, Brazil; Drake Coll. (USNM).
DISTRIBUTION: Brazil.
HOST PLANT: *Panicum maximum.*

*Leptodictya (Hanuala) ecuadoris Drake and Hambleton

Leptodictya ecuadoris Drake and Hambleton 1945, p. 362 [Ecuador; bamboo].

TYPE: Holotype ♂, macropterous; Vinces, Ecuador; Drake Coll. (USNM).
DISTRIBUTION: Ecuador; Brazil.
HOST PLANT: Bamboo.

*Leptodictya (Hanuala) elitha Drake and Ruhoff

Leptodictya elitha Drake and Ruhoff 1962c, p. 136 [Peru].

TYPE: Holotype ♂, macropterous; Queros, Rio Cosñipata, Dept. Cuszo, Peru; Drake Coll. (USNM).
DISTRIBUTION: Peru.
HOST PLANT: Unrecorded.

*Leptodictya (Hanuala) evidens Drake

Leptodictya evidens Drake 1928a, p. 49 [Panama].
Leptodictya (Hanuala) evidens: Drake 1931a, p. 121.

TYPE: Holotype ♀, macropterous; Tabernilla, Panama; Drake Coll. (USNM).
DISTRIBUTION: Panama: Peru.
HOST PLANT: Unrecorded.

Leptodictya (Hanuala) faceta Monte

Leptodictya faceta Monte 1943d, p. 270 [Brazil].

TYPE: Holotype ♂; Palmerias, Ipaussú, São Paulo, Brazil; Monte Coll. (Mus. Nacional).
DISTRIBUTION: Brazil.
HOST PLANT: Unrecorded.

*Leptodictya (Hanuala) formositis Drake (emendation)

Leptodictya formosatis Drake 1928a, p. 50 [Ecuador].
Leptodictya (Hanuala) formosatis: Drake 1931e, p. 121.

TYPE: Holotype ♀, macropterous; Mera, Ecuador; Drake Coll. (USNM).
DISTRIBUTION: Ecuador.
HOST PLANT: Unrecorded.

*Leptodictya (Hanuala) fraterna Monte

Leptodictya fraterna Monte 1941d, p. 96, fig. 3 [Costa Rica].—Drake and Hambleton 1945, p. 362 [bamboo].

TYPE: Holotype ♂, macropterous; San Isidro de Coronado, Alajuela, Costa Rica; Monte Coll. (Mus. Nacional).
DISTRIBUTION: Costa Rica.
HOST PLANT: Bamboo.

*Leptodictya (Hanuala) fuscocincta (Stål)

Monanthia (Physatocheila) fusco-cincta Stål 1858, p. 62 [Brazil].
Monanthia fuscocincta: Walker 1873a, p. 193.
Leptodictya fuscocincta: Stål 1873, p. 127.—Champion 1898b, p. 60, pl. 2, fig. 9.—Drake and Poor 1937d, p. 307.—Drake and Hambleton 1938b, p. 53 [bamboo].—Monte 1938b, p. 131; 1941b, p. 104.
Leptodictya (Hanuala) fuscocincta: Drake 1931e, p. 121.

Type: Holotype ♀; Rio de Janeiro, Brazil; Stockholm Mus.
Distribution: Brazil.
Host Plant: Bamboo.

*Leptodictya (Hanuala) galerita Drake

Leptodictya galerita Drake 1942a, p. 19 [Paraguay].

Type: Holotype ♂, macropterous; Horqueta, Paraguay; Drake Coll. (USNM).
Distribution: Paraguay.
Host Plant: Unrecorded.

*Leptodictya (Hanuala) grandatis Drake

Leptodictya grandatis Drake 1931b, p. 511 [Peru].

Type: Holotype ♂, macropterous; Tambo Eneñas, Cam. del Pichis, Peru; Cornell Univ.
Distribution: Peru.
Host Plant: Unrecorded.

Leptodictya (Hanuala) intermedia Monte

Leptodictya intermedia Monte 1943d, p. 272 [Brazil].

Type: Holotype ♂; Nova Teutonia, S. Catarina, Brazil; Monte Coll. (Mus. Nacional).
Distribution: Brazil.
Host Plant: Unrecorded.

*Leptodictya (Hanuala) laidis Drake and Hambleton

Leptodictya laidis Drake and Hambleton 1945, p. 362 [Colombia; bamboo].

Type: Holotype ♂, macropterous; Villavicencio, Colombia; Drake Coll. (USNM).
Distribution: Colombia.
Host Plant: Bamboo.

*Leptodictya (Hanuala) leinahoni (Kirkaldy)

Hanuala leinahoni Kirkaldy 1905, p. 217 [Peru; Bolivia].
Leptodictya leinahoni: Drake 1922b, p. 42.—Monte 1938b, p. 131.
Leptodictya (Hanuala) leinahoni: Drake 1931c, p. 226; 1931e, p. 121 [Ecuador].—Drake and Davis 1960, fig. 61.

Type: Lectotype ♀, macropterous; Mapiri, Bolivia; USNM.
Distribution: Bolivia; Peru; Ecuador.
Host Plant: Unrecorded.

Leptodictya (Hanuala) lepida (Stål)

Monanthia (Physatocheila) lepida Stål 1858, p. 63 [Brazil].
Monanthia lepida: Walker 1873a, p. 193.
Leptodictya lepida: Stål 1873, p. 127.—Drake and Poor 1937d, p. 307, pl. 36, fig. 2.
Leptodictya (Hanuala) lepida: Drake 1931e, p. 121.

TYPE: Sex unknown; Rio de Janeiro, Brazil; Stockholm Mus.
DISTRIBUTION: Brazil.
HOST PLANT: Unrecorded.

*Leptodictya (Hanuala) litigiosa Monte

Leptodictya litigiosa Monte 1940b, p. 380 [Brazil; bamboo].—Silva 1956, p. 36, fig. 12 [*Phyllostachys castilloni*].
Leptodictya (Hanuala) litigiosa: Monte 1941e, p. 106.

TYPE: Holotype♂; Água Preta, Estado da Baía, Brazil; Monte Coll. (Mus. Nacional).
DISTRIBUTION: Brazil; British Guiana.
HOST PLANT: *Phyllostachys castilloni;* bamboo.

*Leptodictya (Hanuala) lucida Drake and Hambleton

Leptodictya lucida Drake and Hambleton 1945, p. 364 [Peru; bamboo].

TYPE: Holotype♂, macropterous; Tingo María, Peru; Drake Coll. (USNM).
DISTRIBUTION: Peru.
HOST PLANT: Bamboo.

*Leptodictya (Hanuala) luculenta Drake

Leptodictya luculenta Drake 1928a, p. 49 [Ecuador].
Leptodictya (Hanuala) luculenta: Drake 1931e, p. 121.

TYPE: Holotype ♂, macropterous; Mera, Ecuador; Drake Coll. (USNM).
DISTRIBUTION: Ecuador; Peru.
HOST PLANT: Unrecorded.

*Leptodictya (Hanuala) madelinae Drake

Leptodictya madelinae Drake 1928a, p. 47 [Ecuador]; 1931b, p. 511 [Peru].
Leptodictya (Hanuala) madelinae: Drake 1931e, p. 121 [grass].

TYPE: Holotype♂, macropterous; Banos, Ecuador; Drake Coll. (USNM).
DISTRIBUTION: Ecuador; Peru.
HOST PLANT: Grass.

*Leptodictya (Hanuala) madra Drake and Hambleton

Leptodictya madra Drake and Hambleton 1939, p. 158 [Brazil; *Olyra*].
Leptodictya (Hanuala) madra: Monte 1941e, p. 106.

TYPE: Holotype♂, macropterous; Belém, Pará, Brazil; Drake Coll. (USNM).
DISTRIBUTION: Brazil.
HOST PLANT: *Olyra* sp.

*Leptodictya (Hanuala) nema Drake and Hambleton

Leptodictya nema Drake and Hambleton 1939, p. 158 [Brazil].
Leptodictya (Hanuala) nema: Monte 1941e, p. 106.

TYPE: Holotype ♀, macropterous; Viçosa, Minas Gerais, Brazil; Drake Coll. (USNM).

DISTRIBUTION: Brazil.

HOST PLANT: Unrecorded.

*Leptodictya (Hanuala) nicholi Drake

Leptodictya nicholi Drake 1926c, p. 126 [Ariz.].
Leptodictya (Hanuala) nicholi: Drake 1931e, p. 121.

TYPE: Holotype ♂, macropterous; Santa Rita Mountains, Arizona, U.S.; Drake Coll. (USNM).

DISTRIBUTION: U.S. (Ariz.).

HOST PLANT: Unrecorded.

Leptodictya (Hanuala) nigra Monte

Leptodictya nigra Monte 1941d, p. 97 [Costa Rica].

TYPE: Holotype ♂; San Isidro de Coronado, Alajuela, Costa Rica; Monte Coll. (Mus. Nacional).

DISTRIBUTION: Costa Rica.

HOST PLANT: Unrecorded.

*Leptodictya (Hanuala) nigrosis Drake and Hambleton

Leptodictya nigrosis Drake and Hambleton 1945, p. 363 [Peru; bamboo].

TYPE: Holotype ♂, macropterous; Tingo María, Peru; Drake Coll. (USNM).

DISTRIBUTION: Peru.

HOST PLANT: Bamboo.

*Leptodictya (Hanuala) nota Drake and Hambleton

Leptodictya nota Drake and Hambleton 1939, p. 157 [Brazil; *Olyra*].
Leptodictya (Hanuala) nota: Monte 1941e, p. 106.

TYPE: Holotype ♂, macropterous; Belém, Pará, Brazil; Drake Coll. (USNM).

DISTRIBUTION: Brazil.

HOST PLANT: *Olyra* sp.

*Leptodictya (Hanuala) olyrae Drake

Leptodictya (Hanuala) olyrae Drake 1931e, p. 121 [Brazil; *Olyra*].
Leptodictya olyrae: Costa Lima 1936, p. 128.—Drake and Hambleton 1938a, p. 48; 1938b, p. 54.—Monte 1938b, p. 131 [*Olyra latifolia*].— Silva 1956, p. 38.

TYPE: Holotype ♀, macropterous; Bahia, Brazil; Drake Coll. (USNM).

DISTRIBUTION: Brazil.

HOST PLANTS: *Olyra latifolia; Olyra* sp.

*Leptodictya (Hanuala) parilis Drake and Hambleton

Leptodictya parilis Drake and Hambleton 1945, p. 363 [El Salvador; bamboo].

TYPE: Holotype ♂, macropterous; San Andrés, El Salvador; Drake Coll. (USNM).

DISTRIBUTION: El Salvador.

HOST PLANT: Bamboo.

*Leptodictya (Hanuala) paspalii Drake and Hambleton

Leptodictya paspalii Drake and Hambleton 1934, p. 443 [Brazil; Paspalum].—Costa Lima 1936, p. 128.

Leptodictya (Hanuala) paspalii: Monte 1939b, p. 72; 1941e, p. 107.

TYPE: Holotype ♂, macropterous; Viçosa, Minas Gerais, Brazil; Drake Coll. (USNM).

DISTRIBUTION: Brazil.

HOST PLANT: Paspalum sp.

*Leptodictya (Hanuala) paulana Drake and Hambleton

Leptodictya paulana Drake and Hambleton 1944b, p. 125 [Brazil].

TYPE: Holotype ♂, macropterous; Taquaretinga, São Paulo, Brazil; Drake Coll. (USNM).

DISTRIBUTION: Brazil.

HOST PLANT: Unrecorded.

*Leptodictya (Hanuala) perita Drake

Leptodictya perita Drake 1935, p. 17 [Brazil].—Monte 1940b, p. 380.

Leptodictya (Hanuala) perita: Monte 1939b, p. 72; 1941e, p. 107.

TYPE: Holotype ♂; Rio Grande do Sul, Brazil; Vienna Mus.

DISTRIBUTION: Brazil.

HOST PLANT: Unrecorded.

*Leptodictya (Hanuala) plana Heidemann

Leptodictya plana Heidemann 1913b, p. 1, fig. 1 [Okla.].—Drake 1925c, p. 38 [Miss.].—Blatchley 1926, p. 478, fig. 108.

Leptodictya (Hanuala) plana: Drake 1931e, p. 121 [Fla.; Ala.; Tex.].

TYPE: Holotype ♂, macropterous; Wistar, Indian Territory, U.S.; USNM.

DISTRIBUTION: U.S. (Okla.; Tex.; Ariz.; Kans.; Ala.; Miss.; Fla.); Mexico.

HOST PLANT: Gramineae.

*Leptodictya (Hanuala) simulans Heidemann

Leptodictya simulans Heidemann 1913b, p. 3, fig. 2 [Va.; Ala.; S.C.].— Blatchley 1926, p. 478, fig. 109 [Miss.].

Leptodictya (Hanuala) simulans: Drake 1931e, pp. 120, 121 [Tex.; Fla.; N.C.; bamboo].

TYPE: Holotype ♂, macropterous; Drummond, Virginia, U.S.; USNM.

DISTRIBUTION: U.S. (Va.; N.C.; S.C.; Fla.; Ala.; Miss.; Tex.).

HOST PLANT: Bamboo.

*Leptodictya (Hanuala) sinaloana Drake

Leptodictya sinaloana Drake 1954d, p. 75 [Mexico].

TYPE: Holotype ♂, macropterous; Sinaloa, Mexico; USNM.

DISTRIBUTION: Mexico.

HOST PLANT: Unrecorded.

NOTE: Found on orchid plants at port-of-entry, Nogales, Ariz. [Drake 1954d]; found on *Tillandsia usneoides* from Mexico, at port-of-entry, San Pedro, Calif.

*Leptodictya (Hanuala) socorrona Drake

Leptodictya socorrona Drake 1948c, p. 23 [Revilla Gigedo].

TYPE: Holotype ♂; Socorro Island, Mexico; Cal. Acad.

DISTRIBUTION: Mexico (Revilla Gigedo Islands).

HOST PLANT: Unrecorded.

*Leptodictya (Hanuala) sodalatis Drake

Leptodictya sodalatis Drake 1928a, p. 48 [Bolivia].
Leptodictya (Hanuala) sodalatis: Drake 1931e, p. 121.

TYPE: Holotype♂, macropterous; Cochabamba, Bolivia; Drake Coll. (USNM).

DISTRIBUTION: Bolivia.

HOST PLANT: Unrecorded.

*Leptodictya (Hanuala) solita Drake and Hambleton

Leptodictya solita Drake and Hambleton 1938b, p. 53, pl. 9, fig. d [Brazil; *Olyra*].
Leptodictya (Hanuala) solita: Monte 1939b, p. 72; 1941e, p. 107.

TYPE: Holotype ♀, macropterous; Ponte Nova, Minas Gerais, Brazil; Drake Coll. (USNM).

DISTRIBUTION: Brazil.

HOST PLANT: *Olyra* sp.

*Leptodictya (Hanuala) tabida (Herrich-Schaeffer)

Monanthia tabida Herrich-Schaeffer 1840, p. 86, pl. 173, fig. 535 [Mexico].—Stål 1873, p. 134.—Walker 1873a, p. 191.
Monanthia (Phyllontocheila) tabida: Fieber 1844, p. 70, pl. 6, fig. 1.— Herrich-Schaeffer 1850, p. 155.
Leptostyla tabida: Uhler 1886, p. 22.
Leptodictya tabida: Champion 1897, p. 23, pl. 2, figs. 10, 10a [Guatemala]; 1898b, p. 60.—Heidemann 1913a, p. 249, fig. 1 [Panama; sugar].—Drake 1925c, p. 38 [Tex.].—Drake and Hambleton 1946b, p. 122.—Box 1953, p. 37 [Venezuela].—Berry 1959, p. 145, fig. 126 [El Salvador].
Leptodictya (Hanuala) tabida: Drake 1931e, pp. 119, 121 [Cuba; maize; bamboo].

Type: Mexico; sex and deposition of type unknown.
Distribution: Panama; El Salvador; Venezuela; Cuba; Guatemala; Mexico; U.S. (Tex.).
Host Plants: Bamboo; maize; sugar.

Leptodictya (Hanuala) tegeticula Monte

Leptodictya tegeticula Monte 1943d, p. 271 [Brazil].
Type: Holotype♂; São Paulo, Brazil; Monte Coll. (Mus. Nacional).
Distribution: Brazil.
Host Plant: Unrecorded.

*Leptodictya (Hanuala) venezolana Monte

Leptodictya venezolana Monte 1940d, p. 104 [Venezuela; *Bambusa*].
Type: Holotype♂; Caobos, Caracas, Venezuela; Monte Coll. (Mus. Nacional).
Distribution: Venezuela.
Host Plant: *Bambusa* sp.

*Leptodictya (Hanuala) vulgata Drake

Leptodictya vulgata Drake 1928a, p. 46 [Ecuador].
Leptodictya (Hanuala) vulgata: Drake 1931e, p. 121.
Type: Holotype♂, macropterous; Naranjapata, Ecuador; Drake Coll. (USNM).
Distribution: Ecuador; Bolivia.
Host Plant: Unrecorded.

*Leptodictya (Hanuala) williamsi Drake

Leptodictya williamsi Drake 1928a, p. 47 [Ecuador].
Leptodictya (Hanuala) williamsi: Drake 1931e, p. 121.
Type: Holotype♂, macropterous; Banos, Ecuador; Drake Coll. (USNM).
Distribution: Ecuador.
Host Plant: Unrecorded.

Genus LEPTOPHARSA Stål

Leptopharsa Stål 1873, pp. 122, 126.—Lethierry and Severin 1896, p. 14.—Champion 1897, p. 21.—Drake 1928d, p. 21.—Costa Lima 1936, p. 128.—Monte 1939b, p. 72; 1941e, p. 108.—Hurd 1946, p. 465.—Bailey 1951, p. 35.—Silva 1956, pp. 38–41.—Drake and Ruhoff 1960a, p. 65.
Leptostyla Stål 1873, pp. 120, 125.—Lethierry and Severin 1896, p. 14.—Champion 1897, p. 11 (key).—Osborn and Drake 1916a, p. 237.—Van Duzee 1917b, pp. 218, 817.—McAtee 1917a, p. 60 (key).—Drake and Ruhoff 1960a, p. 65.
Gelchossa Kirkaldy 1904, p. 280.—Drake 1922c, p. 372.—Parshley 1923b, p. 704.—Blatchley 1926, p. 475 (key).—Drake and Ruhoff 1960a, p. 58.
Type Species: *Leptopharsa elegantula* Stål.

*Leptopharsa albella Drake

Leptopharsa albella Drake 1935, p. 18 [Paraguay].

TYPE: Holotype♂; S. Bernardino, Paraguay; Vienna Mus.

DISTRIBUTION: Paraguay.

HOST PLANT: Unrecorded.

*Leptopharsa angustata (Champion)

Leptostyla angustata Champion 1897, p. 17, pl. 1, figs. 24, 24a [Guatemala].—Van Duzee 1907, p. 19 [Jamaica].

Gelchossa angustata: Drake and Bruner 1924a, p. 149.—Gowdy 1926a, p. 35.

Leptopharsa angustata: Drake and Hambleton 1945, p. 360.—Hurd 1946, p. 466 [Artocarpus integrifolia].

TYPE: Sex unknown; San Gerónimo, Guatemala; British Mus.

DISTRIBUTION: Guatemala; Jamaica.

HOST PLANT: Artocarpus integrifolia.

*Leptopharsa arta Drake and Poor

Leptopharsa arta Drake and Poor 1942, p. 300 [Argentina; Brazil].

TYPE: Holotype ♂; Loreto, Misiones, Argentina; Argentina Mus.

DISTRIBUTION: Argentina; Brazil.

HOST PLANT: Unrecorded.

*Leptopharsa artocarpi Drake and Hambleton

Leptopharsa artocarpi Drake and Hambleton 1938a, p. 48, fig. 1 [Brazil; Artocarpus integrifolia].

TYPE: Holotype ♀, macropterous; Deodoro, E. do Rio, Brazil; Drake Coll. (USNM).

DISTRIBUTION: Brazil.

HOST PLANT: Artocarpus integrifolia.

*Leptopharsa atibaiae Drake and Ruhoff

Leptopharsa atibaiae Drake and Ruhoff 1962d, p. 489 [Brazil].

TYPE: Holotype ♂, macropterous; Atibaia, São Paulo, Brazil; Drake Coll. (USNM).

DISTRIBUTION: Brazil.

HOST PLANT: Unrecorded.

*Leptopharsa avia Drake

Leptopharsa avia Drake 1953a, p. 15 [Brazil].

TYPE: Holotype ♂, macropterous; Belo Horizonte, Minas Gerais, Brazil; Drake Coll. (USNM).

DISTRIBUTION: Brazil.

HOST PLANT: Unrecorded.

Leptopharsa bifasciata (Champion)

Leptostyla bifasciata Champion 1897, p. 19, pl. 2, figs. 3,3a [Guatemala].

Leptopharsa bifasciata: Hurd 1946, p. 466.

TYPE: Sex unknown; Senahu, Vera Paz, Guatemala; British Mus.

DISTRIBUTION: Guatemala.

HOST PLANT: Unrecorded.

*Leptopharsa bondari Drake and Poor

Leptopharsa bondari Drake and Poor 1939a, p. 33 [Brazil].

TYPE: Holotype ♂, macropterous; Bahia, Brazil; Drake Coll. (USNM).

DISTRIBUTION: Brazil.

HOST PLANT: Unrecorded.

*Leptopharsa bradleyi (Drake)

Leptobyrsa bradleyi Drake 1931b, p. 513 [Peru].

Leptopharsa bradleyi: Drake and Poor 1937c, p. 163.

TYPE: Holotype ♂, macropterous; Matucana, Peru; Cornell Univ.

DISTRIBUTION: Peru.

HOST PLANT: Unrecorded.

*Leptopharsa callangae Drake and Poor

Leptopharsa callangae Drake and Poor 1940, p. 230 [Peru].

TYPE: Holotype ♂; Callanga, Peru; Stockholm Mus.

DISTRIBUTION: Peru.

HOST PLANT: Unrecorded.

*Leptopharsa calopa Drake

Leptopharsa calopa Drake 1928a, p. 54 [Brazil].

TYPE: Holotype ♂; Chapada, Brazil; Carnegie Mus.

DISTRIBUTION: Brazil.

HOST PLANT: Unrecorded.

*Leptopharsa clitoriae (Heidemann)

Leptostyla clitoriae Heidemann 1911a, p. 137, pl. 10, fig. 6; 1911b, p. 180, fig. 4 [D.C.; Md.; Tex.; *Clitoria mariana*].—Osborn and Drake 1916a, p. 239, fig. 8 [S.C.].—Van Duzee 1917b, p. 218 [Mass.; N.Y.; Pa.; Ark.].—McAtee 1917a, p. 61 [*Lespedeza; Meibomia*]; 1919, p. 143 [Ind.].—Hussey 1922b, p. 23 [Mich.].

Leptostyla costofasciata Drake 1916, p. 326, fig. 1 [Tenn.].

Gelchossa clitoriae: McAtee 1923, p. 146.—Blatchley 1926, p. 476, fig. 107.—Blöte 1945, p. 85.

Leptopharsa clitoriae: Froeschner 1944, p. 669 [Mo.].—Proctor 1946, p. 74 [Maine; alder].—Bailey 1951, p. 36 [Conn.; *Lappula*].

TYPE: Holotype ♂, macropterous; Rock Creek, District of Columbia, U.S.; USNM.

DISTRIBUTION: U.S. (Maine; Mass.; N.Y.; Pa.; Md.; D.C.; Va.; W. Va.; N.C.; S.C.; Ark.; Miss.; Tenn.; Tex.; Kans.; Mo.; Iowa; Nebr.; Wis.; Mich.; Ill.; Ind.; Ohio).

HOST PLANTS: *Clitoria mariana; Meibomia* sp.; *Lespedeza* sp.; *Lappula* sp.; alder.

NOTE: Eggs [Heidemann 1911a; Bailey]. Taken at light [Bailey].

*Leptopharsa cognata Drake and Hambleton

    Leptopharsa cognata Drake and Hambleton 1934, p. 448 [Brazil; *Miconia*].

TYPE: Holotype ♀, macropterous; Viçosa, Minas Gerais, Brazil; Drake Coll. (USNM).

DISTRIBUTION: Brazil.

HOST PLANT: *Miconia* sp.

*Leptopharsa constricta (Champion)

    Leptostyla constricta Champion 1897, p. 20, pl. 2, figs. 6, 6a [Guatemala; Panama].—Van Duzee 1907, p. 19 [Jamaica].

    Gelchossa constricta: Drake and Bruner 1924a, p. 149.—Gowdy 1926, p. 35.

    Leptopharsa constricta: Hurd 1946, p. 466.

TYPE: Sex unknown; Pantaleon, Guatemala; British Mus.

DISTRIBUTION: Jamaica; Panama; Guatemala.

HOST PLANT: Unrecorded.

NOTE: Synonymy mentioned in Drake and Bruner incorrect.

*Leptopharsa dampfi (Drake)

    Gelchossa dampfi Drake 1927b, p. 117 [Mexico].

    Leptopharsa dampfi: Hurd 1946, p. 466.

TYPE: Holotype ♂, macropterous; Montaña de Sumidero, Chiapas, Mexico; Drake Coll. (USNM).

DISTRIBUTION: Mexico.

HOST PLANT: Unrecorded.

*Leptopharsa dapsilis Drake and Hambleton

    Leptopharsa dapsilis Drake and Hambleton 1945, p. 359 [Guatemala; *Olmediella betschleriana*].

TYPE: Holotype ♂, macropterous; Guatemala City, Guatemala; Drake Coll. (USNM).

DISTRIBUTION: Guatemala.

HOST PLANT: *Olmediella betschleriana.*

*Leptopharsa deca Drake and Hambleton

    Leptopharsa deca Drake and Hambleton 1945, p. 359 [Ecuador].

TYPE: Holotype ♂, macropterous; Pichilingue, Ecuador; Drake Coll. (USNM).

DISTRIBUTION: Ecuador.

HOST PLANT: Unrecorded.

*Leptopharsa decens Drake and Hambleton

    Leptopharsa decens Drake and Hambleton 1938a, p. 58, fig. 4 [Brazil; *Erythroxylon deciduum*].

TYPE: Holotype ♂, macropterous; São Paulo, Brazil; Drake Coll. (USNM).

DISTRIBUTION: Brazil.

HOST PLANT: *Erythroxylon deciduum.*

*Leptopharsa delicata Monte

Leptopharsa delicata Monte 1945a, p. 249, fig. 1 [Brazil].

TYPE: Holotype ♂; Carmo do Rio Claro, Minas Gerais, Brazil; Monte Coll. (Mus. Nacional).

DISTRIBUTION: Brazil.

HOST PLANT: Unrecorded.

*Leptopharsa difficilis Drake and Hambleton

Leptopharsa difficilis Drake and Hambleton 1938b, p. 56, pl. 10, fig. F [Brazil; *Chlorophora tinctoria*].—Monte 1942d, p. 108.

TYPE: Holotype ♂, macropterous; Campinas, São Paulo, Brazil; Drake Coll. (USNM).

DISTRIBUTION: Brazil.

HOST PLANT: *Chlorophora tinctoria*.

Leptopharsa dilaticollis (Champion)

Leptostyla dilaticollis Champion 1897, p. 18, pl. 2, figs. 2, 2a [Guatemala].
Leptopharsa dilaticollis: Hurd 1946, p. 466.

TYPE: Sex unknown; Cahabon, Vera Paz, Guatemala; British Mus.

DISTRIBUTION: Guatemala.

HOST PLANT: Unrecorded.

*Leptopharsa distans Drake (emendation)

Leptopharsa distantis Drake 1928a, p. 53 [Mexico].

TYPE: Holotype ♂, macropterous; Tamasopa, Mexico; Drake Coll. (USNM).

DISTRIBUTION: Mexico.

HOST PLANT: Unrecorded.

*Leptopharsa distinconis Drake

Leptopharsa distinconis Drake 1928a, p. 54 [Brazil].—Monte 1939b, p. 73 [Rubiaceae]; 1947b, p. 432 [*Siparuna guianensis*].—Drake and Hambleton 1944b, p. 128.
Leptopharsa iridis Drake 1930a, p. 2.

TYPE: Holotype ♂; Chapada, Brazil; Carnegie Mus.

DISTRIBUTION: Brazil.

HOST PLANTS: *Siparuna guianensis;* Rubiaceae.

*Leptopharsa divisa (Champion)

Leptostyla divisa Champion 1897, p. 19, pl. 2, figs. 4, 4a [Panama].
Leptopharsa divisa: Monte 1941d, p. 98 [Costa Rica].—Drake and Hambleton 1945, p. 362 [Guatemala]; 1946b, p. 122 [Rubiaceae].

TYPE: Sex unknown; Volcan de Chiriqui, Panama; British Mus.

DISTRIBUTION: Panama; Guatemala; Costa Rica.

HOST PLANT: Rubiaceae.

*Leptopharsa elachys Drake and Ruhoff

Leptopharsa elachys Drake and Ruhoff 1961b, p. 177, fig. 17b [South-West Africa].

TYPE: Holotype ♂, macropterous; Windhoek, South-West Africa; Drake Coll. (USNM).

DISTRIBUTION: South-West Africa.

HOST PLANT: Unrecorded.

*Leptopharsa elata (Champion)

Leptostyla elata Champion 1897, p. 16, pl. 1, figs. 21, 21 a, b [Mexico; Guatemala].

Leptopharsa elata: Monte 1942a, p. 94 [Costa Rica].

TYPE: Sex unknown; San Geronimo, Guatemala; British Mus.

DISTRIBUTION: Mexico; Guatemala; Costa Rica; El Salvador.

HOST PLANT: Unrecorded.

*Leptopharsa elegans (Hacker)

Gelchossa elegans Hacker 1927, p. 27, pl. 7, fig. 7 [Queensland].

TYPE: Sex unknown; Upper Brookfield, Queensland, Australia; Queensland Mus.

DISTRIBUTION: Australia (Queensland).

HOST PLANT: Unrecorded.

*Leptopharsa elegantula Stål

Leptopharsa elegantula Stål 1873, p. 126 [Colombia].—Champion 1898b, p. 60, pl. 2, fig. 8.—Drake and Poor 1937d, p. 308 [Bolivia; Brazil].

TYPE: Holotype ♂; Bogota, Colombia; Stockholm Mus.

DISTRIBUTION: Colombia; Bolivia; Brazil; Ecuador.

HOST PLANT: Unrecorded.

*Leptopharsa enodata Drake

Leptopharsa enodata Drake 1942b, p. 364 [Queensland].

TYPE: Holotype ♂; North Pine River, Queensland, Australia; Queensland Mus.

DISTRIBUTION: Australia (Queensland).

HOST PLANT: Unrecorded.

*Leptopharsa farameae Drake and Hambleton

Leptopharsa farameae Drake and Hambleton 1938a, p. 62, fig. 11 [Brazil; *Faramea*].

TYPE: Holotype ♂, macropterous; Viçosa, Minas Gerais, Brazil; Drake Coll. (USNM).

DISTRIBUTION: Brazil.

HOST PLANT: *Faramea* sp.

*Leptopharsa fici Drake and Hambleton

Leptopharsa fici Drake and Hambleton 1938a, p. 50, fig. 2 [Brazil; *Ficus elastica*].—Monte 1941e, p. 110 [*Ficus subtriplinervia*].

TYPE: Holotype ♂, macropterous; Campinas, São Paulo, Brazil; Drake Coll. (USNM).

DISTRIBUTION: Brazil.

HOST PLANTS: *Ficus elastica; Ficus subtriplinervia.*

*Leptopharsa fimbriata (Champion)

Leptostyla fimbriata Champion 1897, p. 15, pl. 1, figs. 19, 19a [Mexico].
Leptopharsa fimbriata: Hurd 1946, p. 466.

TYPE: Sex unknown; Atoyac, Vera Cruz, Mexico; British Mus.

DISTRIBUTION: Mexico.

HOST PLANT: Unrecorded.

*Leptopharsa firma Drake and Hambleton

Leptopharsa firma Drake and Hambleton 1938a, p. 53 [Brazil].

TYPE: Holotype ♂, macropterous; Araraquara, São Paulo, Brazil; Drake Coll. (USNM).

DISTRIBUTION: Brazil.

HOST PLANT: Unrecorded.

Leptopharsa flava Monte

Leptopharsa flava Monte 1940e, p. 291 [Brazil].—Silva 1956, p. 40 [coffee; Rubiaceae].

TYPE: Holotype ♂; Água Preta, Baía, Brazil; Monte Coll. (Mus. Nacional).

DISTRIBUTION: Brazil.

HOST PLANTS: Coffee; Rubiaceae.

*Leptopharsa forsteroniae Drake and Hambleton

Leptopharsa forsteroniae Drake and Hambleton 1938a, p. 51, fig. 6 [Brazil; *Forsteronia*].

TYPE: Holotype ♂, macropterous; Viçosa, Minas Gerais, Brazil; Drake Coll. (USNM).

DISTRIBUTION: Brazil.

HOST PLANT: *Forsteronia* sp.

*Leptopharsa fortis Drake and Hambleton

Leptopharsa fortis Drake and Hambleton 1934, p. 447 [Brazil; *Cephaelis hastisepala*].—Monte 1939b, p. 73 [*Psychotria*].

TYPE: Holotype ♂. macropterous; Viçosa, Minas Gerais, Brazil; Drake Coll. (USNM).

DISTRIBUTION: Brazil.

HOST PLANTS: *Cephaelis hastisepala; Psychotria* sp.

*Leptopharsa furcata (Stål)

Leptostyla furcata Stål 1873, p. 126 [Brazil].—Champion 1898b, p. 60, pl. 2, figs. 7, 7a.

Gelchossa furcata: Costa Lima 1930, p. 84.

Leptopharsa furcata: Costa Lima 1936, p. 128.—Drake and Poor 1937d, p. 308, pl. 36, fig. 7.—Drake and Hambleton 1938a, p. 55, fig. 5.— Monte 1940e, p. 292 [*Rudgea villiflora*].

TYPE: Sex unknown; Rio de Janeiro, Brazil; Stockholm Mus.

DISTRIBUTION: Brazil.

HOST PLANT: *Rudgea villiflora*.

Leptopharsa furcata var. **immatura** (Stål)

Leptostyla furcata var. *immatura* Stål 1873, p. 126 [Brazil].

TYPE: Sex unknown; Rio de Janeiro, Brazil; Stockholm Mus.

DISTRIBUTION: Brazil.

HOST PLANT: Unrecorded.

*Leptopharsa furculata (Champion)

Leptostyla furculata Champion 1897, p. 20, pl. 2, figs. 5, 5 a, b [Panama; Guatemala].

Leptopharsa furculata: Hurd 1946, p. 466 [Rubiaceae].

TYPE: Sex unknown; Bugaba, Panama; British Mus.

DISTRIBUTION: Panama; Guatemala; Mexico; Costa Rica.

HOST PLANT: Rubiaceae.

Leptopharsa fuscofasciata (Champion)

Leptostyla fuscofasciata Champion 1897, p. 15, pl. 1, figs. 20, 20a [Panama].

Leptopharsa fuscofasciata: Hurd 1946, p. 466.

TYPE: Sex unknown; Bugaba, Panama; British Mus.

DISTRIBUTION: Panama.

HOST PLANT: Unrecorded.

*Leptopharsa gracilenta (Champion)

Leptostyla gracilenta Champion 1897, p. 17, pl. 1, figs. 23, 23a [Guatemala].

Leptopharsa gracilenta: Drake and Bondar 1932, p. 91 [Brazil].—Drake and Hambleton 1938a, p. 51 [*Machaerium stipitatum*].

TYPE: Sex unknown; Pantaleon, Guatemala; British Mus.

DISTRIBUTION: Guatemala; Brazil.

HOST PLANT: *Machaerium stipitatum*.

*Leptopharsa guatemalensis Drake and Poor

Leptopharsa guatemalensis Drake and Poor 1939a, p. 34 [Guatemala].

TYPE: Holotype ♂, macropterous; Polochic River, Guatemala; Drake Coll. (USNM).

DISTRIBUTION: Guatemala.

HOST PLANT: Unrecorded.

*Leptopharsa heidemanni (Osborn and Drake)

Leptostyla heidemanni Osborn and Drake 1916a, p. 238 [Ark.; D.C.; Mass.].—McAtee 1917a, p. 63 [N.J.; La.; *Baptisia tinctoria*]; 1919, p. 144.—Parshley 1917b, p. 56; 1919b, p. 70.—Barber 1922a, p. 17; 1922b, p. 22.

Gelchossa heidemanni: McAtee 1923, p. 146 [Md.].—Parshley 1923b, p. 705, pl. 17, fig. 5 [Conn.].—Weiss and West 1924, p. 56 [Pa.].—Blatchley 1926, p. 477 [N.Y.].—Drake 1928b, p. 102.—Torre-Bueno 1929, p. 311.—Blöte 1945, p. 85 [Va.].

Leptopharsa heidemanni: Froeschner 1944, p. 669 [Mo.].—Hurd 1946, p. 466 [Ohio].—Bailey 1951, p. 37 [R.I.].

TYPE: Sex unknown; Arkansas, U.S.; Ohio State Univ.

DISTRIBUTION: U.S. (Mass.; R.I.; Conn.; N.Y.; N.J.; Pa.; Md.; D.C.; Va.; Ohio; Ind.; Ill.; Mo.; Iowa; Ark.; Okla.; La.; Miss.).

HOST PLANT: *Baptisia tinctoria*.

NOTE: Life history studies [Weiss and West; Bailey].

*Leptopharsa heveae Drake and Poor

Leptopharsa heveae Drake and Poor 1935, p. 283, fig. 1 [Brazil; *Hevea braziliensis*].—Monte 1940b, p. 378.

TYPE: Holotype ♂, macropterous; Boa Vista Rio Tapajo, Brazil; USNM.

DISTRIBUTION: Brazil.

HOST PLANT: *Hevea braziliensis*.

*Leptopharsa hintoni Drake

Leptopharsa hintoni Drake 1938a, p. 71 [Mexico].—Hurd 1946, p. 466 [Ariz.; Tex.].

TYPE: Holotype ♂; Tejupilco, Temascaltepec, Mexico; Cal. Acad.

DISTRIBUTION: Mexico; U.S. (Ariz.; Tex.).

HOST PLANT: Unrecorded.

*Leptopharsa hoffmani Drake

Leptopharsa hoffmani Drake 1928d, p. 21 [Haiti].

TYPE: Holotype ♂, macropterous; Haiti; USNM.

DISTRIBUTION: Haiti.

HOST PLANT: Unrecorded.

*Leptopharsa hyaloptera (Stål)

Leptostyla hyaloptera Stål 1873, p. 126 [Brazil].

Leptopharsa hyaloptera: Drake and Poor 1937d, p. 308.—Drake and Hambleton 1938a, p. 56 [*Psychotria suterella*].

TYPE: Sex unknown; Rio de Janeiro, Brazil; Stockholm Mus.

DISTRIBUTION: Brazil.

HOST PLANT: *Psychotria suterella*.

*Leptopharsa ignota Drake and Hambleton

Leptopharsa ignota Drake and Hambleton 1934, p. 449 [Brazil; *Psychotria hancorniaefolia*].

TYPE: Holotype♂, macropterous; Viçosa, Minas Gerais, Brazil; Drake Coll. (USNM).

DISTRIBUTION: Brazil.

HOST PLANT: *Psychotria hancorniaefolia*.

*Leptopharsa inannana Drake

Leptopharsa inannana Drake 1953a, p. 13 [Cuba].

TYPE: Holotype♂, macropterous; Imias, Cuba; Drake Coll. (USNM).

DISTRIBUTION: Cuba.

HOST PLANT: Unrecorded.

*Leptopharsa inaudita Drake and Hambleton

Leptopharsa inaudita Drake and Hambleton 1938a, p. 62 [Brazil].

TYPE: Holotype♂, macropterous; Itararé, São Paulo, Brazil; Drake Coll. (USNM).

DISTRIBUTION: Brazil.

HOST PLANT: Unrecorded.

*Leptopharsa jubaris Drake and Hambleton

Leptopharsa jubaris Drake and Hambleton 1945, p. 361 [Ecuador].

TYPE: Holotype♂, macropterous; Pichilingue, Ecuador; Drake Coll. (USNM).

DISTRIBUTION: Ecuador.

HOST PLANT: Unrecorded.

*Leptopharsa laureata Drake and Hambleton

Leptopharsa laureata Drake and Hambleton 1945, p. 360 [Peru].

TYPE: Holotype♂, macropterous; Pucallpa, Peru; Drake Coll. (USNM).

DISTRIBUTION: Peru.

HOST PLANT: Unrecorded.

*Leptopharsa lauta Drake and Hambleton

Leptopharsa lauta Drake and Hambleton 1945, p. 361 [Ecuador].

TYPE: Holotype♂, macropterous; Vinces, Ecuador; Drake Coll. (USNM).

DISTRIBUTION: Ecuador.

HOST PLANT: Unrecorded.

*Leptopharsa lenitis Drake (emendation)

Leptopharsa lenatis Drake 1930d, p. 272 [Peru; Brazil].

TYPE: Holotype ♀, macropterous; Peru; Drake Coll. (USNM).

DISTRIBUTION: Peru; Brazil.

HOST PLANT: Unrecorded.

*Leptopharsa lineata (Champion)

Leptostyla lineata Champion 1897, p. 17, pl. 1, figs. 22, 22a [Guatemala].—Osborn and Drake 1915b, p. 536.

Leptopharsa lineata: Monte 1939b, p. 74 [Gramineae; Brazil].—Drake and Hambleton 1946b, p. 122.

TYPE: Sex unknown; San Isidro, Guatemala; British Mus.

DISTRIBUTION: Guatemala; Brazil; Peru; Argentina.

HOST PLANT: Gramineae.

Leptopharsa livida Monte

Leptopharsa livida Monte 1943d, p. 265, fig. 3 [Brazil].

TYPE: Holotype♂; Viçosa, Minas Gerais, Brazil; Monte Coll. (Mus. Nacional).

DISTRIBUTION: Brazil.

HOST PLANT: Unrecorded.

*Leptopharsa longipennis (Champion)

Leptostyla longipennis Champion 1897, p. 13, pl. 1, figs. 16, 16a,b [Guatemala].

Leptopharsa longipennis: Hurd 1946, p. 466.

TYPE: Sex unknown; Panajachel, Guatemala; British Mus.

DISTRIBUTION: Guatemala.

HOST PLANT: Unrecorded.

*Leptopharsa luxa Drake and Hambleton

Leptopharsa luxa Drake and Hambleton 1945, p. 361 [Ecuador].

TYPE: Holotype♂, macropterous; Vinces, Ecuador; Drake Coll. (USNM).

DISTRIBUTION: Ecuador.

HOST PLANT: Unrecorded.

*Leptopharsa machaerii Drake and Hambleton

Leptopharsa machaerii Drake and Hambleton 1934, p. 446 [Brazil; *Machaerium nictitans*].

TYPE: Holotype♂, macropterous; Viçosa, Minas Gerais, Brazil; Drake Coll. (USNM).

DISTRIBUTION: Brazil.

HOST PLANT: *Machaerium nictitans.*

*Leptopharsa machalana Drake and Hambleton

Leptopharsa machalana Drake and Hambleton 1946a, p. 12 [Ecuador; *Desmodium*].

TYPE: Holotype ♂, macropterous; Machala, Ecuador; Drake Coll. (USNM).

DISTRIBUTION: Ecuador.

HOST PLANT: *Desmodium* sp.

*Leptopharsa machalana var. **vinnula** Drake and Hambleton

    Leptopharsa machalana var. *vinnula* Drake and Hambleton 1946a, p. 13 [Fla.; Guatemala; *Desmodium;* Caesar's burr; beggars' lice].—Stahler 1946, p. 545, fig. 1 [*Boehmeria cylindrica drummondiana; Urena lobata; Bidens pilosa radiata*].

    Leptophersa [sic] *vinnula:* Gibson and Carrillo 1959, p. 19 [Mexico].

TYPE: Holotype ♂, macropterous; Fort Pierce, Florida, U.S.; USNM.

DISTRIBUTION: U.S. (Fla.); Mexico; Guatemala.

HOST PLANTS: *Bidens pilosa radiata; Boehmeria cylindrica drummondiana; Desmodium* sp.; *Urena lobata.*

NOTE: Fungus *Hirsutella* sp. found on adults [Stahler].

Leptopharsa marginella (Stål)

    Monanthia (Tropidocheila) marginella Stål 1858, p. 62 [Brazil].

    Monanthia marginella: Walker 1873a, p. 192.

    Leptopharsa marginella: Stål 1873, p. 126.—Drake and Poor 1937d, p. 309, pl. 36, fig. 6.

TYPE: Sex unknown; Rio de Janeiro, Brazil; Stockholm Mus.

DISTRIBUTION: Brazil.

HOST PLANT: Unrecorded.

*Leptopharsa miconiae Drake and Hambleton

    Leptopharsa miconiae Drake and Hambleton 1938b, p. 55, fig. 2 [Brazil; *Miconia*].

TYPE: Holotype ♂, macropterous; Alto da Serra, São Paulo, Brazil; Drake Coll. (USNM).

DISTRIBUTION: Brazil.

HOST PLANT: *Miconia* sp.

*Leptopharsa milleri Drake

    Leptopharsa milleri Drake 1954f, p. 6 [Congo; Rhodesia; polony].

TYPE: Holotype ♀; Salisbury, Southern Rhodesia; British Mus.

DISTRIBUTION: Southern Rhodesia; Congo.

HOST PLANT: Polony tree.

*Leptopharsa mira Drake and Hambleton   FIGURE 2

    Leptopharsa mira Drake and Hambleton 1934, p. 446 [Brazil; *Swartzia*].— Monte 1939b, p. 74 [*Cassia;* Annonaceae].

TYPE: Holotype ♂, macropterous; Viçosa, Minas Gerais, Brazil; Drake Coll. (USNM).

DISTRIBUTION: Brazil.

HOST PLANTS: *Cassia* sp.; *Swartzia* sp.; Annonaceae.

*Leptopharsa modica Drake and Hambleton

    Leptopharsa modica Drake and Hambleton 1939, p. 161 [Brazil].

TYPE: Holotype ♂, macropterous; São Paulo, Brazil; Drake Coll. (USNM).

DISTRIBUTION: Brazil.

HOST PLANT: Unrecorded.

*Leptopharsa nota Drake and Hambleton

Leptopharsa nota Drake and Hambleton 1938a, p. 52 [Brazil; *Rudgea blanchetiana*].

TYPE: Holotype ♂, macropterous; São Paulo, Brazil; Drake Coll. (USNM).

DISTRIBUTION: Brazil.

HOST PLANT: *Rudgea blanchetiana*.

*Leptopharsa oblonga (Say)

Tingis oblonga Say 1825, p. 325.—Le Conte 1859, p. 248 [Mo.].

Leptostyla oblonga: Stål 1873, p. 126 [N.J.].—Provancher 1886, p. 159 [Canada].—Van Duzee 1912, p. 323.—Drake 1916, p. 327 [Ark.; D.C.].—Osborn and Drake 1916a, p. 238.—McAtee 1917a, p. 62 [Nebr. Iowa; Ill.; Wis.; Md.; *Falcata comosa; Petalostemon*]; 1919, p. 144.—Parshley 1922b, p. 11 [S. Dak.].

Gelchossa oblonga: McAtee 1923, p. 147 [Va.].—Drake 1925c, p. 37 [*Amorpha fruticosa*].—Blatchley 1926, p. 477 [Ind.; *Kuhnistera*].—Blöte 1945, p. 85.

Leptopharsa oblonga: Froeschner 1944, p. 669.—Bailey 1951, p. 39.

TYPE: Missouri, U.S.; sex and deposition of type unknown.

DISTRIBUTION: U.S. (N.J.; Md.; D.C.; Va.; Ind.; Ill.; Wis.; Ark.; Mo.; Nebr.; Iowa; S. Dak.); Canada.

HOST PLANTS: *Amorpha fruticosa; Falcata comosa; Kuhnistera* sp.; *Petalostemon* sp.

*Leptopharsa ocoteae Drake and Hambleton

Leptopharsa ocoteae Drake and Hambleton 1938a, p. 59, fig. 9 [Brazil; *Ocotea pretiosa*].

TYPE: Holotype ♂, macropterous; Viçosa, Minas Gerais, Brazil; Drake Coll. (USNM).

DISTRIBUTION: Brazil.

HOST PLANT: *Ocotea pretiosa*.

*Leptopharsa ogloblini Drake

Leptopharsa ogloblini Drake 1936b, p. 701 [Argentina].—Drake and Hambleton 1938a, p. 51 [Brazil; *Machaerium pedicillatum*].

TYPE: Holotype ♀, macropterous; Loreto, Argentina; Leningrad Inst.

DISTRIBUTION: Argentina; Brazil.

HOST PLANT: *Machaerium pedicillatum*.

Leptopharsa ornata Monte

Leptopharsa ornata Monte 1940e, p. 294 [Bolivia].

TYPE: Holotype ♀; Sur Yungas, Chulumani, Bolivia; Monte Coll. (Mus. Nacional).

DISTRIBUTION: Bolivia.

HOST PLANT: Unrecorded.

*Leptopharsa ovantis Drake and Hambleton

  Leptopharsa ovantis Drake and Hambleton 1945, p. 360 [Peru].

TYPE: Holotype ♂, macropterous; Tingo María, Peru; Drake Coll. (USNM).

DISTRIBUTION: Peru; Guatemala.

HOST PLANT: Unrecorded.

*Leptopharsa pacis Drake and Hambleton

  Leptopharsa pacis Drake and Hambleton 1939a, p. 160 [Brazil].—Drake 1948j, p. 434.—Silva 1956, p. 40.

  Leptopharsa perbona (not Drake): Monte 1944b, p. 461, figs. 2, 3.

TYPE: Holotype ♀, macropterous; Baia, Brazil; Drake Coll. (USNM).

DISTRIBUTION: Brazil.

HOST PLANT: Unrecorded.

Leptopharsa pallens Monte

  Leptopharsa pallens Monte 1943d, p. 267 [Peru].

TYPE: Holotype ♀; Satipo, Dep. Junin, Peru; Monte Coll. (Mus. Nacional).

DISTRIBUTION: Peru.

HOST PLANT: Unrecorded.

*Leptopharsa papella Drake

  Leptopharsa papella Drake 1941a, p. 143 [Md.].—Hurd 1946, p. 466 [Ind.].

TYPE: Holotype ♀, macropterous; Ashton, Maryland, U.S.; USNM.

DISTRIBUTION: U.S. (Ind.; Md.).

HOST PLANT: Unrecorded.

*Leptopharsa partita (Champion)

  Leptostyla partita Champion 1898a, p. 48, pl. 3, fig. 26 [Mexico].

  Leptopharsa partita: Hurd 1946, p. 466.

TYPE: Sex unknown; Pedregal, Mexico; British Mus.

DISTRIBUTION: Mexico.

HOST PLANT: Unrecorded.

*Leptopharsa paulana Drake

  Leptopharsa paulana Drake 1953a, p. 16 [Brazil].

TYPE: Holotype ♂, macropterous; São Paulo, Brazil; Drake Coll. (USNM).

DISTRIBUTION: Brazil.

HOST PLANT: Unrecorded.

*Leptopharsa pensa Drake and Hambleton

  Leptopharsa pensa Drake and Hambleton 1939, p. 160 [Brazil; *Scleria myricocarpa*].

TYPE: Holotype ♂, macropterous; São Paulo, Brazil; Drake Coll. (USNM).

DISTRIBUTION: Brazil.

HOST PLANT: *Scleria myricocarpa.*

*Leptopharsa perbona Drake

Leptopharsa perbona Drake 1930a, p. 2 [Brazil]; 1948j, p. 434.—Drake and Bondar 1932, p. 91 [Rudgea].—Drake and Hambleton 1944b, p. 128.

Leptopharsa spectabilis Monte 1940e, p. 290, fig. 7.

TYPE: Holotype ♂; Chapada, Brazil; Carnegie Mus.

DISTRIBUTION: Brazil.

HOST PLANT: Rudgea sp.

*Leptopharsa peruensis Drake

Leptopharsa peruensis Drake 1928a, p. 55 [Peru].

TYPE: Holotype ♀, macropterous; Peru; Drake Coll. (USNM).

DISTRIBUTION: Peru.

HOST PLANT: Unrecorded.

*Leptopharsa posoqueriae Drake and Hambleton

Leptopharsa posoqueriae Drake and Hambleton 1938a, p. 56, fig. 8 [Brazil; Posoqueria acutifolia].

TYPE: Holotype ♂, macropterous; São Paulo, Brazil; Drake Coll. (USNM).

DISTRIBUTION: Brazil.

HOST PLANT: Posoqueria acutifolia.

*Leptopharsa principis Drake and Hambleton

Leptopharsa principis Drake and Hambleton 1938a, p. 54 [Brazil].— Monte 1939b, p. 75 [Cassia].

TYPE: Holotype ♂, macropterous; Viçosa, Minas Gerais, Brazil; Drake Coll. (USNM).

DISTRIBUTION: Brazil.

HOST PLANT: Cassia sp.

*Leptopharsa probala Drake and Hambleton

Leptopharsa probala Drake and Hambleton 1938a, p. 57, fig. 3 [Brazil].— Monte 1939b, p. 75 [Leguminosae].

TYPE: Holotype ♀, macropterous; Viçosa, Minas Gerais, Brazil; Drake Coll. (USNM).

DISTRIBUTION: Brazil.

HOST PLANT: Leguminosae.

*Leptopharsa psychotriae Drake and Hambleton

Leptopharsa psychotriae Drake and Hambleton 1939, p. 161 [Brazil; Psychotria].

TYPE: Holotype ♂, macropterous; Viçosa, Minas Gerais, Brazil; Drake Coll. (USNM).

DISTRIBUTION: Brazil.

HOST PLANT: Psychotria sp.

*Leptopharsa pudens Drake and Hambleton

Leptopharsa pudens Drake and Hambleton 1938a, p. 52 [Brazil; Machaerium].

TYPE: Holotype ♂, macropterous; São Paulo, Brazil; Drake Coll. (USNM).
DISTRIBUTION: Brazil.
HOST PLANT: Machaerium sp.

*Leptopharsa quadrata Drake

Leptopharsa quadrata Drake 1954f, p. 7 [Natal].

TYPE: Holotype ♀, macropterous; Durban, Natal, South Africa; Drake Coll. (USNM).
DISTRIBUTION: South Africa (Natal).
HOST PLANT: Unrecorded.

*Leptopharsa retrusa Drake and Hambleton

Leptopharsa retrusa Drake and Hambleton 1939, p. 159 [Brazil].
Leptodictya (Hanuala) retrusa: Monte 1941e, p. 107.

TYPE: Holotype ♂, macropterous; Belém, Pará, Brazil; Drake Coll. (USNM).
DISTRIBUTION: Brazil.
HOST PLANT: Unrecorded.

*Leptopharsa reuniona Drake

Leptopharsa reuniona Drake 1957e, p. 404 [Reunion].

TYPE: Holotype ♂; Béloune, Reunion; Madagascar Sci. Inst.
DISTRIBUTION: Mascarene Islands (Reunion).
HOST PLANT: Unrecorded.

*Leptopharsa rudgeae Drake and Hambleton

Leptopharsa rudgeae Drake and Hambleton 1934, p. 447 [Brazil; Rudgea].—Costa Lima 1936, p. 129.

TYPE: Holotype ♂, macropterous; Viçosa, Minas Gerais, Brazil; Drake Coll. (USNM).
DISTRIBUTION: Brazil.
HOST PLANT: Rudgea sp.

*Leptopharsa rumiana Drake and Hambleton

Leptopharsa rumiana Drake and Hambleton 1946a, p. 11 [El Salvador; Guatemala; Malvaviscus arboreus].

TYPE: Holotype ♂, macropterous; San Andres, El Salvador; Drake Coll. (USNM).
DISTRIBUTION: El Salvador; Guatemala.
HOST PLANT: Malvaviscus arboreus.

*Leptopharsa ruris Drake

> *Leptopharsa ruris* Drake 1942a, p. 20 [Antigua].—Drake and Cobben 1960, p. 83, fig. 83 [St. Martin; *Croton flavens*].

TYPE: Holotype ♂, macropterous; Antigua, British West Indies; Drake Coll. (USNM).

DISTRIBUTION: Leeward Islands (Antigua; St. Martin).

HOST PLANT: *Croton flavens*.

*Leptopharsa satipona Drake and Hambleton

> *Leptopharsa satipona* Drake and Hambleton 1944b, p. 128 [Peru].

TYPE: Holotype ♂, macropterous; Satipo, Peru; Drake Coll. (USNM).

DISTRIBUTION: Peru.

HOST PLANT: Unrecorded.

*Leptopharsa sera Drake and Poor

> *Leptopharsa sera* Drake and Poor 1939a, p. 35 [Brazil; Bolivia].

TYPE: Holotype ♀, macropterous; Chapada, Brazil; Drake Coll. (USNM).

DISTRIBUTION: Brazil; Bolivia.

HOST PLANT: Unrecorded.

Leptopharsa setigera (Champion)

> *Leptostyla setigera* Champion 1897, p. 14, pl. 1, figs. 18, 18a [Panama].
> *Leptopharsa setigera:* Hurd 1946, p. 466.

TYPE: Sex unknown; Bugaba, Panama; British Mus.

DISTRIBUTION: Panama.

HOST PLANT: Unrecorded.

*Leptopharsa siderea Drake and Hambleton

> *Leptopharsa siderea* Drake and Hambleton 1946a, p. 13 [Guatemala].

TYPE: Holotype ♀, macropterous; Esquintla, Guatemala; Drake Coll. (USNM).

DISTRIBUTION: Guatemala.

HOST PLANT: Unrecorded.

*Leptopharsa simulans (Stål)

> *Monanthia (Phyllontocheila) simulans* Stål 1858, p. 61 [Brazil].
> *Monanthia (Gargaphia) simulans:* Stål 1862, p. 324.
> *Monanthia simulans:* Walker 1873a, p. 192.
> *Gargaphia simulans:* Stål 1873, p. 124.—Lethierry and Severin 1896, p. 13.—Drake and Poor 1937d, p. 310, pl. 36, fig. 8.—Monte 1941e, p. 119.
> *Leptopharsa scita* Drake and Hambleton 1939, p. 160.
> *Leptopharsa simulans:* Monte 1947a, p. 236.

TYPE: Holotype ♀; Rio de Janeiro, Brazil; Stockholm Mus.

DISTRIBUTION: Brazil.

HOST PLANT: Unrecorded.

Leptopharsa sobrina Monte

Leptopharsa sobrina Monte 1940b, p. 377 [Brazil; *Aspidosperma warmingii*].
TYPE: Holotype ♀; Belo Horizonte, Brazil; Monte Coll. (Mus. Nacional).
DISTRIBUTION: Brazil.
HOST PLANT: *Aspidosperma warmingii.*

*****Leptopharsa tenuatis** Drake

Leptopharsa tenuatis Drake 1928a, p. 52 [Brazil].—Monte 1939b, p. 75 [*Dalbergia*].
TYPE: Holotype ♂, macropterous; Brazil; Drake Coll. (USNM).
DISTRIBUTION: Brazil.
HOST PLANT: *Dalbergia* sp.

*****Leptopharsa tenuis** (Champion)

Leptostyla tenuis Champion 1897, p. 18, pl. 1, figs. 25, 25 a, b [Guatemala].
Leptopharsa tenuis: Drake and Hambleton 1945, p. 360 [*Ichthyomethia grandifolia*].
TYPE: Sex unknown; Capetillo, Guatemala; British Mus.
DISTRIBUTION: Guatemala.
HOST PLANT: *Ichthyomethia grandifolia.*

Leptopharsa unicarinata Champion

Leptopharsa unicarinata Champion 1897, p. 21, pl. 2, figs. 7, 7a [Panama].
TYPE: Sex unknown; Volcan de Chiriqui, Panama; British Mus.
DISTRIBUTION: Panama.
HOST PLANT: Unrecorded.

*****Leptopharsa usingeri** Drake

Leptopharsa usingeri Drake 1938a, p. 72 [Mexico].
TYPE: Holotype ♀; Temascaltepec, Mexico; Cal. Acad.
DISTRIBUTION: Mexico.
HOST PLANT: Unrecorded.

*****Leptopharsa valida** Drake and Hambleton

Leptopharsa valida Drake and Hambleton 1938a, p. 54 [Brazil; *Condylocarpon rauwolfiae*].
TYPE: Holotype ♂, macropterous; São Paulo, Brazil; Drake Coll. (USNM).
DISTRIBUTION: Brazil.
HOST PLANT: *Condylocarpon rauwolfiae.*

Leptopharsa variegata Monte

Leptopharsa variegata Monte 1943d, p. 267 [Brazil].
TYPE: Holotype ♂; São Paulo, Brazil; Monte Coll. (Mus. Nacional).
DISTRIBUTION: Brazil.
HOST PLANT: Unrecorded.

*Leptopharsa velifer (McAtee)

Leptostyla velifer McAtee 1917a, p. 60 [Ariz.].

Leptopharsa velifer: Hurd 1946, p. 466.

TYPE: Holotype ♀, macropterous; Arizona, U.S.; USNM.

DISTRIBUTION: U.S. (Ariz.).

HOST PLANT: Unrecorded.

*Leptopharsa vicina Drake and Poor

Leptopharsa vicina Drake and Poor 1939a, p. 33 [Haiti].

TYPE: Holotype ♂, macropterous; Williamson, Haiti; Drake Coll. (USNM).

DISTRIBUTION: Haiti.

HOST PLANT: Unrecorded.

Leptopharsa vittipennis (Stål)

Leptostyla vittipennis Stål 1873, p. 126 [Brazil].

Leptopharsa vittipennis: Drake and Poor 1937d, p. 307, pl. 36, fig. 11 [Peru].—Drake and Hambleton 1938a, p. 52.—Monte 1940e, p. 292.

Leptopharsa vitipennis [sic]: Monte 1941e, p. 120.—Silva 1956, p. 41, fig. 14 [*Artocarpus integrifolia*].

TYPE: Holotype ♂; Rio de Janeiro, Brazil; Stockholm Mus.

DISTRIBUTION: Brazil; Peru.

HOST PLANT: *Artocarpus integrifolia.*

*Leptopharsa zeteki Drake

Leptopharsa zeteki Drake 1939f, p. 69 [Canal Zone].

TYPE: Holotype ♂, macropterous; Barro Colorado Island, Panama Canal Zone; Drake Coll. (USNM).

DISTRIBUTION: Panama (Canal Zone).

HOST PLANT: Unrecorded.

Genus LEPTOYPHA Stål

Leptoypha Stål 1873, pp. 121, 129.—Lethierry and Severin 1896, p. 21.—Van Duzee 1916, p. 26; 1917b, pp. 220, 817.—McAtee 1917a, p. 55 (key).—Blatchley 1926, p. 498 (key).—Monte 1941e, p. 121.—Hurd 1946, p. 456.—Bailey 1951, p. 27.—Drake and Maa 1953, p. 94.—Drake and Ruhoff 1960a, p. 65.—Stichel 1960b, p. 400; 1960c, p. 139.

Tingis (*Birgitta*) Lindberg 1927, p. 18.—Drake and Ruhoff 1960a, p. 40.

TYPE SPECIES: *Tingis mutica* Say.

*Leptoypha anceps (Horváth)

Paracopium ? anceps Horváth 1925a, p. 9 [Queensland].

Leptoypha anceps: Drake 1947c, p. 112.

TYPE: Holotype ♂; Yarrabah, Queensland, Australia; Stockholm Mus.

DISTRIBUTION: Australia (Queensland).

HOST PLANT: Unrecorded.

*Leptoypha barberi Drake and Ruhoff

Leptoypha brevicornis (not Champion): Barber 1910, p. 38 [Ariz.].—Van Duzee 1917b, p. 220 (in part).

Leptoypha minor (not McAtee 1917a): McAtee 1919, p. 142 (in part).— Hurd 1946, p. 457 [*Fraxinus berlandierana*].

Leptoypha barberi Drake and Ruhoff 1960d, p. 152, fig. 1.

TYPE: Holotype ♂, macropterous; Huachuca Mountains, Arizona, U.S.; Barber Coll. (USNM).

DISTRIBUTION: U.S. (Ariz.).

HOST PLANT: *Fraxinus berlandierana*.

*Leptoypha binotata Champion

Leptoypha binotata Champion 1897, p. 32, pl. 2, fig. 27 [Guatemala].

TYPE: Sex unknown; Cerro Zunil, Guatemala; British Mus.

DISTRIBUTION: Guatemala.

HOST PLANT: Unrecorded.

*Leptoypha braziliensis Drake and Hambleton

Leptoypha braziliensis Drake and Hambleton 1939, p. 154 [Brazil].

TYPE: Holotype ♀, macropterous; Amazon region, Brazil; Drake Coll. (USNM).

DISTRIBUTION: Brazil.

HOST PLANT: Unrecorded.

*Leptoypha brevicornis Champion

Leptoypha brevicornis Champion 1897, p. 32, pl. 2, fig. 28 [Mexico].—Van Duzee 1917b, p. 220 (in part).

TYPE: Sex unknown; Omilteme, Guerrero, Mexico; British Mus.

DISTRIBUTION: Mexico.

HOST PLANT: Unrecorded.

*Leptoypha capitata (Jakovlev)

Monanthia capitata Jakovlev 1876a, p. 110 [Siberia].

Monosteira capitata: Lethierry and Severin 1896, p. 25.—Horváth 1906a, p. 106.—Kiritshenko 1913b, p. 482.

Monostira capitata: Oshanin 1908, p. 456; 1912, p. 46.

Tingis (Birgitta) tenuimarginata Lindberg 1927, p. 19, fig. 5.

Leptoypha capitata: Kiritshenko 1931, p. 269 [*Malus manschurica; Pyrus ussuriensis*].—Drake and Maa 1953, p. 94 [China; Japan].

TYPE: Holotype ♀, macropterous; Ussuri, Russia; Leningrad Inst.

DISTRIBUTION: U.S.S.R. (Siberia); Japan; China.

HOST PLANTS: *Malus manschurica; Pyrus ussuriensis*.

*Leptoypha costata Parshley

Leptoypha costata Parshley 1917a, 16 [Md.].—McAtee 1917a, p. 57; 1919, p. 143 [ash]; 1923, p. 146 [*Franxinus caroliniana*].—Drake 1918d, p. 87 [Colo.; Ark.; Ill.]; 1925c, p. 38 [Miss.].—Blatchley 1926, p. 498.—Bailey 1951, p. 27 [Conn.; La.; *Hicoria alba*].

Leptoypha distinguenda Heidemann 1917, p. 218, pl. 17, fig. 1 [D.C.; Va.; *Hamamelis*].

TYPE: Holotype ♀; Marshall Hall, Maryland, U.S.; MCZ.

DISTRIBUTION: U.S. (Conn.; Md.; D.C.; Va.; Miss.; La.; Ark.; Ill; Colo.).

HOST PLANTS: *Fraxinus caroliniana; Hicoria alba; Hamamelis* sp.

*Leptoypha drakei McAtee

Leptoypha mutica (not Say): Uhler 1893b, p. 264.

Leptoypha brevicornis (not Champion): McAtee 1917a, p. 59; 1919, p. 143.

Leptoypha drakei McAtee 1919, p. 143 [Calif.; Tex.].—Hurd 1946, p. 457 [Ariz.].

TYPE: Holotype ♂, macropterous; Argus Mountains, California, U.S.; USNM.

DISTRIBUTION: U.S. (Calif.; Ariz.; Tex.).

HOST PLANT: Ash.

*Leptoypha elliptica McAtee

Leptoypha elliptica McAtee 1917a, p. 57 [Tex.]; 1919, p. 143.—Drake 1918d, p. 87 [Ga.; Fla.; *Ilex*].—Blatchley 1926, p. 499 [Ind.].— Froeschner 1944, p. 670 [Mo.].

TYPE: Holotype ♂, macropterous; Texas, U.S.; USNM.

DISTRIBUTION: U.S. (Tex.; Fla.; Ga.; Tenn.; Ind.; Mo.).

HOST PLANT: *Ilex* sp.

*Leptoypha hospita Drake and Poor

Leptoypha hospita Drake and Poor 1937a, p. 12 [Penang]; 1937b, p. 402.

TYPE: Holotype ♀, macropterous; Penang Island, Straits Settlements; USNM.

DISTRIBUTION: Federation of Malaya (Penang Island); China.

HOST PLANT: Unrecorded.

*Leptoypha ilicis Drake

Leptoypha ilicis Drake 1919a, p. 420 [Ga.; *Ilex*].—Blatchley 1926, p. 500 [Fla.]; 1928, p. 5 [*Vaccinium*].—Hurd 1946, p. 457 [Tex.; Okla.].— Bailey 1951, p. 28.

TYPE: Holotype ♂, macropterous; Stone Mountain, Georgia, U.S.; Drake Coll. (USNM).

DISTRIBUTION: U.S. (Ga.; Fla.; Tex.; Okla.).

HOST PLANTS: *Ilex* sp.; *Vaccinium* sp.

*Leptoypha luzona Drake and Ruhoff

Leptoypha luzona Drake and Ruhoff 1961b, p. 140 [Luzon].

TYPE: Holotype ♂, macropterous; Los Banos, Philippines; Drake Coll. (USNM).

DISTRIBUTION: Philippine Islands (Luzon).

HOST PLANT: Unrecorded.

*Leptoypha mcateei Drake

    Leptoypha mcateei Drake 1921b, p. 49 [Fla.; *Osmanthus americana*].—
    Blatchley 1926, p. 499 [*Xolisma ferruginea*].

    Leptoypha mcatella [sic]: Drake 1925c, p. 38.

TYPE: Holotype ♂, macropterous; Gainesville, Florida, U.S.; Drake Coll. (USNM).

DISTRIBUTION: U.S. (Fla.).

HOST PLANTS: *Osmanthus americana; Xolisma ferruginea.*

*Leptoypha minor McAtee

    Leptoypha minor McAtee 1917a, p. 56 [Calif.]; 1919, p. 142 (in part).—
    Van Duzee 1917a, p. 260.—Drake 1918d, p. 87 (in part).—Usinger
    1946b, p. 286, figs. [*Populus candicans; Fraxinus velutina; Fraxinus
    oregona;* olive].—Drake and Ruhoff 1962a, p. 156.

    Leptoypha nubilis Drake 1941b, p. 141 [*Ceanothus*].

TYPE: Holotype ♂, macropterous; Siskiyou County, California, U.S.; USNM.

DISTRIBUTION: U.S. (Calif.).

HOST PLANTS: *Ceanothus* sp.; *Fraxinus oregona; Fraxinus velutina; Populus candicans;* "olive tree next to infested ash."

NOTE: Life history study [Usinger].

*Leptoypha morrisoni Drake

    Leptoypha morrisoni Drake 1922b, p. 43 [Dominican Republic].—Drake
    and Bruner 1924a, p. 146.—Gowdy 1926, p. 35.—Drake and Ham-
    bleton 1939, p. 155 [Canal Zone].—Hurd 1946, p. 457 [Fla.].

    Leptoypha binotata ? (not Champion): Van Duzee 1907, p. 21 [Jamaica].

TYPE: Holotype ♂, macropterous; San Pedro de Macoris, Dominican Republic; USNM.

DISTRIBUTION: Dominican Republic; Panama (Canal Zone); Jamaica; Haiti; Cuba; U.S. (Fla.).

HOST PLANT: Mangle.

*Leptoypha mutica (Say)

    Tingis mutica Say 1832, p. 27 [Ind.].—Fitch 1858, p. 794.—Le Conte
    1859, p. 349.

    Monanthia mutica: Walker 1873a, p. 190.

    Leptoypha mutica: Stål 1873, p. 129 [Tex.].—Provancher 1886, p. 160
    [Que.].—Uhler 1886, p. 22.—Champion 1898b, p. 61.—Wirtner
    1904, p. 203 [Pa.].—Smith 1910, p. 149 [N.J.].—Banks 1910, p. 57.—
    Van Duzee 1912, p. 323.—Dickerson and Weiss 1916, p. 308, pl. 16
    [*Chionanthus virginica*].—McAtee 1917a, p. 58 [D.C.; Nebr.; Wis.;
    Ohio; Ont.; Tenn.; *Fraxinus*]; 1919, p. 143; 1923, p. 146.—Drake
    1918d, p. 87 [Mich.; Ill.; Md.; Va.; Ga.; *Adelia acuminata*]; 1928b,
    p. 102 [N.Y.].—Barber 1914, p. 507 [Fla.].—Barber and Weiss 1922,
    p. 14, fig. 8.—Hussey 1922a, p. 11 [N. Dak.]; 1922b, p. 22 [*Fraxinus*

americana].—Parshley 1922a, p. 236 [Mass.]; 1922b, p. 11 [S. Dak.]; 1923b, p. 706 [Conn.].—Blatchley 1926, p. 500, fig. 121.—Froeschner 1944, p. 670 [Mo.].—Bailey 1951, p. 28 [Maine; N.H.]; 1959, p. 63.

Leptophya [sic] *mutica:* Osborn and Drake 1916a, p. 241, pl. 10, fig. b.

TYPE: Indiana, U.S.; type apparently lost.

DISTRIBUTION: U.S. (Maine; N.H.; Mass.; Conn.; N.Y.; N.J.; Pa.; Md.; D.C.; Va.; N.C.; S.C.; Ga.; Fla.; Tenn.; Ind.; Ohio; Ill.; Nebr.; Kans.; Wis.; Mich.; Mo.; Iowa; S. Dak.; N. Dak.; Tex.; Minn.); Canada (Ont.; Que.); Mexico (Socorro Island).

HOST PLANTS: *Adelia acuminata; Chionanthus virginica; Fraxinus americana; Fraxinus* sp.

NOTE: Taken at light [Drake 1918d]. Life history studies [Dickerson and Weiss; Bailey].

*Leptoypha wuorentausi (Lindberg)

Tingis (Birgitta) wuorentausi Lindberg 1927, p. 18, fig. 4 [Russia].

Tingis (Birgitta) crispifolii Takeya 1932, p. 12, pl. 1, fig. 3 [Korea; *Fraxinus mandshurica japonica*]; 1951a, p. 17.

Tingis crispifolii: Saitô 1933, p. 7 [*Fraxinus pubinervis; Fraxinus rhynchophylla*].

Leptoypha wuorentausi: Drake and Maa 1953, p. 95.

TYPE: Sex unknown; Ussuri, Spasskaja, Russia; Helsin. Mus.

DISTRIBUTION: U.S.S.R. (Siberia); Korea.

HOST PLANTS: *Fraxinus mandshurica japonica; Fraxinus pubinervis; Fraxinus rhynchophylla.*

Genus LEPTURGA Stål

Lepturga Stål 1873, pp. 119, 124.—Drake 1943b, pp. 175–177.—Drake and Ruhoff 1960a, p. 66.

TYPE SPECIES: *Lepturga nigritarsis* Stål.

*Lepturga dignata Drake

Lepturga dignata Drake 1943b, p. 176 [New Guinea]; 1960, p. 367, fig. 19.

TYPE: Holotype ♀, macropterous; Madang, New Guinea; Drake Coll. (USNM).

DISTRIBUTION: New Guinea.

HOST PLANT: Unrecorded.

NOTE: The type locality (Drake 1943b) is incorrectly given as "Pedang, Pedang, New Guinea." The label on the type specimen reads "F. Wilhelmshaven, Germ. N. Guinea" which today is known as "Madang." The distribution record (Drake 1960) of "Penang I., Malaya" is also in error.

*Lepturga magnifica (Hacker)

Leptobyrsa magnifica Hacker 1929, p. 331, pl. 35, fig. 13 [Queensland].

Lepturga magnifica: Drake 1943b, p. 176.

TYPE: Sex unknown; Mt. Tambourine, Queensland, Australia; Queensland Mus.

DISTRIBUTION: Australia (Queensland).

HOST PLANT: Unrecorded.

*Lepturga major (Hacker)

Leptobyrsa major Hacker 1929, p. 332, pl. 35, fig. 14 [Queensland].

Lepturga major: Drake 1943b, p. 176.

TYPE: Sex unknown; Blackbutt, Queensland, Australia; Queensland Mus.

DISTRIBUTION: Australia (Queensland).

HOST PLANT: Unrecorded.

*Lepturga nigritarsis Stål

Lepturga nigritarsis Stål 1873, p. 124 [Queensland].—Lethierry and Severin 1896, p. 13.—Drake 1943b, p. 175.

TYPE: Holotype ♀; Cape York, Australia; Stockholm Mus.

DISTRIBUTION: Australia (Queensland).

HOST PLANT: Unrecorded.

Genus LIOTINGIS Drake

Liotingis Drake 1930d, p. 270.—Drake and Hambleton 1935, p. 146.— Monte 1939b, p. 76; 1941e, p. 122.—Drake and Ruhoff 1960a, p. 66.

TYPE SPECIES: *Liotingis evidens* Drake.

*Liotingis affinata Drake and Hambleton

Liotingis affinatus Drake and Hambleton 1935, p. 147 [Brazil; *Aspidosperma*].

TYPE: Holotype ♂, macropterous; São Paulo, Brazil; Drake Coll. (USNM).

DISTRIBUTION: Brazil.

HOST PLANT: *Aspidosperma* sp.

*Liotingis aspidospermae Drake and Hambleton

Liotingis aspidospermae Drake and Hambleton 1935, p. 147, fig. 3 [Brazil; *Aspidosperma*].

TYPE: Holotype ♂, macropterous; São Paulo, Brazil; Drake Coll. (USNM).

DISTRIBUTION: Brazil.

HOST PLANT: *Aspidosperma* sp.

*Liotingis evidens Drake (emendation)

Liotingis evidentis Drake 1930d, p. 271 [Brazil].—Drake and Hambleton 1935, p. 146; 1938a, p. 63.—Monte 1939b, p. 76 [*Aspidosperma*].

TYPE: Holotype ♀, macropterous; Minas Gerais, Brazil; Drake Coll. (USNM).

DISTRIBUTION: Brazil.

HOST PLANT: *Aspidosperma* sp.

*Liotingis immaculata (Drake and Hambleton)

Allotingis immaculata Drake and Hambleton 1934, p. 443 [Brazil; *Aspidosperma*].—Costa Lima 1936, p. 125.

Liotingis immaculata: Drake and Hambleton 1935, p. 146.

TYPE: Holotype ♀, macropterous; Viçosa, Minas Gerais, Brazil; Drake Coll. (USNM).

DISTRIBUTION: Brazil.

HOST PLANT: *Aspidosperma* sp.

Genus LULLIUS Distant

Lullius Distant 1904, p. 429.—Drake and Ruhoff 1960a, p. 24.

TYPE SPECIES: *Lullius major* Distant.

*Lullius insolens Drake

Lullius insolens Drake 1944a, p. 68 [Cape Province].

TYPE: Holotype ♂, macropterous; Camps Bay, Cape Peninsula, Africa; Drake Coll. (USNM).

DISTRIBUTION: South Africa (Cape Province).

HOST PLANT: Unrecorded.

*Lullius major Distant

Lullius major Distant 1904, p. 430, pl. 8, fig. 7 [Cape Province].—Drake 1956f, p. 429; 1961c, p. 130.

TYPE: Sex unknown; Cape Colony, South Africa; British Mus.

DISTRIBUTION: South Africa (Cape Province).

HOST PLANT: Unrecorded.

*Lullius spinifemur Drake   PLATE 15

Lullius spinifemur Drake 1961c, p. 130, pl. 10 [Cape Province].

TYPE: Holotype ♂; Seven Weeks Poort, Laingsburg District, West Cape Province, South Africa; Natal Museum, Pietermaritzberg, Natal, South Africa.

DISTRIBUTION: South Africa (Cape Province).

HOST PLANT: Unrecorded.

Genus MACROCORYTHA Stål

Corythucha (Macrocorytha) Stål 1873, p. 123.

Macrocorytha: Drake and Ruhoff 1960a, p. 66.

TYPE SPECIES: *Tingis rhomboptera* Fieber.

Macrocorytha rhomboptera (Fieber)

Tingis rhomboptera Fieber 1844, p. 103, pl. 8, figs. 37, 38 [Luzon; Malvaceae].—Herrich-Schaeffer 1850, p. 161.

Corythucha (Macrocorytha) rhomboptera: Stål 1873, p. 123.

Corythucha rhomboptera: Lethierry and Severin 1896, p. 11.

Macrocorytha rhomboptera: Drake and Ruhoff 1960a, p. 66.

TYPE: Sex unknown; Luzon, Philippine Islands; Vienna Mus.

DISTRIBUTION: Philippine Islands (Luzon).

HOST PLANT: Malvaceae.

Genus MACROTINGIS Champion

Macrotingis Champion 1897, p. 22.—Hurd 1946, p. 469.—Drake and Ruhoff 1960a, p. 66.

TYPE SPECIES: *Macrotingis biseriata* Champion.

*Macrotingis biseriata Champion

Macrotingis biseriata Champion 1897, p. 22, pl. 2, figs. 8, 8a, b [Panama].—Drake 1928e, p. 4 [Honduras].

TYPE: Sex unknown; Panama; British Mus.

DISTRIBUTION: Panama; Honduras.

HOST PLANT: Unrecorded.

*Macrotingis biseriata var. novicis Drake

Macrotingis biseriata var. *novicis* Drake 1928e, p. 4 [Honduras].

TYPE: Holotype ♂; Progreso, Honduras; Michigan Univ.

DISTRIBUTION: Honduras.

HOST PLANT: Unrecorded.

NOTE: Taken at light.

Macrotingis uniseriata Champion

Macrotingis uniseriata Champion 1897, p. 22, pl. 2, figs. 9, 9a [Guatemala].

TYPE: Sex unknown; Capetilla, Guatemala; British Mus.

DISTRIBUTION: Guatemala.

HOST PLANT: Unrecorded.

*Macrotingis zeteki Drake

Macrotingis zeteki Drake 1950b, p. 299 [Canal Zone].

TYPE: Holotype ♂, macropterous; Barro Colorado Island, Panama Canal Zone; USNM.

DISTRIBUTION: Panama (Canal Zone).

HOST PLANT: Unrecorded.

Genus MAFA Hesse

Mafa Hesse 1925, p. 88.—Drake and Ruhoff 1960a, p. 67.

TYPE SPECIES: *Mafa lanceolata* Hesse.

*Mafa lanceolata Hesse

Mafa lanceolata Hesse 1925, p. 89, pl. 4, fig. 4 [South-West Africa].

TYPE: Sex unknown; brachypterous form; Mafa, Ovamboland, South-West Africa; So. Afr. Mus.

DISTRIBUTION: South-West Africa.

HOST PLANT: Unrecorded.

Genus MALANDIOLA Horváth

Malandiola Horváth 1925a, p. 13.—Drake and Ruhoff 1960a, p. 67.

TYPE SPECIES: *Malandiola simplex* Horváth.

*Malandiola acares Drake and Ruhoff

Malandiola acares Drake and Ruhoff 1962d, p. 494 [Queensland].

TYPE: Holotype ♂, macropterous; Bluff, Queensland, Australia; Drake Coll. (USNM).

DISTRIBUTION: Australia (Queensland).

HOST PLANT: Unrecorded.

*Malandiola minys Drake and Ruhoff

Malandiola minys Drake and Ruhoff 1962d, p. 493 [Queensland].

TYPE: Holotype ♂; Castle Hill, Queensland, Australia; Drake Coll. (USNM).

DISTRIBUTION: Australia (Queensland).

HOST PLANT: Unrecorded.

*Malandiola semota Drake

Malandiola semota Drake 1942b, p. 360 [Victoria; South Australia].—Drake and Ruhoff 1962b, p. 250.

TYPE: Holotype ♂, macropterous; Murray Bridge, South Australia; Drake Coll. (USNM).

DISTRIBUTION: Australia (South Australia; Victoria; Western Australia).

HOST PLANT: Tea tree (myrtaceous shrubs).

*Malandiola similis Hacker

Malandiola similis Hacker 1927, p. 21, pl. 9, fig. 11 [Queensland].
Melandiola [sic] *similis:* Drake and Poor 1937b, p. 402 [New South Wales].

TYPE: Sex unknown; Sunnybank, Queensland, Australia; Queensland Mus.

DISTRIBUTION: Australia (Queensland; Bribie Island; New South Wales).

HOST PLANT: Unrecorded.

Malandiola simplex Horváth

Malandiola simplex Horváth 1925a, p. 14, fig. 8 [Queensland].

TYPE: Holotype ♂; Malanda, Queensland, Australia; Stockholm Mus.

DISTRIBUTION: Australia (Queensland).

HOST PLANT: Unrecorded.

*Malandiola syscena Drake and Ruhoff

Malandiola syscena Drake and Ruhoff 1962d, p. 788 [Northern Territory].

TYPE: Holotype ♀, macropterous; Darwin, Northern Territory, Australia; Drake Coll. (USNM).

DISTRIBUTION: Australia (Northern Territory).

HOST PLANT: Unrecorded.

Genus MECOPHARSA Drake

Mecopharsa Drake 1953b, p. 96.—Drake and Ruhoff 1960a, p. 67.

TYPE SPECIES: *Mecopharsa hackeri* Drake.

*Mecopharsa hackeri Drake   PLATE 39

Macropharsa [sic] *hackeri* Drake 1953b, p. 97 [Queensland].—Drake and Davis 1960, fig. 48.

TYPE: Holotype ♀, macropterous; Connondal, Queensland, Australia; Drake Coll. (USNM).

DISTRIBUTION: Australia (Queensland).

HOST PLANT: Unrecorded.

NOTE: Through typographical errors the generic name *Mecopharsa* was spelled *Mecropharsa* and *Macropharsa* (Drake 1953b, p. 97).

*Mecopharsa secta Drake

Mecopharsa secta Drake 1960, p. 366, fig. 18 [New Guinea].

TYPE: Holotype ♀, macropterous; Eubenangee, New Guinea; Drake Coll. (USNM).

DISTRIBUTION: New Guinea.

HOST PLANT: Unrecorded.

Genus MEGALOCYSTA Champion

Megalocysta Champion 1897, p. 5.—Monte 1942c, p. 301.—Hurd 1946, p. 474.—Drake and Ruhoff 1960a, p. 67.

TYPE SPECIES: *Megalocysta pellucida* Champion.

*Megalocysta pellucida Champion

Megalocysta pellucida Champion 1897, p. 6, pl. 1, figs. 5, 5a, b, c [Panama].—Monte 1942c, p. 301.

TYPE: Sex unknown; Panama; British Mus.

DISTRIBUTION: Panama.

HOST PLANT: Unrecorded.

Genus MELANORHOPALA Stål

Tingis (*Melanorhopala*) Stål 1873, p. 130.

Tingis (not Fabricius): Uhler 1886, p. 22.—Banks 1910, p. 57.

Melanorhopala: Horváth 1908, p. 564.—Van Duzee 1916, p. 26; 1917b, pp. 220, 818.—Parshley 1917a, p. 17 (key).—Blatchley 1926, p. 490 (key).—Hurd 1946, p. 446.—Drake and Ruhoff 1960a, p. 68.

TYPE SPECIES: *Tingis* (*Melanorhopala*) *clavata* Stål.

*Melanorhopala balli Drake

Melanorhopala balli Drake 1928f, p. 3 [Colo.].

TYPE: Holotype ♀, brachypterous; Fort Collins, Colorado, U.S.; Drake Coll. (USNM).

DISTRIBUTION: U.S. (Colo.).

HOST PLANT: Unrecorded.

*Melanorhopala clavata (Stål)

Tingis (Melanorhopala) clavata Stål 1873, p. 130 [N.Y.; Wis.].—Parshley 1914, p. 145 [Maine].

Tingis (Melanorhopala) lurida Stål 1873, p. 131 [Ill.].

Tingis (Melanorhopala) uniformis Stål 1873, p. 131.

Cantacader henshawi Ashmead 1886, p. 20 [Mass.].—Lethierry and Severin 1896, p. 4.

Lasiacantha clavata: Lethierry and Severin 1896, p. 19.

Lasiacantha lurida: Lethierry and Severin 1896, p. 19.

Lasiacantha uniformis: Lethierry and Severin 1896, p. 19.

Melanorhopala clavata: Horváth 1908, p. 564.—Torre-Bueno 1908, p. 231; 1910, p. 30.—Smith 1910, p. 149 [N.J.].—Osborn and Drake 1916a, p. 244, pl. 8, fig. a; pl. 10, fig. d; 1917a, p. 159, pl. 8, figs. a–c [Iowa; Nebr.].—Van Duzee 1917b, p. 220 [Man.].—Parshley 1917b, p. 56 [R.I.; Conn.]; 1919c, p. 102; 1920a, p. 274; 1923b, p. 706, pl. 17, fig. 3.—Barber 1922a, p. 17.—Drake 1922d, p. 66; 1926b, p. 376, pl. 34, fig. b [Colo.; oak]; 1928b, p. 102; 1930d, p. 269.—Blatchley 1926, p. 491, pl. 4, fig. 3; figs. 116, 117 [Ind.].—Froeschner 1944, p. 670 [Mo.].—Proctor 1946, p. 75.—Hurd 1946, p. 446 [Wyo.].— Bailey 1951, p. 21 [Fla.; N.H.; *Solidago*].

Tingis clavata: Osborn and Drake 1915a, p. 506 [Ohio].

Melanorhopala lurida: Osborn and Drake 1916a, p. 244, pl. 8, fig. b; 1917a, p. 160, pl. 8, figs. g, h.—Van Duzee 1917b, p. 220 [Kans.].— Parshley 1917a, p. 19.—Hussey 1922a, p. 11 [N. Dak.].—Drake 1926b, pl. 34, fig. a.

Melanorhopala uniformis: Osborn and Drake 1916a, p. 245, pl. 8, fig. c [S. Dak.]; 1917a, p. 160, pl. 8, fig. f.—Parshley 1917a, p. 19.—Drake 1926b, pl. 34, fig. c.

Melanorhopala obscura Parshley 1916a, p. 167; 1917b, p. 57; 1917c, p. 47.

Melanorhopala reflexa Blatchley 1926, p. 492.

TYPE: Unknown.

DISTRIBUTION: U.S. (Maine; N.H.; Mass.; R.I.; Conn.; N.Y.; N.J.; Fla.; Ohio; Ill.; Ind.; Kans.; Nebr.; Mo.; Wis.; Iowa; Wyo.; N. Dak.; S. Dak; Colo.); Canada (Man.).

HOST PLANTS: *Solidago* sp.; oak.

NOTE: Discovered in ocean drift [Parshley 1916a].

*Melanorhopala infuscata Parshley

Melanorhopala infuscata Parshley 1917a, p. 19, fig. 1a [Va.; *Liriodendron*];
1920a, p. 274.—McAtee 1923, p. 145 [D.C.; *Ceanothus americanus*].—
Blatchley 1926, p. 493 [Md.; *Ceanothus*].—Bailey 1951, p. 22.

TYPE: Holotype ♂; Falls Church, Virginia, U.S.; MCZ.

DISTRIBUTION: U.S. (Md.; D.C.; Va.).

HOST PLANTS: *Ceanothus americanus; Ceanothus* sp.; *Liriodendron* sp.

Genus MONOSTEIRA Costa

Monosteira Costa 1863, p. 7.—Lethierry and Severin 1896, p. 25.—
Horváth 1906a, pp. 15, 104 (key).—Stichel 1926, pp. 105, 116 (key);
1960a, p. 343; 1960b, p. 401; 1960c, p. 140.—de Seabra 1931, p.
438.—Silvestri 1934, p. 259.—Kiritshenko 1951, pp. 243, 254.—
Drake and Ruhoff 1960a, p. 69.

Monostira [sic]: Oshanin 1908, p. 454; 1912, p. 46.—Stichel 1935, p.
349; 1938a, p. 408.—Gulde 1938, pp. 245, 319 (key).—Gomez-
Menor 1949, p. 158; 1950, p. 2; 1954, p. 382; 1955a, p. 257.—Priesner
and Alfieri 1953, pp. 63, 65.

TYPE SPECIES: *Monanthia unicornis* Mulsant and Rey.

*Monosteira discoidalis (Jakovlev)

Monanthia (Monosteira) discoidalis Jakovlev 1883, p. 107 [Russia].
Monosteira discoidalis: Lethierry and Severin 1896, p. 25 [Turkmen].—
Horváth 1906a, p. 106 [Turkestan].

TYPE: Holotype ♂, macropterous; Tajikistan, Russia; Leningrad Inst.

DISTRIBUTION: U.S.S.R. (Turkestan; Turkmen).

HOST PLANT: Unrecorded.

*Monosteira inermis Horváth

Monosteira inermis Horváth 1899, p. 449 [Turkestan]; 1906a, p. 106.—
Kiritshenko 1959, p. 105.

TYPE: Holotype ♀; Turkestan, Russia; Hungarian Mus.

DISTRIBUTION: U.S.S.R. (Turkestan).

HOST PLANT: Unrecorded.

*Monosteira lobulifera Reuter

Monosteira lobulifera Reuter 1888, p. 225 [Greece]; 1891a, p. 27.—
Horváth 1906a, p. 105 [Syria].—Hoberlandt 1955, p. 95 [Turkey;
Israel; Transcaucasus; *Quercus coccifera; Quercus ilex*].
Monostira lobulifera: Priesner and Alfieri 1953, p. 66 [Egypt; *Salix*].

TYPE: Attica, Greece; sex and deposition of type unknown.

DISTRIBUTION: Greece; Turkey; Syria; Israel; U.S.S.R. (Transcaucasus);
Egypt.

HOST PLANTS: *Quercus coccifera; Quercus ilex; Salix* sp.

*Monosteira minutula Montandon

Monosteira minutula Montandon 1897, p. 101 [Algeria].—Horváth 1906a, p. 106 [Tunisia; Egypt].—Drake 1957a, p. 420 [Aden; Yemen; *Indigofera*].

Monostira minutula: Priesner and Alfieri 1953, p. 66 [*Zizyphus spina-christi*].

TYPE: Sex unknown; Taguin, Algeria; Bucharest Mus.

DISTRIBUTION: Algeria; Tunisia; Egypt; Senegal; Yemen; Aden Protectorate.

HOST PLANTS: *Indigofera* sp.; *Zizyphus jujuba*; *Zizyphus spinachristi*.

NOTE: Taken at light [Priesner and Alfieri].

*Monosteira unicostata (Mulsant and Rey)

Monanthia unicostata Mulsant and Rey 1852a, p. 134 [France]; 1852b, p. 153.—Fieber 1861, p. 383.—Walker 1873a, p. 187.—Stål 1874, p. 58.—Horváth 1874b, p. 432 [Hungary].—Ferrari 1878, p. 66.—Bolivar and Chicote 1879, p. 166.

Monanthia aliena Fieber 1861, p. 124 [Turkey; Syria].—Walker 1873a, p. 185.—Jakovlev 1876b, p. 67.—Ferrari 1874, p. 170; 1878, p. 66.

Monosteira unicostata: Costa 1863, p. 7, pl. 1, fig. 3.—Garbiglietti 1869, p. 274 [Italy].—Reuter 1891a, p. 27 [Greece]; 1908, p. 88.—Horváth 1892b, p. 131 [*Pinus halepensis; Spartium scoparium*]; 1906a, p. 106 [Yugoslavia; Rumania; Caucasus; Armenia; Turkmen; Tunisia].—Lethierry and Severin 1896, p. 25 [Morocco].—Stichel 1926, p. 116; 1960a, p. 344, fig. 181 [Sardinia; Bulgaria; *Prunus persica; Prunus cerasus*].—de Seabra 1931, pp. 439, 444, figs. 510 (1–4), 511 [Portugal; *Pyrus malus*].—Silvestri 1934, p. 259, fig. 222 [Sicily].—Hoberlandt 1942, p. 126 [Czechoslovakia; Transcaucasus]; 1955, p. 96.—Blöte 1945, p. 92.—Kiritshenko 1951, p. 254.

Monanthia (Monosteira) unicostata: Puton 1879c, p. 124 [Algeria; Russia; *Populus alba*].

Monostira unicostata: Horváth 1906d, p. 2; 1916, p. 9 [Albania].—Lindberg 1932a, p. 44 [*Alnus glutinosa*]; 1948, p. 60 [Cyprus].—Vidal 1937, p. 199; 1939, p. 27, fig. 1 [*Pyrus communis*].—Bremond 1938, p. 294, pls. 1–3; figs. 1, 2 [*Populus nigra; Populus tremula; Pyrus mamorensis; Salix; Cydonia vulgaris; Prunus; Crataegus monogyna; Cerasus; Amygdalus communis*].—Gulde 1938, p. 320, fig.—González 1948, p. 51.—Gomez-Menor 1950, p. 99, figs. 1–5; 1954, p. 383, figs. 5–7 [*Prunus amygdalus*]; 1955a, p. 257, figs. 34, 35 (a–e); 1955b, p. 249; 1956a, pp. 111, 112, pl. 1, figs. 6, 8.—Novak and Wagner 1951, p. 71.—Mancini 1953b, p. 186; 1953c, p. 22; 1953d, p. 16.—Seidenstücker 1954, p. 236.

TYPE: Languedoc, France; sex and deposition of type unknown.

DISTRIBUTION: Portugal; Spain; France; Italy; Sicily; Hungary; Czechoslovakia; Yugoslavia; Greece; Albania; Sardinia; Bulgaria; Rumania;

Turkey; Cyprus; Syria; U.S.S.R. (Armenia; Caucasus; Turkmen; Transcaucasus); Algeria; Tunisia; Morocco.

HOST PLANTS: *Alnus glutinosa; Amygdalus communis; Cerasus* sp.; *Crataegus monogyna; Cydonia vulgaris; Pinus halepensis; Populus alba; Populus nigra; Populus tremula; Populus* sp.; *Prunus amygdalus; Prunus cerasus; Prunus persica; Prunus* sp.; *Pyrus communis; Pyrus malus; Pyrus mamorensis; Salix* sp.; *Spartium scoparium.*

NOTE: Life history studies [Vidal 1939; Gomez-Menor 1950; 1955a; Bremond 1938].

*Monosteira unicostata var. buccata Horváth

Monosteira buccata Horváth 1902a, p. 600 [Spain].

Monosteira unicostata var. *buccata:* Horváth 1906a, p. 106.—Stichel 1960a, p. 344.

Monostira unicostata var. *buccata:* Lindberg 1932a, p. 44 [*Nerium olean-der*].—Gulde 1938, p. 320.—Gomez-Menor 1955b, p. 249 [*Persica vulgaris*].

Monostira var. *bucata* [sic]: González 1948, p. 51.

TYPE: Sex unknown; Ciudad Real, Spain; Hungarian Mus.

DISTRIBUTION: Spain.

HOST PLANTS: *Persica vulgaris; Nerium oleander.*

Genus MUMMIUS Horváth

Mummius Horváth 1910, p. 65.—Drake and Ruhoff 1960a, p. 69.

TYPE SPECIES: *Mummius bicorniger* Horváth.

Mummius bicorniger Horváth

Mummius bicorniger Horváth 1910, p. 65 [Tanganyika].

Mummius corniger [sic]: Drake 1954e, p. 5 [Congo].

TYPE: Holotype ♀; Kibongoto, Kilimandjaro; Stockholm Mus.

DISTRIBUTION: Tanganyika; Congo.

HOST PLANT: Unrecorded.

Mummius denigratus Drake

Mummius denigratus Drake 1954e, p. 5, fig. 1 [Congo].

TYPE: Holotype ♀; Dipidi, Parc National de l'Upemba, Belgian Congo; Brussels Mus.

DISTRIBUTION: Congo.

HOST PLANT: Unrecorded.

Genus NAITINGIS Drake and Ruhoff

Naitingis Drake and Ruhoff 1962c, p. 133.

TYPE SPECIES: *Tropidocheila maynei* Schouteden.

Naitingis blukwana (Drake)

Tingis (Tropidocheila) blukwana Drake 1954e, p. 2 [Congo].
Naitingis blukwana: Drake and Ruhoff 1962c, p. 134.
TYPE: Holotype♂; Blukwa, Belgian Congo; Brussels Mus.
DISTRIBUTION: Congo.
HOST PLANT: Unrecorded.

Naitingis maynei (Schouteden)

Tropidocheila maynei Schouteden 1923, p. 105 [Tanganyika].
Tingis (Tropidocheila) maynei: Drake 1954e, p. 2 [Congo].
Tingis (Tropidochila) maynei: Drake 1958a, p. 104 [Angola].
Naitingis maynei: Drake and Ruhoff 1962c, p. 134.
TYPE: Sex unknown; Albertville, Tanganyika; Cent. Afr. Mus.
DISTRIBUTION: Tanganyika; Congo; Angola.
HOST PLANT: Unrecorded.

Naitingis maynei var. biseriata (Schouteden)

Tropidocheila maynei var. *biseriata* Schouteden 1923, p. 106 [Tanganyika].
Naitingis maynei var. *biseriata:* Drake and Ruhoff 1962c, p. 134.
TYPE: Sex unknown; Albertville, Tanganyika; Cent. Afr. Mus.
DISTRIBUTION: Tanganyika.
HOST PLANT: Unrecorded.

Naitingis nyanzae (Schouteden)

Tropidocheila nyanzae Schouteden 1955a, p. 30 [Congo].
Naitingis nyanzae: Drake and Ruhoff 1962c, p. 134.
TYPE: Sex unknown; Ukewere, Victoria-Nyanza, Belgian Congo; Cent. Afr. Mus.
DISTRIBUTION: Congo.
HOST PLANT: Unrecorded.

Genus NAOCHILA Drake

Naochila Drake 1957f, p. 127.—Drake and Ruhoff 1960a, p. 70.
TYPE SPECIES: *Cochlochila boxiana* Drake.

*Naochila arete Drake and Mohanasundarum

Naochila arete Drake and Mohanasundarum 1961, p. 108, fig. 1 [India; *Cordia*].
TYPE: Holotype ♂, brachypterous; Coimbatore, India; Drake Coll. (USNM).
DISTRIBUTION: India.
HOST PLANT: *Cordia* sp.

*Naochila boxiana (Drake)

Cochlochila boxiana Drake 1953d, p. 214 [Ghana; *Hoslundia oppositifolia;* Uganda]; 1955b, p. 85 [Angola].
Naochila boxiana: Drake 1957f, p. 128.

TYPE: Holotype ♂; Tafo, Gold Coast; British Mus.
DISTRIBUTION: Ghana; Uganda; Angola.
HOST PLANT: *Hoslundia oppositifolia.*

*Naochila bukobana (Drake)

Cochlochila bukobana Drake 1953d, p. 214 [Tanganyika].
Naochila bukobana: Drake 1957f, p. 128.

TYPE: Holotype ♂, macropterous; Lake Victoria, Tanganyika; Drake Coll. (USNM).
DISTRIBUTION: Tanganyika.
HOST PLANT: Unrecorded.

*Naochila bullana (Drake)

Cysteochila bullana Drake 1958c, p. 319 [Malagasy].
Naochila bullana: Drake and Ruhoff 1961c, p. 145.

TYPE: Holotype ♂; Ankaratra, Madagascar; Madagascar Sci. Inst.
DISTRIBUTION: Malagasy Republic.
HOST PLANT: Unrecorded.

*Naochila kivuensis (Schouteden)

Monanthia kivuensis Schouteden 1953e, p. 199 [Congo; *Acanthus; Ficus*]; 1957c, p. 318 [Ruanda].
Naochila kivuensis: Drake 1957f, p. 128.

TYPE: Sex unknown; Belgian Congo; Cent. Afr. Mus.
DISTRIBUTION: Congo; Ruanda-Urundi.
HOST PLANTS: *Acanthus* sp.; *Ficus* sp.

*Naochila natalana (Drake)

Cochlochila natalana Drake 1954b, p. 8 [Natal; Pondoland].
Naochila natalana: Drake 1957f, p. 128.

TYPE: Holotype ♂; Port Shepstone, Natal, South Africa; British Mus.
DISTRIBUTION: South Africa (Natal; Pondoland); Kenya.
HOST PLANT: Unrecorded.

*Naochila parvella (Drake)

Cochlochila parvella Drake 1954b, p. 7 [Natal; Pondoland; Cape Province]; 1958c, p. 320 [Malagasy].
Naochila parallela [sic]: Drake 1957f, p. 128.

TYPE: Holotype ♂; Weenan, Natal, South Africa; British Mus.
DISTRIBUTION: South Africa (Natal; Pondoland; Cape Province); Malagasy Republic.
HOST PLANT: Unrecorded.

*Naochila sufflata (Drake and Poor)

Monanthia sufflata Drake and Poor 1939c, p. 203 [India; *Lantana*].
Dictyla sufflata: Drake and Ruhoff 1960a, p. 51.
Naochila sufflata: Drake and Ruhoff 1960c, p. 29.

TYPE: Holotype ♀, macropterous; Dharampur, Dehra Dun, India; Drake Coll. (USNM).

DISTRIBUTION: India.

HOST PLANTS: *Ehretia laevis; Lantana* sp.

*Naochila turgida Drake

Naochila turgida Drake 1957f, p. 128 [Malagasy].

TYPE: Holotype ♂; Ankaratra, Madagascar; Madagascar Sci. Inst.

DISTRIBUTION: Malagasy Republic.

HOST PLANT: Unrecorded.

Genus NEOTINGIS Drake

Neotingis Drake 1922c, p. 366.—Drake and Ruhoff 1960a, p. 70.

TYPE SPECIES: *Neotingis hollandi* Drake.

*Neotingis hollandi Drake

Neotingis hollandi Drake 1922c, p. 367, pl. 39, fig. 5 [Brazil].—Monte 1941e, p. 126.

TYPE: Holotype ♀; Chapada, Brazil; Carnegie Mus.

DISTRIBUTION: Brazil.

HOST PLANT: Unrecorded.

Genus NESOCYPSELAS Kirkaldy

Nesocypselas Kirkaldy 1908b, p. 364.—Drake and Ruhoff 1960a, p. 70.

TYPE SPECIES: *Nesocypselas dicysta* Kirkaldy.

Nesocypselas bellatula Drake

Nesocypselas bellatula Drake 1960, p. 375, fig. 25 [New Guinea].

TYPE: Holotype ♀; Wesselmeren, Duroto, E. of Enarotadi, Netherlands New Guinea; Bishop Mus.

DISTRIBUTION: New Guinea (Netherlands).

HOST PLANT: Unrecorded.

*Nesocypselas dicysta Kirkaldy

Nesocypselas dicysta Kirkaldy 1908b, p. 365, pl. 4, figs. 8, 9 [Viti Levu; *Artocarpus incisa*].—Drake and Poor 1943, p. 200.

TYPE: Holotype ♂; Viti Levu, Fiji Islands; Hawaii. Sugar Plant. Assn.

DISTRIBUTION: Fiji Islands (Viti Levu).

HOST PLANT: *Artocarpus incisa.*

*Nesocypselas evansi Drake

Nesocypselas evansi Drake 1953b, p. 98 [Taveuni].

TYPE: Holotype ♂; Waiyero, Taveuni, Fiji Islands; British Mus.

DISTRIBUTION: Fiji Islands (Taveuni).

HOST PLANT: Unrecorded.

*Nesocypselas evansi subsp. **aemulus** Drake

Nesocypselas evansi subsp. *aemulus* Drake 1953b, p. 99 [Fiji].

TYPE: Holotype ♀; Bau, Fiji Islands; British Mus.

DISTRIBUTION: Fiji Islands.

HOST PLANT: Unrecorded.

*Nesocypselas inannana Drake

Nesocypselas inannana Drake 1953d, p. 222 [Espiritu Santo].

TYPE: Holotype ♀, macropterous; Espiritu Santo, New Hebrides; USNM.

DISTRIBUTION: New Hebrides Islands (Espiritu Santo).

HOST PLANT: Unrecorded.

Nesocypselas muiri Drake and Poor (emendation)

Nesocypselas muri Drake and Poor 1943, p. 203, fig. 7 [Viti Levu].

TYPE: Holotype ♀; Nandarivatu, Viti Levu, Fiji Islands; Bishop Mus.

DISTRIBUTION: Fiji Islands (Viti Levu).

HOST PLANT: Unrecorded.

*Nesocypselas piperica Drake

Nesocypselas piperica Drake 1957d, p. 203, figs. 1, 2 [New Britain; pepper]; 1960, p. 374, fig. 24 [Papua].—Drake and Ruhoff 1960a, p. 5, fig. 1.

TYPE: Holotype ♂; Keravat, New Britain, Melanesia; British Mus.

DISTRIBUTION: New Britain Island, Bismarck Archipelago; New Guinea (Papua).

HOST PLANT: Cultivated pepper.

Nesocypselas simulis Drake and Poor

Nesocypselas simulis Drake and Poor 1943, p. 203, fig. 6 [Viti Levu].

TYPE: Holotype ♀; Nandarivatu, Viti Levu, Fiji Islands; Bishop Mus.

DISTRIBUTION: Fiji Islands (Viti Levu).

HOST PLANT: Unrecorded.

*Nesocypselas vicinalis Drake and Poor (emendation)

Nesocypselas vicinatis Drake and Poor 1943, p. 201 [Viti Levu].

TYPE: Holotype ♀; Nandarivatu, Viti Levu, Fiji Islands; Bishop Mus.

DISTRIBUTION: Fiji Islands (Viti Levu).

HOST PLANT: Unrecorded.

Genus NESOCYSTA Kirkaldy

Nesocysta Kirkaldy 1908b, p. 365.—Drake and Ruhoff 1960a, p. 70.

TYPE SPECIES: *Nesocysta rugata* Kirkaldy.

*Nesocysta rugata Kirkaldy

Nesocysta rugata Kirkaldy 1908b, p. 366 [Viti Levu].—Drake and Poor 1943, p. 204.

TYPE: Holotype ♀; Rewa, Fiji Islands; Hawaii. Sugar Plant. Assn.

DISTRIBUTION: Fiji Islands (Viti Levu).

HOST PLANT: Unrecorded.

Genus NESOTINGIS Drake

Nesotingis Drake 1957e, p. 402.—Drake and Ruhoff 1960a, p. 70.
TYPE SPECIES: *Nesotingis pauliani* Drake.

Nesotingis pauliani Drake

Nesotingis pauliani Drake 1957e, p. 403 [Reunion].
TYPE: Holotype ♀; Bélouve, Reunion; Madagascar Sci. Inst.
DISTRIBUTION: Mascarene Islands (Reunion).
HOST PLANT: Unrecorded.

*Nesotingis vinsoni (Drake and Mamet)

Eteoneus vinsoni Drake and Mamet 1956, p. 301, fig. 6 [Mauritius].—
    Mamet 1957, p. 57.
Nesotingis vinsoni: Drake 1957e, p. 404 [Reunion].
TYPE: Holotype ♀, macropterous; Les Mares, Mauritius Island; Drake
Coll. (USNM).
DISTRIBUTION: Mascarene Islands (Mauritius; Reunion).
HOST PLANT: Unrecorded.

Genus NETHERSIA Horváth

Nethersia Horváth 1925a, p. 14.—Drake and Ruhoff 1960a, p. 71.
TYPE SPECIES: *Nethersia maculosa* Horváth.

*Nethersia absimilis Drake

Nethersia absimilis Drake 1944a, p. 74 [Queensland].
TYPE: Holotype ♀, macropterous; Roma, Queensland, Australia; Drake
Coll. (USNM).
DISTRIBUTION: Australia (Queensland).
HOST PLANT: Unrecorded.

*Nethersia haplotes Drake and Ruhoff

Nethersia haplotes Drake and Ruhoff 1962d, p. 505 [New South Wales].
TYPE: Holotype ♂, macropterous; Mullahey, New South Wales, Aus-
tralia; Drake Coll. (USNM).
DISTRIBUTION: Australia (New South Wales).
HOST PLANT: Unrecorded.

*Nethersia maculosa Horváth

Nethersia maculosa Horváth 1925a, p. 15, fig. 9 [Western Australia].—
    Hacker 1928, p. 186 [South Australia; Queensland].—Drake and
    Ruhoff 1962a, p. 156; 1962b, p. 250; 1962d, p. 505.
Nethersia pugna Drake 1944a, p. 76.
Nathersea [sic] *maculosa:* Drake 1947c, p. 111.
TYPE: Holotype ♀; Broome, Australis occidentalis; Stockholm Mus.
DISTRIBUTION: Australia (Queensland; Western Australia; Northern Ter-
ritory; South Australia).
HOST PLANT: Unrecorded.

*Nethersia nigritarsis (Horváth)

Tingis (*Tropidochila*) *nigritarsis* Horváth 1925a, p. 7 [Queensland].
Nethersia poorae Drake 1944a, p. 72, fig. 1.
Nethersia nigritarsis: Drake and Ruhoff 1962d, p. 505.

TYPE: Holotype ♀; Herberton, Queensland, Australia; Stockholm Mus.
DISTRIBUTION: Australia (Queensland).
HOST PLANT: Unrecorded.

*Nethersia setosa (Hacker)

Ischnotingis setosus Hacker 1927, p. 23, pl. 6, fig. 3 [Queensland; *Acacia*].
Nethersia setosa: Hacker 1928, p. 186.

TYPE: Sex unknown; Mount Coot-tha, Queensland, Australia; Queensland Mus.
DISTRIBUTION: Australia (Queensland; New South Wales).
HOST PLANT: *Acacia* sp.

Genus NOBARNUS Distant

Nobarnus Distant 1920, p. 156.—Drake and Ruhoff 1960a, p. 71.
TYPE SPECIES: *Nobarnus typicus* Distant.

Nobarnus signatus (Distant)   PLATE 41

Compseuta signata Distant 1920, p. 156 [New Caledonia].
Nobarnus signatus: China 1926, p. 228.—Drake and Davis 1960, fig. 38.

TYPE: Sex unknown; Paompai, New Caledonia; British Mus.
DISTRIBUTION: New Caledonia.
HOST PLANT: Unrecorded.

Nobarnus typicus Distant

Nobarnus typicus Distant 1920, p. 157 [New Caledonia].
TYPE: Sex unknown; Mt. Arago, New Caledonia; British Mus.
DISTRIBUTION: New Caledonia.
HOST PLANT: Unrecorded.

Genus NYCTOTINGIS Drake

Nyctotingis Drake 1922c, p. 362.—Drake and Ruhoff 1960a, p. 71.
TYPE SPECIES: *Nyctotingis osborni* Drake.

*Nyctotingis nexilis Drake

Nyctotingis nexilis Drake 1948j, p. 431 [Peru].
TYPE: Holotype ♀, macropterous; Tingo Maria, Peru; Drake Coll. (USNM).
DISTRIBUTION: Peru; Bolivia.
HOST PLANT: Unrecorded.

*Nyctotingis osborni Drake

Nyctotingis osborni Drake 1922c, p. 363, fig. 1 [Brazil]; 1928a, p. 42 [Ecuador].—Monte 1938b, p. 132; 1941e, p. 126 [*Bambusa*].—Drake and Hambleton 1945, p. 357 [Peru].—Silva 1956, p. 46, fig. 17.

TYPE: Holotype ♀; Chapada, Brazil; Carnegie Mus.

DISTRIBUTION: Brazil; Ecuador; Peru.

HOST PLANT: *Bambusa* sp.

Genus OCTACYSTA Drake and Ruhoff

Octacysta Drake and Ruhoff 1960a, p. 71.—Stichel 1960b, p. 401; 1960c, p. 140.

TYPE SPECIES: *Tingis rotundata* Herrich-Schaeffer = *Tingis echii* Fabricius (not Schrank).

*Octacysta echii (Fabricius)

Tingis echii Fabricius 1803, p. 126 [Austria; *Echium*].—Burmeister 1835, p. 259 [*Echium vulgare*].—Amyot and Serville 1843, p. 297 [France].

Tingis rotundata Herrich-Schaeffer 1835, p. 59.

Monanthia rotundata: Herrich-Schaeffer 1838, pp. 52, 59, pl. 124, figs. 392, f–g; pl. 125, fig. 2 [Czechoslovakia].—Horváth 1906a, pp. 99, 103 [Hungary; Rumania; Russia; Caucasus].—Mužik 1907, p. 64.— Oshanin 1908, p. 454 [Turkestan]; 1912, p. 46.—Moroder Sala 1920, p. 13 [Spain].—Stichel 1926, p. 115; 1935, p. 349; 1938a, p. 408.—Börner 1935, p. 78.—Gulde 1938, p. 318.—Hoberlandt 1942, p. 126; 1943a, p. 119; 1943b, p. 124; 1955, p. 95 [Transcaucasus].— Blöte 1945, p. 91.—Kiritshenko 1951, p. 254.—Seidenstücker 1954, p. 236 [Turkey].—Štušák and Stys 1959, p. 199, figs. 41–46 [*Anchusa officinalis*].—Putshkov 1960, p. 305 [*Cynoglossum*].—Štušák 1961a, p. 86, figs. 5c, 14, 15; pl. 2.

Monanthia (Physatocheila) echii: Fieber 1844, p. 88, pl. 7, figs. 27–32 [Italy].—Herrich-Schaeffer 1850, p. 153.

Tingis (Physatocheila) echii: Kolenati 1856, p. 428 [*Echium rubrum; Echium italicum;* Armenia].

Monanthia echii: Fieber 1861, p. 126.—Garbiglietti 1869, p. 273.— Walker 1873a, p. 187.—Stål 1874, p. 59.—Puton 1879c, p. 123.— Hüeber 1893, p. 355 [Germany; Switzerland].

Octacysta rotundata: Drake and Ruhoff 1960a, p. 71, pls. 6, 7.—Stichel 1960b, p. 401; 1960c, p. 140.

Dictyla rotundata: Stichel 1960a, p. 342, fig. 180a [Poland; Bulgaria].

Octacysta echii: Drake and Ruhoff 1960b, p. 74, fig. 22.

TYPE: Lectotype ♀, brachypterous; Austria; Copenhagen Mus.

DISTRIBUTION: Spain; France; Germany; Switzerland; Czechoslovakia; Austria; Italy; Hungary; Rumania; Bulgaria; Poland; U.S.S.R. (Armenia; Caucasus; Transcaucasus; Turkestan); Turkey.

HOST PLANTS: *Anchusa officinalis; Cynoglossum* sp.; *Echium italicum; Echium rubrum; Echium vulgare; Echium* sp.

NOTE: Study of nymphs and eggs [Štuśak and Stys; Štuśak]. Resurrection of name [Drake and Ruhoff 1960b].

Genus OEDOTINGIS Drake

Oedotingis Drake 1942a, p. 19.—Drake and Ruhoff 1960a, p. 72.
TYPE SPECIES: *Australotingis williamsi* Drake.

*Oedotingis mexicana Drake

Odeotingis [sic] *mexicana* Drake 1948d, p. 17 [Mexico].
TYPE: Holotype ♀, macropterous; Guerrero, Mexico; USNM.
DISTRIBUTION: Mexico.
HOST PLANT: Unrecorded.
NOTE: Intercepted on orchid plants at port-of-entry, Laredo, Texas. The sex of the type species was erroneously reported as male in the original description.

*Oedotingis williamsi (Drake)

Australotingis williamsi Drake 1928a, p. 51 [Ecuador].
Oedotingis williamsi: Drake 1942a, p. 20.
TYPE: Holotype ♀, macropterous; Mera, Ecuador; Drake Coll. (USNM).
DISTRIBUTION: Ecuador.
HOST PLANT: Unrecorded.

Genus OGYGOTINGIS Drake

Ogygotingis Drake 1948e, p. 149.—Drake and Ruhoff 1960a, p. 72.
TYPE SPECIES: *Teleonemia insularis* China.

*Ogygotingis insularis (China)

Teleonemia insularis China 1924, p. 436, fig. 2b [Rodriguez].
Ogygotingis insularis: Drake 1948e, p. 149.
Orygotingis [sic] *insularis:* Drake and Davis 1960, fig. 41.
TYPE: Sex unknown; Rodriguez Island; British Mus.
DISTRIBUTION: Mascarene Islands (Rodriguez).
HOST PLANT: Unrecorded.

Genus OLASTRIDA Schouteden

Olastrida Schouteden 1956, p. 205.—Drake and Ruhoff 1960a, p. 72.
TYPE SPECIES: *Olastrida oleae* Schouteden.

*Olastrida oleae Schouteden

Olastrida oleae Schouteden 1956, p. 205 [Ruanda; *Olea europea*].
TYPE: Sex unknown; Astrida, Ruanda; Cent. Afr. Mus.
DISTRIBUTION: Ruanda-Urundi.
HOST PLANT: *Olea europea.*

Genus ONCOCHILA Stål

Oncochila Stål 1873, p. 121; 1874, p. 57.—Kirkaldy 1904, p. 281.—
Horváth 1906a, pp. 15, 96 (key).—Oshanin 1908, p. 449; 1912, p.
45.—Stichel 1926, pp. 105, 114 (key); 1935, p. 349; 1938a, p. 408;
1960a, p. 336; 1960b, p. 400; 1960c, p. 139.—Börner 1935, pp. 74,
78.—Gulde 1938, pp. 245, 309 (key).—China 1943, p. 248.—
Kiritshenko 1951, pp. 242, 252.—Drake and Ruhoff 1960a, p. 72.
Type Species: *Monanthia* (*Physatocheila*) *scapularis* Fieber.

*Oncochila scapularis (Fieber)

Monanthia (*Physatocheila*) *scapularis* Fieber 1844, p. 80, pl. 6, figs. 38–40
[Czechoslovakia; Austria; Italy; Germany; *Senecio jacobaea*].
Monanthia scapularis: Scholz 1847, p. 120.—Mayr 1858, p. 571 [Hun-
gary].—Fieber 1861, p. 125.—Garbiglietti 1869, p. 273.—Walker
1873a, p. 186.—Reiber and Puton 1876, p. 69.—Horváth 1889, p.
326.—Hüeber 1893, p. 349 [Yugoslavia; Rumania].
Oncochila scapularis: Stål 1873, p. 121; 1874, p. 57.—Horváth 1906a,
p. 97 [Russia; Siberia; *Euphorbia gerardiana*].—Mužik 1907, p. 62.—
Stichel 1926, p. 115; 1938a, p. 408 [Albania; Poland]; 1960a, p.
336 [Bulgaria].—Hoberlandt 1942, p. 126; 1943b, pp. 119, 124.—
Štusak 1958, p. 367, figs. 12–14.
Physatochila scapularis: Lethierry and Severin 1896, p. 21.
Type: Unknown.

Distribution: Czechoslovakia; Hungary; Austria; Italy; Germany;
Rumania; Yugoslavia; Albania; Poland; Bulgaria; U.S.S.R. (Siberia).
Host Plants: *Euphorbia gerardiana; Senecio jacobaea.*
Note: Eggs [Štusak].

*Oncochila simplex (Herrich-Schaeffer)

Tingis simplex Herrich-Schaeffer 1830, heft 118, tab. 21 [Germany];
1835, p. 59.
Monanthia simplex: Herrich-Schaeffer 1838, p. 59.—Douglas and Scott
1865, p. 245 [England].—Horváth 1874b, p. 432 [Hungary].—
Jakovlev 1876b, p. 66 [Russia]; 1880b, p. 108 [Caucasus].—Saunders
1875, p. 250.—Puton 1879c, p. 119 [France; *Euphorbia cyparissias*].—
Chicote 1880, p. 189 [Spain].—Dubois 1888, p. 121.—d'Antessanty
1890, p. 33.—Hüeber 1893, p. 347 [Austria; Switzerland].—Butler
1923, p. 214 [Turkestan].
Monanthia (*Physatocheila*) *simplex:* Herrich-Schaeffer 1850, p. 153.—
Saunders 1892, p. 136, pl. 12, fig. 10.
Physatochila (*Oncochila*) *simplex:* Sahlberg 1878, p. 21.
Physatochila simplex: Lethierry and Severin 1896, p. 21.—Reichensperger
1920, p. 62.

Oncochila simplex: Horváth 1906a, pp. 96, 97 [Belgium; Italy; Yugoslavia; Rumania; Armenia].—Mužik 1907, p. 62 [Czechoslovakia].—Stichel 1926, p. 115; 1960a, p. 336 [Poland; Bulgaria; *Thymus*].—Lindberg 1927, p. 20.—Scholte 1935, p. 90, fig. 23 [Netherlands].—Gulde 1938, p. 310, fig. [Denmark].—Hoberlandt 1942, p. 126; 1943b, p. 124.—Blöte 1945, p. 89 [Tunisia].—Bator 1953, p. 326, pl. 4, fig. 1.—Cobben 1958a, p. 12, fig. 15 [*Euphorbia gerardiana*].—Southwood and Leston 1959, p. 151, pl. 19, fig. 3; pl. 21, fig. 6.

Type: Regensburg, Germany; sex and deposition of type unknown.

Distribution: Germany; France; England; Italy; Austria; Poland; Switzerland; Yugoslavia; Hungary; Belgium; Rumania; Bulgaria; Czechoslovakia; Netherlands; Spain; Denmark; Albania; U.S.S.R. (Armenia; Turkestan; Caucasus); Tunisia.

Host Plants: *Euphorbia cyparissias; Euphorbia gerardiana; Thymus* sp.

†Oncochila wollastoni (Heer)

Tingis wollastoni Heer 1865, fig. 307; 1872, fig. 307; 1876, fig. 307; 1879, fig. 307.—Scudder 1891, p. 449.

Monanthia wollastoni: Heer 1865, p. 392 [Baden]; 1872, p. 480; 1876, p. 50; 1879, p. 417.—Scudder 1891, p. 422 [Horizon: Tortonian].

Dictyla wollastoni: Drake and Ruhoff 1960a, pp. 11, 51.

Oncochila wollastoni: Drake and Ruhoff 1960c, p. 32.

Type: Sex undeterminable; fossil; Oeningen, Baden; deposition unknown.

Distribution: Fossil.

Note: In the above publications by Heer, *wollastoni* was placed in the genus *Tingis* in figure captions (which preceded the text) and in *Monanthia* in the description.

Genus ONCOPHYSA Stål

Oncophysa Stål 1873, pp. 121, 129.—Drake and Ruhoff 1960a, p. 73.

Type Species: *Monanthia (Physatocheila) vesiculata* Stål.

*Oncophysa leai Drake

Oncophysa leai Drake 1948e, p. 154 [Western Australia].

Type: Holotype ♀; Australia; Hungarian Mus.

Distribution: Australia (Western Australia).

Host Plant: Unrecorded.

*Oncophysa rufescens Hacker

Oncophysa rufescens Hacker 1928, p. 178, pl. 21, fig. 8 [South Australia].

Type: Sex unknown; Port Noarlunga, South Australia, Australia; Queensland Mus.

Distribution: Australia (South Australia).

Host Plant: Unrecorded.

*Oncophysa vesiculata (Stål)

Monanthia (*Physatocheila*) *vesiculata* Stål 1859, p. 259 [New South Wales].
Monanthia vesiculata: Walker 1873a, p. 197.
Oncophysa vesiculata: Stål 1873, p. 129.—Lethierry and Severin 1896, p. 22.—Horváth 1925a, p. 2 [Queensland].—Hacker 1927, p. 25 [*Pimelea*]; 1928, p. 177 [Victoria].—Drake 1961b, p. 108.
TYPE: Holotype ♀; New Holland, Sydney, Australia; Stockholm Mus.
DISTRIBUTION: Australia (New South Wales; Queensland; Victoria).
HOST PLANT: *Pimelea* sp.

Oncophysa vesiculata var. gracilis Hacker

Oncophysa vesiculata var. *gracilis* Hacker 1928, p. 178, pl. 21, fig. 7 [South Australia].—Drake 1961b, p. 108 [New South Wales].
TYPE: Sex unknown; Cape Jarvis, South Australia, Australia; Queensland Mus.
DISTRIBUTION: Australia (South Australia; New South Wales).
HOST PLANT: Unrecorded.

*Oncophysa vesiculata var. nigra Hacker

Oncophysa vesiculata var. *nigra* Hacker 1928, p. 178, pl. 21, fig. 6 [Tasmania; Victoria].—Drake 1961b, p. 108 [New South Wales].—Drake and Ruhoff 1962b, p. 250.
TYPE: Sex unknown; Mount Arthur, Tasmania, Australia; Queensland Mus.
DISTRIBUTION: Australia (Tasmania; New South Wales; Victoria).
HOST PLANT: Unrecorded.

Genus ONYMOCHILA Drake

Onymochila Drake 1948e, p. 152.—Drake and Ruhoff 1960a, p. 73.
TYPE SPECIES: *Cysteochila dichapetali* Horváth.

*Onymochila dichapetali (Horváth) (emendation)　　　PLATE 17

Cysteochila dichopetali Horváth 1929, p. 324 [Transvaal; *Dichapetalum cymosum*].
Onymochila dichopatali [sic]: Drake 1948e, p. 152.
Onymochila dichopetali: Drake and Davis 1960, figs. 50, 51.
TYPE: Sex unknown; Pretoria, Transvaal, South Africa; British Mus.
DISTRIBUTION: South Africa (Transvaal).
HOST PLANT: Causes extensive down-curl of the leaves of *Dichapetalum cymosum* (see pl. 17).

Genus OROTINGIS Drake and Poor

Orotingis Drake and Poor 1941, p. 161.—Drake and Ruhoff 1960a, p. 73.
TYPE SPECIES: *Orotingis muiri* Drake and Poor.

Orotingis eueides Drake

Orotingis eueides Drake 1960, p. 364, fig. 16 [New Guinea].

TYPE: Holotype ♂; Wisselmeren, Duroto, Netherlands New Guinea; Bishop Mus.

DISTRIBUTION: New Guinea (Netherlands).

HOST PLANT: Unrecorded.

***Orotingis muiri** Drake and Poor

Orotingis muiri Drake and Poor 1941, p. 161 [Amboina].—Drake and Davis 1960, fig. 64.

TYPE: Holotype ♂; Amboina Island; Cal. Acad.

DISTRIBUTION: Moluccas (Amboina Island).

HOST PLANT: Unrecorded.

Genus OTTOICUS Drake

Ottoicus Drake 1960, p. 358.

TYPE SPECIES: *Ottoicus dissitus* Drake.

***Ottoicus dissitus** Drake

Ottoicus dissitus Drake 1960, p. 358, fig. 12 [New Guinea].

TYPE: Holotype ♂; Mt. Otto, above Kabebe, New Guinea; Bishop Mus.

DISTRIBUTION: New Guinea.

HOST PLANT: Unrecorded.

Genus PACHYCYSTA Champion

Pachycysta Champion 1898b, p. 59.—Drake 1928g, pp. 184–185 (key).— Monte 1941e, p. 126.—Hurd 1946, p. 474.—Drake and Ruhoff 1960a, p. 74.

TYPE SPECIES: *Pachycysta diaphana* Champion.

***Pachycysta adolpha** Drake

Pachycysta adolpha Drake 1948j, p. 431 [Peru].

TYPE: Holotype ♀, macropterous; Maracapata, Peru; Drake Coll. (USNM).

DISTRIBUTION: Peru.

HOST PLANT: Unrecorded.

***Pachycysta championi** Drake

Pachycysta championi Drake 1921a, p. 344, figs. a, b [Bolivia]; 1928g, p. 184.—Drake and Davis 1960, fig. 57.

TYPE: Sex unknown; Cochabamba, Bolivia; Paris Mus.

DISTRIBUTION: Boliva.

HOST PLANT: Unrecorded.

*Pachycysta diaphana Champion

Pachycysta diaphana Champion 1898b, p. 59, pl. 2, figs. 6, 6a [Brazil].—Drake 1928g, p. 184.—Monte 1940e, p. 300; 1942a, p. 97.—Drake and Hambleton 1944b, p. 124 [Venezuela].

TYPE: Holotype ♀; Amazons; Oxford Mus.

DISTRIBUTION: Brazil; Venezuela.

HOST PLANT: Unrecorded.

*Pachycysta hambletoni Drake and Poor

Pachycysta hambletoni Drake and Poor 1938a, p. 31 [Brazil].—Monte 1941e, p. 127 [*Guettarda viburnoides*].

TYPE: Holotype ♂, macropterous; São Paulo, Brazil; Drake Coll. (USNM).

DISTRIBUTION: Brazil.

HOST PLANT: *Guettarda viburnoides.*

*Pachycysta schildi Drake

Pachycysta schildi Drake 1928g, p. 185 [Costa Rica].

Pachycysta shildi [sic]: Monte 1942a, p. 96 [Venezuela].

TYPE: Holotype ♂, macropterous; Suize Tur'lba, Costa Rica; Drake Coll. (USNM).

DISTRIBUTION: Costa Rica; Venezuela.

HOST PLANT: Unrecorded.

Genus PALAUELLA Drake

Palauella Drake 1956d, pp. 105, 110.—Drake and Ruhoff 1960a, p. 74.

TYPE SPECIES: *Palauella gressitti* Drake.

*Palauella gressitti Drake

Palauella gressitti Drake 1956d, pp. 105, 112, fig. 6 [Palau].

TYPE: Holotype ♀, macropterous; Ulimang, Babelthuap, Palau Islands; USNM.

DISTRIBUTION: Palau Islands.

HOST PLANT: Unrecorded.

Genus PARACOPIUM Distant

Paracopium Distant 1902b, p. 354; 1903b, p. 128.—Horváth 1929, p. 322.—Drake and Ruhoff 1960a, p. 74.

TYPE SPECIES: *Dictyonota cingalensis* Walker.

*Paracopium africum Drake

Paracopium africum Drake 1956g, p. 472 [Natal]; 1961c, p. 129.

TYPE: Holotype ♂, macropterous; Natal, South Africa; Drake Coll. (USNM).

DISTRIBUTION: South Africa (Natal).

HOST PLANT: Unrecorded.

*Paracopium albofasciatum Hacker

Paracopium albofasciata Hacker 1927, p. 21, pl. 6, fig. 2 [Queensland].— Drake 1961b, p. 110.

TYPE: Sex unknown; Prairie, Queensland, Australia; Queensland Mus.

DISTRIBUTION: Australia (Queensland).

HOST PLANT: Unrecorded.

*Paracopium antennatum (Schouteden)

Copium antennatum Schouteden 1923, p. 86 [Congo].

Paracopium antennatum: Drake 1954f, p. 4.

TYPE: Sex unknown; Belgian Congo; Cent. Afr. Mus.

DISTRIBUTION: Congo; Cameroun.

HOST PLANT: Unrecorded.

*Paracopium assimile Horváth

Paracopium assimile Horváth 1929, pp. 321, 322 [Uganda].

TYPE: Holotype ♀; Nagunga, Uganda; British Mus.

DISTRIBUTION: Uganda; Nigeria; Tanganyika.

HOST PLANT: Unrecorded.

*Paracopium australicum (Stål)

Catoplatus australicus Stål 1873, p. 128 [Queensland].—Lethierry and Severin 1896, p. 20.

Paracopium australicus: Hacker 1927, p. 20, pl. 6, fig. 1; 1928, p. 183 [New South Wales; Melville; Moa].

Paracopium australicum: Horváth 1929, p. 322.—Drake 1961b, p. 110.— Drake and Ruhoff 1962b, p. 250.

TYPE: Holotype ♀; Port Denison, Cape York, Australia; Stockholm Mus.

DISTRIBUTION: Australia (Queensland; New South Wales; Moa and Melville Islands).

HOST PLANT: Unrecorded.

*Paracopium bequaerti (Schouteden)

Copium bequaerti Schouteden 1923, p. 86 [Congo].

Copium (Paracopium) bequaerti: Mayné and Ghesquière 1934, p. 20 [*Clerodendron giletii*].

Paracopium bequaerti: Drake 1954f, p. 4; 1958b, p. 29.

TYPE: Sex unknown; Sankisia, Katanga, Belgian Congo; Cent. Afr. Mus.

DISTRIBUTION: Congo.

HOST PLANT: *Clerodendron giletii*.

Paracopium burgeoni (Schouteden)

Catoplatus burgeoni Schouteden 1923, p. 89 [Congo].

Paracopium burgeoni: Drake 1954f, p. 4.

TYPE: Sex unknown; Kindu, Manyema, Belgian Congo; Cent. Afr. Mus.

DISTRIBUTION: Congo.

HOST PLANT: Unrecorded.

*Paracopium caledonicum Drake

Paracopium caledonicum Drake 1956g, p. 474 [New Caledonia].

TYPE: Holotype ♂, macropterous; New Caledonia; Drake Coll. (USNM).

DISTRIBUTION: New Caledonia.

HOST PLANT: Unrecorded.

*Paracopium cingalense (Walker)

Dictyonota cingalensis Walker 1873a, p. 178 [Ceylon].—Kirby 1891, p. 109.—Lethierry and Severin 1896, p. 25.

Paracopium cingalensis: Distant 1902b, p. 354.

Paracopium cingalense: Distant 1903b, p. 128, fig. 92.—Maxwell-Lefroy 1909, p. 693 [India; *Clerodendron phlomoides*].—Horváth 1929, p. 322.

TYPE: Sex unknown; Ceylon; British Mus.

DISTRIBUTION: Ceylon; India.

HOST PLANT: *Clerodendron phlomoides*.

Paracopium coloratum Schouteden

Paracopium coloratum Schouteden 1955b, p. 164 [Congo].

TYPE: Sex unknown; Lukenie, Belgian Congo; Cent. Afr. Mus.

DISTRIBUTION: Congo.

HOST PLANT: Unrecorded.

*Paracopium comatum Drake (emendation)

Paracopium comantis Drake 1953d, p. 217 [India].

TYPE: Holotype ♂; West Almora, United Province, India; British Mus.

DISTRIBUTION: India.

HOST PLANT: Unrecorded.

*Paracopium congruum Drake

Paracopium congruum Drake 1956g, p. 471, fig. 1 [Congo; Rhodesia].

TYPE: Holotype ♂, macropterous; Victoria Falls, Rhodesia; Drake Coll. (USNM).

DISTRIBUTION: Rhodesia; Congo.

HOST PLANT: Unrecorded.

*Paracopium dauphinicum Drake

Paracopium dauphinicum Drake 1956g, p. 473, fig. 2 [Malagasy].

TYPE: Holotype ♀, macropterous; Fort Dauphin, Madagascar; Drake Coll. (USNM).

DISTRIBUTION: Malagasy Republic.

HOST PLANT: *Clerodendron micans*.

*Paracopium fenestellatum (Bergroth)

Copium fenestellatum Bergroth 1894, p. 168 [Malagasy].—Lethierry and Severin 1896, p. 16.

Paracopium fenestellatum: Horváth 1929, p. 322.—Drake 1958c, p. 325.

TYPE: Sex unknown; Madagascar; Helsin. Mus.

DISTRIBUTION: Malagasy Republic.

HOST PLANT: Unrecorded.

*Paracopium floricolum (Horváth)

Copium floricola Horváth 1910, p. 61 [Tanganyika].
Paracopium floricola: Horváth 1929, p. 322.

TYPE: Sex unknown; Usambara, Tanganyika; Stockholm Mus.
DISTRIBUTION: Tanganyika.
HOST PLANT: Unrecorded.

Paracopium fraterculum Schouteden

Paracopium fraterculum Schouteden 1955b, p. 166 [Congo].

TYPE: Sex unknown; Belgian Congo; Cent. Afr. Mus.
DISTRIBUTION: Congo.
HOST PLANT: Unrecorded.

*Paracopium furvum (Horváth)

Copium furvum Horváth 1925a, p. 2 [Queensland].
Paracopium furvum: Horváth 1929, p. 322.

TYPE: Holotype ♂; Queensland, Australia; Stockholm Mus.
DISTRIBUTION: Australia (Queensland).
HOST PLANT: Unrecorded.

*Paracopium ghesquierei (Schouteden)

Copium ghesquierei Schouteden 1923, p. 87 [Congo].
Paracopium ghesquierei: Drake 1954f, p. 4.

TYPE: Sex unknown; Belgian Congo; Cent. Afr. Mus.
DISTRIBUTION: Congo.
HOST PLANT: Unrecorded.

*Paracopium gigantos Drake

Paracopium gigantos Drake 1954f, p. 3 [Malagasy].

TYPE: Holotype ♀, macropterous; Perinet, Analamasotra, Madagascar;
Drake Coll. (USNM).
DISTRIBUTION: Malagasy Republic.
HOST PLANT: Unrecorded.

*Paracopium glabricorne (Montandon)

Eurycera glabricornis Montandon 1892, p. 267 [Mozambique].—Distant
1904, p. 430, pl. 8, fig. 9 [Cape Province; Natal; Transvaal].
Copium glabricorne: Lethierry and Severin 1896, p. 16.—Distant 1902a,
p. 241.—Schouteden 1916b, p. 292 [Congo]; 1923, p. 88.—Mancini
1939c, p. 308 [Somali].—Blöte 1945, p. 85.
Paracopium glabricorne: Horváth 1929, p. 322.—Drake and Slater
1955, p. 49 [Zululand].

TYPE: Sex unknown; Rikatla, Mozambique; Montandon Coll. (Bucharest Mus.).
DISTRIBUTION: Mozambique; Congo; South Africa (Cape Province;
Natal; Transvaal; Zululand); No. Rhodesia; Somali.
HOST PLANT: Unrecorded.

*Paracopium hamadryas (Drake) PLATES 23, 24

Copium hamadryas Drake 1925a, p. 1 [Congo; *Clerodendron*].
Paracopium hamadryas: Horváth 1929, p. 322 [Ghana; *Clerodendron buchholzi*].—Drake and Davis 1960, fig. 52 [Uganda].
Copium (Paracopium) hamadryas: Mayné and Ghesquière 1934, p. 20 [*Clerodendron subreniforme*].
TYPE: Holotype ♀; Thysville, Belgian Congo; American Mus.
DISTRIBUTION: Congo; Ghana; Uganda; Tanganyika.
HOST PLANTS: *Clerodendron buchholzi; Clerodendron subreniforme; Clerodendron* sp.
NOTE: Figures of floral cecidia formed on *Clerodendron* sp. [Drake and Davis].

*Paracopium hirsutum Drake

Paracopium hirsutum Drake 1953d, p. 218 [Malagasy]; 1958c, p. 326.
TYPE: Holotype ♂, macropterous; Perinet, Analamasotra, Madagascar; Drake Coll. (USNM).
DISTRIBUTION: Malagasy Republic.
HOST PLANT: Unrecorded.

*Paracopium hirticorne (Bergroth)

Copium hirticorne Bergroth 1912, p. 145 [Guinea].
Paracopium hirticorne: Horváth 1929, p. 323.
Paracopium histocorne [sic]: Drake 1954a, p. 232 [Ghana].
TYPE: Holotype ♂; Assini, Guinea; deposition unknown.
DISTRIBUTION: Guinea; Ghana.
HOST PLANT: Unrecorded.

*Paracopium insigne Schouteden

Paracopium ? insigne Schouteden 1955b, p. 163 [Congo; Ruanda]; 1957c, p. 313.
TYPE: Sex unknown; Belgian Congo; Cent. Afr. Mus.
DISTRIBUTION: Congo; Ruanda-Urundi.
HOST PLANT: Unrecorded.

Paracopium kollari (Fieber)

Laccometopus kollari Fieber 1844, p. 98, pl. 8, figs. 17–22 [Mauritius].— Herrich-Schaeffer 1850, p. 158.
Eurycera kollari: Stål 1873, p. 129.
Copium kollari: Lethierry and Severin 1896, p. 16.
Paracopium kollari: Horváth 1929, p. 323.—Drake and Mamet 1956, p. 300; 1961, p. 223, fig.—Orian 1956, p. 647.—Mamet 1957, p. 56.
TYPE: Holotype ♂, macropterous; Mauritius Island; Vienna Mus.
DISTRIBUTION: Mascarene Islands (Mauritius).
HOST PLANT: Unrecorded.
NOTE: Taken at light [Drake and Mamet 1961].

*Paracopium lewisi Distant

> *Paracopium lewisi* Distant 1903a, p. 48 [Ceylon]; 1903b, p. 128.—Horváth 1929, p. 323.

TYPE: Sex unknown; Ceylon; British Mus.

DISTRIBUTION: Ceylon; Greater Sunda Islands (Sumatra).

HOST PLANT: Unrecorded.

*Paracopium longulum Drake

> *Paracopium longulum* Drake 1958c, p. 323 [Malagasy].

TYPE: Holotype ♀; Forêt au Nord d'Anosibe, Madagascar; Madagascar Sci. Inst.

DISTRIBUTION: Malagasy Republic.

HOST PLANT: Unrecorded.

*Paracopium lupakense (Schouteden)

> *Copium lupakense* Schouteden 1923, p. 88 [Congo].
> *Paracopium lupakense:* Drake 1954f, p. 4.

TYPE: Sex unknown; Lupaka, Luapula, Belgian Congo; Cent. Afr. Mus.

DISTRIBUTION: Congo.

HOST PLANT: Unrecorded.

Paracopium modestum Schouteden

> *Paracopium modestum* Schouteden 1955b, p. 165 [Congo].

TYPE: Sex unknown; Moto, Ituri, Belgian Congo; Cent. Afr. Mus.

DISTRIBUTION: Congo.

HOST PLANT: Unrecorded.

*Paracopium parvum Drake

> *Paracopium parvum* Drake 1958c, p. 326 [Malagasy].

TYPE: Holotype ♂; Tongobory, Madagascar; Madagascar Sci. Inst.

DISTRIBUTION: Malagasy Republic.

HOST PLANT: Unrecorded.

*Paracopium philippinense Drake

> *Paracopium philippinensis* Drake 1930e, p. 165 [Sibuyan].

TYPE: Holotype ♂, macropterous; Sibuyan Island, Philippine Islands; USNM.

DISTRIBUTION: Philippine Islands (Sibuyan; Negros).

HOST PLANT: Unrecorded.

*Paracopium proprium Drake

> *Paracopium proprium* Drake 1958c, p. 325 [Malagasy].

TYPE: Holotype ♂; Réserve Naturelle, Nosivola, Madagascar; Madagascar Sci. Inst.

DISTRIBUTION: Malagasy Republic.

HOST PLANT: Unrecorded.

*Paracopium sauteri Drake

　　Paracopium sauteri Drake 1951, p. 171 [Taiwan].

TYPE: Holotype ♂; Anping, Formosa; Hungarian Mus.

DISTRIBUTION: Taiwan.

HOST PLANT: Unrecorded.

*Paracopium stolidum (Horváth)

　　Copium stolidum Horváth 1912a, p. 355 [Congo].—Schouteden 1916b, p. 292; 1923, p. 88.—Mayné and Ghesquière 1934, p. 20 [*Kalaharia (Clerodendron) spinescens*].

　　Paracopium stolidum: Horváth 1929, p. 323.—Drake 1955b, p. 89 [Angola].

TYPE: Holotype ♀; Leopoldville, Belgian Congo; Cent. Afr. Mus.

DISTRIBUTION: Congo; Angola.

HOST PLANTS: *Kalaharia (Clerodendron) spinescens;* "in galls of old fallen flowers of the herb called by the Batshick 'kakolu-uá-hachi' " [Drake 1955b].

*Paracopium summervillei (Hacker)

　　Teleonemia summervillei Hacker 1927, p. 22, pl. 6, fig. 4 [Queensland; *Scaevola koenigii*].

　　Paracopium summetvillei [sic]: Drake 1947c, p. 112 [Dunk; Prince Wales Islands; New Hebrides].

TYPE: Sex unknown; Palm Island, Queensland, Australia; Queensland Mus.

DISTRIBUTION: Australia (Queensland; Palm, Dunk, Prince Wales Islands); New Hebrides Islands.

HOST PLANT: *Scaevola koenigii.*

Genus PARADA Horváth

　　Cysteochila (Parada) Horváth 1925a, p. 3.

　　Parada: Drake 1942a, p. 4; 1952a, pp. 143–147.—Drake and Ruhoff 1960a, p. 74.

TYPE SPECIES: *Cysteochila (Parada) taeniophora* Horváth.

*Parada absona Drake

　　Parada absona Drake 1952, p. 146 [Queensland].

TYPE: Holotype ♂; Lake Barrine, Queensland, Australia; MCZ.

DISTRIBUTION: Australia (Queensland).

HOST PLANT: Unrecorded.

*Parada darlingtoni Drake

　　Parada darlingtoni Drake 1952, p. 143 [Queensland].

TYPE: Holotype ♂; National Park, McPherson Range, Queensland, Australia; MCZ.

DISTRIBUTION: Australia (Queensland).

HOST PLANT: Unrecorded.

*Parada hackeri Drake

Parada hackeri Drake 1952, p. 145 [Queensland].

TYPE: Holotype ♂, macropterous; Mt. Gipps, Queensland, Australia; Drake Coll. (USNM).

DISTRIBUTION: Australia (Queensland).

HOST PLANT: Unrecorded.

*Parada popla Drake

Cysteochila (Parada) taeniophora (not Horváth): Hacker 1927, p. 24 [New South Wales; Queensland]; 1928, p. 180.

Parada popla Drake 1942a, p. 3; 1952, p. 147; 1961b, p. 110.

TYPE: Holotype ♂, macropterous; National Park, Queensland, Australia; Drake Coll. (USNM).

DISTRIBUTION: Australia (Queensland; New South Wales).

HOST PLANT: Unrecorded.

*Parada popula var. **nigrans** Drake (emendation)

Parada popla var. *nigrantis* Drake 1942a, p. 4 [Queensland].

TYPE: Holotype ♂, macropterous; Mount Glorious, Queensland, Australia; Drake Coll. (USNM).

DISTRIBUTION: Australia (Queensland).

HOST PLANT: Unrecorded.

*Parada solla Drake and Ruhoff

Parada solla Drake and Ruhoff 1961b, p. 139 [Queensland].

TYPE: Holotype ♂; Mt. Spurgeon, Queensland, Australia; MCZ.

DISTRIBUTION: Australia (Queensland).

HOST PLANT: Unrecorded.

*Parada taeniophora (Horváth)

Cysteochila (Parada) taeniophora Horváth 1925a, p. 2, fig. 1 [Queensland].

Parada taeniophora: Drake 1952, p. 147.—Drake and Ruhoff 1962b, p. 250 [New South Wales].

TYPE: Sex unknown; Malanda, Queensland, Australia; Stockholm Mus.

DISTRIBUTION: Australia (Queensland; New South Wales).

HOST PLANT: Unrecorded.

*Parada torta Drake

Parada torta Drake 1942a, p. 4 [Queensland]; 1952, p. 147 [New South Wales]; 1961b, p. 110.

TYPE: Holotype ♂, macropterous; Mt. Gipps, Queensland, Australia; Drake Coll. (USNM).

DISTRIBUTION: Australia (Queensland; New South Wales).

HOST PLANT: Unrecorded.

Parada torta var. **pulla** Drake

Parada torta var. *pulla* Drake 1952, p. 147 [New South Wales].

TYPE: Holotype ♀; Mt. Wilson, New South Wales, Australia; MCZ.

DISTRIBUTION: Australia (New South Wales).

HOST PLANT: Unrecorded.

Genus PASEALA Schouteden

Paseala Schouteden 1923, p. 93.—Drake and Ruhoff 1960a, p. 74.
TYPE SPECIES: *Paseala arnoldi* Schouteden.

*Paseala arnoldi Schouteden

Paseala arnoldi Schouteden 1923, p. 94 [Congo].—Mayné and Ghesquière 1934, p. 20 [Apocynaceae].—Drake and Gomez-Menor 1954, p. 92 [Spanish Guinea].
TYPE: Sex unknown; Belgian Congo; Cent. Afr. Mus.
DISTRIBUTION: Congo; Spanish Guinea.
HOST PLANT: Apocynaceae.

Genus PENOTTUS Distant

Penottus Distant 1903c, p. 254.—Drake and Ruhoff 1960a, p. 75.
Cetiocysta Drake and Poor 1939c, p. 205.—Drake and Ruhoff 1960a, p. 44.
TYPE SPECIES: *Penottus jalorensis* Distant=*Monanthia monticollis* Walker.

*Penottus bunus Drake and Ruhoff

Penottus bunus Drake and Ruhoff 1961b, p. 179, fig. 20 [Borneo].
TYPE: Holotype ♀, macropterous; Sandakan, Borneo; Drake Coll. (USNM).
DISTRIBUTION: Greater Sunda Islands (Borneo).
HOST PLANT: Unrecorded.

*Penottus monticollis (Walker)

Monanthia monticollis Walker 1873a, p. 196 [Sarawak].—Distant 1902b, p. 356.
Penottus jalorensis Distant 1903c, p. 254, pl. 14 [Malaya].—Blöte 1945, p. 92 [Sumatra].
Diplocysta nubila Drake 1927a, p. 55 [Singapore]; 1930e, p. 167 [Negros].—Drake and Poor 1937a, p. 11.
Cetiocysta nubilia [sic]: Drake and Poor 1939c, p. 205.
Penottus monticollis: Drake and Ruhoff 1960a, p. 75, pl. 8; 1962c, p. 133.
TYPE: Sex unknown; Sarawak; British Mus.
DISTRIBUTION: Greater Sunda Islands (Sarawak; Sumatra); Federation of Malaya; Singapore; Philippine Islands (Negros).
HOST PLANT: Unrecorded.
NOTE: Only hemelytron remains of type specimen.

*Penottus nimius (Drake)

Diplocysta nimia Drake 1927a, p. 54 [Negros].—Drake and Poor 1937a, p. 11 [Mindanao; Samar].
Cetiocysta nimia: Drake and Poor 1939c, p. 205.
Penottus nimius: Drake and Ruhoff 1960c, p. 29.

Type: Holotype ♂, macropterous; Curenos Mountains, Negros, Philippine Islands; Drake Coll. (USNM).

Distribution: Philippine Islands (Mindanao; Negros; Samar).

Host Plant: Unrecorded.

*Penottus opiparus (Drake)

> *Diplocysta opipara* Drake 1927c, p. 18 [Luzon].
> *Cetiocysta opipara:* Drake and Poor 1939c, p. 205.
> *Penottus opiparus:* Drake and Ruhoff 1960c, p. 29.

Type: Holotype ♂, macropterous; Bagnio, Luzon, Philippine Islands; Drake Coll. (USNM).

Distribution: Philippine Islands (Luzon).

Host Plant: Unrecorded.

*Penottus oresbius Drake and Ruhoff

> *Penottus oresbius* Drake and Ruhoff 1961b, p. 178, figs. 19 a, b [Borneo; Malaya].

Type: Holotype ♀, macropterous; Malacca, Southern Malay Peninsula; Drake Coll. (USNM).

Distribution: Federation of Malaya; Greater Sunda Islands (Borneo).

Host Plant: Unrecorded.

*Penottus tibetanus Drake and Maa

> *Penottus tibetanus* Drake and Maa 1954, p. 115 [Tibet].

Type: Holotype ♂, macropterous; Tibet; Drake Coll. (USNM).

Distribution: Tibet.

Host Plant: Unrecorded.

*Penottus verdicus Drake and Maa

> *Penottus verdicus* Drake and Maa 1953, p. 88 [Taiwan].

Type: Holotype ♂, macropterous; Formosa; Drake Coll. (USNM).

Distribution: Taiwan.

Host Plant: Unrecorded.

Genus PERBRINCKEA Drake

Perbrinckea Drake 1956f, p. 427.—Drake and Ruhoff 1960a, p. 75.

Type Species: *Perbrinckea brincki* Drake.

*Perbrinckea brincki Drake   Plate 16

> *Perbrinckea brincki* Drake 1956f, p. 427, fig. 1 [Basutoland].

Type: Holotype ♂; Mount Morosi, Basutoland, South Africa; Lund Zool. Inst.

Distribution: Basutoland.

Host Plant: Unrecorded.

Genus PERISSONEMIA Drake and Poor

Perissonemia Drake and Poor 1937a, p. 2.—Drake and Ruhoff 1960a, p. 75.

Type Species: *Perissonemia torquata* Drake and Poor.

*Perissonemia absita Drake and Ruhoff

Perissonemia absita Drake and Ruhoff 1961b, p. 137, fig. 11 [Mindanao].

TYPE: Holotype ♂, macropterous; Butuan, Mindanao, Philippines; Drake Coll. (USNM).

DISTRIBUTION: Philippine Islands (Mindanao).

HOST PLANT: Unrecorded.

*Perissonemia bimaculata (Distant)

Teleonemia bimaculata Distant 1909c, p. 166, pl. 10, figs. 6, 6a [Borneo].

Cromerus bimaculatus: Drake 1953b, p. 92.

Perissonemia bimaculata: Drake and Ruhoff 1961c, p. 145.

TYPE: Holotype ♂; Kuching, Borneo; British Mus.

DISTRIBUTION: Greater Sunda Islands (Borneo); India.

HOST PLANT: Unrecorded.

*Perissonemia borneenis (Distant)

Teleonemia borneenis Distant 1909c, p. 166, pl. 10, figs. 1, 1a [Borneo].

Perissonemia (Ulonemia) borneensis [sic]: Drake and Poor 1937a, p. 4 [Singapore].

Perissonemia borneensis [sic]: Drake and Poor 1937b, p. 401 [Mindanao; Sibuyan].—Drake 1938b, p. 195 [China].

Perissonemia borneenis: Drake 1960, p. 356 [New Guinea].

TYPE: Sex unknown; Kuching, Borneo; British Mus.

DISTRIBUTION: Greater Sunda Islands (Borneo); Singapore; China; Philippine Islands (Luzon; Mindanao; Sibuyan); New Guinea (Northeast).

HOST PLANT: Unrecorded.

*Perissonemia delagoana Drake

Perissonemia delagoana Drake 1954b, p. 9 [Mozambique].

TYPE: Holotype ♂; Dalagoa Bay, Mozambique; British Mus.

DISTRIBUTION: Mozambique.

HOST PLANT: Unrecorded.

*Perissonemia ecmeles Drake and Mohanasundarum   PLATE 25

Perissonemia ecmeles Drake and Mohanasundarum 1961, p. 110, fig. 2 [India; *Ficus*].

TYPE: Holotype ♂, macropterous; Coimbatore, India; Drake Coll. (USNM).

DISTRIBUTION: India.

HOST PLANT: *Ficus* sp.

*Perissonemia gressitti Drake and Poor

Perissonemia gressitti Drake and Poor 1936a, p. 440 [Hainan].

TYPE: Holotype ♂, macropterous; Nodoa, Hainan Island; Drake Coll. (USNM).

DISTRIBUTION: China (Hainan Island).

HOST PLANT: Unrecorded.

*Perissonemia illustris Drake and Poor

Perissonemia (Ulonemia) illustris Drake and Poor 1937a, p. 4 [Luzon].
Perissonemia illustrus [sic]: Drake and Poor 1937b, p. 401.

TYPE: Holotype ♂, macropterous; Imugin, Nueva Vizcaya Province, Luzon, Philippine Islands; USNM.
DISTRIBUTION: Philippine Islands (Luzon); Singapore.
HOST PLANT: Unrecorded.

*Perissonemia kietana Drake and Ruhoff

Perissonemia kietana Drake and Ruhoff 1961b, p. 136 [Bougainville].

TYPE: Holotype ♂, macropterous; Kieta, Solomon Islands; Drake Coll. (USNM).
DISTRIBUTION: Solomon Islands (Bougainville).
HOST PLANT: Unrecorded.

*Perissonemia nigerrima (Schouteden)

Teleonemia nigerrima Schouteden 1923, p. 104 [Congo].
Perissonemia nigerrima: Drake and Ruhoff 1960c, p. 29.

TYPE: Sex unknown; Belgian Congo; Cent. Afr. Mus.
DISTRIBUTION: Congo.
HOST PLANT: Unrecorded.

*Perissonemia occasa Drake

Perissonemia occasa Drake 1942a, p. 2 [Japan].—Drake and Ruhoff
    1961b, p. 135, fig. 10.
Perissonemia (Ulonemia) occasa: Takeya 1951a, p. 18.

TYPE: Holotype ♂, macropterous; Japan; Drake Coll. (USNM).
DISTRIBUTION: Japan; China.
HOST PLANT: Unrecorded.

*Perissonemia onerosa Drake and Poor

Perissonemia onerosa Drake and Poor 1939c, p. 204 [India; sandal].

TYPE: Holotype ♀, macropterous; Vellore, Madras, India; Drake Coll. (USNM).
DISTRIBUTION: India.
HOST PLANT: Taken on "unspiked sandal."

*Perissonemia pagnana Drake

Perissonemia pagnana Drake 1954b, p. 8 [Uganda].

TYPE: Holotype ♀, macropterous; Kampala, Uganda; Drake Coll. (USNM).
DISTRIBUTION: Uganda.
HOST PLANT: Unrecorded.

*Perissonemia sandakana Drake and Ruhoff

Perissonemia sandakana Drake and Ruhoff 1961b, p. 134, fig. 9 [Borneo].

TYPE: Holotype ♂, macropterous; Sandakan, Borneo; Drake Coll. (USNM).
DISTRIBUTION: Greater Sunda Islands (Borneo).
HOST PLANT: Unrecorded.

*Perissonemia sierrana Drake

Perissonemia sierrana Drake 1954b, p. 9 [Sierra Leone; "Bomamagbai"].
TYPE: Holotype ♂; Njala, Sierra Leone; British Mus.
DISTRIBUTION: Sierra Leone.
HOST PLANT: Taken on "Bomamagbai."

*Perissonemia sodalis Drake

Perissonemia sodalis Drake 1948e, p. 151 [Queensland].—Drake and Davis 1960, fig. 65.
TYPE: Holotype ♂, macropterous; Redlynch, Queensland, Australia; Drake Coll. (USNM).
DISTRIBUTION: Australia (Queensland).
HOST PLANT: Unrecorded.

*Perissonemia torquata Drake and Poor

Perissonemia torquata Drake and Poor 1937a, p. 2, pl. 1 [Mindanao]; 1937b, p. 401.—Drake 1960, p. 356 [Solomon; New Guinea].
TYPE: Holotype ♂, macropterous; Surigao, Mindanao, Philippine Islands; Drake Coll. (USNM).
DISTRIBUTION: Philippine Islands (Mindanao); New Guinea; Solomon Islands.
HOST PLANT: Unrecorded.

*Perissonemia vegata Drake and Poor

Perissonemia (*Ulonemia*) *vegata* Drake and Poor 1937b, p. 401 [Borneo].
TYPE: Holotype ♀, macropterous; Sandakan, Borneo; Drake Coll. (USNM).
DISTRIBUTION: Greater Sunda Islands (Borneo).
HOST PLANT: Unrecorded.

Genus PHAENOTROPIS Horváth

Monosteira (*Phaenotropis*) Horváth 1906a, p. 106.—Oshanin 1908, p. 456; 1912, p. 46.
Phaenotropis: Drake 1957a, p. 415.—Drake and Ruhoff 1960a, p. 76.
TYPE SPECIES: *Monanthia* (*Monosteira*) *parvula* Signoret.

*Phaenotropis cleopatra (Horváth)

Monosteira cleopatra Horváth 1905b, p. 572 [Egypt]; 1911c, p. 109.
Monosteira (*Phaenotropis*) *cleopatra:* Horváth 1906a, p. 107.
Monostira [sic] (*Phaenotropis*) *cleopatra:* Priesner and Alfieri 1953, p. 66 [*Panicum turgidum*].
Phaenotropis cleopatra: Drake 1957a, p. 415 [Aden].
TYPE: Sex unknown; Egypt; Vienna Mus.
DISTRIBUTION: Egypt; Aden Protectorate; India; Israel.
HOST PLANTS: *Panicum turgidum; Tephrosia* sp.

*Phaenotropis parvula (Signoret)

Monanthia (*Monosteira*) *parvula* Signoret 1865, p. 117 [France].
Monanthia parvula: Walker 1873a, p. 190.—Puton 1879c, p. 124.—Rey
1893, p. 97 [*Dorycnium suffruticosum*].
Monosteira (*Phaenotropis*) *parvula:* Horváth 1906a, p. 107.
Monosteira parvula: Stichel 1926, p. 116; 1935, p. 349; 1938a, p. 408;
1960a, p. 344, fig. 182 [Sardinia]; 1960b, p. 401; 1960c, p. 140.—
Blöte 1945, p. 92.
Monostira [sic] *parvula:* Gulde 1938, p. 321.—Gomez-Menor 1949,
p. 161, fig. [Spain]; 1955b, p. 249.
Phaenotropis parvula: Drake 1957a, p. 415.
TYPE: Sex unknown; France; Vienna Mus.
DISTRIBUTION: France; Spain; Sardinia; Senegal.
HOST PLANT: *Dorycnium suffruticosum.*

Genus PHAEOCHILA Drake and Hambleton

Phaeochila Drake and Hambleton 1945, p. 358.—Drake and Ruhoff
1960a, p. 75.
TYPE SPECIES: *Amblystira hirta* Monte.

*Phaeochila hirta (Monte)

Amblystira hirta Monte 1940e, p. 284, fig. 5 [Brazil].
Phaeochila hirta: Drake and Hambleton 1945, p. 359 [Peru].
TYPE: Holotype ♀; Catanduva, São Paulo, Brazil; Monte Coll. (Mus.
Nacional).
DISTRIBUTION: Brazil; Peru.
HOST PLANT: Unrecorded.

Genus PHYMACYSTA Monte

Phymacysta Monte 1942d, p. 106.—Hurd 1946, p. 476.—Drake and
Ruhoff 1960a, p. 77.
TYPE SPECIES: *Leptostyla tumida* Champion.

*Phymacysta magnifica (Drake)

Gelchossa magnifica Drake 1922c, p. 373 [Brazil].
Leptopharsa magnifica: Drake 1930a, p. 1; 1931b, p. 511; 1935, p. 18
[Paraguay].—Drake and Hambleton 1938a, p. 63 [*Chuquiragua
glabra*].—Monte 1939b, p. 74; 1941e, p. 115 [Argentina].
Phymacysta magnifica: Monte 1942d, p. 107.
TYPE: Holotype ♀; Chapada, Brazil; Carnegie Mus.
DISTRIBUTION: Brazil; Paraguay; Argentina.
HOST PLANT: *Chuquiragua glabra.*

*Phymacysta mcelfreshi (Drake)

Leptostyla mcelfreshi Drake 1918a, p. 176 [Haiti].
Gelchossa mcelfreshi: Drake and Bruner 1924a, p. 149.
Phymacysta mcelfreshi: Hurd 1946, p. 476.

TYPE: Holotype ♂, macropterous; Port-au-Prince, Haiti; Drake Coll. (USNM).
DISTRIBUTION: Haiti.
HOST PLANT: Unrecorded.

*Phymacysta praestans (Drake) (emendation)

Gelchossa praestantis Drake 1927b, p. 116 [Mexico].
Phymacysta praestantis: Monte 1942d, p. 107.

TYPE: Holotype ♀, macropterous; Montaña de Sumidero, Chiapas, Mexico; Drake Coll. (USNM).
DISTRIBUTION: Mexico.
HOST PLANT: Unrecorded.

*Phymacysta tumida (Champion)

Leptostyla tumida Champion 1897, p. 14, pl. 1, figs. 17, 17a [Guatemala].—Van Duzee 1907, p. 19 [Jamaica].
Leptostyla malpigheae Drake 1922b, p. 38 [Cuba; *Malpighia urens*].
Gelchossa malpigheae: Drake and Bruner 1924a, p. 149.
Gelchossa tumida: Drake and Bruner 1924a, p. 150 [Haiti; Trinidad; cherry].—Gowdy 1926, p. 35.
Leptopharsa walcotti Drake 1928a, p. 55.
Leptopharsa cubana Drake 1928a, p. 56.
Leptopharsa tumida: Monte 1939b, p. 75 [Brazil; Venezuela; *Adenocalymma bracteatum*]; 1940d, p. 105 [*Malpighia punicifolia*]; 1941e, p. 119.
Phymacysta tumida: Monte 1942d, p. 106, fig. 2.—Drake and Hambleton 1945, p. 362 [Peru; Ecuador; Panama].—Hurd 1946, p. 477 [*Malpighia glabra*].—Drake and Cobben 1960, p. 85, fig. 85 [Tex.; Mexico; Aruba; Curaçao; Bonaire; St. Eustatius].—Drake and Ruhoff 1962a, p. 156.
Phymacysta malpigheae: Monte 1942d, p. 107.
Phymacysta cubana: Monte 1942d, p. 107.
Phymacysta walcotti: Monte 1942d, p. 107.
Leptopharsa malpigheae: Bruner, Scaramuzza, and Otero 1945, p. 105.
Phymacysta malpighae [sic]: Drake and Hambleton 1945, p. 362.

TYPE: Sex unknown; Pantaleon, Guatemala; British Mus.

DISTRIBUTION: Brazil; Ecuador; Venezuela; Peru; Panama; Guatemala; Mexico; U.S. (Tex.); Jamaica; Haiti; Trinidad; Cuba; Netherlands Antilles (Aruba; Bonaire; Curaçao); Leeward Islands (St. Eustatius).

HOST PLANTS: *Adenocalymma bracteatum; Malpighia glabra; Malpighia punicifolia; Malpighia urens;* cherry.

Phymacysta vesiculosa (Champion)

Leptostyla vesiculosa Champion 1897, p. 13, pl. 1, figs. 15, 15a [Panama].
Phymacysta vesiculosa: Monte 1942d, p. 107.

TYPE: Sex unknown; Bugaba, Panama; British Mus.
DISTRIBUTION: Panama.
HOST PLANT: Unrecorded.

Genus PHYSATOCHEILA Fieber

Monanthia (Physatocheila) Fieber 1844, p. 80.
Physatochila: Stål 1873, pp. 120, 129; 1874, p. 56.—Lethierry and
    Severin 1896, p. 21.—Oshanin 1908, p. 447; 1912, p. 45.—Banks
    1910, p. 57.—Osborn and Drake 1916a, p. 242 (key).—Stichel 1935,
    p. 349; 1938a, p. 408; 1938b, p. 454.—Gulde 1938, pp. 245, 305
    (key).—Singer 1952, p. 54.
Phyllochisme Kirkaldy 1904, p. 280.—Drake and Ruhoff 1960a, p. 76.
Physatocheila: Horváth 1906a, pp. 15, 94 (key).—Mužik 1907, pp. 51,
    61.—Van Duzee 1916, p. 25; 1917b, p. 219.—Osborn and Drake
    1917a, p. 155 (key).—Stichel 1926, pp. 105, 114 (key); 1960a, p. 332;
    1960b, p. 399; 1960c, p. 138.—de Seabra 1931, pp. 408, 432.—China
    1943, p. 247; 1952, p. 50 (key).—Hurd 1946, p. 451.—Kiritshenko
    1951, pp. 242, 252 (key).—Drake and Ruhoff 1960a, p. 77.

TYPE SPECIES: *Acanthia quadrimaculata* Wolff=*Acanthia costata* Fabricius.

*Physatocheila aglaia Drake and Ruhoff

Physatocheila aglaia Drake and Ruhoff 1961b, p. 131, fig. 8 [Burma].

TYPE: Holotype ♂, macropterous; Mandalay, Burma; Drake Coll.
(USNM).
DISTRIBUTION: Burma.
HOST PLANT: Unrecorded.

*Physatocheila arbicola Drake

Physatocheila arbicola Drake 1958a, p. 102 [Angola].

TYPE: Holotype ♂; Cazombo, Angola; Cent. Afr. Mus.
DISTRIBUTION: Angola.
HOST PLANT: Unrecorded.

*Physatocheila biseriata Hacker

Physatochila biseriata Hacker 1929, p. 327, pl. 33, fig. 5 [Queensland].

TYPE: Sex unknown; Brookfield, Queensland, Australia; Queensland
Mus.
DISTRIBUTION: Australia (Queensland).
HOST PLANT: Unrecorded.

*Physatocheila brevirostris Osborn and Drake

Physatochila brevirostris Osborn and Drake 1916a, p. 243 [Ohio; N.Y.].
Physatocheila brevirostris: Osborn and Drake 1917a, p. 155.—Parshley
    1917b, p. 56 [Mass.]; 1922a, p. 236 [Conn.]; 1923b, p. 706.—Barber

1922a, p. 17.—McAtee 1923, p. 145 [Md.; Va.].—Blatchley 1926, p. 484 [N.J.].—Drake 1928b, p. 102.—Hurd 1946, p. 452 [Que.; Pa.; Ill.].—Bailey 1951, p. 24.—Ash 1954, p. 185 [Ind.].

TYPE: Holotype ♀, macropterous; Chillicothe, Ross Co., Ohio, U.S.; Ohio State Univ.

DISTRIBUTION: U.S. (Mass.; Conn.; N.Y.; Pa.; N.J.; Md.; Va.; Ohio; Ill.; Ind.; Iowa); Canada (Que.).

HOST PLANT: Unrecorded.

*Physatocheila chatterjeei Drake and Poor

Physatocheila chatterjeei Drake and Poor 1936b, p. 142 [India].

TYPE: Holotype ♀, macropterous; Bodyar, Chakrata Division, United Province; Drake Coll. (USNM).

DISTRIBUTION: India.

HOST PLANT: Unrecorded.

*Physatocheila civatis Drake

Physatocheila civatis Drake 1942a, p. 10 [New South Wales]; 1961b, p. 107 [Queensland].

TYPE: Holotype ♂, macropterous; Mt. Wilson, New South Wales, Australia; Drake Coll. (USNM).

DISTRIBUTION: Australia (New South Wales; Queensland).

HOST PLANT: Unrecorded.

*Physatocheila confinis Horváth

Tingis (Physatocheila) quadrimaculata (not Wolff): Kolenati 1856, p. 427 (in part) [Caucasus].

Physatocheila confinis Horváth 1905b, p. 570 [Crimea; Armenia; Hungary; Yugoslavia; Turkey; Greece]; 1906a, p. 95 [Syria; Pyrus communis].—Stichel 1926, p. 114; 1960a, p. 333 [France].—Kiritshenko 1951, p. 252.—Novak and Wagner 1951, p. 71 [Quercus pubescens; Ostrya carpinifolia].—Hoberlandt 1955, p. 94 [Transcaucasus; Quercus ilex; Quercus coccifera].

Physatochila confinis: Stichel 1938a, p. 408 [Austria; Albania].—Gomez–Menor 1954, p. 390.

TYPE: Unknown.

DISTRIBUTION: France; Austria; Hungary; Yugoslavia; Albania; Greece; Turkey; Syria; U.S.S.R. (Caucasus; Transcaucasus; Crimea; Armenia).

HOST PLANTS: Ostrya carpinifolia; Pyrus communis; Quercus coccifera; Quercus ilex; Quercus pubescens.

Physatocheila confinis var. putoni Horváth

Monanthia dumetorum var. Puton 1881, p. 123.

Physatocheila confinis var. putoni Horváth 1911b, p. 584 [Syria].

TYPE: Holotype ♀; Damascus, Syria; Hungarian Mus.

DISTRIBUTION: Syria.

HOST PLANT: Unrecorded.

*Physatocheila costata (Fabricius)

Acanthia costata Fabricius 1794, p. 77.

Tingis costata: Fabricius 1803, p. 125.—Latrielle 1804, p. 253.

Acanthia quadrimaculata Wolff 1804, p. 132, pl. 13, fig. 127.

Tingis 4-maculata: Fallén 1829, p. 144.—Herrich–Schaeffer 1835, p. 58.

Tingis corticea Herrich–Schaeffer 1830, heft 18, tab. 22 [Germany].

Monanthia 4-maculata: Burmeister 1835, p. 261.—Thomson 1871, p. 398.—Jakovlev 1893, p. 294.

Monanthia quadrimaculata: Herrich-Schaeffer 1838, p. 58, pl. 125, fig. a.— Mayr 1858, p. 571.—Fieber 1861, p. 124.—Frey-Gessner 1865, p. 232 [Switzerland; *Chrysanthemum*].—Garbiglietti 1869, p. 273.—Gredler 1870, p. 75.—Jakovlev 1875b, p. 262; 1880b, p. 108.—Reiber and Puton 1876, p. 69.—Hüeber 1893, p. 345.—Jensen-Haarup 1912, pp. 155, 156, fig. 99 [Denmark].

Monanthia (Physatocheila) quadrimaculata: Fieber 1844, p. 81, pl. 7, figs. 1–3 [Czechoslovakia; Austria; Italy; Sweden].—Herrich-Schaeffer 1850, p. 154.

Monanthia costata: Scholz 1847, p. 120.—Mayr 1858, p. 570.—Frey-Gessner 1865, p. 232.—Garbiglietti 1869, p. 273.—Gredler 1870, p. 75.—Puton 1874a, p. 227.—Ferrari 1885, p. 411.—d'Antessanty 1890, p. 33.

Monanthia (Tropidocheila) quadrimaculata: Sahlberg 1848, p. 132 [Finland].

Monanthia (Physatocheila) 4-maculata: Flor 1860, p. 350 [France; Caucasus; Transcaucasus; Estonia; Latvia; *Arnebia cornuta*].

Laccometopus costata: Stål 1868, p. 92.

Eurycera costata: Stål 1873, p. 129.

Physatochila quadrimaculata: Stål 1873, p. 129; 1874, p. 57.—Reuter 1882b, p. 120 [*Alnus*].—Oshanin 1908, p. 448 [Belgium; Hungary].— Schumacher 1914, p. 258 (in part) [*Quercus*].—Scholte 1935, p. 78, fig. 22 [Netherlands].—Börner 1935, p. 78.—Gulde 1938, p. 308, fig. [*Alnus incana*].

Monanthia 4-macalata [sic]: Siebke 1874, p. 23 [Norway].

Physatochila 4-maculata: Sahlberg 1878, p. 21.—Lindberg 1927, p. 20; 1932a, p. 43 [Spain].

Monanthia (Physatochila) quadrimaculata: Puton 1879c, p. 120.

Copium costatum: Horváth 1906a, p. 94.

Physatocheila quadrimaculata: Horváth 1906a, pp. 94, 95 [Siberia; *Alnus glutinosa*].—Reichensperger 1920, p. 62.—Sahlberg 1920, p. 84 [*Populus tremula*].—Stichel 1926, p. 114, fig. 204; 1960a, p. 164 [Poland; Yugoslavia; Rumania; *Betula*].—Hoberlandt 1942, p. 126; 1943b, p. 124.—Blöte 1945, p. 89.—Kiritshenko 1951, p. 252.— China 1952, p. 49, figs. 1 b, d [*Alnus montana*].—Štušak 1957b, p. 140.—Bator 1953a, p. 326, pl. 3, fig. 4.—Cobben 1958a, p. 10, figs. 11, 12, 14.

Paracopium costatum: Horváth 1929, p. 322.

Physatocheila costata: Drake and Ruhoff 1960a, p. 77, pl. 9.

TYPE: Sex unknown; "Europa boreali"; Kiel Coll. (Copenhagen Mus.).

DISTRIBUTION: Spain; France; Belgium; Netherlands; Germany; Czechoslovakia; Switzerland; Austria; Hungary; Poland; Italy; Yugoslavia; Rumania; Norway; Sweden; Finland; Denmark; Turkey; U.S.S.R. (Estonia; Latvia; Siberia; Caucasus; Transcaucasus).

HOST PLANTS: *Alnus glutinosa; Alnus montana; Alnus incana; Alnus* sp.; *Arnebia cornuta; Betula* sp.; *Chrysanthemum* sp.; *Populus tremula; Quercus* sp.

NOTE: Species not found in England [China].

*Physatocheila costata subsp. smreczynskii China

Tingis quadrimaculata (not Wolff): Curtis 1839, tab. 741 [England; apple].

Monanthia quadrimaculata: Douglas and Scott 1865, p. 247.—Saunders 1875, p. 249.

Monanthia (Physatochila) quadrimaculata: Saunders 1892, p. 135, pl. 12, fig. 9.

Physatochila quadrimaculata: Oshanin 1908, p. 448 (in part); 1912, p. 45 (in part).—Schumacher 1914, p. 258 (in part).—Butler 1923, p. 213, fig. (in part).

Physatocheila quadrimaculata: China 1936, p. 271, fig. 1b; 1943, p. 247.

Physatocheila smreczynskii China 1952, p. 49, fig. 1c [Poland; Austria; *Prunus padus; Sorbus*].—Cobben 1958a, p. 10, figs. 11a-c [Netherlands; *Sorbus aucuparia*].—Förster 1959, p. 75.—Southwood and Leston 1959, p. 150, fig. 53.—Stichel 1960a, p. 334 [*Sorbus intermedia; Pyrus communis; Pyrus malus*].

Physatochila smreczynskii: Gomez-Menor 1955a, p. 260 [Spain]; 1955b, p. 249.

Physatocheila smreczynsky [sic]: Gomez-Menor 1956a, p. 112.

Physatocheila quadrimaculata subsp. *smreczynskii:* Wagner 1960, pp. 83–92, 4 pls.

TYPE: Holotype ♂; New Forest, Hants, England; British Mus.

DISTRIBUTION: England; Spain; Poland; Austria; Netherlands; Germany.

HOST PLANTS: *Crataegus* sp.; *Prunus padus; Pyrus communis; Pyrus malus; Sorbus aucuparia; Sorbus intermedia; Sorbus* sp.

*Physatocheila delicatula Horváth

Physatocheila delicatula Horváth 1903a, p. 78 [Algeria]; 1906a, p. 95.— Drake and Ruhoff 1961c, p. 145.

Physatocheila chanceli Bergevin 1920, p. 412, fig. 1.

TYPE: Holotype ♂; Mont Edough, Algeria; deposition unknown.

DISTRIBUTION: Algeria.

HOST PLANT: Unrecorded.

Physatocheila distinguenda (Jakovlev)

Monanthia (Physatochila) distinguenda Jakovlev 1880a, p. 139 [Russia].
Physatocheila distinguenda: Horváth 1906a, p. 96.—Kiritshenko 1951, p. 252.—Stichel 1960a, p. 335 [Turkestan].

TYPE: Holotype ♀, macropterous; Sarepta, Russia; Leningrad Inst.
DISTRIBUTION: U.S.S.R. (Turkestan).
HOST PLANT: Unrecorded.

*Physatocheila dryadis Drake and Poor

Physatocheila dryadis Drake and Poor 1936b, p. 143 [India; *Quercus dilatata*].—Singh 1953, p. 119.

TYPE: Holotype ♂, macropterous; Ramgarh, Naini Tal, United Provinces; Drake Coll. (USNM).
DISTRIBUTION: India.
HOST PLANT: *Quercus dilatata*.

*Physatocheila dumetorum (Herrich-Schaeffer)

Monanthia dumetorum Herrich-Schaeffer 1838, p. 57, pl. 124, figs. 391, a, b, d, e.—Scholz 1847, p. 120.—Mayr 1858, p. 571 [Hungary].—Fieber 1861, p. 125 [*Mespilus oxyacantha*].—Douglas and Scott 1865, p. 246.—Frey-Gessner 1865, p. 232 [Switzerland; *Juniperus*].—Garbiglietti 1869, p. 273 [Italy].—Jakovlev 1876b, p. 67 [Russia].—Horváth 1874b, p. 432.—Saunders 1875, p. 249.—Reiber and Puton 1876, p. 69.—Bolivar and Chicote 1879, p. 166 [Spain].—Dubois 1888, p. 121.—d'Antessanty 1890, p. 33.—Hüeber 1893, p. 346 [*Prunus padus*].—Jensen-Haarup 1912, pp. 155, 157 [Denmark].—Butler 1923, p. 214 [Wales].

Tingis oxyacanthae Curtis 1839, pl. 16, tab. 741 [England; whitethorns].

Monanthia (Physatocheila) dumetorum: Fieber 1844, p. 82, pl. 7, figs. 4–6 [Czechoslovakia; Germany; Austria].—Herrich-Schaeffer 1850, p. 154.—Saunders 1892, p. 135.

Monanthia quadrimaculata (not Wolff): Costa 1847a, p. 22; 1847c, p. 162.—Vollenhoven 1878, p. 276, pl. 9, figs. 8, 8a [Netherlands].

Physatochila dumetorum: Stål 1874, p. 57.—Reuter 1891a, p. 26 [Greece]; 1908, p. 88 [*Crataegus*].—Oshanin 1908, p. 447 [Belgium; Portugal; Crimea].—Schumacher 1914, p. 258.—Lindberg 1932a, p. 43 [Morocco]; 1948, p. 59 [Cyprus; *Amygdalus; Acer obtusifolium*].—Scholte 1935, p. 78.—Börner 1935, p. 78.—Stichel 1938a, p. 408 [Turkey]; 1938b, p. 455.—Blöte 1945, p. 88 [Tunisia; Algeria].—Mancini 1949b, p. 37; 1953b, p. 186; 1953c, p. 22; 1953d, p. 16 [Sicily].—Priesner and Alfieri 1953, p. 65.—Gomez-Menor 1954, p. 388, fig. 8 [*Pinus*]; 1955a, p. 261, fig. 36; 1955b, p. 249; 1956a, p. 115, fig. 9.

Monanthia (Physatochila) dumetorum: Puton 1879c, p. 120 [France].

Physatocheila dumetorum: Horváth 1906a, p. 95 [Yugoslavia; Bulgaria; Egypt; *Crataegus oxycantha; Crataegus monogyna; Prunus domestica; Prunus spinosa*]; 1906d, p. 1; 1916, p. 9 [Albania].—Reichensperger 1920, p. 62.—Stichel 1926, p. 114 [*Pyrus malus; Pyrus communis*]; 1960a, p. 332, fig. 159 [Poland; *Acer creticum*].—de Seabra 1931, pp. 433, 444, figs. 504(1–5), 505.—China 1936, p. 271, fig. 1a.—Hoberlandt 1942, p. 126; 1943b, p. 124; 1955, p. 94 [Israel].—Kiritshenko 1951, p. 252.—Štušak 1957b, p. 140; 1961a, p. 82, fig. 10; pl. 1, fig. a.—Cobben 1958a, p. 12, fig. 13.—Southwood and Leston 1959, p. 150, pl. 21, fig. 5; pl. 25, fig. 1; fig. 51.

TYPE: Unknown.

DISTRIBUTION: Portugal; Spain; France; Netherlands; Belgium; Wales; England; Denmark; Germany; Czechoslovakia; Poland; Austria; Switzerland; Hungary; Italy; Sicily; Yugoslavia; Greece; Bulgaria; Albania; Cyprus; Turkey; U.S.S.R. (Crimea); Israel; Egypt; Algeria; Morocco; Tunisia.

HOST PLANTS: *Acer creticum; Acer obtusifolium; Amygdalus* sp.; *Crataegus monogyna; Crataegus oxycantha; Crataegus* sp.; *Juniperus* sp.; *Mespilus oxyacantha; Pinus* sp.; *Prunus domestica; Prunus padus; Prunus spinosa; Pyrus communis; Pyrus malus.*

NOTE: Life history study [Butler]. Eggs [Štušak].

*Physatocheila enalla Drake and Ruhoff

Physatocheila enalla Drake and Ruhoff 1961b, p. 132 [Burma].

TYPE: Holotype ♀, macropterous; Mandalay, Burma; Drake Coll. (USNM).

DISTRIBUTION: Burma.

HOST PLANT: Unrecorded.

*Physatocheila enodis Drake

Physatochila enodis Drake 1948a, p. 3 [China].

TYPE: Holotype ♂, macropterous; Tsinleong, East Kwantungs, China; Drake Coll. (USNM).

DISTRIBUTION: China.

HOST PLANT: Unrecorded.

*Physatocheila exolasca Drake

Physatocheila exolasca Drake 1954b, p. 2 [India].

TYPE: Holotype ♂, macropterous; Dehra Dun, India; Drake Coll. (USNM).

DISTRIBUTION: India.

HOST PLANT: Unrecorded.

Physatocheila fasciata (Fieber)

Monanthia (*Physatocheila*) *fasciata* Fieber 1844, p. 84, pl. 7, figs. 13–16 [Ostindien].—Herrich-Schaeffer 1850, p. 154.

Monanthia fasciata: Stål 1873, p. 134 [India orientalis].—Distant 1903b, p. 145 [India].

Physatocheila fasciata: Drake 1937b, p. 592 [China].

TYPE: "Ostindien"; sex and deposition of type unknown.

DISTRIBUTION: China; India.

HOST PLANT: Unrecorded.

Physatocheila ferruginea Bergroth

Physatocheila ferruginea Bergroth 1912, p. 146 [Guinea].

TYPE: Holotype ♀; Assini, Guinea; Helsin. Mus.

DISTRIBUTION: Guinea.

HOST PLANT: Unrecorded.

*Physatocheila fulgoris Drake

Physatocheila fulgoris Drake 1937b, p. 592 [China].

TYPE: Holotype ♂, macropterous; Wong-sa-shue, S. Kiangsi, South China; Drake Coll. (USNM).

DISTRIBUTION: China.

HOST PLANT: Unrecorded.

Physatocheila gibba (Fieber)

Monanthia (*Physatocheila*) *gibba* Fieber 1844, p. 83, pl. 7, figs. 7–12 [Ostindien].—Herrich-Schaeffer 1850, p. 154.

Monanthia gibba: Stål 1873, p. 134.—Lethierry and Severin 1896, p. 25.

Physatocheila gibba: Drake and Ruhoff 1960c, p. 29.

TYPE: "Ostindien"; sex and deposition of type unknown.

DISTRIBUTION: Uncertain.

HOST PLANT: Unrecorded.

*Physatocheila harwoodi China

Physatocheila harwoodi China 1936, p. 271, fig. 1c [England; maples]; 1943, p. 247.—Stichel 1938b, p. 455 [Germany; *Acer*]; 1960a, p. 335 [*Acer platanoides; Acer pseudoplatanus*].—Southwood and Leston 1959, p. 151, fig. 52.

TYPE: Sex unknown; Witchamton, Dorsetshire, England; British Mus.

DISTRIBUTION: England; Germany.

HOST PLANTS: *Acer platanoides; Acer pseudoplatanus; Acer* sp.

Physatocheila irregularis Montrouzier

Physatocheila irregularis Montrouzier 1861, p. 68 [Lifu].—Stål 1873, p. 134.—Drake and Ruhoff 1961c, p. 145, fig. 1.

Monanthia irregularis: Walker 1873a, p. 196.

TYPE: Holotype ♂, macropterous; Lifu, Loyalty Islands; Vienna Mus.

DISTRIBUTION: Loyalty Islands (Lifu).

HOST PLANT: Unrecorded.

*Physatocheila katbergana Drake

Physatochelia [sic] *katbergana* Drake 1953d, p. 212 [Cape Province].
TYPE: Holotype ♂; Katberg, Cape Province, South Africa; British Mus.
DISTRIBUTION: South Africa (Cape Province).
HOST PLANT: Unrecorded.

*Physatocheila lautana Drake and Ruhoff

Physatocheila lautana Drake and Ruhoff 1961b, p. 133 [Laut].
TYPE: Holotype ♂, macropterous; Laut Island, Macassar Strait, near Borneo; Drake Coll. (USNM).
DISTRIBUTION: Laut Island.
HOST PLANT: Unrecorded.

*Physatocheila lenis Drake and Poor

Physatocheila lenis Drake and Poor 1939c, p. 204 [India].
TYPE: Holotype ♀, macropterous; Chakrata, United Provinces; Drake Coll. (USNM).
DISTRIBUTION: India.
HOST PLANT: Unrecorded.

*Physatocheila major Osborn and Drake

Physatocheila major Osborn and Drake 1917a, pp. 155, 158, fig. 1d [Ill.].—McAtee 1923, p. 145 [Md.; Va.; D.C.].—Blatchley 1926, p. 484.—Froeschner 1944, p. 669.—Hurd 1946, p. 452 [Ind.].
TYPE: Holotype ♀, macropterous; Urbana, Illinois, U.S.; Drake Coll. (USNM).
DISTRIBUTION: U.S. (Ill.; Ind.; Md.; Va.; D.C.).
HOST PLANT: Unrecorded.

*Physatocheila marginata (Distant)

Teleonemia marginata Distant 1909a, p. 121 [India]; 1910a, p. 123, fig. 64.
Physatochila marginata: Bergroth 1921, p. 105.—Drake and Poor 1937b, p. 399 [Luzon].
Cysteochila (Parada) marginata: Horváth 1925a, p. 3.
TYPE: Sex unknown; Margherita, Assam; British Mus.
DISTRIBUTION: India; Philippine Islands (Luzon).
HOST PLANT: Unrecorded.

*Physatocheila muluana Drake

Physatocheila muluana Drake 1954g, p. 661, fig. 3 [Ethiopia].
TYPE: Holotype ♀; Mulu, Ethiopia; British Mus.
DISTRIBUTION: Ethiopia.
HOST PLANT: Unrecorded.

Physatocheila municeps Horváth

Physatocheila municeps Horváth 1903a, p. 78 [Algeria]; 1906a, p. 95.

TYPE: Holotype ♂; Oued-Harris, Algeria; deposition unknown.

DISTRIBUTION: Algeria.

HOST PLANT: Unrecorded.

*Physatocheila objicis Drake

Physatocheila objicis Drake 1942a, p. 10 [Victoria]; 1961b, p. 108 [New South Wales; Queensland].

TYPE: Holotype ♂, macropterous; Kista, Victoria, Australia; Drake Coll. (USNM).

DISTRIBUTION: Australia (Victoria; Queensland; New South Wales).

HOST PLANT: Unrecorded.

*Physatocheila orientis Drake

Physatocheila orientis Drake 1942a, p. 9 [Japan].—Takeya 1953a, p. 2 [Manchuria]; 1953d, p. 173, pl. 6, fig. 2.

Physatochila orientis: Takeya 1951a, p. 20.

TYPE: Holotype ♀, macropterous; Sapporo, Hokkaido, Japan; Drake Coll. (USNM).

DISTRIBUTION: Japan; China (Manchuria).

HOST PLANT: Unrecorded.

*Physatocheila plexa (Say)

Tingis plexus Say 1832, p. 27.—Fitch 1857, p. 794.—Le Conte 1859, p. 349.

Physatochila plexa: Stål 1873, p. 129 [Ill.].—Provancher 1886, p. 160 [Canada].—Uhler 1886, p. 22.—Wirtner 1904, p. 202 [Pa.].—Van Duzee 1905, p. 549 [N.Y.]; 1912, p. 323.—Torre-Bueno 1910, p. 31.—Parshley 1914, p. 145 [Maine].

Physatocheila plexa: Smith 1910, p. 149 [N.J.].—Parshley 1916a, p. 165 [R.I.]; 1917b, p. 56 [Mass.]; 1923b, p. 705, fig. 164 [Conn.].—Van Duzee 1917b, p. 219 [Ind.; W. Va.; Mich.; Que.; Ont.].—Osborn and Drake 1917a, p. 156 [Nebr.; Kans.; Iowa; Wis.].—Barber 1922a, p. 17 [willow].—McAtee 1923, p. 145 [*Kalmia latifolia*].—Torre-Bueno 1926a, p. 54; 1929, p. 311.—Blatchley 1926, p. 484, pl. 4, fig. 4 [Va.; D.C.; oak; hickory].—Drake 1928b, p. 102.—Froeschner 1944, p. 669.—Proctor 1946, p. 75.—Bailey 1951, p. 25 [N.H.].

Physatocheila parshleyi Osborn and Drake 1917a, pp. 155, 156, figs. 1 a-c (in part).

TYPE: Presumably lost.

DISTRIBUTION: U.S. (Maine; N.H.; Mass.; R.I.; Conn.; N.Y.; N.J.; Pa.; Md.; D.C.; Va.; W. Va.; Ind.; Ill.; Mich.; Wis.; Nebr.; Iowa; Kans.); Canada (Ont.; Que.; N.S.).

HOST PLANTS: *Kalmia latifolia;* hickory; willow; oak.

*Physatocheila pulchella Lindberg

Physatochila pulchella Lindberg 1932a, p. 43, pl. 2, fig. 6 [Morocco].
TYPE: Sex unknown; Morocco; Helsin. Mus.
DISTRIBUTION: Morocco.
HOST PLANT: Unrecorded.

*Physatocheila ruris Drake

Physatocheila ruris Drake 1942a, p. 11 [China].
TYPE: Holotype ♀, macropterous; Krvangtung, Kan-lin San, South China; Drake Coll. (USNM).
DISTRIBUTION: China.
HOST PLANT: Unrecorded.

*Physatocheila scotti Drake

Physatocheila scotti Drake 1954g, p. 660, fig. 2 [Ethiopia].
TYPE: Holotype ♂; Doukam, Ethiopia; British Mus.
DISTRIBUTION: Ethiopia.
HOST PLANT: Unrecorded.

*Physatocheila senegalensis Drake

Physatocheila senegalensis Drake 1954a, p. 234 [Senegal].
TYPE: Holotype ♂; Bambery, Senegal; Inst. Fr. Afr. N.
DISTRIBUTION: Senegal.
HOST PLANT: Unrecorded.

*Physatocheila stricta Bergevin

Physatocheila stricta Bergevin 1929, p. 114, fig. 1 [Algeria].
TYPE: Holotype ♀; Tamanrasset, Algeria; Paris Mus.
DISTRIBUTION: Algeria.
HOST PLANT: Unrecorded.

*Physatocheila suttoni Drake

Physatochila irregularis (not Montrouzier) Hacker 1929, p. 328, pl. 33, fig. 6 [Queensland].
Physatocheila suttoni Drake 1947c, p. 121.
TYPE: Sex unknown; Stanthorpe, Queensland, Australia; Queensland Mus.
DISTRIBUTION: Australia (Queensland).
HOST PLANT: Unrecorded.

*Physatocheila thomasi Drake

Physatocheila thomasi Drake 1956b, p. 111 [Kenya].
TYPE: Holotype ♂, macropterous; Limuru, Kenya Colony; Drake Coll. (USNM).
DISTRIBUTION: Kenya.
HOST PLANT: Unrecorded.

*Physatocheila uniseriata Hacker

  Physatochila uniseriata Hacker 1929, p. 327, pl. 33, fig. 7 [South Australia; Western Australia; New South Wales].

TYPE: Sex unknown; Mount Lofty Ranges, South Australia; So. Austr. Mus.

DISTRIBUTION: Australia (South Australia; Western Australia; New South Wales).

HOST PLANT: Unrecorded.

*Physatocheila variegata Parshley

  Physatocheila variegata Parshley 1916a, p. 166 [N.Y.; W.Va.; Mass., Conn.; pine]; 1917b, p. 56 [Maine]; 1919a, p. 24 [B.C.]; 1923b, p. 705.—Barber 1922a, p. 17 [N.J.; hickory; willow].—Downes 1925, p. 18, fig. 9 [*Salix lasiandra*].—Blatchley 1926, p. 485 [Ind.].—Froeschner 1944, p. 669 [Mo.].—Hurd 1946, p. 452 [Ill.].—Proctor 1946, p. 75.—Bailey 1951, p. 26 [N.H.; Va.].

  Physatochila plexa (not Say): Osborn and Drake 1916a, p. 242 [Iowa; Mich.; Ont.].—Downes 1927a, p. 10 [alder; cottonwood].

  Physatocheila plexa var. *variegata:* Drake 1928b, p. 102.

TYPE: Holotype ♂; Gowanda, New York, U.S.; deposition unknown.

DISTRIBUTION: U.S. (Maine; N.H.; Mass.; Conn.; N.Y.; N.J.; Va.; W. Va.; Ill.; Ind.; Mo.; Iowa; Mich.); Canada (Ont.).

HOST PLANTS: *Salix lasiandra;* hickory; pine; cottonwood; alder.

*Physatocheila variegata var. **ornata** Van Duzee

  Physatochila plexa (not Say): Van Duzee 1914, p. 11.

  Physatocheila ornata Van Duzee 1917a, p. 259 [Calif.].

  Physatocheila parshleyi Osborn and Drake 1917a, p. 156 (in part) [Oreg.].

  Physatocheila plexa: Osborn and Drake 1917a, p. 156 (in part) [Idaho].

  Physatocheila variegata var. *ornata:* Hurd 1946, p. 452.

TYPE: Holotype ♀; Lake County, California, U.S.; Cal. Acad.

DISTRIBUTION: U.S. (Calif.; Oreg.; Idaho).

HOST PLANT: Unrecorded.

*Physatocheila veteris Drake

  Physatocheila veteris Drake 1942a, p. 10 [Japan].

  Physatochila veteris: Takeya 1951a, p. 20.

TYPE: Holotype ♂, macropterous; Sapporo, Hokkaido, Japan; Drake Coll. (USNM).

DISTRIBUTION: Japan.

HOST PLANT: Unrecorded.

*Physatocheila weenenana Drake

  Physatocheila weenenana Drake 1953d, p. 212 [Natal; Kenya; Cape Province].

TYPE: Holotype ♂; Weenen, Natal, South Africa; British Mus.

DISTRIBUTION: South Africa (Natal; Cape Province); Kenya.

HOST PLANT: Unrecorded.

Physatocheila witmeri Mancini

Physatochila dumetorum subsp. *witmeri* Mancini 1960a, p. 105 [Lebanon].
Physatocheila witmeri: Stichel 1960a, p. 332.

TYPE: Sex unknown; Hasrun, Lebanon; Museo Civico Storia Naturale Milano, Milan, Italy.
DISTRIBUTION: Lebanon.
HOST PLANT: Unrecorded.

Genus PLACOTINGIS Drake

Placotingis Drake 1960, p. 369.
TYPE SPECIES: *Placotingis merga* Drake.

Placotingis merga Drake

Placotingis merga Drake 1960, p. 370, fig. 21 [New Guinea].
TYPE: Holotype ♂; Mt. Wilhelm, Northeast New Guinea; Bishop Mus.
DISTRIBUTION: New Guinea (Northeast).
HOST PLANT: Unrecorded.

Placotingis par Drake

Placotingis par Drake 1960, p. 370, fig. 22 [New Guinea].
TYPE: Holotype ♂; Wisselmeren, Entarotadi, Netherlands New Guinea; Bishop Mus.
DISTRIBUTION: New Guinea (Netherlands).
HOST PLANT: Unrecorded.

Genus PLANIBYRSA Drake and Poor

Planibyrsa Drake and Poor 1937c, p. 164.—Monte 1939b, p. 77; 1941e, p. 127.—Drake and Ruhoff 1960a, p. 78.
TYPE SPECIES: *Leptobyrsa splendida* Drake.

*Planibyrsa elegantula (Drake)

Leptobyrsa elegantula Drake 1922c, p. 373, fig. 2b [Brazil]; 1931b, p. 511 [Peru]; 1936b, p. 700 [Argentina].—Monte 1937a, p. 32, fig. 11 [Bignoniaceae].
Planibyrsa elegantula: Drake and Poor 1937c, p. 165.—Drake and Hambleton 1938a, p. 65.—Kormilev 1955a, p. 66 [Bolivia].
TYPE: Holotype ♂; Chapada, Brazil; Carnegie Mus.
DISTRIBUTION: Brazil; Argentina; Peru; Bolivia.
HOST PLANT: Bignoniaceae.

*Planibyrsa montei Drake and Hambleton   PLATE 40

Leptobyrsa splendida (not Drake): Monte 1937a, p. 32, fig. 2 [Brazil; Serjania].
Planibyrsa montei Drake and Hambleton 1938a, p. 65.—Monte 1938b, p. 129.—Singh 1953, p. 119.

TYPE: Holotype ♂; Belo Horizonte, Minas Gerais, Brazil; Drake Coll. (USNM).

DISTRIBUTION: Brazil.

HOST PLANT: *Serjania* sp.

*Planibyrsa sodalis (Drake and Bondar)

Leptobyrsa sodalis Drake and Bondar 1932, p. 91 [Brazil; *Arrabidaea*].— Costa Lima 1936, p. 128.

Planibyrsa sodalis: Drake and Poor 1937c, p. 165.—Silva 1956, p. 46.

TYPE: Holotype ♂, macropterous; Bahia, Brazil; Drake Coll. (USNM).

DISTRIBUTION: Brazil.

HOST PLANT: *Arrabidaea* sp.

*Planibyrsa splendida (Drake)

Leptobyrsa splendida Drake 1922c, p. 374, fig. 2a [Brazil].

Planibyrsa spendida [sic]: Drake and Poor 1937c, p. 164.

Planibyrsa splendida: Monte 1940e, p. 287.—Silva 1956, p. 48.

TYPE: Holotype ♀; Chapada, Brazil; Carnegie Mus.

DISTRIBUTION: Brazil.

HOST PLANT: Unrecorded.

Genus PLATYTINGIS Drake

Platytingis Drake 1925b, p. 107.—Drake and Ruhoff 1960a, p. 78.

TYPE SPECIES: *Platytingis pediades* Drake.

*Platytingis pediades Drake

Platytingis pediades Drake 1925b, p. 108, fig. [Malagasy].

TYPE: Holotype ♂, macropterous; Imamonto, Madagascar; Drake Coll. (USNM).

DISTRIBUTION: Malagasy Republic; Tanganyika.

HOST PLANT: Unrecorded.

Genus PLEROCHILA Drake

Plerochila Drake 1954c, p. 69.—Drake and Ruhoff 1960a, p. 78.

TYPE SPECIES: *Teleonemia australis* Distant.

*Plerochila australis (Distant)

Teleonemia australis Distant 1904, p. 432, pl. 8, fig. 13 [Cape Province; *Olea europea*].

Cysteochila (Parada) australis: Horváth 1925a, p. 3.

Plerochila australis: Drake 1954c, p. 69 [Mozambique; Transvaal]; 1954g, p. 663 [Ethiopia].—Orian 1956, p. 647 [Mauritius].

TYPE: Sex unknown; Capetown, South Africa; British Mus.

DISTRIBUTION: South Africa (Cape Province; Transvaal); Mozambique; Ethiopia; Mascarene Islands (Mauritius).

HOST PLANT: *Olea europea.*

*Plerochila horvathi (Schouteden)

Cysteochila horvathi Schouteden 1907, p. 286 [Mauritius].

Cysteochila (Parada) horvathi: Horváth 1925a, p. 3.

Plerochila horvathi: Drake 1954c, p. 69 [Kenya; Tanganyika]; 1957e, p. 401 [Reunion; Congo; South-West Africa].—Orian 1956, p. 647.—Mamet 1957, p. 57.

Pleurochila [sic] *horvathi:* Drake and Mamet 1956, p. 301 [*Olea europea; Jasminum*].

TYPE: Sex unknown; Mauritius Island; Cent. Afr. Mus.

DISTRIBUTION: Mascarene Islands (Reunion; Mauritius); Tanganyika; Kenya; Congo; South-West Africa.

HOST PLANTS: *Jasminum* sp.; *Olea europea.*

*Plerochila rutshurica Schouteden

Plerochila rutshurica Schouteden 1954, p. 140 [Congo; Ruanda; *Olea*].

TYPE: Unknown.

DISTRIBUTION: Congo; Ruanda-Urundi.

HOST PLANT: *Olea* sp.

*Plerochila zululandana Drake

Plerochila (nom. nud.) *zululandana* Drake 1953d, p. 213 [Zululand].

TYPE: Holotype ♂; Eshowe, Zululand; British Mus.

DISTRIBUTION: South Africa (Zululand).

HOST PLANT: Unrecorded.

Genus PLESEOBYRSA Drake and Poor

Pleseobyrsa Drake and Poor 1937c, p. 165.—Hurd 1946, p. 470.—Drake and Ruhoff 1960a, p. 79.

TYPE SPECIES: *Pleseobyrsa boliviana* Drake and Poor.

*Pleseobyrsa ablusa Drake and Hambleton

Pleseobyrsa ablusa Drake and Hambleton 1946b, p. 124 [Peru].

TYPE: Holotype ♂, macropterous; Changos, Peru; Drake Coll. (USNM).

DISTRIBUTION: Peru.

HOST PLANT: Unrecorded.

*Pleseobyrsa atratarsis Drake and Hambleton

Pleseobyrsa atratarsis Drake and Hambleton 1944b, p. 127, fig. 1 [Brazil].—Drake and Davis 1960, fig. 49.

TYPE: Holotype ♀, macropterous; Poças de Caldas, Minas Gerais, Brazil; Drake Coll. (USNM).

DISTRIBUTION: Brazil.

HOST PLANT: Unrecorded.

Pleseobyrsa bicincta Monte

Pleseobyrsa bicincta Monte 1946b, p. 283 [Brazil].

TYPE: Holotype ♀; Palmerias, Monte Alegre, Mato Grosso, Brazil; Monte Coll. (Mus. Nacional).

DISTRIBUTION: Brazil.

HOST PLANT: Unrecorded.

*Pleseobyrsa boliviana Drake and Poor

Pleseobyrsa boliviana Drake and Poor 1937c, p. 165 [Bolivia].—Monte 1938b, p. 129.

TYPE: Holotype ♂, macropterous; Cochabamba, Bolivia; Drake Coll. (USNM).

DISTRIBUTION: Bolivia.

HOST PLANT: Avocado.

*Pleseobyrsa chiriquensis (Champion)

Leptobyrsa chiriquensis Champion 1897, p. 27, pl. 2, figs. 16, 16a [Panama].

Pleseobyrsa chiriquensis: Drake and Poor 1937c, p. 165.—Monte 1942a, p. 97 [Venezuela]; 1947b, p. 432 [Colombia; *Persea americana*].— Hurd 1946, p. 471 [Costa Rica].

TYPE: Sex unknown; Panama; British Mus.

DISTRIBUTION: Panama; Colombia; Venezuela; Costa Rica.

HOST PLANT: *Persea americana.*

Pleseobyrsa lichyi Monte

Pleseobyrsa lichyi Monte 1945a, p. 251 [Venezuela].

TYPE: Holotype ♂; Carreteras Maracay-Ocumare, Aragua, Venezuela; Monte Coll. (Mus. Nacional).

DISTRIBUTION: Venezuela.

HOST PLANT: Unrecorded.

Pleseobyrsa nigriceps (Champion)

Leptobyrsa nigriceps Champion 1897, p. 27, pl. 2, fig. 17 [Panama; Guatemala].

Pleseobyrsa nigriceps: Drake and Poor 1937c, p. 165.

TYPE: Sex unknown; Cerro Zunil, Guatemala; British Mus.

DISTRIBUTION: Panama; Guatemala.

HOST PLANT: Unrecorded.

*Pleseobyrsa peruana Drake

Pleseobyrsa peruana Drake 1939d, p. 529 [Peru].

TYPE: Holotype ♂, macropterous; Peru; Drake Coll. (USNM).

DISTRIBUTION: Peru.

HOST PLANT: Unrecorded.

*Pleseobyrsa plicata (Champion)

Leptobyrsa plicata Champion 1897, p. 26, pl. 2, fig. 15 [Panama].—
Swezey 1945, p. 372 [Costa Rica].
Pleseobyrsa plicata: Drake and Poor 1937c, p. 165.—Monte 1940e,
p. 286 [Venezuela].
Pleseobyrsa parana Drake and Hambleton 1944a, p. 95 [Brazil].
TYPE: Sex unknown; Bugaba, Panama; British Mus.
DISTRIBUTION: Panama; Venezuela; Brazil; Costa Rica.
HOST PLANT: Unrecorded.
NOTE: Intercepted on *Cattleya dowiana aurea* from Costa Rica at port-of-
entry, Washington, D.C. [Swezey].

Genus PLIOBYRSA Drake and Hambleton

Pliobyrsa Drake and Hambleton 1946b, p. 123.—Drake and Ruhoff
1960a, p. 79.
TYPE SPECIES: *Leptopharsa inflexa* Drake and Hambleton.

*Pliobyrsa adversa (Drake and Hambleton)

Leptopharsa adversa Drake and Hambleton 1938a, p. 60, fig. 10 [Brazil;
Ocotea].—Monte 1941e, p. 108.
Pleseobyrsa adversa: Monte 1940e, p. 286.
Pliobyrsa adversa: Drake and Hambleton 1946b, p. 123.
TYPE: Holotype ♂, macropterous; São Paulo, Brazil; Drake Coll.
(USNM).
DISTRIBUTION: Brazil.
HOST PLANT: *Ocotea* sp.

*Pliobyrsa inflexa (Drake and Hambleton)

Leptopharsa inflexa Drake and Hambleton 1938b, p. 54, fig. 1 [Brazil;
Ocotea lanata].—Monte 1941e, p. 113.
Pliobyrsa inflata [sic]: Drake and Hambleton 1946b, p. 123.
TYPE: Holotype ♂, macropterous; São Paulo, Brazil; Drake Coll.
(USNM).
DISTRIBUTION: Brazil.
HOST PLANT: *Ocotea lanata.*

*Pliobyrsa lateris Drake and Hambleton

Pliobyrsa lateris Drake and Hambleton 1946b, p. 124 [Guatemala].
TYPE: Holotype ♂, macropterous; Mazatenango, Guatemala; Drake Coll.
(USNM).
DISTRIBUTION: Guatemala.
HOST PLANT: Unrecorded.

*Pliobyrsa mollinediae (Drake and Hambleton)

Leptobyrsa mollinediae Drake and Hambleton 1934, p. 445 [Brazil; *Mollinedia*].—Costa Lima 1936, p. 127.

Pleseobyrsa mollinediae: Drake and Poor 1937c, p. 165.—Monte 1939b, p. 77; 1941e, p. 128.

Pliobyrsa mollinediae: Drake and Hambleton 1946b, p. 123.—Drake and Davis 1960, fig. 63.

TYPE: Holotype ♂, macropterous; Viçosa, Minas Gerais, Brazil; Drake Coll. (USNM).

DISTRIBUTION: Brazil.

HOST PLANT: *Mollinedia* sp.

*Pliobyrsa pulcherrima Monte

Pliobyrsa pulcherrima Monte 1947b, p. 430 [Brazil].

TYPE: Holotype ♂; Parque Nacional, Serra des Órgãos, Teresópolis, Estado do Rio, Brazil; Monte Coll. (Mus. Nacional).

DISTRIBUTION: Brazil.

HOST PLANT: Unrecorded.

Pliobyrsa translucida (Champion)

Leptobyrsa translucida Champion 1897, p. 26, pl. 2, figs. 14, 14a [Guatemala].

Stephanitis translucida: Hurd 1946, p. 482.

Pliobyrsa translucida: Drake and Hambleton 1946b, p. 123.

TYPE: Holotype macropterous; sex unknown; San Gerónimo, Guatemala; British Mus.

DISTRIBUTION: Guatemala.

HOST PLANT: Unrecorded.

NOTE: Champion states type apterous; his figure shows unique specimen with long elytra and no hind pair of wings.

Genus POGONOSTYLA Drake

Pogonostyla Drake 1953d, p. 221.—Drake and Ruhoff 1960a, p. 79.

TYPE SPECIES: *Pogonostyla intonsa* Drake.

*Pogonostyla afra Drake and Smithers

Pogonostyla afra Drake and Smithers 1958, p. 315 [Natal].

TYPE: Holotype ♂, macropterous; Sweetwater, Natal, South Africa; Drake Coll. (USNM).

DISTRIBUTION: South Africa (Natal).

HOST PLANT: Unrecorded.

Pogonostyla crispa Drake

Pogonostyla crispa Drake 1958c, p. 327 [Malagasy].

TYPE: Holotype ♂; Périnet, Madagascar; Magadascar Sci. Inst.

DISTRIBUTION: Malagasy Republic.

HOST PLANT: Unrecorded.

*Pogonostyla discrega Drake and Smithers

  Pogonostyla discrega Drake and Smithers 1958, p. 313, figs. 1 a, b [So. Rhodesia].

TYPE: Holotype ♂, macropterous; Penhalonga, Southern Rhodesia; Drake Coll. (USNM).
DISTRIBUTION: Southern Rhodesia.
HOST PLANT: Unrecorded.

*Pogonostyla herana Drake

  Pogonostyla herana Drake 1958c, p. 328 [Malagasy].

TYPE: Holotype ♂; Tongobory, Madagascar; Madagascar Sci. Inst.
DISTRIBUTION: Malagasy Republic.
HOST PLANT: Unrecorded.

*Pogonostyla intonsa Drake

  Pogonostyla intonsa Drake 1953d, p. 222 [Natal].

TYPE: Holotype ♂; Verulan, Natal, South Africa; British Mus.
DISTRIBUTION: South Africa (Natal).
HOST PLANT: Unrecorded.

*Pogonostyla natalicola (Distant)

  Leptostyla natalicola Distant 1902a, p. 240, pl. 15, fig. 15 [Natal].
  Pogonostyla natalicola: Drake 1953d, p. 222.

TYPE: Sex unknown; Natal, South Africa; British Mus.
DISTRIBUTION: South Africa (Natal).
HOST PLANT: Unrecorded.

Genus PONTANUS Distant

  Pontanus Distant 1902b, p. 354.—Drake 1956f, p. 425.—Drake and Ruhoff 1960a, p. 79.
  Teratochila Drake and Poor 1936b, p. 147.—Drake and Ruhoff 1960a, p. 84.

TYPE SPECIES: *Monanthia gibbifera* Walker.

*Pontanus accedens (Drake) (emendation)

  Teratocheila [sic] *accedentis* Drake 1947c, p. 120 [Australia].

TYPE: Holotype ♀, macropterous; Aldgate, Australia; Drake Coll. (USNM).
DISTRIBUTION: Australia.
HOST PLANT: Unrecorded.

*Pontanus cafer (Distant)

  Phyllontochila cafer Distant 1902a, p. 241, pl. 15, fig. 17 [Cape Province].
  Tingis cafer: Blöte 1945, p. 86.
  Pontanus cafer: Drake 1956f, p. 426.

TYPE: Sex unknown; Cape Colony, South Africa; So. Afr. Mus.
DISTRIBUTION: South Africa (Cape Province).
HOST PLANT: Unrecorded.

Pontanus gibbiferus (Walker)

Monanthia gibbifera Walker 1873a, p. 197 [Australia].—Lethierry and Severin 1896, p. 25.

Pontanus gibbiferus: Distant 1902b, p. 354.

TYPE: Sex unknown; Australia; British Mus.

DISTRIBUTION: Australia.

HOST PLANT: Unrecorded.

*Pontanus puerilis (Drake and Poor)

Teratochila puerilis Drake and Poor 1936b, p. 147 [India; teak].—Singh 1953, p. 119.

TYPE: Holotype ♀, macropterous; Rahatgaon, Hoshangabad, Central Provinces; Drake Coll. (USNM).

DISTRIBUTION: India.

HOST PLANT: Teak.

Genus PSEUDACYSTA Blatchley

Pseudacysta Blatchley 1926, p. 497.—Hurd 1946, p. 459.—Drake and Ruhoff 1960a, p. 80.

TYPE SPECIES: *Acysta perseae* Heidemann.

*Pseudacysta perseae (Heidemann)

Acysta perseae Heidemann 1908, p. 103, pl. 4, figs. a–c [Fla.; La.; *Persea carolinensis; Persea gratissima; Camphora officinalis*].—Barber 1914, p. 507.—Van Duzee 1917b, p. 223.—Moznette 1922, p. 17, figs. 12, 13.

Pseudacysta persea [sic]: Blatchley 1926, p. 497, fig. 120.—Gibson and Carrillo 1959, p. 19.

Pseudacysta perseae: Hurd 1946, p. 459 [Tex.; Mexico].

TYPE: Holotype ♂, macropterous; Miami, Florida, U.S.; USNM.

DISTRIBUTION: U.S. (Fla.; La.; Tex.); Mexico.

HOST PLANTS: *Comphora officinalis; Persea carolinensis; Persea gratissima*.

NOTE: Life history study [Heidemann].

Genus PSILOBYRSA Drake and Hambleton

Psilobyrsa Drake and Hambleton 1935, p. 148.—Drake and Ruhoff 1960a, p. 80.

Psylobyrsa [sic]: Monte 1941e, p. 129.

TYPE SPECIES: *Psilobyrsa aechemeae* Drake and Hambleton.

*Psilobyrsa aechemeae Drake and Hambleton

Psilobyrsa aechemeae Drake and Hambleton 1935, p. 149 [Brazil; *Aechmea*].

TYPE: Holotype ♂, macropterous; S. Vicente, São Paulo, Brazil; Drake Coll. (USNM).

DISTRIBUTION: Brazil.

HOST PLANT: *Aechmea* sp.

*Psilobyrsa vriesiae Drake and Hambleton

Psilobyrsa vriesiae Drake and Hambleton 1935, p. 149, fig. 4 [Brazil; *Vriesia hoehneana*].

TYPE: Holotype ♂, macropterous; São Paulo, Brazil; Drake Coll. (USNM).

DISTRIBUTION: Brazil.

HOST PLANT: *Vriesia hoehneana.*

Genus RADINACANTHA Hacker

Radinacantha Hacker 1929, p. 330.—Drake and Ruhoff 1960a, p. 80.

TYPE SPECIES: *Radinacantha reticulata* Hacker.

*Radinacantha prudens Drake and Poor (emendation)

Radinacantha prudentis Drake and Poor 1937a, p. 15 [Malagasy].

TYPE: Sex unknown (abdomen broken); Ambalamadakana, Madagascar; Drake Coll. (USNM).

DISTRIBUTION: Malagasy Republic.

HOST PLANT: Unrecorded.

*Radinacantha reticulata Hacker

Radinacantha reticulata Hacker 1929, p. 330, pl. 34, fig. 11 [Queensland; Bribie].

TYPE: Sex unknown; Samsonvale, Queensland, Australia; Queensland Mus.

DISTRIBUTION: Australia (Queensland; Bribie Island).

HOST PLANT: Unrecorded.

*Radinacantha tasmanica Hacker

Radinacantha tasmanica Hacker 1929, p. 331, pl. 34, fig. 12 [Tasmania]·

TYPE: Sex unknown; Strahan, Tasmania, Australia; So. Austr. Mus·

DISTRIBUTION: Australia (Tasmania; New South Wales).

HOST PLANT: Unrecorded.

Genus RECAREDUS Distant

Recaredus Distant 1909b, p. 361; 1910a, p. 104.—Drake 1950a, p. 166.— Drake and Ruhoff 1960a, p. 29.

TYPE SPECIES: *Recaredus rex* Distant.

*Recaredus rex Distant

Recaredus rex Distant 1909b, p. 361 [West Bengal]; 1910a, p. 104, fig. 51.

TYPE: Sex unknown; Paresnath, West Bengal, India; Indian Mus.

DISTRIBUTION: India.

HOST PLANT: Unrecorded.

NOTE: Taken at light. This genus belongs to subfamily Tinginae, tribe Tingini, not Cantacaderinae, and is here so transferred.

Genus RENAUDEA Drake

Renaudea Drake 1958c, p. 332.—Drake and Ruhoff 1960a, p. 80.

TYPE SPECIES: *Renaudea pauliani* Drake.

Renaudea pauliani Drake

Renaudea pauliani Drake 1958c, p. 333, fig. 2 [Comoro].

TYPE: Holotype ♀; Fomboni, Mohéli, Iles Comores; Madagascar Sci. Inst.

DISTRIBUTION: Comoro Islands (Mohéli).

HOST PLANT: Unrecorded.

Genus SABESTENA Drake

Sabestena Drake 1944a, p. 67.—Drake and Ruhoff 1960a, p. 25.

TYPE SPECIES: *Sabestena africana* Drake.

*Sabestena africana Drake

Sabestena africana Drake 1944a, p. 67, fig. 6 [Kenya]; 1956a, p. 6 [Congo; Ethiopia].—Schouteden 1957c, p. 312.

TYPE: Holotype ♀, macropterous; Naburu, Kenya; Drake Coll. (USNM).

DISTRIBUTION: Kenya; Congo; Ethiopia.

HOST PLANT: Unrecorded.

*Sabestena alfierii Drake and Ruhoff

Ceratinoderma sp. Priesner and Alfieri 1953, p. 66 [Egypt; *Gymnocarpos decandrum*].

Sabestena alfierii Drake and Ruhoff 1961b, p. 166.

TYPE: Holotype ♀, macropterous; Wadi Nouega, Egypt; Drake Coll. (USNM).

DISTRIBUTION: Egypt.

HOST PLANT: *Gymnocarpos decandrum.*

Genus SANAZARIUS Distant

Sanazarius Distant 1904, p. 431.—Drake and Ruhoff 1960a, p. 81.

TYPE SPECIES: *Sanazarius cuneatus* Distant.

*Sanazarius biseriatus Drake

Sanazarius biseriatus Drake 1953d, p. 217 [Cape Province].

TYPE: Holotype ♂, brachypterous; Swellendam, Cape Province, South Africa; British Mus.

DISTRIBUTION: South Africa (Cape Province).

HOST PLANT: Unrecorded.

*Sanazarius cuneatus Distant

Sanazarius cuneatus Distant 1904, p. 431, pl. 8, fig. 11 [Cape Province].

TYPE: Sex unknown; Grahamstown, Cape Colony, South Africa; British Mus.

DISTRIBUTION: South Africa (Cape Province).

HOST PLANT: Unrecorded.

*Sanazarius productus Distant

Sanazarius productus Distant 1911a, p. 43, fig. [Cape Province].—Drake 1956f, p. 426 [*Protea*].

TYPE: Sex unknown; Grahamstown, Cape Colony, South Africa; So. Afr. Mus.

DISTRIBUTION: South Africa (Cape Province).

HOST PLANT: *Protea* sp.

NOTE: Figure p. 44 incorrectly labeled by Distant as "*Sanazarius inflatus*" instead of "*S. productus.*"

Genus SCYMNOTINGIS Drake

Scymnotingis Drake 1960, p. 354.

TYPE SPECIES: *Scymnotingis sigillata* Drake.

Scymnotingis sigillata Drake

Scymnotingis sigillata Drake 1960, p. 355, fig. 10 [New Guinea].

TYPE: Holotype ♀; Daulo Pass, Asaro-Chimbu Divide, Northeast New Guinea; Bishop Mus.

DISTRIBUTION: New Guinea (Northeast).

HOST PLANT: Unrecorded.

Genus SINUESSA Horváth

Phyllontochila [sic] (*Sinuessa*) Horváth 1910, p. 63.

Phyllontocheila (*Sinuessa*): Horváth 1911a, pp. 329, 332 (key).

Sinuessa: Drake 1957c, p. 32.—Drake and Ruhoff 1960a, p. 81.

TYPE SPECIES: *Phyllontochila* (*Sinuessa*) *subinermis* Horváth.

*Sinuessa colens (Drake) (emendation)

Belenus colentis Drake 1953d, p. 218 [Cape Province].

Sinuessa calentis [sic]: Drake 1957c, p. 32.

TYPE: Holotype ♂; Queenstown, Cape Province, South Africa; British Mus.

DISTRIBUTION: South Africa (Cape Province).

HOST PLANT: Unrecorded.

*Sinuessa nairobia Drake

Sinuessa nairobia Drake 1957c, p. 34 [Kenya; Transvaal; Congo].

TYPE: Holotype ♀, macropterous; Nairobi, Kenya Colony; Drake Coll. (USNM).

DISTRIBUTION: Kenya; Congo; South Africa (Transvaal).

HOST PLANT: Unrecorded.

*Sinuessa subinermis (Horváth)

Phyllontochila (Sinuessa) subinermis Horváth 1910, p. 64 [Tanganyika].
Phyllontocheila (Sinuessa) subinermis: Horváth 1911a, pp. 329, 332.
Phyllontocheila subinermis: Schouteden 1916a, p. 272 [Eritrea].—Mancini 1939b, p. 162; 1954a, p. 143; 1956b, p. 78.—Drake 1954g, p. 663 [Ethiopia]; 1957a, p. 416 [Aden].
Sinuessa subinermis: Drake 1957c, p. 32.
Ammianus (Sinuessa) subinermis: Drake 1958a, p. 106 [Angola; Uganda; Kenya; So. Rhodesia].

TYPE: Sex unknown; Kibongoto, Kilimandjaro; Stockholm Mus.
DISTRIBUTION: Tanganyika; Kenya; Southern Rhodesia; Uganda; Angola; Aden Protectorate; Eritrea; Ethiopia.
HOST PLANT: Unrecorded.

*Sinuessa waelbroecki (Schouteden)

Phyllontocheila waelbroecki Schouteden (*in* Bergroth and Schouteden 1905, p. 381, fig. 1) [Congo]; 1916b, p. 292; 1923, p. 102.—Drake 1956f, p. 424 [Transvaal].
Phyllontochila (Sinuessa) waelbroecki: Horváth 1910, p. 63.
Phyllontocheila (Sinuessa) waelbroecki: Horváth 1911b, pp. 329, 332.
Sinuessa waelbroecki: Drake 1957c, p. 32; 1958b, p. 28 [Kenya].
Ammianus (Sinuessa) waelbroecki: Drake 1958a, p. 106 [Angola].

TYPE: Sex unknown; Kinchassa, Belgian Congo; Cent. Afr. Mus.
DISTRIBUTION: Congo; Kenya; Angola; South Africa (Transvaal).
HOST PLANT: Unrecorded.

Genus SPHAERISTA Kiritshenko

Sphaerista Kiritshenko 1951, pp. 240, 245.—Drake and Ruhoff 1960a, p. 81.
TYPE SPECIES: *Orthostira paradoxa* Jakovlev.

*Sphaerista paradoxa (Jakovlev)

Orthostira paradoxa Jakovlev 1880a, p. 128 [Russia]; 1893, p. 293.—Lethierry and Severin 1896, p. 7.
Acalypta paradoxa: Horváth 1906a, p. 34 [Siberia].—Oshanin 1908, p. 412; 1912, p. 42.
Sphaerista paradoxa: Kiritshenko 1951, p. 245, fig. 324.

TYPE: Holotype ♂, brachypterous; Russia; Leningrad Inst.
DISTRIBUTION: U.S.S.R. (Siberia).
HOST PLANT: Unrecorded.

Genus SPHAEROCYSTA Stål

Sphaerocysta Stål 1873, pp. 120, 128.—Lethierry and Severin 1896, p. 15.—Drake 1928a, p. 42.—Monte 1939b, p. 78; 1941e, p. 129.—Drake and Ruhoff 1960a, p. 82.
TYPE SPECIES: *Tingis globifera* Stål.

Sphaerocysta angulata Monte

Sphaerocysta angulata Monte 1941a, p. 373, fig. 1 [Brazil; Bignoniaceae].

TYPE: Holotype ♂; Chavantes, São Paulo, Brazil; Monte Coll. (Mus. Nacional).

DISTRIBUTION: Brazil.

HOST PLANT: Bignoniaceae.

*****Sphaerocysta biseriata** Drake

Sphaerocysta inflata var. *biseriata* Drake 1928a, p. 43 [Brazil].

Sphaerocysta biseriata: Drake and Hambleton 1934, p. 438.

TYPE: Holotype ♂; Chapada, Brazil; Carnegie Mus.

DISTRIBUTION: Brazil.

HOST PLANT: Unrecorded.

*****Sphaerocysta brasiliensis** Monte

Sphaerocysta brasiliensis Monte 1938c, p. 64, fig. [Brazil]; 1939a, p. 516 fig. [redescribed].

TYPE: Holotype ♂; Brazil; Monte Coll. (Mus. Nacional).

DISTRIBUTION: Brazil.

HOST PLANT: Unrecorded.

*****Sphaerocysta egregia** Drake

Sphaerocysta egregia Drake 1928a, p. 44 [Brazil].

TYPE: Holotype ♂; Corumba, Brazil; Carnegie Mus.

DISTRIBUTION: Brazil.

HOST PLANT: Unrecorded.

*****Sphaerocysta fumosa** Drake

Sphaerocysta fumosa Drake 1928a, p. 44 [Brazil].

TYPE: Holotype ♀, macropterous; Para, Brazil; Drake Coll. (USNM).

DISTRIBUTION: Brazil.

HOST PLANT: Unrecorded.

*****Sphaerocysta globifera** (Stål)

Tingis ? globifera Stål 1858, p. 65 [Brazil].—Walker 1873a, p. 181.

Sphaerocysta globifera: Stål 1873, p. 128.—Drake 1929, p. 35; 1930b, p. 25; 1935, p. 11.—Drake and Hambleton 1934, p. 438 [Bignoniaceae].—Costa Lima 1936, p. 130.—Drake and Poor 1937d, p. 305.—Silva 1956, p. 48, figs. 18, 18a.

Sphaerocysta globiffera [sic]: Drake 1928a, p. 43.

TYPE: Sex unknown; Brazil; Stockholm Mus.

DISTRIBUTION: Brazil; Paraguay.

HOST PLANTS: Bignoniaceae; hollyhocks.

*Sphaerocysta inflata (Stål)

Tingis ? inflata Stål 1858, p. 64 [Brazil].—Walker 1873a, p. 181.

Sphaerocysta inflata: Stål 1873, p. 128.—Drake 1930a, p. 1; 1935, p. 11
[Paraguay]; 1936b, p. 699 [Argentina].—Drake and Hambleton
1934, p. 438 [Bignoniaceae].—Costa Lima 1936, p. 130.—Drake and
Poor 1937d, p. 305, pl. 36, fig. 5; 1939b, p. 96.—Monte 1938b, p.
131; 1939b, p. 78 [Bolivia].—Kormilev 1955a, p. 67.—Drake and
Davis 1960, fig. 69.

TYPE: Holotype ♀; Brazil; Stockholm Mus.

DISTRIBUTION: Brazil; Argentina; Paraguay; Bolivia.

HOST PLANT: Bignoniaceae.

Sphaerocysta maculata Monte

Sphaerocysta maculata Monte 1942a, p. 95, fig. 2 [Brazil].

TYPE: Holotype ♂; Palmeiras, Impaussu, São Paulo, Brazil; Monte
Coll. (Mus. Nacional).

DISTRIBUTION: Brazil.

HOST PLANT: Unrecorded.

*Sphaerocysta nosella Drake and Hambleton

Sphaerocysta nosella Drake and Hambleton 1945, p. 358 [Ecuador].

TYPE: Holotype ♂, macropterous; Vinces, Ecuador; Drake Coll.
(USNM).

DISTRIBUTION: Ecuador.

HOST PLANT: Unrecorded.

*Sphaerocysta paris Drake

Sphaerocysta paris Drake 1939d, p. 529 [Brazil].—Silva 1956, p. 48.—
Drake and Ruhoff 1961c, p. 145.

Sphaerocysta romani Drake 1947, p. 2.

TYPE: Holotype ♀; Bahia, Brazil; Hungarian Mus.

DISTRIBUTION: Brazil.

HOST PLANT: Unrecorded.

*Sphaerocysta propria Drake and Poor

Sphaerocysta propria Drake and Poor 1939a, p. 31 [Brazil].

TYPE: Holotype ♀, macropterous; Rio Grande do Sul, Brazil; Drake
Coll. (USNM).

DISTRIBUTION: Brazil.

HOST PLANT: Unrecorded.

*Sphaerocysta stali Drake

Sphaerocysta globifera (not Stål): Champion 1898b, pl. 2, figs. 11, 11a
(fig. only).

Sphaerocysta stali Drake 1928a, p. 43 [Brazil].—Drake and Bondar
1932, p. 87.—Silva 1956, p. 51.

TYPE: Holotype ♂; Rio de Janeiro, Brazil; Drake Coll. (USNM).

DISTRIBUTION: Brazil.

HOST PLANT: Unrecorded.

Genus STENOCYSTA Champion

Stenocysta Champion 1897, p. 28.—Hurd 1946, p. 473.—Drake and Ruhoff 1960a, p. 82.

TYPE SPECIES: *Stenocysta pilosa* Champion.

Stenocysta pilosa Champion

Stenocysta pilosa Champion 1897, p. 29, pl. 2, figs. 18, 18 a, b [Panama].

TYPE: Holotype ♀; Bugaba, Panama; British Mus.

DISTRIBUTION: Panama.

HOST PLANT: Unrecorded.

Genus STEPHANITIS Stål

Stephanitis Stål 1873, pp. 119, 123; 1874, p. 53.—Horváth 1906a, pp. 14, 54 (key); 1912b, pp. 319–339 (key).—Oshanin 1908, p. 424; 1912, p. 43.—Van Duzee 1917b, p. 216.—Stichel 1926, p. 110; 1935, p. 349; 1938a, p. 406; 1960a, p. 300; 1960b, p. 394; 1960c, p. 133.—de Seabre 1931, pp. 407, 419.—Börner 1935, pp. 73, 76 (key).—Gulde 1938, pp. 243, 277 (key).—China 1943, p. 246.—Blöte 1945, p. 83.—Hurd 1946, p. 481.—González 1948, p. 50.—Drake 1948b, pp. 45–56 (catalog).—Kiritshenko 1951, pp. 242, 247.—Takeya 1951a, p. 7.—Drake and Maa 1953, pp. 99–101 (catalog).—Gomez-Menor 1954, p. 369.—Drake and Ruhoff 1960a, p. 82.

Tingis (not Fabricius): Laporte 1833, p. 48.—Drake and Ruhoff 1960a, p. 86.

Tingis (not Fabricius): Lethierry and Severin 1896, p. 12.—Drake and Ruhoff 1960a, p. 86.

Cadamustus Distant 1903a, p. 47; 1903b, p. 132; 1910a, p. 108.—Drake and Ruhoff 1960a, p. 41.

Maecenas Kirkaldy 1904, p. 280.—Drake and Ruhoff 1960a, p. 67.

Calliphanes Horváth 1906b, p. 34.—Drake and Ruhoff 1960a, p. 41.

Mokanna Distant 1910a, p. 111.—Drake and Ruhoff 1960a, p. 68.

TYPE SPECIES: *Acanthia pyri* Fabricius.

Subgenus STEPHANITIS (STEPHANITIS) Stål

TYPE SPECIES: *Acanthia pyri* Fabricius.

*Stephanitis agaica Drake

Stephanitis agaica Drake 1960, p. 374 [New Guinea].

TYPE: Holotype ♂; Wisselmeren, Enarotadi, Netherlands New Guinea; Bishop Mus.

DISTRIBUTION: New Guinea (Northeast; Netherlands).

HOST PLANT: Unrecorded.

*Stephanitis ambigua Horváth

   Tingis pyrioides (not Scott): Matsumura 1905, p. 33.

   Stephanitis ambigua Horváth 1912b, pp. 321, 328, fig. 2 [Japan].—
      Esaki and Takeya 1931, p. 54, figs. 1c, 2c; pl. 4, fig. 3; pl. 5, fig. 3;
      pl. 6, fig. 3.—Takeya 1932, p. 8 [Korea; *Lindera obtusiloba*]; 1951a,
      p. 9 [Taiwan]; 1953d, p. 168 [*Lindera glauca*].—Drake 1938b, p. 197
      [China].

   TYPE: Sex unknown; Japan; Hungarian Mus.

   DISTRIBUTION: Japan; China; Korea; Taiwan.

   HOST PLANTS: *Lindera glauca; Lindera obtusiloba.*

Stephanitis amboinae Drake and Poor

   Stephanitis amboinae Drake and Poor 1941, p. 163 [Amboina].

   TYPE: Holotype ♀; Amboina Island; Cal. Acad.

   DISTRIBUTION: Moluccas (Amboina Island).

   HOST PLANT: Unrecorded.

*Stephanitis assamana Drake and Maa

   Stephanitis assamana Drake and Maa 1954, p. 117 [India].

   TYPE: Holotype ♀; Cha Che, Delai Valley, Mishmi Hills, Assam, India;
British Mus.

   DISTRIBUTION: India.

   HOST PLANT: Unrecorded.

Stephanitis assamana subsp. **eremnoa** Drake and Ruhoff

   Stephanitis assamana subsp. *marginata* Drake and Maa 1954, p. 118
      [India].

   Stephanitis assamana subsp. *eremnoa* Drake and Ruhoff 1960c, p. 36.

   TYPE: Holotype ♀; Cha Che, Delai Valley, Mishmi Hills, Assam, India;
British Mus.

   DISTRIBUTION: India.

   HOST PLANT: Unrecorded.

*Stephanitis aucta Drake

   Stephanitis aucta Drake 1942a, p. 20 [Brazil].

   TYPE: Holotype ♀, macropterous; Chapoda, Brazil; Drake Coll. (USNM).

   DISTRIBUTION: Brazil.

   HOST PLANT: Unrecorded.

*Stephanitis blatchleyi Drake

   Stephanitis blatchleyi Drake 1925c, p. 37 [Fla.].

   Leptobyrsa blatchleyi: Blatchley 1926, p. 470.

   TYPE: Holotype ♂, macropterous; Dunedin, Florida, U.S.; Drake Coll.
(USNM).

   DISTRIBUTION: U.S. (Fla.).

   HOST PLANT: Unrecorded.

   NOTE: Wrongly transferred by Blatchley to genus *Leptobyrsa.*

*Stephanitis caucasica Kiritshenko

Stephanitis caucasica Kiritshenko 1939, p. 10 (nom. nud.); 1951, p. 247, fig. 325 [Caucasus; Transcaucasus; *Rhododendron*].—Stichel 1960a, p. 304, fig. 107.

TYPE: Sex unknown; Transcaucasia, Russia; Leningrad Inst.

DISTRIBUTION: U.S.S.R. (Caucasus; Transcaucasus).

HOST PLANT: *Rhododendron* sp.

*Stephanitis chlorophana (Fieber)

Tingis chlorophana Fieber 1861, p. 129 [Portugal].—Walker 1873a, p. 179.—Chicote 1880, p. 189 [Spain].

Stephanitis chlorophana: Horváth 1905b, p. 568; 1906a, p. 56; 1912b, p. 333.—de Seabra 1931, p. 421, figs. 492 (2–6), 494 [*Viburnum tinus*].— Gomez-Menor 1954, p. 381, fig. 4.—Stichel 1960a, p. 303, fig. 104.

TYPE: Portugal; sex and deposition of type unknown.

DISTRIBUTION: Portugal; Spain.

HOST PLANT: *Viburnum tinus.*

*Stephanitis colocasiae Horváth

Stephanitis colocasiae Horváth 1912b, pp. 320, 326 [New Guinea; *Colocasia esculenta*].—Drake 1960, p. 372.

TYPE: Sex unknown; Friedrich-Wilhelmshafen, New Guinea; Hungarian Mus.

DISTRIBUTION: New Guinea (Northeast).

HOST PLANT: *Colocasia esculenta.*

Stephanitis depressa Blöte

Stephanitis depressa Blöte 1945, p. 83 [Sumatra].

TYPE: Sex unknown; Gunung Teleman, Sumatra; Leiden Zool. Inst.

DISTRIBUTION: Greater Sunda Islands (Sumatra).

HOST PLANT: Unrecorded.

*Stephanitis farameae Drake and Hambleton

Stephanitis farameae Drake and Hambleton 1935, p. 151 [Brazil; *Faramea montevidensis*].—Monte 1939b, p. 78; 1941e, p. 132.

TYPE: Holotype ♂, macropterous; Parque do Estado, São Paulo, Brazil; Drake Coll. (USNM).

DISTRIBUTION: Brazil.

HOST PLANT: *Faramea montevidensis.*

*Stephanitis fasciicarina Takeya

Stephanitis fasciicarina Takeya 1931, p. 70, pl. 7, fig. 2; pl. 8, fig. 6 [Japan; *Machilus thunbergii; Cinnamomum camphora*]; 1951a, p. 10; 1953d, p. 168.—Drake and Poor 1937b, p. 403.

Stephanitis kyushuana Drake 1948b, p. 52.

TYPE: Holotype ♂; Akama, Kyushu, Japan; Kyushu Univ.

DISTRIBUTION: Japan.

HOST PLANTS: *Cinnamomum camphora; Machilus thunbergii.*

*Stephanitis gallarum Horváth

Stephanitis gallarum Horváth 1906b, p. 33 [India; *Machilus gamblei*]; 1912b, p. 330.—Distant 1910a, p. 108.—Drake and Poor 1936b, p. 148.—Drake 1937a, p. 387; 1938b, p. 197 [China].—Singh 1953, p. 119.—Drake and Maa 1953, p. 100.

Stephanitis distinctissima Esaki and Takeya 1933, p. 1, figs. 1, 2 [Taiwan; *Machilus pseudo-longifolia*].—Takeya 1951a, p. 9 [*Machilus longifolia*].

TYPE: Sex unknown; Kurseong, Bengal, India; Hungarian Mus.

DISTRIBUTION: India; China; Taiwan.

HOST PLANTS: *Alnus nepalensis; Machilus gamblei; Machilus longifolia; Machilus pseudo-longifolia.*

*Stephanitis gressitti Drake

Stephanitis gressitti Drake 1948b, p. 50 [China].

TYPE: Holotype ♀, macropterous; Szechwan, north of Chengtu, West China; Drake Coll. (USNM).

DISTRIBUTION: China.

HOST PLANT: Unrecorded.

*Stephanitis hikosana Drake

Stephanitis hikosana Drake 1948b, p. 53 [Japan].—Takeya 1951a, p. 10 [*Rhododendron hymenanthes* var. *heptamerum*]; 1953d, p. 171.

TYPE: Holotype ♂; Hikosan (Buzen), Kyushu, Japan; Kyushu Univ.

DISTRIBUTION: Japan.

HOST PLANT: *Rhododendron hymenanthes* var. *heptamerum.*

*Stephanitis hydrangeae Drake and Maa

Stephanitis hydrangeae Drake and Maa 1955, p. 8 [Taiwan; *Hydrangea integra*].

TYPE: Holotype ♂, macropterous; Arisan, Formosa; Drake Coll. (USNM).

DISTRIBUTION: Taiwan.

HOST PLANT: *Hydrangea integra.*

*Stephanitis laudata Drake and Poor

Stephanitis laudata Drake and Poor (*in* Drake and Maa 1953, p. 98) [China; Hainan; Taiwan].

TYPE: Holotype ♂, macropterous; Ta Han, Hainan Island, China; Drake Coll. (USNM).

DISTRIBUTION: China (Hainan Island); Taiwan.

HOST PLANT: Unrecorded.

*Stephanitis ligyra Drake   FIGURE 1a

Stephanitis ligyra Drake 1960, p. 372, fig. 23 [New Guinea].

TYPE: Holotype ♀; Okaitadi, Wisselmeren, Netherlands New Guinea; Bishop Mus.

DISTRIBUTION: New Guinea (Netherlands).

HOST PLANT: Unrecorded.

*Stephanitis luzonana Drake

Stephanitis luzonana Drake 1948b, p. 50 [Luzon].

TYPE: Holotype ♂, macropterous; Mt. Makiling, Luzon, Philippine Islands; Drake Coll. (USNM).

DISTRIBUTION: Philippine Islands (Luzon).

HOST PLANT: Unrecorded.

*Stephanitis matsumurae Horváth

Stephanitis matsumurae Horváth 1912b, pp. 322, 332 [Japan].

TYPE: Sex unknown; Sapporo, Japan; Hungarian Mus.

DISTRIBUTION: Japan.

HOST PLANT: Unrecorded.

Stephanitis mitrata (Stål)

Tingis mitrata Stål 1858, p. 64 [Brazil].—Walker 1873a, p. 181.—Lethierry and Severin 1896, p. 12.

Stephanitis mitrata: Stål 1873, p. 123.—Champion 1898b, p. 58, pl. 2, figs. 3, 3a.—Drake and Poor 1937d, p. 309.—Drake and Hambleton 1938a, p. 66 [*Merostachys*].—Monte 1941e, p. 133.

Calliphanes mitratus: Horváth 1906b, p. 34.

TYPE: Holotype ♀; Rio de Janeiro, Brazil; Stockholm Mus.

DISTRIBUTION: Brazil.

HOST PLANT: *Merostachys* sp.

*Stephanitis nashi Esaki and Takeya

Tingis pyri (not Fabricius): Matsumura 1908, p. 147, fig.

Stephanitis ambigua (not Horváth): Matsumura 1917, p. 440, fig.; 1930, p. 158, pl. 14, fig. 11.

Stephanitis pyri (not Fabricius): Drake 1923a, p. 104.

Stephanitis nashi Esaki and Takeya 1931, p. 54, pl. 4, fig. 1; pl. 5, fig. 1; pl. 6, fig. 1; figs. 1a, 2a [Japan; Korea; *Pyrus; Prunus; Malus floribunda; Chaenomeles cathayensis; Cormus tschonoskii; Kerria japonica; Crataegus; Malus*].—Takeya 1932, p. 8; 1951a, p. 9 [*Crataegus cuneata*]; 1953d, p. 168.—Esaki 1932, p. 1635, fig.; 1954, p. 236, fig. 609.—Kato 1933, pl. 31, fig. 3.—Saito 1933, p. 6 [*Pyrus ussuriensis*].—Drake and Hsiung 1936, p. 288 [China].—Drake and Poor 1937b, p. 403.—Drake 1937b, p. 594; 1938b, p. 197.—Fukui 1938, pl. 50, fig. 35.—Shinji 1938, p. 316.—Maa 1957, pp. 128, 133.

TYPE: Holotype ♂; Fukuoka, Kyushu, Japan; Kyushu Univ.

DISTRIBUTION: China; Japan; Korea; Taiwan.

HOST PLANTS: *Chaenomeles cathayensis; Cormus tschonoskii; Crataegus cuneata; Crataegus* sp.; *Kerria japonica; Malus floribunda; Malus* sp.; *Prunus* sp.; *Pyrus ussuriensis; Pyrus* sp.

Stephanitis nashi var. **suigensis** Saitô

　　Stephanitis nashi var. *suigensis* Saitô 1933, p. 5 [Korea; *Potentilla freyniana*].—Takeya 1951a, p. 10.

　　TYPE: Korea; sex and deposition of type unknown.

　　DISTRIBUTION: Korea.

　　HOST PLANT: *Potentilla freyniana*.

*Stephanitis oberti (Kolenati)

　　Tingis pyri (not Fabricius): Fallén 1807, p. 39 [Sweden; *Carduus lanceolatus*]; 1829, p. 149 [*Myrica gale*].—Sahlberg 1848, p. 136 [Finland].

　　Campylosteira (*Dictyonota*) *oberti* Kolenati 1856, p. 433 [Estonia].

　　Tingis oberti: Flor 1860, p. 369 [*Pinus sylvestris*].—Jakovlev 1875b, p. 262; 1880b, p. 102 (in part) [Caucasus]; 1902b, p. 276.—Hüeber 1893, p. 326 [Austria].—Lethierry and Severin 1896, p. 12.

　　Stephanitis oberti: Stål 1873, p. 123.—Reuter 1882b, p. 118 [*Myrtillus niger; Ledum palustre*].—Horváth 1906a, p. 56 [Siberia; Netherlands; Germany; *Vaccinium myrtillus; Vaccinium vitis-idaea*]; 1912b, pp. 322, 332 [*Rhododendron*].—Lindberg 1919, p. 42.—Sahlberg 1920, p. 83 [*Calluna vulgaris; Myrtillus uliginosus*].—Stichel 1926, p. 110; 1928a, p. 206; 1938a, p. 406 [Czechoslovakia; Albania; Norway; Denmark]; 1960a, p. 303 [Yugoslavia; *Vaccinium uliginosum*].—Scholte 1935, p. 60.— Gulde 1938, p. 280, fig.—Kiritshenko 1951, p. 248.—Cobben 1958a, p. 5, figs. 5–10.

　　TYPE: Dorpat, Livonia; sex and deposition of type unknown.

　　DISTRIBUTION: Netherlands; Germany; Austria; Czechoslovakia; Albania; Yugoslavia; Denmark; Norway; Sweden; Finland; U.S.S.R. (Estonia; Caucasus; Siberia).

　　HOST PLANTS: *Calluna vulgaris; Carduus lanceolatus; Ledum palustre; Myrica gale; Myrtillus niger; Myrtillus uliginosus; Pinus sylvestris; Rhododendron* sp.; *Vaccinium myrtillus; Vaccinium uliginosum; Vaccinium vitis-idaea*.

Stephanitis oberti var. **biseriata** Sahlberg

　　Stephanitis oberti var. *biseriata* Sahlberg 1920, p. 83 [Finland].—Stichel 1960a, p. 303.

　　TYPE: Sex unknown; Finland; Helsin. Mus.

　　DISTRIBUTION: Finland.

　　HOST PLANT: Unrecorded.

*Stephanitis olyrae Drake and Hambleton

　　Stephanitis olyrae Drake and Hambleton 1935, p. 150, fig. 5 [Brazil; *Olyra micrantha*].—Monte 1939b, p. 78; 1941e, p. 133.

　　TYPE: Holotype ♂, macropterous; Ponte Nova, Minas Gerais, Brazil; Drake Coll. (USNM).

　　DISTRIBUTION: Brazil.

　　HOST PLANT: *Olyra micrantha*.

*Stephanitis parana Drake and Hambleton

Stephanitis parana Drake and Hambleton 1944b, p. 128 [Brazil].

TYPE: Holotype ♂, macropterous; Para, Brazil; Drake Coll. (USNM).

DISTRIBUTION: Brazil.

HOST PLANT: Unrecorded.

*Stephanitis princeps (Distant)

Mokanna princeps Distant 1910a, p. 112, fig. 55 [India].

Stephanitis princeps: Horváth 1912b, pp. 321, 329.

TYPE: Sex unknown; Trichinopoly, India; British Mus.

DISTRIBUTION: India.

HOST PLANT: Unrecorded.

*Stephanitis propinqua Horváth

Stephanitis propinqua Horváth 1912b, pp. 322, 331 [Japan].—Takeya 1932, p. 9, pl. 1, fig. 1 [Korea; Rhododendron].

TYPE: Sex unknown; Kagoshima, Japan; Hungarian Mus.

DISTRIBUTION: Japan; Korea.

HOST PLANT: Rhododendron sp.

*Stephanitis pyri (Fabricius)

Acanthia pyri Fabricius 1775, p. 696 [Pyrus]; 1781, p. 338; 1787, p. 280; 1794, p. 78.—Rossi 1790, p. 225.—Walckenaer 1802, p. 338.

Cimex appendiceus Fourcroy 1785, p. 212.—Villers 1789, p. 488, pl. 3, fig. 19.

Cimex pyri: Gmelin 1790, p. 2127.

Tingis pyri: Fabricius 1803, p. 126.—Latrielle 1804, p. 254; 1829, p. 201.—Le Peletier and Serville 1828, p. 653.—Laporte 1833, p. 48.— Burmeister 1835, p. 259 [Germany; Portugal].—Spinola 1837, p. 166.—Herrich-Schaeffer 1838, p. 69, pl. 126, fig.; pl. 130, fig. d; 1850, p. 162.—Blanchard 1840, p. 112, pl. 2, fig. 7.—Westwood 1840a, p. 478 [England; pear].—Amyot and Serville 1843, p. 297 [France].—Guérin-Méneville 1844, p. 349, pl. 56, fig. 13.—Fieber 1844, p. 102, pl. 8, figs. 34–36 [Czechoslovakia; Austria; Hungary; Italy; Sweden]; 1861, p. 129.—Costa 1847a, p. 21; 1847c, p. 161.— Mayr 1858, p. 572.—Frey-Gessner 1865, p. 233 [Switzerland].— Garbiglietti 1869, p. 275.—Gredler 1870, p. 76.—Walker 1873a, p. 179.—Horváth 1874b, p. 432.—Ferrari 1874, p. 171; 1878, p. 66; 1885, p. 411.—Reiber and Puton 1876, p. 69.—Bolivar and Chicote 1879, p. 166 [Spain].—Puton 1879c, p. 105; 1881, p. 123 [Syria].— Jakovlev 1880b, p. 102 [Caucasus].—Dubois 1888, p. 120.—d'Antessanty 1890, p. 31.—Reuter 1891, p. 26 [Greece].—Hüeber 1893, p. 325 [Sorbus aria; Vaccinium myrtillus].—Champion 1898b, p. 58.— Reichensperger 1920, p. 61.—Gautier 1925, p. 321; 1927a, p. 12; 1927b, p. 26.

Tingis marginata Lamarck 1816, p. 504.

Tingis appendicea: Le Peletier and Serville 1828, p. 653.

Stephanitis pyri: Stål 1873, p. 123.—Horváth 1906a, pp. 54, 55 [Turkestan; Armenia; Turkey; *Pyrus malus; Castanea sativa*]; 1906d, p. 1; 1912b, pp. 320, 327 [*Prunus lusitanica*]; 1916, p. 9 [Albania].—Muzik 1907, p. 57.—Blanchard 1926, p. 362.—Stichel 1926, p. 110 [*Pyrus aria*]; 1938a, p. 406 [Belgium; Rumania]; 1960a, p. 301, fig. 98 [Sicily; Sardinia; Poland; *Sorbus torminalis; Pyrus aucuparia; Prunus mahaleb; Prunus armeniaca; Cotoneaster integerrima; Crataegus crus-galli; Robina pseudoacacia; Ulmus effusa; Ulmus campestris; Populus; Tilia; Ligustrum; Cormus; Ribes nigrum; Juglans regia*].—Esaki and Takeya 1931, p. 53, figs. 1b, 2b; pl. 4, fig. 2; pl. 5, fig. 2; pl. 6, fig. 2.—de Seabra 1931, p. 420, figs. 492(1), 493.—Silvestri 1934, p. 257, fig. 221.—Balachowsky and Mesnil 1935, p. 277, fig. 212.—Scholte 1935, p. 60 [Netherlands].—Vidal 1937, p. 197 [Morocco].—Lindberg 1948, p. 58 [Bulgaria; Yugoslavia; *Prunus cerasus; Amygdalus; Rosa;* Cyprus].—Mancini 1949b, p. 36; 1952, p. 12; 1953b, p. 186; 1953d, p. 16.—Novak and Wagner 1951, p. 70 [*Crataegus pyracantha; Cydonia vulgaris; Prunus marasca; Prunus persica; Prunus avium*].—Kiritshenko 1951, p. 247, fig. 327.—Poisson 1951, p. 1798, fig. 1591.—Gomez-Menor 1954, p. 371, figs. 1, 2 [*Crataegus*]; 1955a, p. 255, figs. 32, 33a–d; 1955b, p. 249 [*Malus communis*].—Hoberlandt 1955, p. 98 [Iraq; Israel; *Quercus ilex; Quercus coccifera*].—Carayon 1960, p. 111.—Drake and Ruhoff 1962c, p. 133.

Stephanitis piri [sic]: Börner 1935, p. 76.

Stephanitis oschanini Vasiliev 1935, p. 151.

Phyllontocheila schoutedeni (not Distant): Gomez-Menor 1956a, fig. 14 (fig. only).

Maecenas pyri: Drake and Ruhoff 1960a, p. 67.

Type: Holotype ♀, macropterous; locality unknown; Kiel Coll. (Copenhagen Mus.).

Distribution: Portugal; Spain; France; Belgium; Netherlands; England; Germany; Austria; Switzerland; Czechoslovakia; Hungary; Italy; Sicily; Sardinia; Yugoslavia; Albania; Rumania; Bulgaria; Poland; Sweden; Greece; Cyprus; Turkey; Iran; Iraq; Syria; Israel; U.S.S.R. (Caucasus; Armenia; Turkestan); Morocco.

Host Plants: *Amygdalus* sp.; *Castanea sativa; Chaenomeles japonica; Cormus* sp; *Cotoneaster integerrima; Crataegus crus-galli; Crataegus pyracantha; Crataegus* sp.; *Cydonia vulgaris; Juglans regia; Malus communis; Ligustrum* sp.; *Populus* sp.; *Prunus armeniaca; Prunus avium; Prunus cerasus; Prunus lusitanica; Prunus mahaleb; Prunus marasca; Prunus persica; Pyrus aria; Pyrus aucuparia; Pyrus communius; Pyrus malus; Pyrus* sp.; *Quercus coccifera; Quercus ilex; Ribes nigrum; Rosa* sp.; *Sorbus aria; Sorbus torminalis; Robina pseudoacacia; Tilia* sp.; *Ulmus campestris; Ulmus effusa; Vaccinium myrtillus.*

Note: Predators and parasites [Silvestri; Gautier; Carayon]. Notes on hibernation [Gautier 1925, 1927a].

LACEBUGS OF THE WORLD **361**

*Stephanitis pyri var. **sareptana** Horváth

Stephanitis pyri var. *sareptana* Horváth 1912b, pp. 320, 327 [Russia].—Stichel 1960a, p. 302.

TYPE: Sarepta, Russia; sex and deposition of type unknown.

DISTRIBUTION: U.S.S.R.

HOST PLANT: Unrecorded.

*Stephanitis pyrioides (Scott)

Tingis pyrioides Scott 1874, pp. 291, 440 [Japan].—Uhler 1896, p. 265.

Stephanitis azaleae Horváth 1905b, p. 568 [Netherlands; azalea]; 1906a, pp. 55, 56; 1912b, p. 333 [D.C.].—Stichel 1926, p. 110; 1928, p. 206.—Scholte 1935, p. 60.

Stephanitis pyrioides: Oshanin 1908, p. 425.—Dickerson and Weiss 1917, p. 101, pl. 9 [N.J.; Pa.; *Rhododendron hinodegeri; amoena; ledifolia alba; benigeri; yodogawa; kaempheri; pontica; mollis; indica; shirogeri; hatsugeri; shibori; amurasaki; schilippenbachii*].—Weiss 1918, p. 8, figs. 7–9.—Barber and Weiss 1922, p. 10, fig. 4.—Parshley 1922a, p. 236 [Conn.]; 1923b, p. 704, pl. 17, fig. 8.—McAtee 1923, p. 149.—Drake 1923a, p. 104; 1928b, p. 101 [N.Y.; *Kalmia latifolia*]; 1961b, p. 112 [New South Wales].—Blatchley 1926, p. 468, pl. 4, fig. 8.—Blanchard 1926, p. 361, fig. [Argentina].—Esaki and Takeya 1931, p. 53, figs. 1d, 2d; pl. 4, fig. 4; pl. 5, fig. 4; pl. 6, fig. 4.—Esaki 1932, p. 1635, fig.; 1954, p. 236, fig. 610.—Takeya 1932, p. 10 [Korea]; 1951a, p. 12 [Taiwan; *Pieris ovalifolia*]; 1953c, pp. 8–12; 1953d, p. 168.—White 1933, p. 631.—Kato 1933, pl. 31, fig. 2.—Saito 1933, p. 6 [*Rhododendron mucronatum; yedoense poukhanense*].—Shinji 1938, p. 316.—Froeschner 1944, p. 668 [Mo.].—Bailey 1950, p. 144; 1951, p. 56 [Mass.; R.I.; *Rhododendron calendulaceum*]; 1959, p. 65.—Gomez-Menor 1954, p. 377, fig. 3 [Morocco].—Maa 1957, pp. 128, 133.—Cobben 1958a, p. 9, fig. 10.—Stichel 1960a, p. 302 [England].—Drake and Ruhoff 1926b, p. 250.

Stephanitis pyriodes [sic]: Barber 1922a, p. 16.

Stephanitis oberti (not Kolenati): Lindlinger 1927, p. 36 [Germany].

Stephanitis pyroides [sic]: Drake 1937b, p. 594 [China].—Bosq 1937, p. 131.

Stephanitis pyri (not Fabricius): Gomez-Menor 1956a, fig. 7 (fig. only).

TYPE: Sex unknown; Japan; British Mus.

DISTRIBUTION: Japan; China; Korea; Taiwan; Germany; Netherlands; England; Argentina; Morocco; U.S. (N.Y.; Conn.; Mass.; R.I.; N.J.; Pa.; D.C.; Fla.; Mo.); Australia (New South Wales).

HOST PLANTS: *Kalmia latifolia; Pieris ovalifolia; Rhododendron* species (including azalea) especially: *amoena; amurasaki; benigeri; calendulaceum; hinodegeri; hatsugeri; indica; kaempheri; ledifolia alba; mollis; mucronatum; obtusum amoenum; pontica; shirogeri; shibori; schilippenbachii; yedoense poukhanense; yodogawa.*

NOTE: Life history studies [Bailey; Dickerson and Weiss].

681–552—64——24

*Stephanitis queenslandensis Hacker

Stephanitis queenslandensis Hacker 1927, p. 28, pl. 7, fig. 8 [Queensland; *Stephania hernandifolia*]; 1928, p. 183.

TYPE: Sex unknown; Queensland, Australia; Queensland Mus.

DISTRIBUTION: Australia (Queensland).

HOST PLANT: *Stephania hernandifolia.*

*Stephanitis querca Bergroth

Stephanitis quercus Bergroth 1924, p. 83 [Luzon; oak].—Drake 1930e, p. 168.

Stephanitis querca: Drake and Poor 1937a, p. 17.

TYPE: Sex unknown; Luzon, Philippine Islands; Helsin. Mus.

DISTRIBUTION: Philippine Islands (Luzon; Mindanao).

HOST PLANT: Oak.

*Stephanitis rhododendri Horváth

Stephanitis rhododendri Horváth 1905b, p. 567 [Netherlands; *Rhododendron*]; 1906a, p. 55; 1912b, pp. 321, 329.—Distant 1910c, p. 395, fig. [England].—Theobald 1911, p. 206; 1913, p. 297, figs. 40–43.— Steyer 1915, p. 434 [Germany].—Van den Broeck and Schenk 1915, p. 170.—Green 1916, p. 207.—Marchal 1917, p. 93 [France].— Barber and Weiss 1922, p. 11, figs. 5–7.—Lounsbury 1923, p. 548 [Cape Province].—Wilson 1925, p. 52 [Switzerland].—Stichel 1928, p. 206; 1960a, p. 300, fig. 94 [Scotland; Denmark; Sweden; Finland].—Schmidt 1928, p. 205.—Scholte 1935, p. 60, fig. 13.— Balachowsky and Mesnil 1936, p. 1532, fig. 1225.—Proctor 1946, p. 74.—Van der Bruel 1947, p. 191, fig. 1 [Belgium].—Bailey 1951, p. 58 [N.H.; R.I.; *Kalmia angustifolia*]; 1959, p. 65.—Cobben 1958a, p. 5, figs. 5–8 [*Rhododendron Van der Hoop; Mme. Mason; Mme. Carvalho; parsons gloriosium; Mr. R.S. Holford; america; caratacus; Cunningham's White; Antoon van Welie; fastuosum; cynthia; everestianum; Peter Koster; hollandia; Dr. V. H. Rutgers; Mme. de Bruin*].—Southwood and Leston 1959, p. 146, pl. 18, fig. 5.

Leptobyrsa species nova? Wirtner 1904, p. 202.

Leptobyrsa explanata Heidemann 1908, p. 105, pl. 4, figs. e, f [Fla.; Mass.; D.C.; N.C.; Md.; Pa.; N.Y.; W. Va.; Ohio; *Kalmia latifolia; Rhododendron maximum*].—Felt 1910, p. 72, fig. 1.—Banks 1910, p. 56.— Torre-Bueno 1910, p. 31.—Smith 1910, p. 148 [N.J.].—Parshley 1914, p. 145 [Maine].—Crosby and Hadley 1915, pp. 409–415, pl. 23, figs. 1–6; pl. 22 [Conn.].—Osborn and Drake 1916a, p. 240, pl. 7.

Leptobyrsa rhododendri: Parshley 1917a, p. 15; 1917b, p. 55; 1923b, p. 703.—Dickerson 1917, pp. 105–112, pl. 8.—Weiss 1918, p. 5, figs. 4–6.—McAtee 1923, p. 149.—Downes 1925, p. 17, fig. 8 [B.C.]; 1927a, p. 10.—Blatchley 1926, p. 469, fig. 105 [Va.].—Drake 1928b, p. 102.—Ascot 1930, p. 238.—Johnson 1936, p. 342, figs. 2–4; pls. 13–15.

Type: Sex unknown; Boskoop, Netherlands; Hungarian Mus.

Distribution: Netherlands; Belgium; France; Germany; Switzerland; Finland; Sweden; Denmark; Scotland; England; South Africa (Cape Province); Canada (Nfld.; B.C.); U.S. (Maine; N.H.; Mass.; Conn.; R.I.; N.Y.; N.J.; Pa.; Ohio; Md.; D.C.; Va.; W. Va.; N.C.; S. C.; Fla.; Oreg.; Wash.; Vt.); New Zealand.

Host Plants: *Kalmia angustifolia; Kalmia latifolia; Pieris floribunda; Pieris japonica; Rhododendron* species, those reported: *america; Antoon van Welie; caractacus; Cunningham's White; cynthia; Dr. V.H. Rutgers; everestianum; fastuosum; hollandia; maximum; Mme. Mason; Mme. Carvalho; Mr. R.S. Holford; Mme. de Bruin; parsons gloriosum; Peter Koster; Van der Hoop.*

Note: Life history studies [Heidemann; Crosby and Hadley; Dickerson; Johnson; Wilson; Felt; Bruel; Balachowsky and Mesnil]. Found on 120 species of *Rhododendron* [Van den Broek and Schenk].

*Stephanitis steeleae Drake and Maa

Stephanitis steeleae Drake and Maa 1954, p. 116 [India].

Type: Holotype ♂, macropterous; Cha Che, Delai Valley, Mishmi Hills, Assam, India; British Mus.

Distribution: India.

Host Plant: Unrecorded.

*Stephanitis subfasciata Horváth

Stephanitis subfasciata Horváth 1912b, pp. 320, 325 [China; Taiwan].— Esaki 1926, p. 163.—Drake and Poor 1937b, p. 404 [Java].—Drake 1948b, p. 56 [India]; 1956d, p. 115 [Burma; *Cocculus; Hernandia;* Peleliu; Argaut].—Maa 1957, pp. 129, 132 [*Cocculus trilobus*].

Stephanitis (Menodora) subfasciata: Wu 1935, p. 449.

Type: Unknown.

Distribution: China; Taiwan; Burma; India; Palau Islands (Peleliu; Argaut); Greater Sunda Islands (Java).

Host Plants: *Cocculus trilobus; Cocculus* sp.; *Hernandia* sp.

*Stephanitis svensoni Drake

Stephanitis svensoni Drake 1948b, p. 51 [Japan].—Takeya 1953d, p. 169, fig. 1a.

Stephanitis shirozui Takeya 1951b, p. 60, fig. 2 [*Illicium religiosum*].

Type: Holotype ♂, macropterous; Shimabara Pen., Japan; Drake Coll. (USNM).

Distribution: Japan.

Host Plant: *Illicium religiosum.*

*Stephanitis tabidula Horváth

Stephanitis tabidula Horváth 1912b, pp. 323, 333 [Japan].

Type: Sex unknown; Kanagawa, Japan; Hungarian Mus.

Distribution: Japan.

Host Plant: Unrecorded.

*Stephanitis takeyai Drake and Maa   PLATE 48

Tingis globulifera Matsumura 1905, p. 36, pl. 19, fig. 16 [Japan].
Stephanitis globulifera: Matsumura 1908, p. 148, fig.; 1930, p. 161, pl. 14,
fig. 16; 1931, p. 1203, fig. 7.—Horváth 1912b, pp. 322, 330 [*Cinnamomum camphora*].—Drake 1923a, p. 104.—Kato 1933, pl. 31, fig.
4.—Takeya 1930b, p. 72; 1951a, p. 11 [*Lindera citriodora; Styrax
iaponica; Pierus ovalifolia*]; 1953d, p. 168, fig. 1b [*Lyonia neziki; Lindera
obtusiloba; Lindera umbellata; Salix; Aperula citriodora; Pierus japonica*].—
Drake and Poor 1937b, p. 403.—Bailey 1950, pp. 143–145 [Conn.];
1951, p. 53; 1959, p. 65.—Warner 1956, p. 6 [N.J.].
Stephanitis takeyai Drake and Maa 1955, p. 10 [India].
TYPE: Unknown.
DISTRIBUTION: Japan; India; U.S. [Conn.; N.J.].
HOST PLANTS: *Andromedea* sp.; *Aperula citriodora; Cinnamomum camphora;
Lindera sericea; Lindera citriodora; Lindera obtusiloba; Lindera umbellata; Lyonia
neziki; Pierus japonica; Pierus ovalifolia; Salix* sp.; *Styrax japonica*.

*Stephanitis typica (Distant)   PLATE 47

Cadamustus typicus Distant 1903a, p. 47 [Ceylon]; 1903b, p. 132, fig. 95
[*Hedychium; Musa*].
Stephanitis typicus: Distant 1910a, p. 108 [India; Luzon]. —Drake 1926e,
p. 335; 1933, p. 1016; 1937b, p. 594; 1938b, p. 197 [Hong Kong].—
Nagaraj and Menon 1956, pp. 161–165.—Mathen 1960, pp. 8–24,
figs. 1–6, pls. 1–2, tables 1–6 [*Artocarpus integrifolia*].—Shanta,
Menon, and Pillai 1960, p. 58–62.
Stephanitis typica: Horváth 1912b, pp. 320, 325 [Java; *Musa paradisiaca
sapientum*]; 1912c, p. 341; 1926, p. 329 [Sumatra].—Bergroth 1914a,
p. 361 [Taiwan].—Fletcher 1920, p. 263.—Drake 1923a, p. 104;
1960, p. 373 [Korea; Papua].—Esaki 1926, p. 163.—Takeya 1931, p.
70 [*Alpinia nutans*]; 1951a, p. 8 [Japan; *Zingiber mioga*]; 1952, pp. 39–46,
fig. 1 [Pakistan; Malaya; *Alpinia japonica; Alpinia speciosa; Zingiber
kawangoii*].—Hoffman 1935, p. 643, pl. 47 [China; *Elettaria cardamomum;* coconut; camphor].—Takahashi 1936, p. 295.—Drake and Poor
1936a, p. 443 [Hainan]; 1937a, p. 16; 1937b, p. 404 [Mindanao;
Annona muricata].—Shirôzu 1939, p. 205 [*Alpinia chinensis*].—Maa 1957,
pp. 127, 133.
Stephanitis indiana Drake 1948b, p. 51.
TYPE: Sex unknown; Pundalu-oya, Ceylon; British Mus.
DISTRIBUTION: Ceylon; India; Pakistan; Hong Kong; China (Hainan
Island); Japan; Korea; Taiwan; New Guinea (Papua); Greater Sunda
Islands (Sumatra; Java); Federation of Malaya; Philippine Islands (Luzon;
Mindanao; Leyte).
HOST PLANTS: *Alpinia chinensis; Alpinia nutans; Alpinia japonica; Alpinia speciosa;
Annona muricata; Artocarpus integrifolia; Elettaria cardamomum; Hedychium* sp.;

Musa paradisciaca sapientum; Musa sp.; *Zingiber kawagoii; Zingiber mioga;* camphor; coconut.

NOTE: (1) Life history studies [Hoffman; Mathen]; (2) possible vector of wilt (root) disease of coconut palm [Nagaraj and Menon; Mathen; Shanta, Menon and Pillai]; (3) *indiana* here placed in synonymy. (New synonymy.)

*Stephanitis veridica Drake

Stephanitis veridica Drake 1948b, p. 54 [Taiwan].

TYPE: Holotype ♂, macropterous; Tainansliu, Formosa; Drake Coll. (USNM).

DISTRIBUTION: Taiwan.

HOST PLANT: Unrecorded.

*Stephanitis yasumatsui Takeya

Stephanitis yasumatsui Takeya 1951b, p. 58, fig. 1 [Japan].

TYPE: Holotype ♂; Sobo-san, Prov. Bungo, Japan; Kyushu Univ.

DISTRIBUTION: Japan.

HOST PLANT: Unrecorded.

*Stephanitis yunnana Drake and Maa

Stephanitis yunnana Drake and Maa 1955, p. 9 [China].

TYPE: Holotype ♀, macropterous; Yunnan, China; Drake Coll. (USNM).

DISTRIBUTION: China.

HOST PLANT: Unrecorded.

Subgenus STEPHANITIS (MENODORA) Horváth

Stephanitis (Menodora) Horváth 1912b, pp. 319, 324.—Takeya 1951a, p. 7.—Drake and Maa 1953, p. 99 (catalog).—Drake and Ruhoff 1960a, p. 83.

TYPE SPECIES: *Stephanitis (Menodora) formosa* Horváth.

*Stephanitis (Menodora) charieis Drake and Mohanasundarum

Stephanitis (Menodora) charieis Drake and Mohanasundarum 1961, p. 111, fig. 3 [India; *Artocarpus integrifolia*].

TYPE: Holotype ♂, macropterous; Coimbatore, India; Drake Coll. (USNM).

DISTRIBUTION: India.

HOST PLANT: *Artocarpus integrifolia.*

*Stephanitis (Menodora) formosa Horváth

Stephanitis (Menodora) formosa Horváth 1912b, pp. 319, 324, fig. 1 [Taiwan].

Stephanitis formosa: Esaki 1926, p. 163.

TYPE: Sex unknown; Takao, Formosa; Hungarian Mus.

DISTRIBUTION: Taiwan.

HOST PLANT: Unrecorded.

*Stephanitis (Menodora) kardia Drake and Ruhoff

Stephanitis (Menodora) kardia Drake and Ruhoff 1960c, p. 36, fig. 5 a, b [Singapore].

TYPE: Holotype ♂, macropterous; Singapore; Drake Coll. (USNM).
DISTRIBUTION: Singapore.
HOST PLANT: Unrecorded.

*Stephanitis (Menodora) sondaica Horváth

Stephanitis (Menodora) sondaica Horváth 1912b, p. 338 [Java; *Musa sapientum*].—Takeya 1951a, p. 8 [Taiwan].
Stephanitis sondaica: Horváth 1912c, p. 341.

TYPE: Sex unknown; Muara Antjol near Batavia, Java; Hungarian Mus.
DISTRIBUTION: Greater Sunda Islands (Java); Taiwan.
HOST PLANT: *Musa paradisiaca sapientum*.

Subgenus STEPHANITIS (NORBA) Horváth

Stephanitis (Norba) Horváth 1912b, pp. 323, 334.—Takeya 1951a, p. 12.—Drake and Maa 1953, p. 100 (catalog).—Drake and Ruhoff 1960a, p. 83.

TYPE SPECIES: *Stephanitis (Norba) mendica* Horváth.

*Stephanitis (Norba) aperta Horváth

Stephanitis (Norba) aperta Horváth 1912b, pp. 323, 335 [Japan].—Takeya 1931, p. 75, pl. 7, fig. 4; pl. 9, fig. 1; 1951a, p. 13 [Taiwan; *Cinnamomum camphora; Machilus thunbergii*].
Stephanitis aperta: Maa 1957, pp. 127, 132.

TYPE: Sex unknown; Sakuna, Japan; Hungarian Mus.
DISTRIBUTION: Japan; Taiwan; China.
HOST PLANTS: *Cinnamomum camphora; Machilus thunbergii*.

*Stephanitis (Norba) astralis Drake and Poor

Stephanitis astralis Drake and Poor 1941, p. 164 [Amboina].

TYPE: Holotype ♂; Amboina Island; Cal. Acad.
DISTRIBUTION: Moluccas (Amboina Island).
HOST PLANT: Unrecorded.

*Stephanitis (Norba) chinensis Drake

Stephanitis (Norba) chinensis Drake 1948b, pp. 46, 48, 55, figs. 3, 4 [China; tea].

TYPE: Holotype ♂, macropterous; Meitanhsieh, Kweichow Province, China; Drake Coll. (USNM).
DISTRIBUTION: China.
HOST PLANT: Tea.

*Stephanitis (Norba) esakii Takeya

Stephanitis (Norba) esakii Takeya 1931, p. 72, pl. 8, figs. 7–10 [Taiwan; *Machilus thunbergii*].
Stephanitis (Norba) shintenana Drake 1948b, pp. 46, 48, 56.
Stephanitis esakii: Maa 1957, pp. 125, 132 [*Machilus; Tetradenia dolichocarpa*].

TYPE: Holotype ♂; Musha, Formosa; Kyushu Univ.
DISTRIBUTION: Taiwan.
HOST PLANTS: *Machilus thunbergii; Machilus* sp.; *Tetradenia dolichocarpa.*

*Stephanitis (Norba) exigua Horváth

Stephanitis (Norba) exigua Horváth 1912b, pp. 323, 336 [Okinawa; Japan; Lycopodiaceae].—Takeya 1953d, p. 168 [*Machilus thunbergii*].
Stephanitis (Norba) vitrea Takeya 1931, p. 74, pl. 7, fig. 3; pl. 8, figs. 11, 12.
Stephanitis exigua: Drake 1937b, p. 594 [China].

TYPE: Unknown.
DISTRIBUTION: Ryukyu Islands (Okinawa); Japan; China.
HOST PLANTS: *Machilus thunbergii;* Lycopodiaceae.

*Stephanitis (Norba) laratana Drake

Stephanitis (Norba) laratana Drake 1948b, pp. 46, 55 [Larat].

TYPE: Holotype ♂, macropterous; Larat; Drake Coll. (USNM).
DISTRIBUTION: Tanimbar Islands (Larat).
HOST PLANT: Unrecorded.

*Stephanitis (Norba) macaona Drake

Stephanitis (Norba) macaona Drake 1948b, pp. 46, 47, 55 [China].

TYPE: Holotype ♂, macropterous; Macao, Kwangtung Province, China; Drake Coll. (USNM).
DISTRIBUTION: China.
HOST PLANT: Unrecorded.

*Stephanitis (Norba) mendica Horváth

Stephanitis (Norba) mendica Horváth 1912b, pp. 323, 334 [Japan].—Takeya 1931, p. 77, pl. 9, figs. 2–6 [*Cinnamomum pedunculatum*].

TYPE: Sex unknown; Japan; Hungarian Mus.
DISTRIBUTION: Japan.
HOST PLANT: *Cinnamomum pedunculatum.*

*Stephanitis (Norba) nitor Drake and Poor (emendation)

Stephanitis nitoris Drake and Poor 1937a, p. 17 [Luzon; Negros]; 1937b, p. 403 [*Uvaria rufa*].

TYPE: Holotype ♂, macropterous; Mount Maquiling, Laguna Province, Luzon, Philippine Islands; USNM.
DISTRIBUTION: Philippine Islands (Luzon; Negros); Greater Sunda Islands (Borneo).
HOST PLANT: *Uvaria rufa.*

*Stephanitis (Norba) outouana Drake and Maa

Stephanitis (Norba) outouana Drake and Maa 1953, p. 97 [China].

TYPE: Holotype ♂, macropterous; Outou, Kienyang Hsien, Fukien, China; Drake Coll. (USNM).

DISTRIBUTION: China.

HOST PLANT: Unrecorded.

*Stephanitis (Norba) pagana Drake and Maa

Stephanitis (Norba) pagana Drake and Maa 1953, p. 98 [China].

TYPE: Holotype ♂, macropterous; Tsinleong Shan, E. Kwangtung, China; Drake Coll. (USNM).

DISTRIBUTION: China.

HOST PLANT: Unrecorded.

*Stephanitis (Norba) sordida Distant

Stephanitis sordidus Distant 1909a, p. 114 [Burma]; 1910a, p. 109.

Stephanitis sordida: Horváth 1912b, p. 338.

Stephanitis (Stephanitis) sordida: Drake and Maa 1953, p. 101.

Stephanitis (Norba) sordida: Drake and Maa 1954, p. 116.

TYPE: Sex unknown; Tenasserim, Merqui, Burma; British Mus.

DISTRIBUTION: Burma.

HOST PLANT: Unrecorded.

*Stephanitis (Norba) suffusa (Distant)

Cadamustus suffusus Distant 1903a, p. 47 [Ceylon]; 1903b, p. 133 [Burma].

Stephanitis suffusa: Horváth 1912b, p. 338.

Stephanitis (Norba) bankana Drake 1948b, pp. 46, 47, 54 [Bangka; China; Persea gratissima].

Stephanitis (Stephanitis) suffusa: Drake and Maa 1953, p. 101.

Stephanitis (Norba) suffusa: Drake and Maa 1954, p. 116.

TYPE: Sex unknown; Matale, Ceylon; British Mus.

DISTRIBUTION: Ceylon; Burma; China; Bangka Island.

HOST PLANT: *Persea gratissima.*

Subgenus STEPHANITIS (OMOPLAX) Horváth

Stephanitis (Omoplax) Horváth 1912b, pp. 323, 336.—Takeya 1951a, p. 14.—Drake and Maa 1953, p. 100 (catalog).—Drake and Ruhoff 1960a, p. 83.

TYPE SPECIES: *Stephanitis (Omoplax) desecta* Horváth.

*Stephanitis (Omoplax) desecta Horváth

Stephanitis (Omoplax) desecta Horváth 1912b, pp. 323, 337, fig. 3 [Japan].— Drake 1956d, p. 116, fig. 8.

TYPE: Sex unknown; Ogasawara, Japan; Hungarian Mus.

DISTRIBUTION: Japan.

HOST PLANT: Unrecorded.

Genus STYMNONOTUS Reuter

Stymnonotus Reuter 1887, p. 103.—Drake and Ruhoff 1960a, p. 83.
TYPE SPECIES: *Stymnonotus apicalis* Reuter.

Stymnonotus apicalis Reuter

Stymnonotus apicalis Reuter 1887, p. 104 [Malagasy].—Lethierry and Severin 1896, p. 13.
TYPE: Holotype ♂; Nossibé, Madagascar; Frankfort Mus.
DISTRIBUTION: Malagasy Republic.
HOST PLANT: Unrecorded.

Genus TANYBYRSA Drake

Tanybyrsa Drake 1942a, p. 21.—Drake and Ruhoff 1960a, p. 83.
TYPE SPECIES: *Compseuta secundus* Hacker.

*Tanybyrsa ampliata (Hacker)

Compseuta ampliatus Hacker 1927, p. 26, pl. 7, fig. 5 [Queensland].
Tanybyrsa ampliata: Drake 1942a, p. 21; 1961b, p. 112.
TYPE: Sex unknown; Southport, Queensland, Australia; Queensland Mus.
DISTRIBUTION: Australia (Queensland).
HOST PLANT: Unrecorded.

Tanybyrsa cumberi Drake

Tanybyrsa cumberi Drake 1959, p. 67, fig. 1 [New Zealand].
TYPE: Holotype ♂; Arapae, Te Kuiti-Tawaro Range, Waitomo County, New Zealand; Entomology Division, Dept. Scientific and Industrial Research, Nelson, New Zealand.
DISTRIBUTION: New Zealand.
HOST PLANT: Unrecorded.

*Tanybyrsa secunda (Hacker)

Compseuta secundus Hacker 1927, p. 27, pl. 7, fig. 6 [Queensland; New South Wales].
Tanybyrsa secunda: Drake 1942a, p. 21.
TYPE: Sex unknown; Australia; Queensland Mus.
DISTRIBUTION: Australia (Queensland; New South Wales).
HOST PLANT: Unrecorded.

Genus TANYTINGIS Drake

Tanytingis Drake 1939b, p. 205.—Drake and Ruhoff 1960a, p. 83.
TYPE SPECIES: *Tanytingis takahashii* Drake.

*Tanytingis assamana Drake and Lutz

Tanytingis assamana Drake and Lutz 1953, p. 105 [India].

TYPE: Holotype ♂, macropterous; Shillong, Assam, India; Drake Coll. (USNM).

DISTRIBUTION: India.

HOST PLANT: Unrecorded.

*Tanytingis takahashii Drake

Tanytingis takahashii Drake 1939b, p. 206 [Taiwan].—Takeya 1951a, p. 17.

TYPE: Holotype ♂; Buta, Taihoku-shu, Formosa; Kyushu Univ.

DISTRIBUTION: Taiwan.

HOST PLANT: Unrecorded.

Genus TELEONEMIA Costa

Teleonemia Costa 1864, p. 144.—Stål 1873, pp. 122, 131.—Uhler 1886, p. 22.—Lethierry and Severin 1896, p. 22.—Champion 1898a, p. 34 (key).—Banks 1910, p. 57.—Van Duzee 1916, p. 26; 1917b, p. 221.—Drake 1918b, pp. 323–332 (key).—Horváth 1925b, p. 219.—Blatchley 1926, p. 487 (key).—Monte 1939b, p. 79; 1941e, p. 133.—Hurd 1946, p. 447.—Drake and Ruhoff 1960a, p. 84.

Tingis (Amaurosterphus) Stål 1868, p. 92.

Teleonemia (Amaurosterphus): Stål 1873, p. 131.—Drake and Ruhoff 1960a, p. 35.

Tingis (Americia) Stål 1873, p. 131.—Drake and Ruhoff 1960a, p. 36.

TYPE SPECIES: *Teleonemia funerea* Costa.

*Teleonemia abdita Drake

Teleonemia abdita Drake 1939d, p. 527 [Brazil].

TYPE: Holotype ♂; Rio de Janeiro, Brazil; Stockholm Mus.

DISTRIBUTION: Brazil.

HOST PLANT: Unrecorded.

*Teleonemia absimilis Drake and Hambleton

Teleonemia absimilis Drake and Hambleton 1944b, p. 122 [Colombia].

TYPE: Holotype ♀, macropterous; Villa Vicenzio, Colombia; Drake Coll. (USNM).

DISTRIBUTION: Colombia.

HOST PLANT: Unrecorded.

*Teleonemia aemula Monte

Teleonemia aemula Monte 1942b, p. 137, fig. 2 [Brazil].

TYPE: Holotype ♀; Nova Teutonia, Santa Catarina, Brazil; Monte Coll. (Mus. Nacional).

DISTRIBUTION: Brazil.

HOST PLANT: Unrecorded.

*Teleonemia altilis Drake and Hambleton

Teleonemia altilis Drake and Hambleton 1944b, p. 122 [Bolivia].

TYPE: Holotype ♀, macropterous; Las Juntas, Bolivia; Drake Coll. (USNM).

DISTRIBUTION: Bolivia.

HOST PLANT: Unrecorded.

Teleonemia amazonica Horváth

Teleonemia (Americia) amazonica Horváth 1925b, p. 220 [Brazil].

TYPE: Holotype ♀; Manáos, Brazil; Hungarian Mus.

DISTRIBUTION: Brazil.

HOST PLANT: Unrecorded.

Teleonemia angustata Monte

Teleonemia angustata Monte 1943d, p. 268 [Brazil].

TYPE: Holotype ♂; Belo Horizonte, Minas Gerais, Brazil; Monte Coll. (Mus. Nacional).

DISTRIBUTION: Brazil.

HOST PLANT: Unrecorded.

*Teleonemia annae (Kirkaldy)

Americia annae Kirkaldy 1905, p. 216 [Peru].

Teleonemia annae: Drake and Hambleton 1938b, p. 52 [Brazil].

TYPE: Holotype ♀, macropterous; Marcapata, Peru; Drake Coll. (USNM).

DISTRIBUTION: Peru; Brazil.

HOST PLANT: Unrecorded.

*Teleonemia argentinensis Drake and Poor

Teleonemia argentinensis Drake and Poor 1942, p. 300 [Argentina].

TYPE: Holotype ♂; Estacion Experimental de Loreto, Misiones, Argentina; Argentina Mus.

DISTRIBUTION: Argentina.

HOST PLANT: Unrecorded.

*Teleonemia aterrima Stål

Teleonemia aterrima Stål 1873, p. 131 [Colombia].—Champion 1898b, p. 62, pl. 3, fig. 3 [Brazil].—Drake 1922c, p. 356 [Peru]; 1930b, p. 25.—Drake and Poor 1937d, p. 303, pl. 36, fig. 15.—Drake and Hambleton 1938b, p. 52.—Blöte 1945, p. 89.—Silva 1956, p. 51, fig. 19.

TYPE: Holotype ♂; Bogota, Nova Granada; Stockholm Mus.

DISTRIBUTION: Colombia; Brazil; Peru.

HOST PLANT: Unrecorded.

*Teleonemia atrata Champion

> *Teleonemia atrata* Champion 1898a, p. 38, pl. 3, fig. 7 [Panama].—
> Osborn and Drake 1915b, p. 536 [Guatemala].—Hurd 1946, p. 448
> [Brazil].

TYPE: Holotype ♀; Bugaba, Panama; British Mus.

DISTRIBUTION: Panama; Guatemala; Brazil.

HOST PLANT: Unrecorded.

Teleonemia atriflava Monte

> *Teleonemia atriflava* Monte 1943b, p. 204 [Argentina].

TYPE: Holotype ♀; El Dorado, Misiones, Argentina; Monte Coll. (Mus. Nacional).

DISTRIBUTION: Argentina.

HOST PLANT: Unrecorded.

*Teleonemia bahiana Drake

> *Teleonemia bahiana* Drake 1942a, p. 1 [Brazil]; 1947a, p. 1.—Silva
> 1956, p. 51.

TYPE: Holotype ♀, macropterous; Bahia, Brazil; Drake Coll. (USNM).

DISTRIBUTION: Brazil.

HOST PLANT: Unrecorded.

*Teleonemia barberi Drake

> *Teleonemia barberi* Drake 1918b, pp. 325, 328 [Ariz.; Tex.; *Chilopsis*].

TYPE: Holotype ♀, macropterous; Huachuca Mountains, Arizona, U.S.; USNM.

DISTRIBUTION: U.S. (Ariz.; Tex.).

HOST PLANT: *Chilopsis* sp.

*Teleonemia belfragii Stål

> *Teleonemia belfragii* Stål 1873, p. 132 [Tex.].—Champion 1898b, p. 62,
> pl. 3, fig. 8.—Van Duzee 1909, p. 173 [Fla.].—Drake 1926b, p.
> 376.—Hurd 1946, p. 448 [Miss.; Ala.].
> *Teleonemia belfragei* [sic]: Lethierry and Severin 1896, p. 22.—Drake
> 1918b, p. 331 [*Callicarpa americana*].—Blatchley 1926, p. 490.
> *Telconemia belfragei* [sic]: Barber 1914, p. 507.

TYPE: Holotype ♀; Texas, U.S.; Stockholm Mus.

DISTRIBUTION: U.S. (Tex.; Miss.; Ala.; Fla.).

HOST PLANT: *Callicarpa americana*.

Teleonemia bierigi Monte

> *Teleonemia bierigi* Monte 1943d, p. 269 [Costa Rica].

TYPE: Holotype ♂; La Perla, Costa Rica; Monte Coll. (Mus. Nacional).

DISTRIBUTION: Costa Rica.

HOST PLANT: Unrecorded.

*Teleonemia bifasciata Champion

> *Teleonemia bifasciata* Champion 1898a, p. 38, pl. 3, figs. 8, 8a [Guatemala; Panama].—Drake and Bruner 1924a, p. 145 [Grenada].—Drake and Hambleton 1940, p. 534 [Brazil].—Hurd 1946, p. 448 [*Lantana*].

TYPE: Sex unknown; Bugaba, Panama; British Mus.

DISTRIBUTION: Brazil; Panama; Guatemala; Windward Islands (Grenada).

HOST PLANT: *Lantana* sp.

*Teleonemia boliviana Drake

> *Teleonemia boliviana* Drake 1939d, p. 528 [Bolivia; Peru].

TYPE: Holotype ♂; San Antonio, Bolivia; Stockholm Mus.

DISTRIBUTION: Bolivia; Peru.

HOST PLANT: Unrecorded.

Teleonemia bondari Monte

> *Teleonemia bondari* Monte 1943d, p. 270 [Brazil].

TYPE: Holotype ♂; Belo Horizonte, Minas Gerais, Brazil; Monte Coll. (Mus. Nacional).

DISTRIBUTION: Brazil.

HOST PLANT: Unrecorded.

*Teleonemia bosqi Monte

> *Teleonemia bosqi* Monte 1943b, p. 202, fig. [Argentina].

TYPE: Holotype ♂; El Dorado, Misiones, Argentina; Monte Coll. (Mus. Nacional).

DISTRIBUTION: Argentina.

HOST PLANT: Unrecorded.

*Teleonemia brevipennis Champion

> *Teleonemia brevipennis* Champion 1898b, p. 63, pl. 3, fig. 9 [Brazil].— Drake 1922c, p. 357 [Peru]; 1929, p. 35; 1930a, p. 1.—Drake and Hambleton 1934, p. 438 [*Cassia*]; 1938a, p. 45 [*Vernonia polyanthes*].— Costa Lima 1936, p. 130.—Monte 1938d, p. 390 [Argentina]; 1939b, p. 79 [Venezuela]; 1940c, p. 191; 1940d, p. 101.—Drake and Poor 1939b, p. 96 [*Buddleia*].—Silva 1956, p. 51, fig. 20 [*Ipomoea fistulosa*].
> *Teleonemia brevicornis* [sic]: Drake 1935, p. 10 [Paraguay].

TYPE: Holotype ♀; Amazons, Brazil; British Mus.

DISTRIBUTION: Brazil; Argentina; Peru; Paraguay; Venezuela.

HOST PLANTS: *Buddleia* sp.; *Cassia* sp.; *Ipomoea fistulosa; Vernonia polyanthes.*

*Teleonemia carmelana (Berg)

> *Leptostyla carmelana* Berg 1892, p. 99 [Uruguay].
> *Cantacader chilensis* Reed 1900, p. 180 [Chile].
> *Teleonemia (Cantacader) chiliensis* [sic]: Drake 1922b, p. 50.
> *Teleonemia chilensis:* Drake 1922c, p. 358 [Brazil; Argentina]; 1935, p. 10 [Peru; Paraguay]; 1936b, p. 699.

Teleonemia jensoni Bergroth 1922, p. 150.
Teleonemia carmelana: Drake 1935, p. 11; 1939c, p. 332 [Bolivia].— Drake and Poor 1938b, p. 107.—Monte 1938d, p. 390; 1941e, p. 135 [*Lantana*]; 1947b, p. 432 [*Lippia juncea; Rhaphithamnus spinosus*].

TYPE: Sex unknown; Uruguay; La Plata Mus.

DISTRIBUTION: Uruguay; Paraguay; Peru; Argentina; Chile; Brazil; Bolivia.

HOST PLANTS: *Lantana* sp.; *Lippia juncea; Rhaphithamnus spinosus.*

*Teleonemia chacoana Drake

Teleonemia chacoana Drake 1942a, p. 1 [Paraguay].

TYPE: Holotype ♀, macropterous; Chaco, Paraguay; Drake Coll. (USNM).

DISTRIBUTION: Paraguay.

HOST PLANT: Unrecorded.

Teleonemia chapadiana Drake

Teleonemia chapadiana Drake 1922c, p. 356 [Brazil].

TYPE: Holotype ♀; Chapada, Brazil; Carnegie Mus.

DISTRIBUTION: Brazil.

HOST PLANT: Unrecorded.

*Teleonemia consors Drake

Teleonemia consors Drake 1918b, pp. 324, 327 [Ariz.].

TYPE: Holotype ♀, macropterous; Bonita, Post Creek Can., Arizona, U.S.; Drake Coll. (USNM).

DISTRIBUTION: U.S. (Ariz.).

HOST PLANT: Unrecorded.

Teleonemia crassispinosa Monte

Teleonemia crassispinosa Monte 1946b, p. 285 [Brazil].—Silva 1956, p. 54.

TYPE: Holotype ♂; Agua Preta, Baía, Brazil; Monte Coll. (Mus. Nacional).

DISTRIBUTION: Brazil.

HOST PLANT: Unrecorded.

*Teleonemia cylindricornis Champion

Teleonemia cylindricornis Champion 1898a, p. 41, pl. 3, figs. 14, 14a [Guatemala; British Honduras].—Van Duzee 1907, p. 22 [Jamaica]. —Drake 1925c, p. 38 [Miss.; Ill.].—Blatchley 1926, p. 488.— Froeschner 1944, p. 669.

TYPE: Sex unknown; San Geronimo, Vera Paz, Guatemala; British Mus.

DISTRIBUTION: Jamaica; British Honduras; Guatemala; Mexico; U.S. (Miss.; Ill.).

HOST PLANT: Unrecorded.

*Teleonemia dulcis Drake

Teleonemia dulcis Drake 1939d, p. 525 [Brazil].

TYPE: Holotype ♀, macropterous; Belém, Pará, Brazil; Drake Coll. (USNM).

DISTRIBUTION: Brazil.

HOST PLANT: Unrecorded.

*Teleonemia elata Drake

Teleonemia chilensis var. *elata* Drake 1935, p. 10 [Brazil; Paraguay].— Drake and Poor 1938b, p. 107 [Chile; Peru].—Monte 1939b, p. 79 [*Lantana*].

Teleonemia elata: Monte 1942b, p. 138.

TYPE: Holotype ♂; Rio Grande do Sul, Brazil; Vienna Mus.

DISTRIBUTION: Brazil; Paraguay; Chile; Peru.

HOST PLANT: *Lantana* sp.

Teleonemia elevata (Fabricius)

Aradus elevatus Fabricius 1803, p. 120.

Tingis (*Tropidocheila*) *elevata:* Stål 1868, p. 91.

Tingis elevata: Walker 1873a, p. 181 [South America].

Monanthia elevata: Walker 1873a, p. 191.

Teleonemia elevata: Stål 1873, p. 132.

TYPE: Lectotype ♀, macropterous; "Americae meridionalis"; Copenhagen Mus.

DISTRIBUTION: Uncertain, possibly South America.

HOST PLANT: Unrecorded.

*Teleonemia forticornis Champion

Teleonemia forticornis Champion 1898a, p. 36, pl. 3, fig. 5 [Panama].— Drake and Hambleton 1938b, p. 52 [Brazil; Peru; Argentina].— Drake and Poor 1939b, p. 95.—Monte 1939b, p. 79 [*Ipomoea batatas*].

TYPE: Holotype ♂; Bugaba, Panama; British Mus.

DISTRIBUTION: Panama; Brazil; Peru; Argentina.

HOST PLANT: *Ipomoea batatas.*

*Teleonemia funerea Costa

Teleonemia funerea Costa 1864, p. 145, pl. 2, fig. 5.—Stål 1873, p. 132.— Drake and Hambleton 1938b, p. 52 [Brazil].

Monanthia funerea: Walker 1873a, p. 197.

TYPE: Unknown.

DISTRIBUTION: Brazil.

HOST PLANT: Unrecorded.

NOTE: Type specimen apparently lost [Drake and Hambleton].

Teleonemia granulosa Monte

Teleonemia granulosa Monte 1942b, p. 139 [Argentina].

TYPE: Holotype ♂; San Javier, Misiones, Argentina; Monte Coll. (Mus. Nacional).

DISTRIBUTION: Argentina.

HOST PLANT: Unrecorded.

*Teleonemia guyanensis Drake and Carvalho

Teleonemia guyanensis Drake and Carvalho 1944, p. 41 [British Guiana].

TYPE: Holotype ♀, macropterous; Mallali, British Guiana; Drake Coll. (USNM).

DISTRIBUTION: British Guiana.

HOST PLANT: Unrecorded.

*Teleonemia hasemani Drake

Teleonemia hasemani Drake 1922c, p. 357 [Brazil].

TYPE: Holotype ♀; São Antonio de Guaporé, Brazil; Carnegie Mus.

DISTRIBUTION: Brazil.

HOST PLANT: Unrecorded.

*Teleonemia huachucae Drake

Teleonemia huachucae Drake 1941b, p. 140 [Ariz.].

TYPE: Holotype ♂; Huachuca Mountains, Arizona, U.S.; Cal. Acad.

DISTRIBUTION: U.S. (Ariz.).

HOST PLANT: *Anisacanthus thurberi.*

*Teleonemia inops Drake and Hambleton

Teleonemia inops Drake and Hambleton 1944b, p. 122 [Honduras].

TYPE: Holotype ♂, macropterous; La Ceiba, Honduras; Drake Coll. (USNM).

DISTRIBUTION: Honduras.

HOST PLANT: Unrecorded.

Teleonemia inornata Monte

Teleonemia inornata Monte 1941a, p. 377 [Bolivia].

TYPE: Holotype ♂; Caranavi, Coroico, Nor Yungas, Bolivia; Monte Coll. (Mus. Nacional).

DISTRIBUTION: Bolivia.

HOST PLANT: Unrecorded.

Teleonemia jamaicans Hurd (nom. nud.)

Teleonemia jamaicans Hurd 1946, p. 448.

*Teleonemia jubata Drake and Hambleton

Teleonemia jubata Drake and Hambleton 1939, p. 153 [Brazil].

TYPE: Holotype ♀, macropterous; Belo Horizonte, Minas Gerais, Brazil; Drake Coll. (USNM).

DISTRIBUTION: Brazil.

HOST PLANT: Unrecorded.

*Teleonemia jucunda Drake

Teleonemia jucunda Drake 1939d, p. 526 [Brazil; French Guiana; British Guiana]; 1947a, p. 1.—Silva 1956, p. 54.

TYPE: Holotype ♂, macropterous; Bahia, Brazil; Drake Coll. (USNM).

DISTRIBUTION: Brazil; French Guiana; British Guiana.

HOST PLANT: Unrecorded.

*Teleonemia leitei Drake and Hambleton

Teleonemia leitei Drake and Hambleton 1939, p. 153 [Brazil; Pithecoctenium echinatum].

TYPE: Holotype ♂, macropterous; São Paulo, Brazil; Drake Coll. (USNM).

DISTRIBUTION: Brazil.

HOST PLANT: Pithecoctenium echinatum.

*Teleonemia limbata (Stål)

Tingis (Americia) limbata Stål 1873, p. 131 [Brazil; Colombia].
Lasiacantha (Americia) limbata: Lethierry and Severin 1896, p. 19.
Teleonemia limbata: Champion 1898b, p. 62, pl. 3, fig. 10.—Drake 1922c, p. 356; 1930a, p. 1; 1935, p. 10 [Paraguay]; 1936b, p. 699 [Argentina].—Drake and Poor 1937d, p. 302.—Drake and Hambleton 1938b, p. 52.—Monte 1939b, p. 79 [Lantana camara]; 1940c, p. 191.

TYPE: Unknown.

DISTRIBUTION: Brazil; Paraguay; Argentina; Colombia; Venezuela.

HOST PLANT: Lantana camara.

Teleonemia longicornis Champion

Teleonemia longicornis Champion 1898b, p. 62, pl. 3, fig. 7 [Brazil].—Drake 1930, p. 1.

TYPE: Holotype ♂; Amazons; Oxford Mus.

DISTRIBUTION: Brazil.

HOST PLANT: Unrecorded.

*Teleonemia luctuosa (Stål)

Laccometopus luctuosus Stål 1858, p. 65 [Brazil].
Tingis (Amaurosterphus) luctuosus: Stål 1868, p. 92.
Monanthia luctuosa: Walker 1873a, p. 193.
Teleonemia luctuosa: Stål 1873, p. 132.—Champion 1898b, p. 62, pl. 3, fig. 5.—Drake 1935, p. 9 [Paraguay].—Drake and Poor 1937d, p. 303.—Drake and Hambleton 1938b, p. 52.

TYPE: Holotype ♂; Rio de Janeiro, Brazil; Stockholm Mus.

DISTRIBUTION: Brazil; Paraguay.

HOST PLANT: Unrecorded.

Teleonemia lustrabilis Drake

Teleonemia lustrabilis Drake 1953c, p. 151 [Dominican Republic].

TYPE: Holotype ♀; Constanza, Dominican Republic; MCZ.

DISTRIBUTION: Dominican Republic.

HOST PLANT: Unrecorded.

*Teleonemia lutzi Drake

Teleonemia lutzi Drake 1941b, p. 139 [Paraguay].

TYPE: Holotype ♂, macropterous; Horqueta, Paraguay; Drake Coll. (USNM).

DISTRIBUTION: Paraguay; Brazil.

HOST PLANT: Unrecorded.

*Teleonemia mera Drake and Hambleton

Teleonemia mera Drake and Hambleton 1942b, p. 76 [Brazil].

TYPE: Holotype ♂, macropterous; Santarem, Brazil; Drake Coll. (USNM).

DISTRIBUTION: Brazil.

HOST PLANT: Unrecorded.

*Teleonemia molinae Drake

Teleonemia molinae Drake 1940b, p. 243 [Paraguay].

TYPE: Holotype ♂, macropterous; Horqueta, Paraguay; Drake Coll. (USNM).

DISTRIBUTION: Paraguay.

HOST PLANT: Unrecorded.

*Teleonemia monile Van Duzee

Teleonemia monile Van Duzee 1918, p. 279 [Calif.].

TYPE: Holotype ♂; Lundy, Mono County, California, U.S.; Cal. Acad.

DISTRIBUTION: U.S. (Calif.).

HOST PLANT: Unrecorded.

*Teleonemia montivaga Drake

Teleonemia montivaga Drake 1920, p. 52 [Calif.].—Hurd 1946, p. 448 [*Penstemon*].

TYPE: Holotype ♀, macropterous; Mount Diablo, California, U.S.; Drake Coll. (USNM).

DISTRIBUTION: U.S. (Calif.).

HOST PLANT: *Penstemon* sp.

*Teleonemia morio (Stål)

Tropidocheila morio Stål 1855b, p. 187 [Brazil].

Laccometopus morio: Stål 1858, p. 65.

Tingis (Amaurosterphus) morio: Stål 1868, p. 92.

Monanthia morio: Walker 1873a, p. 193.

Teleonemia (Amaurosterphus) morio: Stål 1873, p. 131.—Horváth 1925b, p. 219.

Teleonemia morio: Champion 1898b, p. 62, pl. 3, fig. 2.—Drake 1922c, p. 356; 1930b, p. 25.—Drake and Hambleton 1934, p. 438 [*Annona squamosa*].—Costa Lima 1936, p. 130.—Drake and Poor 1937d, p. 302 [Paraguay].—Bondar 1936, p. 51, figs. a, b [*Annona cherimolia*].—Silva 1956, p. 56, fig. 22.

Teleonemia moria [sic]: Monte 1938b, p. 131 [*Annona reticulata*].

TYPE: Sex unknown; Brazil; Stockholm Mus.

DISTRIBUTION: Brazil; Paraguay.

HOST PLANTS: *Annona cherimola; Annona reticulata; Annona squamosa.*

NOTE: Bondar states this species attacks exclusively the new bark of branches and twigs.

Teleonemia multimaculata Monte

Teleonemia multimaculata Monte 1940e, p. 298 [Brazil].

TYPE: Holotype ♀; Fazenda do Bosque, Cordeiro, Limeira, São Paulo, Brazil; Monte Coll. (Mus. Nacional).

DISTRIBUTION: Brazil.

HOST PLANT: Unrecorded.

*Teleonemia nigrina Champion

Teleonemia nigrina Champion 1898a, p. 41, pl. 3, figs. 13, 13 a, b [Tex.; Mexico; Guatemala].—Uhler 1904, p. 362 [N. Mex.].—Barber 1906, p. 281; 1922a, p. 17; 1922b, p. 23.—Van Duzee 1914, p. 11 [Calif.; *Rhus laurina*]; 1917a, p. 261.—Drake 1918b, pp. 324, 325 [Ariz.; Kans.; Utah; Mo.; Ark.; Ga.; N.C.; S.C.; *Verbena; Sphaeralcea angustifolia; Adenostegia pilosa; Adenostegia filifolia; Helenium tenuifolium;* sugar beets]; 1938a, p. 70.—Blatchley 1926, p. 488, fig. 115.—Hixson 1942, p. 605, fig. 1 [snapdragon].—Froeschner 1944, p. 669 [*Plantago aristata*].—Hurd 1946, p. 448 [*Eriogonum*].

Teleonemia elongata Uhler 1886, p. 22 (nom. nud.).—Smith 1910, p. 149.—Van Duzee 1917b, p. 222.

TYPE: Sex unknown; Duenas, Guatemala; British Mus.

DISTRIBUTION: Mexico; Guatemala; U.S. (Calif.; Ariz.; N. Mex.; Tex.; Okla.; Utah; Kans.; Iowa; Mo.; Ark.; Ga.; S.C.; N.C.; Va.; N.J.).

HOST PLANTS: *Adenostegia filifolia; Adenostegia pilosa; Eriogonum* sp.; *Helenium tenuifolium; Plantago aristata; Rhus laurina; Sphaeralcea angustifolia; Verbena* sp.; sugar beets; snapdragon.

*Teleonemia notata Champion

Teleonemia notata Champion 1898a, p. 40, pl. 3, figs. 11, 11 a, b [Mexico; Guatemala; Panama].—Perkins and Swezey 1924, p. 52 [*Lantana*].—Monte 1942a, p. 97 [Cuba].—Bruner, Scaramuzza and Otero 1945, p. 69 [*Duranta repens*].—Hurd 1946, p. 448 [*Adenostegia filifolia; Adenostegia pilosa*].

TYPE: Sex unknown; El Tumbador, Guatemala; British Mus.

DISTRIBUTION: Guatemala; Mexico; Panama; Cuba.

HOST PLANTS: *Adenostegia filifolia; Adenostegia pilosa; Duranta repens; Lantana* sp.

*Teleonemia novicia Drake

Teleonemia novicia Drake 1920, p. 53 [Calif.].—Hurd 1946, p. 448 [Ariz.].

TYPE: Holotype ♀, macropterous; Oriocle, California, U.S.; Drake Coll. (USNM).

DISTRIBUTION: U.S. (Calif.; Ariz.).

HOST PLANT: Unrecorded.

Teleonemia ochracea Champion

Teleonemia ochracea Champion 1898a, p. 36, pl. 3, fig. 3 [Panama].

TYPE: Holotype ♂; Volcan de Chiriqui, Panama; British Mus.

DISTRIBUTION: Panama.

HOST PLANT: Unrecorded.

*Teleonemia paraguayana Drake

Teleonemia paraguayana Drake 1942a, p. 2 [Paraguay].

TYPE: Holotype ♀, macropterous; Horqueta, Paraguay; Drake Coll. (USNM).

DISTRIBUTION: Paraguay.

HOST PLANT: Unrecorded.

*Teleonemia patagonica Drake

Teleonemia patagonica Drake 1948j, p. 429 [Argentina].

TYPE: Holotype ♀, macropterous; Rio Santa, Patagonia, Argentina; Drake Coll. (USNM).

DISTRIBUTION: Argentina.

HOST PLANT: Unrecorded.

*Teleonemia picta Champion

Teleonemia picta Champion 1898a, p. 42, pl. 3, figs. 16, 16a [Panama].

TYPE: Sex unknown; Caldera, Panama; British Mus.

DISTRIBUTION: Panama.

HOST PLANT: Unrecorded.

*Teleonemia pilicornis Champion

Teleonemia pilicornis Champion 1898a, p. 37, pl. 3, fig. 6 [Guatemala].

TYPE: Holotype ♂; Zapote, Guatemala; British Mus.

DISTRIBUTION: Guatemala.

HOST PLANT: Unrecorded.

*Teleonemia prolixa (Stål)

Laccometopus prolixus Stål 1858, p. 65 [Brazil].

Monanthia (Tropidochila) sacchari (not Fabricius): Stål 1862, p. 325.

Tingis (Amaurosterphus) prolixa: Stål 1868, p. 92.

Monanthia prolixa: Walker 1873a, p. 193.

Teleonemia prolixa: Stål 1873, p. 132.—Berg 1884, p. 103 [Argentina].—
Champion 1898a, p. 39, pl. 3, figs. 9a, b, 10 [Mexico; Guatemala;
Panama]; 1898b, p. 62, pl. 3, fig. 6.—Van Duzee 1907, p. 22 [Jamaica;
British Guiana].—Pennington 1921, p. 20.—Drake and Bruner 1924a,
p. 145 [Trinidad].—Drake 1929, p. 35 [Surinam; Ecuador]; 1930a,
p. 1; 1931b, p. 510 [Peru]; 1932, p. 100 [Barro Colorado]; 1935, p. 9
[Paraguay]; 1936b, p. 699.—Drake and Hambleton 1934, p. 438;
1945, p. 357; 1946b, p. 122.—Drake and Poor 1937d, p. 304 [Co-
lombia]; 1938b, p. 105 [*Cinchona*].—Monte 1938d, p. 390; 1939b, p. 80
[*Lantana camara*]; 1940c, p. 191; 1940d, p. 101 [Venezuela].—Ramos
1946, p. 25 [Mona].—Silva 1956, p. 58, fig. 23.—Gibson and Carrillo
1959, p. 19.
   Teleonemia prollixa [sic]: Gowdy 1926, p. 35.
TYPE: Holotype ♂; Rio de Janeiro, Brazil; Stockholm Mus.
DISTRIBUTION: Venezuela; Surinam; British Guiana; Brazil; Paraguay;
Argentina; Bolivia; Peru; Ecuador; Colombia; Panama; Canal Zone
(Barro Colorado); Guatemala; Mexico; Trinidad; Jamaica; Mona Island.
HOST PLANTS: *Acacia riparia; Cinchona* sp.; *Lantana camara.*

*Teleonemia prunellae Drake and Hambleton
   Teleonemia prunellae Drake and Hambleton 1946b, p. 122 [Guatemala;
   Prunella vulgaris].
TYPE: Holotype ♂, macropterous; Guatemala City, Guatemala; Drake
Coll. (USNM).
DISTRIBUTION: Guatemala.
HOST PLANT: *Prunella vulgaris.*

*Teleonemia quecha Monte
   Teleonemia quecha Monte 1943a, p. 106, fig. 2 [Peru].—Drake and
   Hambleton 1944b, p. 121 [Colombia]; 1945, p. 357.
TYPE: Holotype ♀; Peru; Monte Coll. (Mus. Nacional).
DISTRIBUTION: Peru; Colombia; Brazil.
HOST PLANT: Unrecorded.

*Teleonemia rugosa Champion
   Teleonemia rugosa Champion 1898a, p. 37, pl. 3, fig. 4 [Guatemala;
   Panama].—Drake 1928e, p. 2 [Honduras].
TYPE: Sex unknown; Panzos, Vera Paz, Guatemala; British Mus.
DISTRIBUTION: Guatemala; Honduras; Panama; Bolivia.
HOST PLANT: Unrecorded.

*Teleonemia ruthae Monte
   Teleonemia ruthae Monte 1942b, p. 136, fig. 1 [Brazil].
TYPE: Holotype ♂; Guarujá, Santos, São Paulo, Brazil; Monte Coll.
(Mus. Nacional).
DISTRIBUTION: Brazil.
HOST PLANT: Unrecorded.

*Teleonemia sacchari (Fabricius)

Acanthia sacchari Fabricius 1794, p. 77.

Tingis sacchari: Fabricius 1803, p. 126.—Guérin-Méneville 1857, p. 409 [Cuba; sugar].

Monanthia sacchari: Herrich-Schaeffer 1840, p. 85, pl. 173, fig. 533 [Brazil; Mexico].—Walker 1873a, p. 191.

Monanthia (Tropidocheila) sacchari: Fieber 1844, p. 76, pl. 6, figs. 22–25 [Martinique].—Herrich-Schaeffer 1850, p. 152.—Stål 1858, p. 62.

Tingis (Tropidocheila) sacchari: Stål 1868, p. 92.

Teleonemia sacchari: Stål 1873, p. 132 [St. Bartholemy].—Distant 1888, p. lxxxiii.—Uhler 1894a, p. 202 [Grenada]; 1894b, p. 278.— Champion 1898b, p. 62 [St. Vincent].—Van Duzee 1907, p. 22 [Jamaica].—Barber 1914, p. 507 [Fla.]; 1939, p. 371 [Antigua; St. Croix; St. Thomas].—Drake 1918b, p. 330; 1926a, p. 86 [*Lantana camara*]; 1931b, p. 510; 1932, p. 100 [Panama].—Wolcott 1923, p. 247 [Puerto Rico; *Verbesina*].—Blatchley 1926, p. 490.—Monte 1941e, p. 139 [Calif.].—Blöte 1945, p. 89 [Trinidad].—Bruner, Scaramuzza, and Otero 1945, p. 98 [*Lantana involucrata*].—Box 1953, p. 37.—Drake and Cobben 1960, p. 79, fig. 79c [St. Eustatius; Saba; St. Martin; *Lantana canescens*].

TYPE: Holotype ♂, macropterous; "Americae meridionalis Insulis"; Copenhagen Mus.

DISTRIBUTION: Brazil; Panama; Mexico; U.S. (Calif.; Fla.); Trinidad; Cuba; Jamaica; Puerto Rico; Windward Islands (Grenada; Martinique; St. Vincent); Virgin Islands (St. Croix; St. Thomas); Leeward Islands (Antigua; St. Martin; Saba; St. Eustatius; St. Bartholomy).

HOST PLANTS: *Lantana camara; Lantana canescens; Lantana involucrata; Verbesina* sp.; sugar.

*Teleonemia sandersi Drake and Hambleton

Teleonemia sandersi Drake and Hambleton 1944b, p. 123 [Canal Zone].— Hurd 1946, p. 448 [Honduras].

TYPE: Holotype ♂, macropterous; Panama Canal Zone; Drake Coll. (USNM).

DISTRIBUTION: Panama (Canal Zone); Honduras.

HOST PLANT: Unrecorded.

*Teleonemia schildi Drake

Teleonemia schildi Drake 1940b, p. 242 [Costa Rica].

TYPE: Holotype ♀, macropterous; Suiza tur'bla, Costa Rica; Drake Coll. (USNM).

DISTRIBUTION: Costa Rica.

HOST PLANT: Unrecorded.

*Teleonemia schwarzi Drake

Teleonemia schwarzi Drake 1918b, pp. 324, 326 [Calif.; Ariz.]; 1941b, p. 141 [*Beloperone californica*].—Hurd 1946, p. 448 [*Hymenoclea salsola*].

Teleonemia sororcula Van Duzee 1923, p. 142 [Baja Calif.].

TYPE: Holotype ♀, macropterous; San Diego, California, U.S.; USNM.

DISTRIBUTION: U.S. (Calif.; Ariz.); Mexico (Baja Calif.).

HOST PLANTS: *Beloperone californica; Hymenoclea salsola.*

*Teleonemia scrupulosa Stål

Teleonemia scrupulosa Stål 1873, p. 132 [Brazil; Colombia].—Distant 1888, p. lxxxiii.—Champion 1898a, p. 40, pl. 3, figs. 12, 12a [Mexico; Guatemala; Panama; Grenada; St. Vincent].—Barber 1906, p. 281 [Tex.]; 1914, p. 507 [Fla.].—Van Duzee 1907, p. 22 [Jamaica].— Drake 1918b, p. 329 [Haiti; *Callirhoe involucrata*]; 1926a, p. 86 [Cuba]; 1926b, p. 376; 1930b, p. 25; 1931b, p. 510; 1935, p. 10 [Paraguay]; 1956d, p. 108, fig. 3 [Ponape].—Drake and Burner 1924a, p. 145 [Trinidad].—Blatchley 1926, p. 489, fig. 114 [ebony].—Drake and Hambleton 1934, p. 438; 1944b, p. 123; 1945, p. 357.—Costa Lima 1936, p. 130.—Drake and Poor 1937d, p. 304; 1943, p. 192, fig. 1.— Monte 1938b, p. 131; 1940c, p. 191; 1942d, p. 109; 1944b, p. 459.— Drake and Frick 1939, p. 199, fig. 1 [Peru; British Guiana; French Guiana; Venezuela].—Currie and Fyfe 1939, p. 259.—Khan 1945, p. 149.—Bruner, Scaramuzza, and Otero 1945, p. 98.—Cashmore and Campbell 1946, p. 26.—Zimmerman 1948, p. 121, figs. 44, 45.—Fullaway 1951, p. 208 [*Xanthium; Lantana montevidensis*]; 1958, p. 550.—Roonwal 1952, p. 3, fig. 1.—Singh 1953, p. 119.—van der Vecht 1953, p. 170 [Java].—Maehler 1955, p. 377 [*Myoporum sandwicense*].—Silva 1956, p. 59, figs. 24, 25 [*Lantana brasiliensis*].— Orian 1956, p. 647 [Mauritius].—Drake and Cobben 1960, p. 73, figs. 79a, 81a [Aruba; Curaçao; Klein Bonaire; Bonaire; *Lantana canescens; Lippia alba*].—Štusak 1961, p. 77, fig. 5a.

Teleonemia bifasciata (not Champion): Kirkaldy 1905, p. 216.

Teleonemia lantanae Distant 1907, p. 60 [Hawaii].—Kirkaldy 1907, p. 154 [*Lantana camara*]; 1908d, p. 190.—Swezey 1924, p. 75, fig. 2.— Perkins and Swezey 1924, p. 52.—Simmonds 1929, p. 36, figs. 1–4 [Fiji].—Drake 1929, p. 35 [Costa Rica].—Fyfe 1935, p. 35; 1937, p. 182, pl. 1, figs. 1, 2 [Australia].—Van Duzee 1936, p. 225.—Beeson and Chatterjee 1940, pp. 42, 48 [*Lantana aculeata;* India].

Teleonemia vanduzeei Drake 1919c, p. 24.—Drake and Bruner 1924a, p. 144.—Blatchley 1926, p. 489.—Gowdy 1926, p. 35.—Krauss 1953, p. 123.

TYPE: Unknown.

DISTRIBUTION: Peru; Brazil; Paraguay; British Guiana; French Guiana; Venezuela; Colombia; U.S. (Tex.; Fla.; Hawaii); Cuba; Jamaica; Trinidad; Haiti; Windward Islands (Grenada; St. Vincent); Netherlands Antilles (Aruba; Curaçao; Klein Bonaire; Bonaire); Costa Rica; Panama; Mexico; Guatemala; Fiji Islands; Greater Sunda Islands (Java); Senyavin Islands (Ponape); Australia; India; Mascarene Islands (Mauritius).

HOST PLANTS: *Callirhoe involucrata; Lantana aculeata; Lantana brasiliensis; Lantana camara; Lantana canescens; Lantana montevidensis; Lippia alba; Myoporum sandwicense; Xanthium* sp.; ebony.

NOTE: Life history studies [Khan; Roonwal; Simmonds; Fyfe].

*Teleonemia scrupulosa var. haytiensis Drake

Teleonemia haytiensis Drake 1920, p. 53 [Haiti].—Drake and Bruner 1924a, p. 145; 1924b, p. 155 [Cuba].

Teleonemia scrupulosa var. *haytiensis:* Drake and Frick 1939, p. 201.

TYPE: Holotype ♀, macropterous; Port au Prince, Haiti; Drake Coll. (USNM).

DISTRIBUTION: Haiti; Cuba.

HOST PLANT: Unrecorded.

Teleonemia sidae (Fabricius)

Acanthia sidae Fabricius 1794, p. 77.

Tingis sidae: Fabricius 1803, p. 126.—Fieber 1844, p. 108.—Walker 1873a, p. 180 [West Indies].

Tingis (Tropidocheila) sidae: Stål 1868, p. 92.

Monanthia sidae: Walker 1873a, p. 121.

Teleonemia sidae: Stål 1873, p. 132.

Tropidocheila sidae: Uhler 1886, p. 22.

TYPE: Holotype ♂, macropterous; "Americae meridionalis Insulis Dom."; Kiel Mus. (Copenhagen Mus.).

DISTRIBUTION: Uncertain, possibly West Indies.

HOST PLANT: Unrecorded.

Teleonemia simillima Monte

Teleonemia simillima Monte 1941a, p. 376, fig. 3 [Brazil].

TYPE: Holotype ♂; Puerto America, Rio Putumayo; Monte Coll. (Mus. Nacional).

DISTRIBUTION: Brazil.

HOST PLANT: Unrecorded.

*Teleonemia simulans Drake

Teleonemia simulans Drake 1922c, p. 358 [Argentina]; 1928i, p. 72.—Drake and Poor 1938b, p. 106.—Monte 1940e, p. 298.

TYPE: Holotype ♀, macropterous; "El Gran Chaco, 'Bords du Rio Tapenaga, Colonia Florencia, S.A.' "; Drake Coll. (USNM).

DISTRIBUTION: Argentina.

HOST PLANT: Unrecorded.

*Teleonemia syssita Drake and Cobben

    Teleonemia syssita Drake and Cobben 1960, pp. 67, 75, figs. 79d, 80, 81b [St. Eustatius; Saba; St. Martin; *Lantana canescens*].

TYPE: Holotype ♂, macropterous; Cul de Sac, St. Martin; Drake Coll. (USNM).

DISTRIBUTION: Leeward Islands (St. Eustatius; Saba; St. Martin).

HOST PLANT: *Lantana canescens*.

*Teleonemia tellus Drake and Hambleton (emendation)

    Teleonemia telluris Drake and Hambleton 1939, p. 154 [Brazil].

TYPE: Holotype ♂, macropterous; Chapada, Mato Grosso, Brazil; Drake Coll. (USNM).

DISTRIBUTION: Brazil.

HOST PLANT: Unrecorded.

*Teleonemia teres Drake (emendation)

    Teleonemia teretis Drake 1940b, p. 242 [Brazil].

TYPE: Holotype ♀, macropterous; Chapada, Brazil; Drake Coll. (USNM).

DISTRIBUTION: Brazil.

HOST PLANT: Unrecorded.

*Teleonemia triangularis (Blanchard)

    Tingis triangularis Blanchard 1846, p. 219, pl. 29, fig. 10 [Bolivia].—Stål 1873, p. 134.—Lethierry and Severin 1896, p. 26.—Champion 1898a, p. 43.

    Laccometopus albilaterus Stål 1858, p. 65 [Brazil].

    Tingis (Americia) albilatera: Stål 1873, p. 131.

    Monanthia albilatera: Walker 1873a, p. 193.

    Lasiacantha (Americia) albilatera: Lethierry and Severin 1896, p. 18.

    Teleonemia triangularis: Champion 1898b, p. 61.—Drake 1922c, p. 359; 1935, p. 10 [Paraguay].—Drake and Poor 1937d, p. 302, pl. 36, fig. 14.—Drake and Hambleton 1938b, p. 53.—Monte 1940c, p. 190; 1941e, p. 141 [Argentina].—Silva 1956, p. 64, fig. 26.

TYPE: Holotype ♀; Province de Chiquitos, Bolivia; Paris Mus.

DISTRIBUTION: Bolivia; Paraguay; Argentina; Brazil.

HOST PLANT: Unrecorded.

Teleonemia tricolor (Mayr)

    Monanthia (Gargaphia) tricolor Mayr 1865, p. 442 [Venezuela].—Walker 1873a, p. 192.

    Monanthia lanceolata Walker 1873a, p. 194 [Brazil].—Distant 1902b, p. 357.

    Gargaphia tricolor: Stål 1873, p. 125.

    Teleonemia albomarginata Champion 1898a, p. 43, pl. 3, figs. 18, 18a [Panama].—Drake 1922c, p. 359 [Guatemala]; 1929, p. 35 [Surinam]; 1931c, p. 226 [Paraguay; Colombia]; 1932, p. 100 [Barro

Colorado].—Drake and Bruner 1924a, p. 145 [Trinidad].—Drake and Hambleton 1934, p. 438.—Drake and Poor 1939b, p. 95 [Argentina].—Monte 1940c, p. 190; 1940e, p. 298; 1943a, p. 107; 1944b, p. 454; 1947a, p. 233.

Americia albomarginata: Kirkaldy 1905, p. 216 [Peru].

Teleonemia (Americia) albomarginata: Horváth 1925b, p. 219.

Teleonemia spectabilis Drake 1931c, p. 226; 1935, p. 10.—Drake and Bondar 1932, p. 87.

Teleonemia dispersa Drake 1931c, p. 227, fig. 1 [Ecuador].

Teleonemia lanceolata: Drake and Hambleton 1938b, p. 52, pl. 9, fig. b [*Cucurbita moschata*]; 1944b, p. 121; 1945, p. 357.—Drake and Poor 1942, p. 299.—Drake 1948j, p. 430.—Silva 1956, p. 54, fig. 21 [*Sicana odorifera; Sechium edule*].

Teleonemia tricolor: Drake and Ruhoff 1962c, p. 133.

TYPE: Sex unknown; Venezuela; Vienna Mus.

DISTRIBUTION: Brazil; Venezuela; Colombia; Surinam; Ecuador; Paraguay; Peru; Argentina; Panama; Canal Zone (Barro Colorado); Guatemala; Trinidad.

HOST PLANTS: *Cucurbita moschata; Sechium edule; Sicana odorifera.*

*Teleonemia validicornis Stål

Teleonemia validicornis Stål 1873, p. 132 [Colombia].—Champion 1898b, p. 62, pl. 3, fig. 4.—Van Duzee 1901, p. 348 [British Guiana].—Drake 1929, p. 35 [Surinam]; 1936b, p. 699 [Argentina].—Drake and Bondar 1932, p. 87 [Brazil; *Macherium oblongifolium subglabrum*].—Costa Lima 1936, p. 130.—Drake and Poor 1937d, p. 303 [French Guiana].—Drake and Hambleton 1938b, p. 52.—Monte 1939b, p. 80 [*Jacaranda paucifoliata*]; 1940c, p. 191.—Hurd 1946, p. 448 [Panama; *Macherium oblongifolium*].—Silva 1956, p. 64, fig. 27.—Drake and Cobben 1960, p. 73, figs. 78, 79b [Venezuela; Curaçao; *Lantana camara*].

TYPE: Holotype ♂; Bogota, Colombia; Stockholm Mus.

DISTRIBUTION: Colombia; Surinam; French Guiana; British Guiana; Brazil; Argentina; Venezuela; Panama; Netherlands Antilles (Curaçao).

HOST PLANTS: *Jacaranda paucifoliata; Lantana camara; Macherium oblongifolium; Macherium oblongifolium* v. *subglabrum.*

*Teleonemia variegata Champion

Teleonemia variegata Champion 1898a, p. 42, pl. 3, figs. 15, 15a [Mexico; Guatemala].—Barber 1910, p. 38 [Ariz.].—Drake 1918b, p. 328.—Perkins and Swezey 1924, p. 52 [*Lantana*].—Hurd 1946, p. 449 [Honduras].

TYPE: Sex unknown; Capetillo, Guatemala; British Mus.

DISTRIBUTION: Honduras; Guatemala; Mexico; U.S. (Ariz.).

HOST PLANT: *Lantana* sp.

*Teleonemia veneris Drake

    Teleonemia veneris Drake 1939d, p. 527 [Brazil].

TYPE: Holotype ♀, macropterous; Belém, Pará, Brazil; Drake Coll. (USNM).

DISTRIBUTION: Brazil.

HOST PLANT: Unrecorded.

*Teleonemia vidua Van Duzee

    Teleonemia vidua Van Duzee 1918, p. 278 [Calif.].

TYPE: Holotype ♀; Keen Camp, San Jacinto Mountains, California, U.S.; Cal. Acad.

DISTRIBUTION: U.S. (Calif.).

HOST PLANT: Unrecorded.

*Teleonemia vulgata Drake and Hambleton

    Teleonemia vulgata Drake and Hambleton 1940, p. 533 [Brazil].

TYPE: Holotype ♂, macropterous; Nictheroy, Est. do Rio, Brazil; Drake Coll. (USNM).

DISTRIBUTION: Brazil.

HOST PLANT: Unrecorded.

*Teleonemia vulsa Drake and Hambleton

    Teleonemia vulsa Drake and Hambleton 1944b, p. 123 [Brazil].

TYPE: Holotype ♂, macropterous; Chapada, Brazil; Drake Coll. (USNM).

DISTRIBUTION: Brazil.

HOST PLANT: Unrecorded.

Genus TIGAVA Stål

    Tigava Stål 1858, p. 63; 1873, pp. 121, 130.—Lethierry and Severin 1896, p. 22.—Monte 1939b, p. 80; 1941e, p. 143; 1944a, p. 158.— Hurd 1946, p. 449.—Drake and Ruhoff 1960a, p. 84.

TYPE SPECIES: *Tigava praecellens* Stål.

*Tigava bombacis Drake and Poor

    Tigava convexicollis (not Champion): Drake and Hambleton 1935, p. 143 [Brazil; *Bombax; Chorisia speciosa*].—Monte 1937a, p. 35, fig. 5 [*Chorisia*].

    Tigava bombacis Drake and Poor 1938a, p. 32.—Monte 1940c, p. 193.— Kormilev 1955a, p. 63 [Argentina].

TYPE: Holotype ♂, macropterous; Viçosa, Brazil; Drake Coll. (USNM).

DISTRIBUTION: Brazil; Argentina.

HOST PLANTS: *Bombax* sp.; *Chorisia speciosa; Chorisia* sp.

*Tigava brevicollis Monte

Tigava brevicollis Monte 1944a, p. 157, fig. 1 [Brazil; *Ficus*].

TYPE: Holotype ♂; Rio de Janeiro, Brazil; Monte Coll. (Mus. Nacional).
DISTRIBUTION: Brazil.
HOST PLANT: *Ficus* sp.

*Tigava ceibae Drake and Poor

Tigava seibae Drake and Poor 1938a, p. 28 [Brazil; *Ceiba pentandra*].
Tigava ceibae (emended): Silva 1956, p. 64, fig. 28.

TYPE: Holotype ♀, macropterous; Bahia, Brazil; Drake Coll. (USNM).
DISTRIBUTION: Brazil; Paraguay.
HOST PLANT: *Ceiba pentandra*.

*Tigava convexicollis Champion

Tigava convexicollis Champion 1897, p. 33, pl. 2, figs. 29, 29a [Panama].

TYPE: Sex unknown; Volcan de Chiriqui, Panama; British Mus.
DISTRIBUTION: Panama.
HOST PLANT: Unrecorded.

*Tigava corumbiana Drake

Tigava corumbiana Drake 1942a, p. 12 [Brazil].

TYPE: Holotype ♂, macropterous; Corumba, Matto Grosso, Brazil;
Drake Coll. (USNM).
DISTRIBUTION: Brazil.
HOST PLANT: Unrecorded.

*Tigava ferruginea Monte

Tigava ferruginea Monte 1940b, p. 378 [Brazil; *Bombax*].

TYPE: Holotype ♂; Brazil; Monte Coll. (Mus. Nacional).
DISTRIBUTION: Brazil.
HOST PLANT: *Bombax* sp.

*Tigava gracilis Monte

Tigava gracilis Monte 1940b, p. 379 [Brazil; Papilionaceae]; 1941e, p.
144 [Leguminosae].

TYPE: Holotype ♂; Lapinha, Lagoa Santa, Brazil; Monte Coll. (Mus.
Nacional).
DISTRIBUTION: Brazil.
HOST PLANTS: Leguminosae; Papilionaceae.

*Tigava graminis Drake and Poor

Tigava graminis Drake and Poor 1938a, p. 33 [Brazil; Gramineae].—
Silva 1956, p. 67.

TYPE: Holotype ♀, macropterous; Bahia, Brazil; Drake Coll. (USNM)
DISTRIBUTION: Brazil.
HOST PLANT: Gramineae.

*Tigava hambletoni Drake

Tigava hambletoni Drake 1948d, p. 16 [Peru].

TYPE: Holotype ♂, macropterous; Tingo Maria, Peru; USNM.

DISTRIBUTION: Peru.

HOST PLANT: Unrecorded.

*Tigava notabilis Drake

Tigava notabilis Drake 1922c, p. 364, pl. 39, fig. 9 [Brazil]; 1930a, p. 1.

TYPE: Holotype ♂; Chapada, Brazil; Carnegie Mus.

DISTRIBUTION: Brazil; Bolivia.

HOST PLANT: Unrecorded.

*Tigava praecellens Stål

Tigava praecellens Stål 1858, p. 63 [Brazil]; 1873, p. 130.—Walker 1873b, p. 4.—Champion 1898b, p. 61, pl. 3, fig. 1.—Drake and Poor 1937d, p. 305 [Bolivia].—Drake and Hambleton 1938a, p. 45.—Monte 1939b, p. 81 [Leguminosae]; 1940c, p. 193 [Papilionaceae.].

Tigava pracellens [sic]: Drake 1931b, p. 510.

TYPE: Holotype ♀; Rio de Janeiro, Brazil; Stockholm Mus.

DISTRIBUTION: Brazil; Bolivia.

HOST PLANTS: Leguminosae; Papilionaceae.

*Tigava pulchella Champion

Tigava pulchella Champion 1897, p. 32, pl. 2, fig. 26 [Mexico].—Drake and Bruner 1924a, p. 146 [Solanum torvum].

TYPE: Sex unknown; Vera Cruz, Mexico; British Mus.

DISTRIBUTION: Mexico; Guatemala; Honduras; Cuba.

HOST PLANTS: Solanum torvum; avocado.

*Tigava semota Drake

Tigava semota Drake 1931a, p. 405 [Brazil]; 1935, p. 13 [Paraguay].

TYPE: Holotype ♂, macropterous; Chapada, Brazil; Drake Coll. (USNM).

DISTRIBUTION: Brazil; Paraguay.

HOST PLANT: Unrecorded.

Tigava spatula Monte

Tigava spatula Monte 1945a, p. 250 [Brazil].

TYPE: Holotype ♂; Rio Verde, Goiás, Brazil; Monte Coll. (Mus. Nacional).

DISTRIBUTION: Brazil.

HOST PLANT: Unrecorded.

*Tigava tingoana Drake

Tigava tingoana Drake 1948d, p. 17 [Peru].

TYPE: Holotype ♂, macropterous; Tingo Maria, Peru; USNM.

DISTRIBUTION: Peru.

HOST PLANT: Unrecorded.

Genus TIGAVARIA Drake

Tigavaria Drake 1945, p. 99.—Drake and Ruhoff 1960a, p. 84.

TYPE SPECIES: *Tigava unicarinata* Hacker.

*Tigavaria unicarinata (Hacker)

Tigava unicarinata Hacker 1929, p. 325, pl. 32, fig. 2 [Queensland].

Tigavaria unicarinata: Drake 1945, p. 99.

TYPE: Sex unknown; Gold Creek, Queensland, Australia, Queensland Mus.

DISTRIBUTION: Australia (Queensland).

HOST PLANT: Unrecorded.

Genus TINGIS Fabricius

Tingis Fabricius 1803, p. 124.—Stål 1874, p. 54.—Horváth 1906a, pp. 14, 61 (key).—Mužik 1907, pp. 50, 58 (key).—Oshanin 1908, p. 429; 1912, p. 44.—Schumacher 1914, p. 257.—Stichel 1926, pp. 104, 110; 1935, p. 349; 1938a, p. 406; 1960a, p. 307; 1960b, p. 396; 1960c, p. 135.—Blatchley 1926, p. 487.—de Seabra 1931, pp. 407, 422 (key).— Börner 1935, p. 76.—Gulde 1938, pp. 244, 287 (key).—Monte 1939b, p. 81; 1941e, p. 146.—China 1943, p. 247.—Blöte 1945, p.85.—Hurd 1946, p. 463.—González 1948, p. 50.—Kiritshenko 1951, pp. 242, 248 (key).—Priesner and Alfieri 1953, p. 64 (key).—Drake and Ruhoff 1960a, p. 85.

Phyllontocheila Fieber 1844, p. 59 (in part).—Distant 1903b, p. 135.— Drake and Ruhoff 1960a, p. 76.

Platychilae Fieber 1861, p. 119 (in part; without species).—Drake and Ruhoff 1960a, p. 78.

Monanthia (*Platychila*) Puton 1879c, p. 107.—Drake and Ruhoff 1960a, p. 78.

Phyllontochila: Lethierry and Severin 1896, p. 17 (in part).

TYPE SPECIES: *Cimex cardui* Linnaeus.

Subgenus TINGIS (TINGIS) Fabricius

Tingis (*Tingis*) Fabricius 1803, p. 124.—Horváth 1906a, p. 71.—Drake and Ruhoff 1960a, p. 85.

TYPE SPECIES: *Cimex cardui* Linnaeus.

*Tingis aemula Drake

Tingis aemula Drake 1947c, p. 115 [South Australia].

TYPE: Holotype ♀, macropterous; Oldea, South Australia, Australia; Drake Coll. (USNM).

DISTRIBUTION: Australia (South Australia).

HOST PLANT: Unrecorded.

*Tingis americana Drake

Tingis americana Drake 1922c, p. 366, pl. 39, fig. 11 [Brazil]; 1926d, pp. 83, 84; 1930a, p. 1; 1931b, p. 511; 1935a, p. 11 [Paraguay].— Monte 1937a, p. 34, fig. 15 [*Tecoma*]; 1937c p. 72.—Drake and Hambleton 1938a, p. 64.—Kormilev 1955a, p. 64 [Argentina].

TYPE: Holotype ♀; Chapada, Brazil; Carnegie Mus.

DISTRIBUTION: Brazil; Paraguay; Argentina.

HOST PLANT: *Tecoma* sp.

*Tingis ampliata (Herrich-Schaeffer)

Monanthia ampliata Herrich-Schaeffer 1838, p. 62, pl. 127, fig. 397a [Czechoslovakia; Austria].—Mayr 1858, p. 569.—Fieber 1861, p. 120 [Ukraine].—Douglas and Scott 1865, p. 252.—Garbiglietti 1869, p. 272.—Walker 1873a, p. 183.—Saunders 1875, p. 248.—Reiber and Puton 1876, p. 69.—Dubois 1888, p. 121.—d'Antessanty 1890, p. 32.—Hüeber 1893, p. 329 [Switzerland; Germany].—Butler 1923, p. 209.

Tingis ampliata: Curtis 1839, tab. 741 [England].—Stål 1874, p. 54.— Sahlberg 1878, p. 21.—Horváth 1906a, pp. 63, 71 [Hungary; Caucasus; *Cirsium*].—Reuter 1908, p. 88 [*Pinus*].—Scholte 1935, p. 62, fig. 15 [Netherlands].—Reclaire 1940, p. 109 [*Cirsium arvense*].— Cobben 1948, p. 82.—Kiritshenko 1951, p. 249.—Singer 1952, p. 52 [*Cirsium palustre*].—Bator 1953, p. 325, pl. 3, fig. 5.—Southwood and Scudder 1956, p. 93, figs. 1, 2a, 3–5, 8–13a.—Štusak 1957b, p. 140, fig. 15a.—Southwood and Leston 1959, p. 148, pl. 21, fig. 8; figs. 41, 46.—Stichel 1960a, p. 311 [Poland; Turkestan; *Cirsium lanceolatum*].

Monanthia (Phyllontocheila) ampliata: Fieber 1844, p. 59, pl. 5, figs. 10–11 [*Verbascum;* Italy].—Herrich-Schaeffer 1850, p. 155.

Monanthia (Platychila) ampliata: Puton 1879c, p. 108 [France; *Carduus*].— Saunders 1892, p. 132, pl. 12, fig. 5.

Phyllonthocheila [sic] *ampliata:* Reichensperger 1920, p. 62.

TYPE: Unknown.

DISTRIBUTION: England; Netherlands; France; Germany; Czechoslovakia; Poland; Austria; Switzerland; Italy; Hungary; U.S.S.R. (Caucasus; Turkestan; Ukraine).

HOST PLANTS: *Carduus* sp.; *Cirsium arvense; Cirsium lanceolatum; Cirsium palustre; Cirsium* sp.; *Pinus* sp.; *Verbascum* sp.

NOTE: Life history studies [Butler; Southwood and Scudder; Štusak]. Predators [Southwood and Leston].

*Tingis angustata (Herrich-Schaeffer)

Monanthia angustata Herrich-Schaeffer 1838, p. 61, pl. 127, fig. 397b [Germany].—Scholz 1847, p. 119.—Fieber 1861, p. 121 [Ukraine].— Garbiglietti 1869, p. 272.—Gredler 1870, p. 75.—Walker 1873a,

p. 184.—Chicote 1880, p. 189.—Horváth 1881b, p. xxxiv.—d'Antessanty 1890, p. 32.—Hüeber 1893, p. 333.—Butler 1923, p. 212 [Algeria].

Monanthia (Phyllontocheila) angustata: Fieber 1844, p. 62, pl. 5, fig. 16–18 [Czechoslovakia; Austria].—Herrich-Schaeffer 1850, p. 155.

Catopolatus parallelus Costa 1847b, p. 19 [Italy]; 1847d, p. 255.—Fieber 1861, p. 383.—Stichel 1960d, p. 119.

Catoplatus variolosus Costa 1847b, p. 20; 1847d, p. 256, pl. 3, fig. 2.— Fieber 1861, p. 383.—Stichel 1960d, p. 119.

Monanthia brachycera Fieber 1861, p. 121 [Yugoslavia].

Monanthia parallela: Garbiglietti 1869, p. 273.—Walker 1873a, p. 187.— Bolivar and Chicote 1879, p. 166 [Spain].

Monanthia variolosa: Garbiglietti 1869, p. 273.—Walker 1873a, p. 187.

Tingis angustata: Stål 1874, p. 54.—Horváth 1906a, pp. 63, 73; 1906d, p. 2; 1916, p. 9.—Reuter 1908, p. 88.—Stichel 1926, p. 112; 1960a, p. 313, fig. 117 [Sicily; Sardinia; *Pyrus aria*].—Hoberlandt 1943b, pp. 121, 123; 1955, p. 89.—Lindberg 1948, p. 59 [Greece; Cyprus; *Sorbus cretica*].—Kiritshenko 1951, p. 250.—Mancini 1953b, p. 186; 1953d, p. 16.—Seidenstücker 1954, p. 235.—Southwood and Leston 1959, p. 149.

Monanthia (Platychila) angustata: Puton 1879c, p. 110 [France; Corsica; England].—Saunders 1892, p. 134, pl. 12, fig. 6.

Monanthia angustata var. *sympathica* Horváth 1881a, p. 41 [Hungary].

Monanthia fieberi Puton 1886b, p. 33.—Hüeber 1893, p. 333.

Phyllontochila angustata: Reuter 1891a, p. 26 [Albania].

Phyllontocheila parallela: Horváth 1901, p. 475 [Turkey].

Monanthia (Platychila) taurica Jakovlev 1903b, p. 193 [Crimea].

TYPE: Sex unknown; Regensburg, Germany; Munich Mus.

DISTRIBUTION: England; Spain; France; Corsica; Italy; Sicily; Sardinia; Austria; Czechoslovakia; Germany; Hungary; Albania; Greece; Yugoslavia; Cyprus; Turkey; U.S.S.R. (Crimea; Ukraine); Algeria.

HOST PLANTS: *Pyrus aria; Sorbus cretica.*

Tingis angustata var. diminuta Horváth

Tingis angustata var. *diminuta* Horváth 1906a, p. 74 [Spain].

TYPE: Sex unknown; Albarracin, Spain; Helsin. Mus.

DISTRIBUTION: Spain.

HOST PLANT: Unrecorded.

*Tingis auriculata (Costa)

Monanthia cardui (not Linnaeus): Herrich-Schaeffer 1838, p. 61, pl. 127, fig. b.

Monanthia (Phyllontocheila) sinuata Fieber 1844, p. 60, pl. 5, figs. 12–15 [Czechoslovakia; Austria; Sicily; *Statice*].

Catoplatus auriculatus Costa 1847b, p. 20 [Italy]; 1847d, p. 256, pl. 3, fig. 3.—Stichel 1960d, p. 119.

Monanthia sinuata: Mayr 1858, p. 570 [Hungary].—Fieber 1861, p. 120
[France; Ukraine; Corsica].—Jakovlev 1869, p. 111 [Russia]; 1880b,
p. 104 [Caucasus].—Garbiglietti 1869, p. 272.—Walker 1873a, p.
183.—Horváth 1874b, p. 432.

Monanthia unicolor Garbiglietti 1869, p. 274 [Sardinia].—Walker 1873a,
p. 188.

Monanthia (Platychila) auriculata: Puton 1879c, p. 109 [*Stachys recta*].

Monanthia auriculata: Chicote 1880, p. 189 [Spain].—Puton 1881, p. 123
[Syria].—d'Antessanty 1890, p. 32.—Hüeber 1893, p. 332.—Mancini
1949b, p. 36; 1953b, p. 186; 1953d, p. 16.

Phyllontochila auriculata: Lethierry and Severin 1896, p. 16 [Algeria].

Phyllontocheila auriculata: Horváth 1901, p. 475 [Turkey].

Tingis auriculata: Horváth 1905b, p. 568; 1906a, pp. 62, 71 [Rumania;
Armenia; Turkestan]; 1906d, p. 2; 1916, p. 9 [Albania].—Oshanin
1908, p. 431 [Switzerland; Portugal; Bulgaria; Yugoslavia; Greece].—
Stichel 1926, p. 111 [*Daucus carota; Caucalis daucoides;* Germany];
1938a, p. 406 [Morocco]; 1960a, p. 310 [*Torilis arvensis*].—de Seabra
1931, p. 426, figs. 495(3), 497.—Lindberg 1932a, p. 41; 1948, p. 59
[Cyprus].—Vidal 1937, p. 197.—Hoberlandt 1943b, p. 120; 1955,
p. 89 [Israel].—Kiritshenko 1951, p. 249.—Seidenstücker 1954, p.
235.—Gomez-Menor 1955b, p. 248.—Štusak 1961a, p. 84, figs. 11,
18.—Drake and Ruhoff 1962a, p. 156.

Monanthia ? necopina Drake 1919a, p. 420 [Md.]; 1926d, p. 83.

Tingis necopina: McAtee 1923, p. 145.—Blatchley 1926, p. 487.

TYPE: Sex unknown; Naples, Italy; Naples Mus.

DISTRIBUTION: Spain; Portugal; France; Corsica; Sardinia; Sicily; Italy;
Switzerland; Czechoslovakia; Germany; Austria; Hungary; Albania; Yugo-
slavia; Rumania; Bulgaria; Greece; Turkey, Cyprus; Israel; Syria; U.S.S.R.
(Armenia; Ukraine; Turkestan; Caucasus); Algeria; Morocco; U.S. (Md.).

HOST PLANTS: *Caucalis daucoides; Daucus carota; Stachys recta; Stachys* sp.;
Statice sp.; *Torilus arvensis.*

NOTE: Study of eggs [Štusak].

*Tingis auriculata var. dauci Horváth

Tingis auriculata var. *dauci* Horváth 1905b, p. 568 [Hungary; Rumania;
Spain; Algeria; *Daucus carota*]; 1906a, p. 71.—Mancini 1953c, p. 22
[Italy].—Stichel 1960a, p. 310 [Sardinia; Czechoslovakia; Iraq;
Caucalis daucoides].

TYPE: Unknown.

DISTRIBUTION: Italy; Hungary; Rumania; Spain; Iraq; Sardinia; Czechoslovakia; Algeria.

HOST PLANTS: *Caucalis daucoides; Daucus carota.*

Tingis brevicornis (Horváth)

Phyllontocheila brevicornis Horváth 1902a, p. 595 [Armenia].

Tingis brevicornis: Horváth 1906a, p. 78 [Turkmen; Turkestan].—
Oshanin 1908, p. 436 [Transcaucasus].

TYPE: Holotype ♂; Armenia, Russia; Hungarian Mus.

DISTRIBUTION: U.S.S.R. (Armenia; Turkestan; Turkmen; Transcaucasus).

HOST PLANT: Unrecorded.

*Tingis buddleiae Drake

Tingis buddleiae Drake 1930e, p. 168 [Luzon; *Buddleia asiatica*].—Drake
and Poor 1937b, p. 402.—Drake and Ruhoff 1962c, p. 133.

Tingis himalayae Drake 1948g, p. 173 [India].

TYPE: Holotype ♂, macropterous; Los Banos, Philippine Islands;
USNM.

DISTRIBUTION: Philippine Islands (Luzon); China; India.

HOST PLANTS: *Buddleia asiatica; Vitex trifolia.*

*Tingis capillata Kiritshenko

Tingis capillata Kiritshenko 1914, p. 194 [Turkestan].

TYPE: Sex unknown; Turkestan, Russia; Leningrad Inst.

DISTRIBUTION: U.S.S.R. (Turkestan).

HOST PLANT: Unrecorded.

*Tingis cardui (Linnaeus)　　　　　　　　FIGURES 1*b, c;* 6*c, d*

Cimex sp. 660 Linnaeus 1746, p. 207 [*Carduus*].

Cimex cardui Linnaeus 1758, p. 443; 1761, p. 247; 1767, p. 718.—
Houttuyn 1765, p. 343.—de Geer 1773, p. 309, pl. 16, figs. 1–6.—
Müller 1774, p. 483.—Schrank 1781, p. 266; 1782, p. 276.—Villers
1789, p. 486.—Gmelin 1790, p. 2127.

Acanthia cardui: Fabricius 1775, p. 696; 1781, p. 338; 1787, p. 280;
1794, p. 77.—Panzer 1796, heft 5, tab. 24.—Cederhielm 1798, p.
270.—Wolff 1801, p. 45, pl. 5, fig. 42.—Schrank 1801, p. 65.—
Walckenaer 1802, p. 338.—Meixner 1915, p. 270.

Cimex minutulus Goeze 1778, p. 277.

Acanthia clavicornis (not Linnaeus): Panzer 1793, heft 3, tab. 24.

Tingis cardui: Fabricius 1803, p. 125.—Latrielle 1804, p. 252; 1810,
p. 433.—Fallén 1807, p. 36 [Sweden]; 1829, p. 143.—Le Peletier
and Serville 1828, p. 653.—Zetterstedt 1828, p. 480; 1840, p. 269
[Lapland].—Herrich-Schaeffer 1835, p. 58.—Curtis 1839, tab.
741 [Scotland; England].—Westwood 1840b, p. 120.—Stål 1874,
p. 54.—Sahlberg 1878, p. 21 [Siberia]; 1920, p. 83.—Reuter 1882b,
p. 119 [*Cirsium lanceolatum*].—Horváth 1906a, pp. 63, 72 [Canary
Islands; Algeria; Turkey; Armenia; Causasus; *Marrubium vulgare*];
1906d, p. 2.—Oshanin 1908, p. 432 [Morocco; Turkestan].—Lindberg
1919, p. 42; 1932a, p. 41 [*Galactites tomentosa*]; 1934, p. 29 [China];

1936b, p. 30.—Stichel 1926, p. 112, fig. 301; 1938a, p. 406 [Albania; Yugoslavia]; 1960a, p. 312, fig. 116 [Sicily, Sardinia, Bulgaria, *Silybum*].—de Seabra 1931, p. 426, fig. 498.—Scholte 1935, p. 62, fig. 16.—Börner 1935, p. 77, fig. 116.—Mancini 1935, p. 9; 1952, p. 12; 1953b, p. 186; 1953d, p. 16.—Gulde 1938, p. 294, fig.— Hoberlandt 1942, p. 125; 1943b, p. 123; 1955, p. 89.—Blöte 1945, p. 86 [Belgium].—Cobben 1948, p. 82, fig. 3 [*Cirsium vulgare*].— Novak and Wagner 1951, p. 70.—Kiritshenko 1951, p. 249.—Bator 1953, p. 325, pl. 3, fig. 5.—Strawinski 1953, p. 380.—Gomez-Menor 1955b, p. 248; 1956b, p. 82, fig.—Southwood and Scudder 1956, pp. 93, 102, figs. 2b, 6, 7, 13b [*Cirsium palustre*].—Štušak 1957b, pp. 139, 140, figs. 9, 12a, 15b; 1958, p. 368, fig. 15.—Southwood and Leston 1959, p. 149, pl. 5, fig. 11; pl. 18, fig. 6; pl. 21, fig. 11.—Drake and Davis 1960, figs. 1, 3, 4, 7–10, 12, 16, 17.

Monanthia cardui: Burmeister 1835, p. 260.—Herrich-Schaffer 1838, p. 61, pl. 127, fig. A.—Amyot and Serville 1843, p. 298 [France].—Sahlberg 1848, p. 131 [Finland].—Mayr 1858, p. 570 [Austria; Ukraine; Hungary; *Ligustrum vulgare*].—Fieber 1861, p. 120.—Douglas and Scott 1865, p. 251.—Garbiglietti 1869, p. 272 [Italy].—Gredler 1870, p. 75.—Thomson 1871, p. 398.—Horváth 1874b, p. 432; 1892b, p. 131.—Siebke 1874, p. 22 [Norway].—Saunders 1875, p. 248; 1892, p. 133.—Reiber and Puton 1876, p. 69.—Vollenhoven 1878, p. 272, pl. 9, fig. 5 [Netherlands].—Ferrari 1878, p. 85.— Bolivar and Chicote 1879, p. 166 [Spain; Portugal].—Puton 1886a, p. 5 [Tunisia].—Dubois 1888, p. 121.—d'Antessanty 1890, p. 32.— Hüeber 1893, p. 330 [Czechoslovakia].—Mason 1898a, p. 140.— Kirkaldy 1908e, p. 59 [*Carduus crispus*].—Jensen-Haarup 1912, pp. 155, 156, fig. 98b.—Butler 1923, p. 210 [Wales; Ireland; Madeira; *Pinus austriaca; Pinus sylvestris; Serratula*].

Monanthia (Phyllontocheila) cardui: Fieber 1844, p. 61, pl. 5, figs. 1–8 [*Carduus nutans; Carduus acanthoides*].—Herrich-Schaeffer 1850, p. 155.—Flor 1860, p. 345 [Estonia; Latvia; Denmark; Poland; Iran; Germany].

Catoplatus cardui: Costa 1847a, p. 23; 1847c, p. 163.

Monanthia cardni [sic]: Frey-Gessner 1865, p. 231 [Switzerland].

Monanthia (Platychila) cardui: Puton 1879c, p. 108 [Corsica].—Mason 1898b, p. 210 [*Carduus lanceolatus*].

Phyllontochila cardui: Reuter 1891a, p. 26 [Greece].

Phyllonthocheila [sic] *cardui*: Reichensperger 1920, p. 62.

Tingis montana Lindberg 1932a, p. 42, pl. 2, fig. 5 (fig. only).—Drake and Ruhoff 1962c, p. 134.

Type: Unknown.

Distribution: Ireland; Scotland; Wales; England; Portugal; Spain; France; Belgium; Netherlands, Germany; Czechoslovakia; Switzerland;

Austria; Hungary; Italy; Corsica; Sardinia; Sicily; Yugoslavia; Albania; Bulgaria; Greece; Poland; Denmark; Norway; Sweden; Finland; (Lapland); U.S.S.R. (Estonia; Latvia; Ukraine; Caucasus; Armenia; Turkestan; Siberia); Turkey; Iran; Tunisia; Algeria; Morocco; Canary Islands; Madeira Island; China.

HOST PLANTS: *Carduus acanthoides; Carduus crispus; Carduus lanceolatum; Carduus nutans; Carduus* sp.; *Cirsium lanceolatum; Cirsium palustre; Cirsium vulgare; Galactites tomentosa; Marrubium vulgare; Pinus austriaca; Pinus sylvestris; Serratula* sp.; *Silybum* sp.

NOTE: Life history studies [Southwood and Scudder; Štušak].

*Tingis cardui var. cognata (Fieber)

    Monanthia cognata Fieber 1861, p. 121 [Corsica].—Garbiglietti 1869, p. 272.

    Monanthia (Platychila) cardui var. *cognata:* Puton 1879c, p. 109 [France].

    Tingis cardui var. *cognata:* Horváth 1906a, p. 73 [Italy; Algeria].—Oshanin 1908, p. 433 [Russia].—Lindberg 1932a, p. 41 [Spain].—Hoberlandt 1943b, pp. 121, 123 [Czechoslovakia].—Blöte 1945, p. 86 [Tunisia].—Mancini 1952, p. 13 [Turkey; Iran; Caucasus; Turkestan].

    Tingis auriculata var. *cognata:* Vidal 1937, p. 197 [Morocco].

TYPE: Sex unknown; Corsica; Vienna Mus.

DISTRIBUTION: Spain; France; Corsica; Italy; Czechoslovakia; Turkey; Iran; U.S.S.R. (Caucasus; Turkestan); Tunisia; Morocco; Algeria.

HOST PLANT: Unrecorded.

*Tingis cardui var. maderensis (Reuter)

    Monanthia (Platychila) cardui var. *maderensis* Reuter 1890b, p. 262 [Madeira].

    Tingis cardui var. *maderensis:* Horváth 1906a, p. 73.—China 1938, p. 20.—Lindberg 1960a, p. 13 [La Palma].—Stichel 1960a, p. 312.

TYPE: Sex unknown; Madeira; Berlin Mus.

DISTRIBUTION: Madeira; Canary Islands (La Palma).

HOST PLANT: Unrecorded.

*Tingis colombiana Drake

    Tingis colombiana Drake 1929, p. 35, fig. 1 [Colombia].—Drake and Hambleton 1938a, p. 63 [Brazil].—Monte 1938b, p. 127 [Bignoniaceae].—Drake and Davis 1960, fig. 47.

TYPE: Holotype ♂; Sabanilla, Colombia; Hamburg Mus.

DISTRIBUTION: Colombia; Brazil.

HOST PLANT: Bignoniaceae.

*Tingis comosa (Takeya)

Dictyonota comosa Takeya 1931, p. 66, pl. 7, fig. 1; pl. 8, figs. 1–3 [Japan].—Drake and Hsiung 1936, p. 288.

Tingis modosa Drake 1937b, p. 593 [China].

Tingis comosa: Drake 1948a, p. 2.—Takeya 1951a, p. 15; 1953a, p. 2.—Drake and Maa 1953, p. 91 [*Artemesia*].

TYPE: Holotype ♂; Hikosan, Prov. Buzen, Kyushu, Japan; Kyushu Univ.

DISTRIBUTION: Japan; China; India.

HOST PLANT: *Artemesia* sp.

*Tingis consaepta Drake and Poor

Tingis consaepta Drake and Poor 1939c, p. 205 [India].

TYPE: Holotype ♀, macropterous; Ayur, North Salem, Madras, India; Drake Coll. (USNM).

DISTRIBUTION: India.

HOST PLANT: Unrecorded.

*Tingis coomani Drake

Tingis coomani Drake 1947d, p. 227, fig. [Viet-Nam]; 1947h, no. 70, (color fig.).

TYPE: Holotype ♂; Tonkin, Hoabinh, Indochina; Heude Mus.

DISTRIBUTION: Viet-Nam.

HOST PLANT: Unrecorded.

*Tingis corumbiana Drake

Tingis corumbiana Drake 1926d, pp. 83, 84 [Brazil].

Tingis corubiana [sic]: Drake 1930a, p. 1.

TYPE: Holotype ♂; Corumbá, Matto Grosso, Brazil; Drake Coll. (USNM).

DISTRIBUTION: Brazil.

HOST PLANT: Unrecorded.

*Tingis crispata (Herrich-Schaeffer)

Derephysia crispata Herrich-Schaeffer 1838, p. 72, pl. 128, figs. 399, a–c [Hungary].

Monanthia (Phyllontocheila) crispata: Fieber 1844, p. 66, pl. 5, figs. 28–30.—Herrich-Schaeffer 1850, p. 154.

Monanthia crispata: Fieber 1861, p. 384.—Garbiglietti 1869, p. 273 [Italy].—Horváth 1874b, p. 432.—Hüeber 1893, p. 336.

Phyllantocheila [sic] *crispata:* Costa 1863, p. 6.

Monanthia (Platychila) crispata: Puton 1879c, p. 110 [France].

Lasiotropis crispata: Lethierry and Severin 1896, p. 18.

Tingis crispata: Horváth 1906a, pp. 64, 75 [Caucasus; Bulgaria; Rumania; Austria; *Artemisia vulgaris*]; 1906d, p. 2.—Oshanin 1908, p. 434 [Turkestan].—Stichel 1926, p. 112 [Germany]; 1960a, p. 313, fig. 118 [Switzerland; *Artemisia campestris; Artemisia absinthium*].—

Ross and Hedicke 1927, p. 92.—Hoberlandt 1943b, pp. 121, 123 [Czechoslovakia].—Blöte 1945, p. 86 [Tunisia].—Mancini 1949b, p. 37.—Kiritshenko 1951, p. 250.—Putshkov 1960, p. 303.

TYPE: Sex unknown; Hungary; Munich Mus.

DISTRIBUTION: France; Germany; Czechoslovakia; Austria; Switzerland; Italy; Hungary; Rumania; Bulgaria; U.S.S.R. (Caucasus; Turkestan); Tunisia.

HOST PLANTS: *Artemisia absinthium; Artemisia campestris; Artemisia vulgaris.*

NOTE: Life history study [Putshkov].

Tingis crispata var. addita Horváth

Tingis crispata var. *addita* Horváth 1911b, p. 584 [Rumania].

TYPE: Holotype ♀; Comana, Rumania; Hungarian Mus.

DISTRIBUTION: Rumania.

HOST PLANT: Unrecorded.

Tingis demissa Horváth

Tingis demissa Horváth 1906a, p. 78 [Turkey].—Hoberlandt 1955, p. 90.—Stichel 1960a, p. 315 [*Cirsium*].

TYPE: Holotype ♀; Konia, Turkey; deposition unknown.

DISTRIBUTION: Turkey.

HOST PLANT: *Cirsium* sp.

*Tingis deserticola Horváth

Tingis deserticola Horváth 1906a, p. 71 [Turkestan].

TYPE: Sex unknown; Tshu, Turkestan, Russia; Hungarian Mus.

DISTRIBUTION: U.S.S.R. (Turkestan).

HOST PLANT: Unrecorded.

*Tingis drakei Hacker

Tingis drakei Hacker 1929, p. 328, pl. 33, fig. 8 [Queensland].—Drake 1961b, p. 110.—Drake and Ruhoff 1962b, p. 250 [Lord Howe].

TYPE: Sex unknown; South Pine River, Australia; Queensland Mus.

DISTRIBUTION: Australia (Queensland; Lord Howe Island).

HOST PLANT: Unrecorded.

*Tingis elongata (Fieber)

Monanthia elongata Fieber 1861, p. 121 [Yugoslavia].—Walker 1873a, p. 184.—Chicote 1880, p. 189 [Spain].

Monanthia parallela (not Costa): Puton 1879c, p. 110.

Phyllontochila elongata: Lethierry and Severin 1896, p. 17 [Algeria].

Phyllontocheila fallax Horváth 1902a, p. 596.

Phyllontocheila prolixa Horváth 1902a, p. 597.

Tingis elongata: Horváth 1906a, p. 79, pl. 1, fig. 8.—Vidal 1937, p. 197 [Morocco].—Lindberg 1948, p. 59 [*Juniperus foetidissima;* Cyprus].—Stichel 1960a, p. 315.—Drake and Ruhoff 1962a, p. 156.

TYPE: Sex unknown; Serbia; Vienna Mus.

DISTRIBUTION: Spain; Yugoslavia; Cyprus; Algeria; Morocco.

HOST PLANT: *Juniperus foetidissima.*

†Tingis florissantensis Cockerell

 Tingis florissantensis Cockerell 1914, p. 719, fig. 4 [Colo.; Miocene].—
 Drake and Ruhoff 1960a, p. 11.

TYPE: Sex undeterminable; fossil; Miocene shales; Florissant, Colorado, U.S.; deposition unknown.

DISTRIBUTION: Fossil.

Tingis foleyi Bergevin

 Tingis foleyi Bergevin 1929, p. 115, fig. 2 [Algeria].

TYPE: Holotype ♀; l'Oued Ilaman, Algeria; Paris Mus.

DISTRIBUTION: Algeria.

HOST PLANT: Unrecorded.

Tingis fuentei Horváth

 Tingis fuentei Horváth 1906a, p. 76 [Spain].—Wagner 1958, p. 240
 [France; Centaurea solstitialis].—Stichel 1960a, p. 314.

TYPE: Holotype ♀; Fuencaliente, Spain; Hungarian Mus.

DISTRIBUTION: Spain; France.

HOST PLANT: Centaurea solstitialis.

*Tingis grisea Germar

 Tingis grisea Germar 1835, fasc. 15, tab. 13 [Germany].—Herrich-
 Schaeffer 1835, p. 58.—Horváth 1906a, pp. 65, 77 [Yugoslavia].—
 Oshanin 1908, p. 435 [Turkestan; Transcaucasus].—Stichel 1926,
 p. 112 [Centaurea rhenana]; 1960a, p. 314 [Morocco].—Hoberlandt
 1942, p. 125; 1943a, p. 118; 1943b, p. 120; 1955, p. 90 [Turkey;
 Israel].—Štusak 1957a, p. 23, figs. 6–8; 1959b, p. 181, figs. 1–8;
 1961a, p. 77, fig. 5g.—Putshkov 1960, p. 304.
 Monanthia grisea: Herrich-Schaeffer 1838, pp. 52, 60, pl. 122d [Czecho-
 slovakia].—Scholz 1847, p. 119.—Mayr 1858, p. 570 [Rumania;
 Hungary].—Fieber 1861, pp. 120, 383.—Walker 1873a, p. 183
 [England].—Horváth 1874b, p. 432.—Jakovlev 1876b, p. 67 [Russia];
 1880b, p. 106 [Caucasus].—Puton 1874a, p. 226; 1881, p. 123
 [Syria].—Rey 1893, p. 97.—Hüeber 1893, p. 336.
 Monanthia (Phyllontocheila) grisea: Fieber 1844, p. 64, pl. 5, figs. 25–27
 [Austria; Centaurea paniculata].—Herrich-Schaeffer 1850, p. 154.
 Monanthia pallida Garbiglietti 1869, p. 273 [Italy].—Walker 1873a,
 p. 187.
 Lasiotropis grisea: Stål 1874, p. 55.
 Monanthia (Platychila) grisea: Puton 1879c, p. 110 [France].

TYPE: Germany; sex and deposition of type unknown.

DISTRIBUTION: England; France; Germany; Czechoslovakia; Austria; Italy; Hungary; Yugoslavia; Rumania; Turkey; Syria; Israel; U.S.S.R. (Caucasus; Transcaucasus; Turkestan); Morocco.

400 U.S. NATIONAL MUSEUM BULLETIN 243

HOST PLANTS: *Centaurea paniculata; Centaurea rhenana.*
NOTE: Life history studies [Putshkov; Štušak 1959b]. Study of eggs [Štušak 1957a; 1961a].

*Tingis hackeri Drake
Tingis hackeri Drake 1947c, p. 118 [Queensland].
TYPE: Holotype ♂, macropterous; National Park, Queensland, Australia; Drake Coll. (USNM).
DISTRIBUTION: Australia (Queensland).
HOST PLANT: Unrecorded.

*Tingis hurdae Drake
Tingis hurdae Drake 1947c, p. 113, fig. 25 [Queensland]; 1961b, p. 110.
TYPE: Holotype ♂, macropterous; Queensland, Australia; Drake Coll. (USNM).
DISTRIBUTION: Australia (Queensland).
HOST PLANT: Unrecorded.

*Tingis impensa Drake
Tingis impensa Drake 1947c, p. 112, fig. 24a [Tasmania].
TYPE: Holotype ♀, macropterous; Tasmania, Australia; Drake Coll. (USNM).
DISTRIBUTION: Australia (Tasmania).
HOST PLANT: Unrecorded.

Tingis laetabilis (Horváth)
Phyllontocheila laetabilis Horváth 1903a, p. 77 [Algeria].
Tingis laetabilis: Horváth 1906a, p. 75.
TYPE: Holotype ♂; Ain-Sefra, Algeria; Hungarian Mus.
DISTRIBUTION: Algeria.
HOST PLANT: Unrecorded.

*Tingis lanigera (Puton)
Monanthia lanigera Puton 1886a, p. 5 [Algeria].
Monanthia (Platychila) lanigera: Puton 1886a, p. 16.
Phyllontochila lanigera: Lethierry and Severin 1896, p. 17 [Tunisia].
Tingis lanigera: Horváth 1906a, p. 75.—Lindberg 1932a, p. 41 [Morocco; *Populus nigra; Ephedra*].—Vidal 1937, p. 197.
TYPE: Sex unknown; Philippeville, Algeria; Paris Mus.
DISTRIBUTION: Algeria; Tunisia; Morocco.
HOST PLANTS: *Ephedra* sp.; *Populus nigra.*

*Tingis lasiocera Matsumura
Lasiotropis grisea (not Germar): Matsumura 1905, p. 39.
Tingis lasiocera Matsumura 1908, p. 148, fig.; 1930, p. 163, pl. 14, fig. 20.
Tingis lasicera [sic]: Matsumura 1931, p. 1203, fig.
Tingis laciocera [sic]: Takeya 1933, p. 37, pl. 3, fig. 4, text fig. 4 [Japan; Korea; *Serratura atriplicifolia*]; 1951a, p. 16.

TYPE: Unknown.
DISTRIBUTION: Japan; Korea.
HOST PLANT: *Serratura atriplicifolia.*

Tingis leptochila Horváth

Tingis leptochila Horváth 1906a, p. 74 [Turkestan].
TYPE: Sex unknown; Turkestan, Russia; Hungarian Mus.
DISTRIBUTION: U.S.S.R. (Turkestan).
HOST PLANT: Unrecorded.

Tingis neotropicalis Monte

Tingis neotropicalis Monte 1940e, p. 283 [Brazil; *Byrsonima*].—Silva
1956, p. 67.
TYPE: Holotype ♂; Agua Preta, Baía, Brazil; Monte Coll. (Mus.
Nacional).
DISTRIBUTION: Brazil.
HOST PLANT: *Byrsonima* sp.

Tingis nyogana Drake

Tingis nyogana Drake 1955c, p. 106 [Cameroun].
TYPE: Holotype ♀; Case du Nyong, French Cameroons; Copenhagen
Mus.
DISTRIBUTION: Cameroun.
HOST PLANT: Unrecorded.

†Tingis obscura Heer

Tingis obscura Heer 1853, p. 74, pl. 13, fig. 15 [Yugoslavia].—Giebel
1856, p. 363.—Scudder 1891, p. 449 [Horizon: Mayencian
(Tertiary)].—Drake and Ruhoff 1960a, p. 11.
TYPE: Sex undeterminable; fossil; Radoboj, Croatia; deposition unknown.
DISTRIBUTION: Fossil.

*Tingis perkensi Drake

Tingis perkensi Drake 1947c, p. 117 [Queensland].
TYPE: Holotype ♂, macropterous; National Park, Queensland, Aus-
tralia; Drake Coll. (USNM).
DISTRIBUTION: Australia (Queensland).
HOST PLANT: Unrecorded.

*Tingis populi Takeya

Tingis populi Takeya 1932, p. 10, pl. 1, fig. 2 [Korea; Japan; Taiwan;
Populus; Salix]; 1951a, p. 16 [*Populus tremula; Populus nigra*]; 1953a,
p. 2.—Saitô 1933, p. 7 [*Salix koreensis*].—Drake and Maa 1953, p. 91.—
Maa 1957, pp. 117, 131.
Nobarnus hoffmani Drake 1938b, p. 195 [China].
TYPE: Holotype ♂; Taikyû, Korea; Kyushu Univ.
DISTRIBUTION: Japan; China; Korea; Taiwan.
HOST PLANTS: *Populus nigra; Populus tremula; Populus* sp.; *Salix koreensis;
Salix* sp.

*Tingis rotundicollis (Jakovlev)

Monanthia (Platychila) rotundicollis Jakovlev 1883, p. 105 [Dagestan].
Phyllontochila rotundicollis: Lethierry and Severin 1896, p. 17 [Caucasus].
Tingis rotundicollis: Horváth 1906a, p. 76 [Yugoslavia; Greece; Bulgaria; Rumania; Turkey]; 1916, p. 9.—Stichel 1926, p. 112; 1938a, p. 406 [Albania]; 1960a, p. 314.—Lindberg 1948, p. 59 [Cyprus].—Kiritshenko 1951, p. 250.—Mancini 1952, p. 13 [Italy]; 1953b, p. 186; 1953d, p. 16; 1956a, p. 192.—Seidenstücker 1954, p. 235.—Hoberlandt 1955, p. 90 [Transcaucasus].

TYPE: Holotype ♀, macropterous; Derbent, Dagestan, Russia; Leningrad Inst.

DISTRIBUTION: Italy; Greece; Cyprus; Bulgaria; Yugoslavia; Rumania; Albania; Turkey; U.S.S.R. (Caucasus; Transcaucasus; Dagestan).

HOST PLANT: Unrecorded.

*Tingis silvacata Drake

Tingis silvacata Drake 1926d, p. 83 [Brazil].—Monte 1938b, p. 127 [*Davilla rugosa*].

TYPE: Holotype ♀; Chapada, Brazil; Carnegie Mus.

DISTRIBUTION: Brazil.

HOST PLANT: *Davilla rugosa.*

Tingis similis (Douglas and Scott)

Monanthia similis Douglas and Scott 1869, p. 259.—Walker 1873a, p. 187 [England].
Monanthia ampliata var. *similis:* Saunders 1875, p. 248.
Monanthia (Platychila) ampliata var. *similis:* Saunders 1892, p. 132.
Tingis similis: Horváth 1906a, p. 72.—Stichel 1938a, p. 406 [Austria]; 1960a, p. 311 [Czechoslovakia].

TYPE: Unknown.

DISTRIBUTION: England; Austria; Czechoslovakia.

HOST PLANT: Unrecorded.

NOTE: Douglas and Scott state "Two specimens taken by Mr. Wollaston, but the place and date of capture are not recorded."

Tingis sinuaticollis (Jakovlev)

Monanthia (Platychila) sinuaticollis Jakovlev 1883, p. 103 [Dagestan].
Tingis sinuaticollis: Horváth 1906a, p. 71.—Kiritshenko 1951, p. 249.—Stichel 1960a, p. 311.

TYPE: Holotype ♀, macropterous; Derbent, Dagestan, Russia; Leningrad Inst.

DISTRIBUTION: U.S.S.R. (Dagestan).

HOST PLANT: Unrecorded.

*Tingis strictula (Puton)

Monanthia (*Platychila*) *strictula* Puton 1878, p. lxvi [Algeria].
Monanthia striculata [sic]: Chicote 1880, p. 189 [Spain].
Lasiotropis strictula: Lethierry and Severin 1896, p. 18.
Tingis strictula: Horváth 1906a, p. 77.—Gomez-Menor 1955b, p. 248.—
Stichel 1960a, p. 315.—Drake and Ruhoff 1962c, p. 134.
Tingis montana Lindberg 1932a, p. 42, pl. 2, fig. 5 [Spain].—Stichel
1960a, p. 315.

TYPE: Sex unknown; Oran, Algeria; Vienna Mus.
DISTRIBUTION: Algeria; Spain.
HOST PLANT: Unrecorded.

Tingis stupidula Horváth

Tingis stupidula Horváth 1906a, p. 77 [Syria].
TYPE: Holotype ♀; Baalbeck, Syria; Hungarian Mus.
DISTRIBUTION: Syria.
HOST PLANT: Unrecorded.

Tingis suavis (Horváth)

Phyllontocheila suavis Horváth 1902a, p. 595 [Turkmen].
Monanthia (*Lasiotropis*) *longipennis* Jakovlev 1903a, p. 3 [Transcapia].
Tingis suavis: Horváth 1906a, p. 78.

TYPE: Sex unknown; Beush-berma, Turcomania, Russia; Hungarian
Mus.
DISTRIBUTION: U.S.S.R. (Turkmen; Transcapia).
HOST PLANT: Unrecorded.

Tingis tecomae Monte

Tingis tecomae Monte 1940b, p. 377 [Brazil; *Tecoma*].
TYPE: Holotype ♂; Belo Horizonte, Brazil; Monte Coll. (Mus. Nacional).
DISTRIBUTION: Brazil.
HOST PLANT: *Tecoma* sp.

*Tingis teretis Drake

Tingis teretis Drake 1947c, p. 119 [South Australia].
TYPE: Holotype ♂, macropterous; Oldea, South Australia, Australia;
Drake Coll. (USNM).
DISTRIBUTION: Australia (South Australia).
HOST PLANT: Unrecorded.

*Tingis tonkinana Drake

Tingis tonkinana Drake 1947d, p. 228 [Viet-Nam].
TYPE: Holotype ♂; Tonkin, Hoabinh, Indochina; Heude Mus.
DISTRIBUTION: Viet-Nam.
HOST PLANT: Unrecorded.

Tingis toxopeusi Drake

Tingis toxopeusi Drake 1960, p. 362, fig. 14 [New Guinea].

TYPE: Holotype ♀; Neth. Ind. American, New Guinea Expedition 1939, top camp, 2,100 m.; Leiden Mus.

DISTRIBUTION: New Guinea.

HOST PLANT: Unrecorded.

*Tingis veteris Drake

Phyllontocheila ampliata (not Herrich-Schaeffer): Matsumura 1905, p. 33, pl. 19, fig. 11; 1908, p. 148, fig.; 1930, p. 158, pl. 14, fig. 11.

Tingis ampliata (not Herrich-Schaeffer): Matsumura 1931, p. 1203, fig.—Takeya 1951a, p. 16 (in part) [Japan; Siberia; *Cirsium; Carduus*].—Esaki 1954, p. 237, figs. 6, 13.

Tingis (Tropidocheila) veteris Drake 1942a, p. 13 [China].

Tingis veteris: Drake 1947d, p. 228 [Taiwan].—Takeya 1951a, p. 17.

TYPE: Holotype ♂, macropterous; Kianzu Province, China; Drake Coll. (USNM).

DISTRIBUTION: China; Japan; Taiwan; U.S.S.R. (Siberia).

HOST PLANTS: *Carduus* sp.; *Cirsium* sp.

†Tingis sp. Berendt

Tingis sp. Berendt 1845, p. 55 [fossil, amber].—Scudder 1891, p. 449 [Horizon: Ligurian].—Drake and Ruhoff 1960a, p. 11.

TYPE: Sex undeterminable; fossil in Prussian amber; deposition unknown.

DISTRIBUTION: Fossil.

†Tingis sp. Hope

Tingis sp. Hope 1847, p. 252 [France].—Scudder 1891, p. 449 [Horizon: Ligurian].—Drake and Ruhoff 1960a, p. 11.

TYPE: Sex undeterminable; fossil; Aix, France; deposition unknown.

DISTRIBUTION: Fossil.

†Tingis sp. Scudder

Tingis sp. Scudder 1881, p. 292 [Colo.]; 1891, p. 449 [Horizon: Oligocene].—Drake and Ruhoff 1960a, p. 11.

TYPE: Sex undeterminable; fossil; Florissant, Colorado, U.S.; deposition unknown.

DISTRIBUTION: Fossil.

†Tingis sp. Serres

Tingis sp. Serres 1829, p. 227 [France].—Scudder 1891, p. 449 [Horizon: Ligurian (Tertiary)].—Drake and Ruhoff 1960a, p. 11.

Phyllontocheila sp. Scudder 1890, p. 357.

TYPE: Sex undeterminable; fossil; Aix, France; deposition unknown.

DISTRIBUTION: Fossil.

Subgenus TINGIS (CAENOTINGIS) Drake

Tingis (Caenotingis) Drake 1928h, p. 283.—Drake and Ruhoff 1960a, p. 85.

TYPE SPECIES: *Tingis (Caenotingis) beesoni* Drake.

*Tingis (Caenotingis) beesoni Drake

Tingis (Caenotingis) beesoni Drake 1928h, p. 283 [Burma; *Gmelina arborea*].—Singh 1953, p. 119.

Tingis beesoni: Drake and Poor 1936b, p. 146.—Mathur 1955, p. 248, figs. 1–6.

TYPE: Holotype ♂, macropterous; North Toungoo, Burma; Drake Coll. (USNM).

DISTRIBUTION: Burma.

HOST PLANT: *Gmelina arborea.*

Subgenus TINGIS (LASIOTROPIS) Stål

Lasiotropis Stål 1874, p. 55.—Lethierry and Severin 1896, p. 18.— Blöte 1945, p. 87.

Tingis (Lasiotropis): Horváth 1906a, p. 69.—Oshanin 1908, p. 429; 1912, p. 44.—Stichel 1926, pp. 110, 111 (key); 1935, p. 349; 1960a, p. 307.—de Seabra 1931, pp. 423, 425.—Börner 1935, p. 77.— Gulde 1938, pp. 286, 287, 288 (key).—China 1943, p. 247.— Priesner and Alfieri 1953, p. 64.—Drake and Ruhoff 1960a, p. 85.

TYPE SPECIES: *Monanthia (Platychila) trichonota* Puton.

Tingis (Lasiotropis) aetheria Drake and Ruhoff

Tingis (Lasiotropis) wollastoni China 1938, p. 20, fig. 3 [Madeira].

Tingis aetheria Drake and Ruhoff 1960c, p. 32.

TYPE: Sex unknown; Dezerta Grande, Madeira; British Mus.

DISTRIBUTION: Madeira Island.

HOST PLANT: Unrecorded.

*Tingis (Lasiotropis) ajugarum (Frey-Gessner)

Monanthia ajugarum Frey-Gessner 1872, p. 22, pl. 1, fig. 4 [Switzerland].—d'Antessanty 1890, p. 32.—Horváth 1892b, p. 131.

Monanthia (Platychila) ragusana (not Fieber): Puton 1879c, p. 112 [France; *Ajuga chamaepytis; Ajuga genevensis*].

Tingis (Lasiotropis) ajugarum: Horváth 1906a, p. 70 [Italy; Yugoslavia; Algeria].—Stichel 1926, p. 111; 1960a, p. 390 [Greece].— Ramade 1960, p. 221 [*Ajuga iva*].

Tingis ajugarum: Reuter 1908, p. 88.—Lindberg 1932a, p. 41 [Morocco].—Mancini 1949b, p. 36 [Sicily]; 1953d, p. 16.—Novak and Wagner 1951, p. 70.

TYPE: Switzerland; sex and deposition of type unknown.

DISTRIBUTION: Switzerland; France; Italy; Sicily; Greece; Yugoslavia; Algeria; Morocco.

HOST PLANTS: *Ajuga chamaepytis; Ajuga genevensis; Ajuga iva.*

*Tingis (Lasiotropis) beieri Drake

Tingis beieri Drake 1935, p. 11 [Paraguay; Brazil].—Monte 1937a, p. 33, fig. 14 [*Cordia*]; 1939b, p. 81 [*Croton*].—Drake and Hambleton 1938a, p. 64.—Singh 1953, p. 119.—Kormilev 1955a, p. 64 [Argentina; Bolivia].

TYPE: Holotype ♂; S. Bernardino, Paraguay; Vienna Mus.
DISTRIBUTION: Paraguay; Argentina; Brazil; Bolivia.
HOST PLANTS: *Cordia* sp.; *Croton* sp.

*Tingis (Lasiotropis) ciliaris (Puton)

Monanthia (Platychila) ciliaris Puton 1879a, p. lix [Caucasus].
Monanthia (Platychila) balassogloi Jakovlev 1880b, p. 105.
Tingis (Lasiotropis) ciliaris: Horváth 1906a, p. 70 [Syria; Hungary; Greece; Turkey].—Oshanin 1908, p. 430 [Crimea].—Kiritshenko 1951, p. 249.—Seidenstücker 1954, p. 235.—Hoberlandt 1955, p. 89 [Transcaucasus].—Stichel 1960a, p. 309 [Bulgaria].

TYPE: Sex unknown; Caucasus, Russia; Paris Mus.
DISTRIBUTION: Bulgaria; Hungary; Greece; Syria; Turkey; U.S.S.R. (Caucasus; Crimea; Transcaucasus).
HOST PLANT: Unrecorded.

Tingis (Lasiotropis) denudata Horváth

Tingis denudata Horváth 1906a, p. 75 [Algeria; Egypt].
Tingis (Lasiotropis) denudata: Priesner and Alfieri 1953, p. 64.
TYPE: Unknown.
DISTRIBUTION: Algeria; Egypt.
HOST PLANT: Unrecorded.

*Tingis (Lasiotropis) hellenica (Puton)

Monanthia hellenica Puton 1877, p. lxviii [Greece].—Horváth 1889, p. 329 [Syria].
Phyllontochila hellencia: Reuter 1891a, p. 26.
Monanthia (Lasiotropis) corniculata Jakovlev 1903a, p. 3 [Crimea].
Tingis (Lasiotropis) hellenica: Horváth 1906a, p. 69 [Israel; Turkey; Crete; *Phlomis fruticosa*].—Kiritshenko 1951, p. 249.—Seidenstücker 1954, p. 235.—Hoberlandt 1955, p. 89.—Stichel 1960a, p. 308.
Tingis hellenica: Lindberg 1948, p. 58 [Cyprus; *Pistacia; Ceratonia*].
TYPE: Sex unknown; Corfu, Greece; Paris Mus.
DISTRIBUTION: Greece; Crete; Cyprus; Turkey; Syria; Israel; U.S.S.R. (Crimea).
HOST PLANTS: *Ceratonia* sp.; *Phlomis fruticosa; Pistacia* sp.

*Tingis (Lasiotropis) paranana Drake

Tingis paranana Drake 1954d, p. 75 [Argentina].
TYPE: Holotype ♂; Parana, Entre Rois, Argentina; Hungarian Mus.
DISTRIBUTION: Argentina.
HOST PLANT: Unrecorded.

*Tingis (Lasiotropis) ragusana (Fieber)

Monanthia ragusana Fieber 1861, p. 121 [Yugoslavia].—Garbiglietti 1896, p. 272.—Walker 1873a, p. 184.—Puton 1874a, p. 226.—Ferrari 1874, p. 170 [Italy]; 1878, p. 66.—Horváth 1881b, p. xxxiv [Hungary]; 1889, p. 329.—Rey 1893, p. 97.—Hüeber 1893, p. 336 [Austria].

Lasiotropis ragusana: Stål 1874, p. 55.

Monanthia ovatula Jakovlev 1877, p. 92 [Iran].

Tingis (Lasiotropis) ragusana: Horváth 1906a, p. 69, pl. 1, fig. 9 [Caucasus; Rumania; Greece; Germany; France; *Stachys italica*].—Stichel 1926, p. 111 [*Stachys*]; 1960a, p. 308 [Poland; Malta; *Verbascum phlomoides*].—González 1948, p. 50 [Spain].—Kiritshenko 1951, p. 249.—Hoberlandt 1952, p. 112 [Cyprus]; 1955, p. 88 [Transcaucasus].—Seidenstücker 1954, p. 235 [Turkey].

Tingis ragusana: Novak and Wagner 1951, p. 70 [*Stachys salviaefolia*].

Type: Sex unknown; Dalmatia; Vienna Mus.

Distribution: Spain; France; Germany; Austria; Italy; Malta; Yugoslavia; Rumania; Greece; Cyprus; Hungary; Poland; Turkey; Iran; U.S.S.R. (Caucasus; Transcaucasus).

Host Plants: *Stachys italica; Stachys salviaefolia; Stachys* sp.; *Verbascum phlomoides.*

*Tingis (Lasiotropis) reticulata Herrich-Schaeffer

Tingis reticulata Herrich-Schaeffer 1835, p. 58.—Horváth 1916, p. 9 [Albania]; 1918, p. 334.—Scholte 1935, p. 61, fig. 14 [Netherlands].—Stichel 1938a, p. 406 [Poland].—Poisson 1938, p. 589 [*Psamma*].—Mancini 1953b, p. 186.—Bator 1953, p. 325, pl. 2, fig. 7.—Gomez-Menor 1955b, p. 248.—Štušak 1957a, p. 24, figs. 9–13; 1961a, p. 85, figs. 1, 5b.—Cobben 1958b, p. 16.—Southwood and Leston 1959, p. 148, fig. 47.

Monanthia reticulata: Herrich-Schaeffer 1836, p. 72, pl. 72, fig. 288 [Germany].—Douglas and Scott 1865, p. 250.—Horváth 1874b, p. 432.—Ferrari 1874, p. 170; 1878, p. 66.—Saunders 1875, p. 247.

Derephysia reticulata: Spinola 1837, p. 166 [Italy; France].

Tingis costata (not Fabricius): Schilling 1838, p. 105.

Monanthia (Phyllontocheila) ciliata Fieber 1844, p. 67, pl. 5, figs. 31–33 [Czechoslovakia; Austria; *Senecio jacobaea; Verbascum thapsus*].

Monanthia ciliata: Scholz 1847, p. 119.—Mayr 1858, p. 570 [Hungary; Ukraine; Greece].—Fieber 1861, p. 122.—Frey-Gessner 1865, p. 231 [Switzerland].—Garbiglietti 1869, p. 273.—Gredler 1870, p. 75.—Walker 1873a, p. 184.—Reiber and Puton 1876, p. 69.—Vollenhoven 1879, p. 230, pl. 12, fig. e.—Chicote 1880, p. 189 [Spain].—Jakovlev 1880b, p. 104.—Dubois 1888, p. 121.—d'Antessanty 1890, p. 32.—Hüeber 1893, p. 334.—Jensen-Haarup 1912, p. 155, fig. 98a [Denmark].—Butler 1923, p. 212 [Crimea; *Ajuga*].

Monanthia (Phyllontocheila) reticulata: Herrich-Schaeffer 1850, p. 154.

Campylosteira (Derephysia) reticulata: Kolenati 1856, p. 431 [Caucasus; Transcaucasus; *Cirsium; Verbascum*].

Lasiotropis ciliata: Stål 1874, p. 55.

Monanthia (Platychila) ciliata: Puton 1879c, p. 113 [*Ajuga reptans*].—Saunders 1892, p. 133, pl. 12, fig. 7 [England].

Platychila ciliata: Reuter 1885, p. 44.

Tingis (Lasiotropis) reticulata: Horváth 1906a, p. 70 [*Ajuga genevensis*].—Oshanin 1908, p. 430 [Belgium; Yugoslavia; Rumania].—Stichel 1926, p. 111, fig. 300 [*Erica vulgaris*]; 1960a, p. 309, fig. 113 [Sweden; Bulgaria; *Calluna vulgaris; Salvia verticillata*].—Gulde 1938, p. 291, fig.—Hoberlandt 1942, p. 125; 1943a, p. 118; 1943b, p. 123.—Kiritshenko 1951, p. 249.—Stehlik 1952, p. 205.

Phyllonthocheila [sic] *ciliata:* Reichensperger 1920, p. 62.

Lasiotropis reticulata: Blöte 1945, p. 87 [Tunisia].

TYPE: Unknown.

DISTRIBUTION: England; France; Netherlands; Belgium; Spain; Italy; Switzerland; Czechoslovakia; Germany; Denmark; Sweden; Poland; Austria; Hungary; Albania; Bulgaria; Yugoslavia; Rumania; Greece; U.S.S.R. (Crimea; Ukraine; Caucasus; Transcaucasus); Tunisia.

HOST PLANTS: *Ajuga genevensis; Ajuga reptans; Ajuga* sp.; *Calluna vulgaris; Cirsium* sp.; *Erica vulgaris; Erica* sp.; *Psamma* sp.; *Salvia verticillata; Senecio jacobaea; Verbascum thapsus; Verbascum* sp.

NOTE: Description of species appears in Herrich-Schaeffer 1836. Eggs [Štušak].

Tingis (Lasiotropis) rotundipennis Horváth

Tingis rotundipennis Horváth 1911c, p. 108 [Egypt].

Tingis (Lasiotropis) rotundipennis: Priesner and Alfieri 1953, p. 64 [*Echinops spinosa*].

TYPE: Lectotype ♀, macropterous; Materie, Egypt; USNM.

DISTRIBUTION: Egypt.

HOST PLANT: *Echinops spinosa.*

NOTE: Lectotype here designated.

Tingis (Lasiotropis) shaowuana Drake and Maa

Tingis (Lasiotropis) shaowuana Drake and Maa 1953, p. 91 [China].

TYPE: Holotype ♀, macropterous; Shaowu, Fukien, China; Drake Coll. (USNM).

DISTRIBUTION: China.

HOST PLANT: Unrecorded.

Tingis (Lasiotropis) trichonota (Puton)

Monanthia clavicornis (not Linnaeus): Burmeister 1835, p. 260 [Portugal].

Monanthia (Platychila) trichonota Puton 1874a, p. 216 [France].

Lasiotropis trichonota: Stål 1874, p. 55.

Monanthia (*Platychila*) *trichonota:* Puton 1879c, p. 112 [*Phlomis lychnitis*].
Tingis (*Lasiotropis*) *trichonota:* Horváth 1906a, p. 69.—Oshanin 1908,
p. 429 [Greece].—de Seabra 1931, pp. 425, 444, figs. 495(2), 496.—
González 1948, p. 50 [Spain].—Seidenstücker 1954, p. 235 [Tur-
key].—Stichel 1960a, p. 208.
Tingis trichonota: Stichel 1938a, p. 406 [Switzerland].
TYPE: Sex unknown; Avignon, France; Paris Mus.
DISTRIBUTION: Portugal; Spain; France; Switzerland; Greece; Turkey.
HOST PLANT: *Phlomis lychnitis.*

Subgenus TINGIS (TROPIDOCHEILA) Fieber

Monanthia (*Tropidocheila*) Fieber 1844, p. 72.
Monanthia (*Tropidochila*): Puton 1879c, p. 114.
Tropidochila: Lethierry and Severin 1896, p. 19.—Blöte 1945, p. 87.
Tingis (*Tropidocheila*): Horváth 1906a, p. 79.—Mužik 1907, p. 59.—
Stichel 1926, pp. 111, 113; 1960a, p. 316.—de Seabra 1931, p. 427.—
Drake and Ruhoff 1960a, p. 86.
Tingis (*Tropidochila*): Oshanin 1908, p. 437; 1912, p. 44.—Börner
1935, p. 77.—Stichel 1935, p. 349.—Gulde 1938, pp. 288, 296 (key).—
Priesner and Alfieri 1953, p. 64.
TYPE SPECIES: *Monanthia* (*Tropidocheila*) *stachydis* Fieber.

*Tingis (Tropidocheila) abundans Drake and Hambleton

Tingis abundans Drake and Hambleton 1945, p. 357 [Peru].
TYPE: Holotype ♂, macropterous; Pucallpa, Peru; Drake Coll.
(USNM).
DISTRIBUTION: Peru.
HOST PLANT: Unrecorded.

*Tingis (Tropidocheila) acris Drake

Tingis (*Tropidocheila*) *acris* Drake 1947c, p. 117 [Queensland].
TYPE: Holotype ♂, macropterous; Benakin, Queensland, Australia;
Drake Coll. (USNM).
DISTRIBUTION: Australia (Queensland).
HOST PLANT: Unrecorded.

*Tingis (Tropidocheila) aegyptiaca Priesner

Tingis (*Tropidochila*) *aegyptiaca* Priesner 1951, p. 138, fig. [Egypt].—
Priesner and Alfieri 1953, p. 65.
TYPE: Holotype ♀; Arabian Desert, Wadi Nouega, Egypt; Alfieri Coll.
(USNM).
DISTRIBUTION: Egypt.
HOST PLANT: Unrecorded.

*Tingis (Tropidocheila) bodenheimeri Lindberg

Tingis bodenheimeri Lindberg 1930, p. 69, fig. 1 [Israel].

Tingis (Lasiotropis) bodenheimeri: Seidenstücker 1954, p. 235 [Turkey].

Tingis (Tropidocheila) bodenheimeri: Stichel 1960a, p. 319 [Syria].

TYPE: Sex unknown; Jerusalem, Palestine; Helsin. Mus.

DISTRIBUTION: Turkey; Israel; Syria.

HOST PLANT: Unrecorded.

Tingis (Tropidocheila) cappadocica Horváth

Tingis (Tropidocheila) cappadocica Horváth 1906a, p. 82 [Turkey].—Hoberlandt 1955, p. 91.—Stichel 1960a, p. 319.

TYPE: Holotype ♀; Kaisarie, Asia Minor; Vienna Mus.

DISTRIBUTION: Turkey.

HOST PLANT: Unrecorded.

*Tingis (Tropidocheila) caucasica (Jakovlev)

Monanthia (Tropidochila) caucasica Jakovlev 1880a, pp. 136, 137 [Dagestan]; 1880b, p. 107.

Tingis (Tropidocheila) caucasica: Horváth 1906a, p. 83 [Hungary; Yugoslavia; Crimea].—Stichel 1960a, p. 320.

Tingis (Tropidochila) caucasica: Kiritshenko 1951, p. 250.—Seidenstücker 1954, p. 235 [Turkey].

Tingis caucasica: Stichel 1938a, p. 406 [France; Albania].—Putshkov 1960, p. 304 [*Ajuga*].

Tingis (Tropidocheila) caucasia [sic]: Hoberlandt 1955, p. 91.

TYPE: Holotype ♀, macropterous; Derbent, Dagestan, Russia; Leningrad Inst.

DISTRIBUTION: France; Hungary; Yugoslavia; Albania; Turkey; U.S.S.R. (Dagestan; Crimea).

HOST PLANT: *Ajuga* sp.

*Tingis (Tropidocheila) gamboana Drake and Hambleton

Tingis gamboana Drake and Hambleton 1945, p. 357 [Canal Zone; elm].

Tingis (Tropidocheila) gamboana: Hurd 1946, p. 465.

TYPE: Holotype ♀, macropterous; Gamboa, Panama Canal Zone; Drake Coll. (USNM).

DISTRIBUTION: Panama (Canal Zone).

HOST PLANT: Elm.

*Tingis (Tropidocheila) geniculata (Fieber)

Monanthia (Tropidocheila) geniculata Fieber 1844, p. 75, pl. 6, figs. 19–21 [Hungary; Austria].—Herrich-Schaeffer 1850, p. 152.

Monanthia geniculata: Mayr 1858, p. 570.—Fieber 1861, p. 124 [Ukraine].—Garbiglietti 1869, p. 273 [Italy].—Walker 1873a, p. 185.—Horváth 1874b, p. 432.—Ferrari 1874, p. 170; 1878, p. 66.—Bolivar and Chicote 1879, p. 166 [Spain].—Jakovlev 1880b, p. 106 [Caucasus].—Puton 1886a, p. 5 [Tunisia].—d'Antessanty 1890, p. 32.—Hüeber 1893, p. 339.

Tingis geniculata: Stål 1874, p. 54.—Reuter 1908, p. 88 [*Abies alba; Juniperus communis; Populus*].—Novak and Wagner 1951, p. 71.— Mancini 1953d, p. 16 [Sicily].

Monanthia (*Tropidochila*) *geniculata:* Puton 1879c, p. 115.

Tropidochila geniculata: Reuter 1891a, p. 26 [Greece].—Lethierry and Severin 1896, p. 19 [Algeria].—Vidal 1937, p. 197 [Morocco].

Tingis (*Tropidocheila*) *geniculata:* Horváth 1906a, pp. 68, 83, pl. 1, fig. 7 [France; Germany; Yugoslavia; Rumania; Bulgaria; Turkey].— Mužik 1907, p. 60 [Czechoslovakia].—Stichel 1926, p. 113; 1960a, p. 321, fig. 121 [Sardinia; Poland].—Hoberlandt 1943b, p. 120; 1955, p. 91 [Transcaucasus].

Tingis (*Tropidochila*) *geniculata:* Börner 1935, p. 77, fig. 120b.— Kiritshenko 1951, p. 250.—Gomez-Menor 1955b, p. 248.

TYPE: Unknown.

DISTRIBUTION: Spain; France; Germany; Czechoslovakia; Austria; Hungary; Italy; Sicily; Sardinia; Yugoslavia; Rumania; Poland; Bulgaria; Greece; Turkey; U.S.S.R. (Ukraine; Caucasus; Transcaucasus); Tunisia; Algeria; Morocco.

HOST PLANTS: *Abies alba; Juniperus communis; Populus* sp.

*Tingis (Tropidocheila) granadensis Horváth

Tingis (*Tropidocheila*) *granadensis* Horváth 1960a, p. 80 [Spain].— Stichel 1960a, p. 317.

Tingis granadensis: Lindberg 1932a, p. 42.—Wagner 1958, p. 240 [France; *Phlomis herba-venti*].

TYPE: Holotype ♀; Granada, Spain; Helsin. Mus.

DISTRIBUTION: Spain; France.

HOST PLANT: *Phlomis herba-venti.*

*Tingis (Tropidocheila) griseola (Puton)

Monanthia (*Tropidochila*) *geniculata* var. *griseola* Puton 1879c, p. 116 [France; Corsica; Sardinia; Algeria].—Horváth 1892b, p. 131.

Tropidochila geniculata var. *griseola:* Reuter 1891a, p. 26 [Greece].

Tingis (*Tropidocheila*) *griseola:* Horváth 1906a, p. 84 [Yugoslavia; Italy; Majorca].—Moroder Sala 1920, p. 12 [Spain].—Stichel 1926, p. 113; 1960a, p. 321.

Tingis griseola: Novak and Wagner 1951, p. 71 [*Juniperus phoenicea*].— Mancini 1952, p. 13 [Sicily].

TYPE: Sex unknown; France; Paris Mus.

DISTRIBUTION: Spain; France; Corsica; Balearic Islands (Majorca); Sicily; Italy; Sardinia; Greece; Yugoslavia; Algeria.

HOST PLANT: *Juniperus phoenicea.*

Tingis (Tropidocheila) griseola var. miscella (Horváth)

Phyllontocheila miscella Horváth 1902a, p. 598 [Sardinia; Sicily; Algeria].
Tingis (Tropidocheila) griseola var. miscella: Horváth 1906a, p. 84.—
Stichel 1926, p. 113; 1960a, p. 321.—Hoberlandt 1955, p. 91 [Turkey].
Tingis griseola var. miscella: Novak and Wagner 1951, p. 71 [Yugoslavia].—Mancini 1953c, p. 22 [Italy].
TYPE: Unknown.
DISTRIBUTION: Italy; Sardinia; Sicily; Yugoslavia; Turkey; Algeria.
HOST PLANT: Unrecorded.

*Tingis (Tropidocheila) helvina (Jakovlev)

Monanthia (Platychila) helvina Jakovlev 1876a, p. 111 [Siberia].
Phyllontochila helvina: Lethierry and Severin 1896, p. 17.
Tingis (Tropidocheila) helvina: Horváth 1906a, p. 85.
TYPE: Holotype ♀, macropterous; Ussuri, Russia; Leningrad Inst.
DISTRIBUTION: U.S.S.R. (Siberia).
HOST PLANT: Unrecorded.

*Tingis (Tropidocheila) insularis (Horváth)

Phyllontocheila insularis Horváth 1902a, p. 599 [Madeira].
Tingis (Tropidocheila) insularis: Horváth 1906a, p. 84.—China 1938,
p. 20.
Tingis (Tropidochila) insularis: Gomez-Menor 1955b, p. 248 [Spain].
TYPE: Holotype ♂; Madeira; Vienna Mus.
DISTRIBUTION: Madeira; Spain.
HOST PLANT: Unrecorded.

Tingis (Tropidocheila) juvenca (Horváth)

Phyllontocheila juvenca Horváth 1902a, p. 598 [Algeria].
Tingis (Tropidocheila) juvenca: Horváth 1906a, p. 83 [Spain].—Stichel
1960a, p. 320.
Tingis (Tropidochila) juvenca: Gomez-Menor 1955b, p. 248.
TYPE: Holotype ♀; Algeria; Hungarian Mus.
DISTRIBUTION: Algeria; Spain.
HOST PLANT: Unrecorded.

Tingis (Tropidocheila) kirinana Drake

Tingis (Tropidocheila) kirinana Drake 1948a, p. 1, fig. 1 [China].
TYPE: Holotype ♀; Kao-lin-tze, Kirin Province, Manchuria; Heude Mus.
DISTRIBUTION: China.
HOST PLANT: Unrecorded.

*Tingis (Tropidocheila) liturata (Fieber)

Monanthia (Tropidocheila) liturata Fieber 1844, p. 74, pl. 6, figs. 16–18
[Spain].—Herrich-Schaeffer 1850, p. 152.
Monanthia liturata: Fieber 1861, p. 123.—Walker 1873a, p. 185.—
Bolivar and Chicote 1879, p. 166.

Tingis liturata: Stål 1874, p. 54.—Lindberg 1932a, p. 42.
Monanthia (Tropidochila) liturata: Puton 1879c, p. 116 [France].
Tropidochila liturata: Lethierry and Severin 1896, p. 19 [Algeria].—
Vidal 1937, p. 197.—Blöte 1945, p. 87 [Egypt].
Tingis (Tropidocheila) liturata: Horváth 1906a, p. 84 [Portugal; Sicily;
Tunisia; Mauritania].—Stichel 1960a, p. 322, fig. 124 [Libya].
Tingis (Tropidochila) liturata: Oshanin 1908, p. 441 [Morocco].—
Priesner and Alfieri 1953, p. 65.

TYPE: Andalusia; sex and deposition of type unknown.

DISTRIBUTION: Portugal; Spain; France; Sicily; Italy; Algeria; Tunisia;
Mauritania; Morocco; Libya; Egypt.

HOST PLANT: Unrecorded.

*Tingis (Tropidocheila) marrubii Vallot

Tingis marrubii Vallot 1829, p. 98 [*Marrubium vulgare*].
Monanthia kiesenwetteri Mulsant and Rey 1852a, p. 135 [France]; 1852b,
p. 154.—Fieber 1861, p. 383.—Walker 1873a, p. 187.—Bolivar and
Chicote 1879, p. 166.—Jakovlev 1893, p. 294 [Russia].
Monanthia villosa Costa 1855a, p. 11; 1855b, p. 233.—Puton 1874a,
p. 277.—Stichel 1960d, p. 120.
Lasiotropis kiesenwetteri: Stål 1874, p. 56.
Lasiotropis kiesenwetteri [sic]: Sahlberg 1878, p. 21 [Italy; Spain; Siberia].
Monanthia (Tropidochila) kiesenwetteri: Puton 1879c, p. 115 [*Carduus;
Marrubium*].
Tropidochila kiesenwetteri: Lethierry and Severin 1896, p. 19 [Cauca-
sus].—Vidal 1937, p. 197.—Blöte 1945, p. 87 [Greece].
Tingis (Tropidocheila) kiesenwetteri: Horváth 1906a, p. 81 [Hungary;
Rumania; Turkey; Turkestan; Algeria].—Moroder Sala 1920,
p. 12.—Stichel 1926, p. 113; 1960a, p. 318 [Bulgaria].—Hoberlandt
1955, p. 90.
Tingis kiesenwetteri: Horváth 1906d, p. 2.—Lindberg 1932a, p. 42
[Morocco].—Novak and Wagner 1951, p. 71 [Yugoslavia].—
Mancini 1960b, p. 114.
Tingis (Tropidochila) kiesenwetteri: Gulde 1938, p. 299 [Germany].—
Gomez-Menor 1955b, p. 248.
Tingis (Tropidocheila) marrubii: Drake and Ruhoff 1960c, p. 32.

TYPE: Unknown.

DISTRIBUTION: Spain; France; Germany; Italy; Hungary; Rumania;
Yugoslavia; Bulgaria; Greece; Turkey; U.S.S.R. (Caucasus; Turkestan;
Siberia); Algeria; Morocco.

HOST PLANTS: *Carduus* sp.; *Marrubium vulgare; Marrubium* sp.

*Tingis (Tropidocheila) muiri Drake

Tingis (Tropidocheila) muiri Drake 1947c, p. 116 [Queensland].

TYPE: Holotype ♂, macropterous; Coolangata, Queensland, Australia; Drake Coll. (USNM).

DISTRIBUTION: Australia (Queensland).

HOST PLANT: Unrecorded.

*Tingis (Tropidocheila) oliveirai Drake and Hambleton

Tingis oliveirai Drake and Hambleton 1938a, p. 64 [Brazil].

TYPE: Holotype ♂, macropterous; Curvello, Minas Gerais, Brazil; Drake Coll. (USNM).

DISTRIBUTION: Brazil.

HOST PLANT: Unrecorded.

*Tingis (Tropidocheila) pauperata (Puton)

Monanthia kiesenwetteri var. *pauperata* Puton 1879b, p. 297 [Caucasus].

Monanthia (Tropidochila) kiesenwetteri var. *pauperata:* Puton 1879c, p. 115.

Monanthia (Tropidochila) angustipennis Jakovlev 1880b, p. 107.

Tingis (Tropidocheila) pauperata: Horváth 1906a, p. 81 [Armenia; Spain; France; Albania; Rumania].—Stichel 1960a, p. 318 [Italy; Yugoslavia; Turkey; Turkestan].

Tingis (Tropidochila) pauperata: Kiritshenko 1913b, p. 482; 1951, p. 250.—Gomez-Menor 1955b, p. 248.

Tingis pauperata: Horváth 1916, p. 9.—Mancini 1953b, p. 186.— Putshkov 1960, p. 312 [*Phlomis pungens*].

Tropidochila pauperata: Vidal 1937, p. 197 [Morocco].

TYPE: Sex unknown; Caucasus, Russia; Paris Mus.

DISTRIBUTION: Italy; France; Spain; Yugoslavia; Rumania; Albania; Turkey; U.S.S.R. (Turkestan; Caucasus; Armenia); Morocco.

HOST PLANT: *Phlomis pungens.*

*Tingis (Tropidocheila) pilosa Hummel

Tingis pilosa Hummel 1825, p. 69 [Russia].—Reuter 1885, p. 44.— Lindberg 1932a, p. 42 [Morocco]; 1934, p. 29 [China].—Scholte 1935, p. 62, fig. 17 [Netherlands].—Stichel 1938a, p. 406 [Portugal; Yugoslavia; Bulgaria; Poland].—Bator 1953, p. 326, pl. 4, fig. 4.

Monanthia angusticollis Herrich-Schaeffer 1836, p. 72, fig. 289 [Germany].—d'Antessanty 1890, p. 32.—Hüeber 1893, p. 340.

Tingis cardui (not Linnaeus): Schilling 1838, p. 105.

Derephysia angusticollis: Herrich-Schaeffer 1838, p. 71.

Monanthia (Tropidocheila) pilosa: Fieber 1844, p. 79, pl. 6, figs. 36–37 [Czechoslovakia; Austria].

Monanthia (Tropidocheila) angusticollis: Herrich-Schaeffer 1850, p 152.

Monanthia pilosa: Mayr 1858, p. 571 [Hungary].—Fieber 1861, p. 122 [France].—Frey-Gessner 1865, p. 231 [Switzerland; *Stachys sylvatica; Galeopsis tetrahit*].—Garbiglietti 1869, p. 273 [Italy].—Gredler 1870, p. 75.—Horváth 1874a, p. 432.—Reiber and Puton 1876, p. 69.

Lasiotropis pilosa: Stål 1874, p. 55.

Monanthia (Tropidochila) angusticollis: Puton 1879c, p. 114 [*Leonurus cardiaca; Lappa minor; Ballota nigra*].

Monanthia (Tropidochila) pilosa: Jakovlev 1880a, p. 136.

Tropidochila angusticollis: Reuter 1885, p. 44; 1891b, p. 184.

Tingis (Tropidocheila) pilosa: Horváth 1906a, pp. 66, 79 [Siberia; Turkestan; Caucasus; Turkey].—Stichel 1926, p. 113 [*Humulus; Crepis tectorum; Senecio*]; 1960a, p. 316 [Greece].—Hoberlandt 1943a, p. 119; 1943b, p. 124; 1955, p. 91 [Transcaucasus; Turkmen].

Tingis (Tropidochila) pilosa: Oshanin 1908, p. 437 [Belgium; Rumania].—Wu 1935, p. 450.—Gulde 1938, p. 297, fig.—González 1948, p. 50 [Spain].—Kiritshenko 1951, p. 250.

Phyllonthocheila [sic] *angusticollis:* Reichensperger 1920, p. 62.

TYPE: Russia; sex and deposition of type unknown.

DISTRIBUTION: Portugal; Spain; France; Netherlands; Belgium; Germany; Poland; Czechoslovakia; Switzerland; Austria; Italy; Hungary; Rumania; Yugoslavia; Bulgaria; Greece; Turkey; U.S.S.R. (Caucasus; Transcaucasus; Turkestan; Turkmen; Siberia); Morocco; China.

HOST PLANTS: *Ballota nigra; Crepis tectorum; Galeopsis tetrahit; Lappa minor; Leonurus cardiaca; Humulus* sp; *Senecio* sp.; *Stachys sylvatica.*

Tingis (Tropidocheila) pilosa var. amplicosta (Montandon)

Lasiotropis amplicosta Montandon 1897, p. 100 [Algeria].

Tingis (Tropidocheila) pilosa var. amplicosta: Horváth 1906a, p. 80.—de Seabra 1931, p. 427, figs. 499, 495 (4–6) [Portugal; *Ballota nigra; Galeopsis tetrahit; Lappa minor; Leonurus cardiaca; Stachys sylvatica*].— Stichel 1960a, p. 317.

TYPE: Sex unknown; Tenient-el-Haad, Algeria; Bucharest Mus.

DISTRIBUTION: Algeria; Portugal.

HOST PLANTS: *Ballota nigra; Galeopsis tetrahit; Lappa minor; Leonurus cardiaca; Stachys sylvatica.*

Tingis (Tropidocheila) pilosa var. antennalis (Puton)

Monanthia kiesenwetteri var. antennalis Puton 1879b, p. 297 [Russia].

Monanthia (Tropidochila) kiesenwetteri var. antennalis: Puton 1879c, p. 115.

Monanthia (Tropidochila) tenuicornis Jakovlev 1880a, p. 136.

Phyllontocheila antennalis: Horváth 1898b, p. 279.

Tingis (Tropidocheila) pilosa var. antennalis: Horváth 1906a, p. 80 [Turkestan; Siberia; Mongolia].—Stichel 1960a, p. 317.

Tingis (Tropidochila) pilosa var. antennalis: Wu 1935, p. 450.

TYPE: Sex unknown; Sarepta, Russia; Paris Mus.

DISTRIBUTION: Mongolia Republic; U.S.S.R. (Turkestan; Siberia).

HOST PLANT: Unrecorded.

*Tingis (Tropidocheila) pusilla (Jakovlev)

Monanthia pusilla Jakovlev 1874a, pp. 10, 33 [Russia].

Tingis (Tropidocheila) pusilla: Horváth 1906a, p. 83.—Seidenstücker 1954, p. 235 [Turkey].—Stichel 1960a, p. 319.

Tingis (Tropidochila) pusilla: Kiritshenko 1951, p. 250.

TYPE: Holotype ♀; Russia; Leningrad Inst.

DISTRIBUTION: U.S.S.R.; Turkey.

HOST PLANT: Unrecorded.

Tingis (Tropidocheila) reuteri Horváth

Tingis (Tropidocheila) reuteri Horváth 1906a, p. 81 [Turkmen].— Hoberlandt 1955, p. 91 [Turkey].—Stichel 1960a, p. 318.

TYPE: Holotype ♂; Ashkhabad, Turkmen, Russia; Helsin. Mus.

DISTRIBUTION: U.S.S.R. (Turkmen); Turkey.

HOST PLANT: Unrecorded.

*Tingis (Tropidocheila) saueri Drake and Hambleton

Tingis saueri Drake and Hambleton 1939, p. 156 [Brazil].

TYPE: Holotype ♂, macropterous; Recife, Pernambuco, Brazil; Drake Coll. (USNM).

DISTRIBUTION: Brazil.

HOST PLANT: Unrecorded.

Tingis (Tropidocheila) stachydis (Fieber)

Monanthia maculata Herrich-Schaeffer 1838, pp. 51, 56, pl. 123, figs. 389a–c [Germany].—Ferrari 1884, p. 475 [Tunisia].—Puton 1886a, p. 12.—d'Antessanty 1890, p. 32.—Rey 1893, p. 97.—Hüeber 1893, p. 339.

Monanthia (Tropidocheila) stachydis Fieber 1844, p. 73, pl. 6, figs. 13–15 [Austria; Czechoslovakia; *Stachys recta*].

Monanthia (Tropidocheila) maculata: Herrich-Schaeffer 1850, p. 152.

Monanthia stachydis: Fieber 1861, p. 123.—Frey-Gessner 1865, p. 232 [Switzerland].—Garbiglietti 1869, p. 273 [Italy].—Walker 1873a, p. 185.—Horváth 1874b, p. 432.—Jakovlev 1876b, p. 67 [Russia].— Reiber and Puton 1876, p. 69.—Bolivar and Chicote 1879, p. 166 [Spain].

Tingis maculata: Walker 1873a, p. 179.—Horváth 1874b, p. 432 [Hungary].—Putshkov 1960, p. 304 [*Sideritis*].

Tingis stachydis: Stål 1874, p. 54.—Drake and Ruhoff 1962c, p. 135.

Monanthia stahidis [sic]: Ferrari 1878, p. 66.

Monanthia (Tropidochila) maculata: Puton 1879c, p. 116 [France].

Tingis (Tropidocheila) maculata: Horváth 1906a, pp. 69, 84.—Stichel 1926, p. 113 [*Teucrium chamaedrys*]; 1960a, p. 322 [Sicily; Poland; *Stachys annua*].

Phyllonthocheila [sic] *maculata:* Reichensperger 1920, p. 62.

Tingis (*Tropidochila*) *maculata:* Börner 1935, p. 77, fig. 120a.—Kiritshenko 1951, p. 251.

TYPE: Sex unknown; Regensburg, Germany; Munich Mus.

DISTRIBUTION: Spain; France; Sicily; Italy; Switzerland; Germany; Czechoslovakia; Poland; Austria; Hungary; U.S.S.R.; Tunisia (?).

HOST PLANTS: *Sideritis* sp.; *Stachys annua; Stachys recta; Stachys* sp.; *Teucrium chamaedrys.*

NOTE: See Horváth 1906a re Tunisia distribution.

*Tingis (Tropidocheila) torpida (Horváth)

Tropidochila geniculata var. Reuter 1900, p. 187.

Phyllontocheila geniculata var. *torpida* Horváth 1902a, p. 597 [Algeria; Tunisia; Morocco].

Tingis (*Tropidocheila*) *torpida:* Horváth 1906a, p. 83 [Spain; Mauritania].—Moroder Sala 1920, p. 12.—Stichel 1960a, p. 320 [France].

Tropidochila torpida: Blöte 1945, p. 88 [Sardinia].

TYPE: Unknown.

DISTRIBUTION: Spain; Sardinia; Morocco; Tunisia; Algeria; Mauritania.

HOST PLANT: Unrecorded.

Tingis (Tropidocheila) valida (Puton)

Monanthia (*Lasiotropis*) *valida* Puton 1878, p. lxviii [Syria].

Tingis (*Tropidocheila*) *valida:* Horváth 1906a, p. 79 [Turkey; Lebanon; Iran].—Stichel 1960a, p. 316 [Turkestan].

Tingis (*Tingis*) *valida:* Hoberlandt 1955, p. 90.

TYPE: Sex unknown; Syria; Vienna Mus.

DISTRIBUTION: Syria; Lebanon; Iran; Turkey; U.S.S.R. (Turkestan).

HOST PLANT: Unrecorded.

Tingis (Tropidocheila) valida var. **biseriata** (Horváth)

Phyllontocheila valida var. *biseriata* Horváth 1902a, p. 600 [Turkestan].

Tingis (*Tropidocheila*) *valida* var. *biseriata:* Horváth 1906a, p. 79.—Stichel 1960a, p. 316.

TYPE: Holotype ♀; Varzaminor, Turkestan, Russia; Hungarian Mus.

DISTRIBUTION: U.S.S.R. (Turkestan).

HOST PLANT: Unrecorded.

Tingis (Tropidocheila) valida var. **discessa** (Horváth)

Phyllontocheila valida var. *discessa* Horváth 1902a, p. 600 [Turkestan].

Tingis (*Tropidocheila*) *valida* var. *discessa:* Horváth 1906a, p. 79.—Stichel 1960a, p. 316.

TYPE: Holotype ♀; Varzaminor, Turkestan, Russia; Hungarian Mus.

DISTRIBUTION: U.S.S.R. (Turkestan).

HOST PLANT: Unrecorded.

Genus TRACHYPEPLUS Horváth

Trachypeplus Horváth 1926, p. 329.—Drake and Ruhoff 1960a, p. 86.

TYPE SPECIES: *Trachypeplus jacobsoni* Horváth.

*Trachypeplus bakeri Drake

> *Trachypeplus bakeri* Drake 1927d, p. 308 [Mindanao].—Drake and Poor 1937a, p. 12.

TYPE: Holotype ♂, macropterous; Iligan, Mindanao, Philippine Islands; Drake Coll. (USNM).

DISTRIBUTION: Philippine Islands (Mindanao).

HOST PLANT: Unrecorded.

*Trachypeplus chinensis Drake and Poor

> *Trachypeplus chinensis* Drake and Poor 1936a, p. 440 [Hainan; Hong Kong].—Drake 1937b, p. 593; 1938b, p. 195; 1947d, p. 229, fig. [Viet-Nam]; 1947g, no. 69, fig. (color).

TYPE: Holotype ♂, macropterous; Liamui, Hainan Island; Drake Coll. (USNM).

DISTRIBUTION: China (Hainan Island); Viet-Nam; Hong Kong.

HOST PLANT: Unrecorded.

*Trachypeplus guinaicus Drake

> *Trachypeplus guinaicus* Drake 1960, p. 350 [New Guinea].

TYPE: Holotype ♀; Asama, Morobe, Northeast New Guinea; Drake Coll. (USNM).

DISTRIBUTION: New Guinea (Northeast).

HOST PLANT: Unrecorded.

*Trachypeplus idoneus Drake and Ruhoff

> *Trachypeplus idoneus* Drake and Ruhoff 1962d, p. 491 [Sumatra].

TYPE: Holotype ♀, macropterous; Medan, Sumatra; Drake Coll. (USNM).

DISTRIBUTION: Greater Sunda Islands (Sumatra).

HOST PLANT: Unrecorded.

*Trachypeplus jacobsoni Horváth

> *Trachypeplus jacobsoni* Horváth 1926, p. 330, fig. 3 [Sumatra; *Mallotus philippinensis*].—Drake and Poor 1936b, p. 144 [India].—Blöte 1945, p. 92.—Singh 1953, p. 119.

TYPE: Fort de Kock, Sumatra; sex and deposition of type unknown.

DISTRIBUTION: Greater Sunda Islands (Sumatra); India.

HOST PLANT: *Mallotus philippinensis*.

*Trachypeplus malloti Drake and Poor

> *Trachypeplus malloti* Drake and Poor 1936b, p. 144 [India; *Mallotus philippinensis*].

TYPE: Holotype ♂, macropterous; Dehra Dun, India; Drake Coll. (USNM).

DISTRIBUTION: India.

HOST PLANT: *Mallotus philippinensis*.

Genus UHLERITES Drake

Uhlerites Drake 1927a, p. 56; 1948b, p. 56.—Drake and Ruhoff 1960a, p. 87.

TYPE SPECIES: *Phyllontocheila debile* Uhler.

*Uhlerites debilis (Uhler)

Phyllontochila debile Uhler 1896, p. 265 [Japan].—Matsumura 1931, p. 1202, fig.

Stephanitis (Norba) x-nigrum Lindberg 1927, p. 15, pl. 1, fig. 3 [Siberia].

Uhlerites debile: Drake 1927a, p. 56; 1948b, p. 56 [China].—Takeya 1951a, p. 14 [Taiwan]; 1953d, p. 173.

Uhlerites debilis: Takeya 1931, p. 78, pl. 7, fig. 5; pl. 9, fig. 7 [*Quercus serrata; Quercus glandulifera; Quercus dentata*]; 1932, p. 10 [Korea].— Esaki 1932, p. 1636, fig.; 1954, p. 237, fig. 612.—Saitô 1933, p. 7 [*Quercus acutissima*].—Kato 1933, pl. 31, fig. 1.—Fukui 1938, pl. 50, tab. 36.

TYPE: Holotype ♀, macropterous; Japan; USNM.

DISTRIBUTION: Japan; China; Taiwan; Korea; U.S.S.R. (Siberia).

HOST PLANTS: *Quercus acutissima; Quercus dentata; Quercus glandulifera; Quercus serrata.*

*Uhlerites latius Takeya

Uhlerites latiorus Takeya 1931, p. 80, pl. 9, figs. 8–10 [Japan].

Uhlerites latius (emended): Drake 1948b, p. 56 [China].—Takeya 1951a, p. 14.

TYPE: Sex unknown; Honghû, Prov. Harima, Japan; Kyushu Univ.

DISTRIBUTION: Japan; China.

HOST PLANT: Unrecorded.

Genus ULOCYSTA Drake and Hambleton

Ulocysta Drake and Hambleton 1945, p. 364.—Drake and Ruhoff 1960a, p. 87.

TYPE SPECIES: *Ulocysta praestabilis* Drake and Hambleton.

*Ulocysta praestabilis Drake and Hambleton

Ulocysta praestabilis Drake and Hambleton 1945, p. 365 [Colombia].

TYPE: Holotype ♀, macropterous; San José, Colombia; Drake Coll. (USNM).

DISTRIBUTION: Colombia.

HOST PLANT: Unrecorded.

Genus ULONEMIA Drake and Poor

Perissonemia (Ulonemia) Drake and Poor 1937a, p. 3.

Ulonemia: Drake 1942b, p. 359.—Drake and Ruhoff 1960a, p. 87.

TYPE SPECIES: *Perissonemia (Ulonemia) dignata* Drake and Poor.

Ulonemia aptata Drake

Ulonemia aptata Drake 1960, p. 351, fig. 8 [New Guinea].

TYPE: Holotype ♀; Nondugl, Northeast New Guinea; Bishop Mus.

DISTRIBUTION: New Guinea (Northeast).

HOST PLANT: Unrecorded.

*Ulonemia assamensis (Distant)

Teleonemia assamensis Distant 1903a, p. 49 [India]; 1903b, p. 143, fig. 106.—Drake 1937b, p. 592 [China].

Perissonemia assamensis: Drake and Poor 1936a, p. 439 [Hainan; Taiwan].

Perissonemia (*Ulonemia*) *assamensis:* Takeya 1951a, p. 18.

Ulonemia assamensis: Drake and Ruhoff 1960c, p. 29.

TYPE: Sex unknown; Margherita, Assam, India; British Mus.

DISTRIBUTION: India; Taiwan; China (Hainan Island); Greater Sunda Islands (Borneo).

HOST PLANT: Unrecorded.

*Ulonemia concava Drake

Ulonemia concava Drake 1942b, p. 359 [Queensland].

TYPE: Holotype ♂, macropterous; Cedar Creek, Queensland, Australia; Drake Coll. (USNM).

DISTRIBUTION: Australia (Queensland).

HOST PLANT: Unrecorded.

*Ulonemia decoris Drake

Ulonemia decoris Drake 1942b, p. 360 [Queensland; South Australia].

TYPE: Holotype ♂, macropterous; Mount Glorious, Queensland, Australia; Drake Coll. (USNM).

DISTRIBUTION: Australia (Queensland; South Australia).

HOST PLANT: Unrecorded.

*Ulonemia dignata (Drake and Poor)

Perissonemia (*Ulonemia*) *dignata* Drake and Poor 1937a, p. 3 [Luzon; Mindanao].

Ulonemia dignata: Drake and Ruhoff 1960c, p. 29.

TYPE: Holotype ♂, macropterous; Baguio, Benguet Subprovince, Luzon, Philippine Islands; Drake Coll. (USNM).

DISTRIBUTION: Philippine Islands (Luzon; Mindanao).

HOST PLANT: Unrecorded.

*Ulonemia electa (Drake and Poor)

Perissonemia (*Ulonemia*) *electa* Drake and Poor 1937a, p. 5 [Luzon].

Ulonemia electa: Drake and Ruhoff 1960c, p. 29.

TYPE: Holotype ♂, macropterous; Baguio, Benguet Subprovince, Luzon, Philippine Islands; Drake Coll. (USNM).

DISTRIBUTION: Philippine Islands (Luzon).

HOST PLANT: Unrecorded.

*Ulonemia leai Drake

Ulonemia leai Drake 1942b, p. 360 [Australia].

TYPE: Holotype ♀, macropterous; Cairns District, Australia; Drake Coll. (USNM).

DISTRIBUTION: Australia.

HOST PLANT: Unrecorded.

*Ulonemia malaccae (Drake)

Perissonemia malaccae Drake 1942a, p. 3 [Malaya].

Ulonemia malaccae: Drake and Ruhoff 1960c, p. 29.

TYPE: Holotype ♀, macropterous; Malacca, Perak, Federated Malay States; Drake Coll. (USNM).

DISTRIBUTION: Federation of Malaya.

HOST PLANT: Unrecorded.

*Ulonemia mjobergi (Horváth)

Tingis (Tingis) mjobergi Horváth 1925a, p. 5 [Australia].

Tingis myobergi [sic]: Drake 1947c, p. 114, fig. 24b.

Ulonemia mjobergi: Drake and Ruhoff 1960c, p. 29; 1961b, p. 139, fig. 12.—Drake 1961b, p. 112 [New South Wales].

TYPE: Sex unknown; Australia occidentalis; Stockholm Mus.

DISTRIBUTION: Australia (New South Wales; Western Australia).

HOST PLANT: Unrecorded.

*Ulonemia plesia Drake and Ruhoff

Ulonemia plesia Drake and Ruhoff 1961b, p. 138 [Western Australia].

TYPE: Holotype ♀, macropterous; Swan River, Western Australia, Australia; Drake Coll. (USNM).

DISTRIBUTION: Australia (Western Australia).

HOST PLANT: Unrecorded.

Genus ULOTINGIS Drake and Hambleton

Ulotingis Drake and Hambleton 1935, p. 144.—Monte 1939b, p. 82; 1941e, p. 148.—Drake and Ruhoff 1960a, p. 87.

TYPE SPECIES: *Acysta brasiliensis* Drake.

*Ulotingis brasiliensis (Drake)

Acysta brasiliensis Drake 1922b, p. 42 [Brazil].

Ulotingis brasiliensis: Drake and Hambleton 1935, p. 145; 1938a, p. 64 [*Psidium guajava*].—Silva 1956, p. 67.

TYPE: Holotype ♂, macropterous; Para, Brazil; USNM.

DISTRIBUTION: Brazil.

HOST PLANT: *Psidium guajava.*

*Ulotingis decor Drake and Hambleton

Ulotingis decor Drake and Hambleton 1935, p. 145 [Brazil; Myrtaceae].

TYPE: Holotype ♂, macropterous; Santo Amaro, São Paulo, Brazil; Drake Coll. (USNM).

DISTRIBUTION: Brazil.

HOST PLANT: Myrtaceae.

*Ulotingis nitor Drake and Hambleton (emendation)

Ulotingis nitoris Drake and Hambleton 1935, p. 145, fig. 2 [Brazil; Myrtaceae].

TYPE: Holotype ♂, macropterous; São Paulo, Brazil; Drake Coll. (USNM).

DISTRIBUTION: Brazil.

HOST PLANT: Myrtaceae.

*Ulotingis uniseriata (Drake)

Acysta brasiliensis var. *uniseriata* Drake 1922c, p. 368, pl. 39, fig. 10 [Brazil].

Acysta uniseriata: Drake and Bondar 1932, p. 91 [*Byrsonima sericea*].— Costa Lima 1936, p. 125.—Monte 1937a, p. 35, fig. 13 [*Byrsonima verbascifolia*].

Ulotingis uniseriata: Drake and Hambleton 1935, p. 145; 1938a, p. 65.— Silva 1956, p. 68, fig. 29.

TYPE: Holotype ♀; Chapada, Brazil; Carnegie Mus.

DISTRIBUTION: Brazil.

HOST PLANTS: *Byrsonima sericea; Byrsonima verbascifolia.*

Genus URENTIUS Distant

Urentius Distant 1903b, p. 134.—Bergroth 1911, p. 186; 1914b, p. 183.— Priesner and Alfieri 1953, p. 63 (key).—Stichel 1960a, p. 298; 1960b. p. 394; 1960c, p. 133.—Drake and Ruhoff 1960a, p. 88.

Ayrerus Distant 1903b, p. 140.—Horváth 1909b, p. 632.—Drake and Ruhoff 1960a, p. 38.

Prionostirina Schumacher 1913, p. 457.—Drake and Ruhoff 1960a, p. 79.

TYPE SPECIES: *Urentius echinus* Distant= *Tingis hystricellus* Richter.

*Urentius chobauti Horváth

Urentius chobauti Horváth 1907, p. 304 [France; Spain; *Cistus albidus*].— Oshanin 1908, p. 457; 1912, p. 43.—Stichel 1935, p. 349; 1938a, p. 406; 1960a, p. 298.

TYPE: Unknown.

DISTRIBUTION: France; Spain.

HOST PLANT: *Cistus albidus.*

*Urentius euonymus Distant

    Urentius euonymus Distant 1909a, p. 116 [Ceylon]; 1910a, p. 114, fig. 57.—Drake and Ruhoff 1962a, p. 156; 1962c, p. 133.

    Prionostirina nana Schumacher 1913, p. 458 [Israel].

    Urentius nanus: Bergroth 1914b, p. 183.—Hoberlandt 1955, p. 88 [Turkey; Syria].—Stichel 1960a, p. 299.

    Urentius hoggari Bergevin 1928, p. 336, fig. 1 [Algeria; *Helianthemum lippii*].—Stichel 1960a, p. 299.

    Urentius maculatus Drake 1933, p. 1015 [India].

    Urentius abutilinus Priesner and Alfieri 1953, p. 63 [Egypt; *Abutilon muticum*].—Stichel 1960a, p. 299 [*Abutilon pannosum*].

    TYPE: Sex unknown; Batticaloa, Ceylon; British Mus.

    DISTRIBUTION: Ceylon; India; Israel; Syria; Turkey; Egypt; Sudan; Algeria.

    HOST PLANTS: *Abutilon muticum; Abutilon pannosum; Abutilon* sp.; *Cajanus indicus; Helianthemum lippii; Sida cordifolia.*

Urentius euphorbiae Menon and Hakk (nom. nud.)

    Urentius euphorbiae Menon and Hakk 1959b, p. 393.

*Urentius hystricellus (Richter)

    Tingis hystricellus Richter 1869, p. 84, fig. 55 [Ceylon].—Green 1882, p. 161.

    Ayrerus hystricellus: Distant 1903b, p. 141, fig. 104 [*Solanum melongena*].

    Urentius echinus Distant 1903b, p. 134, fig. 97.—Maxwell-Lefroy 1909, p. 693 [India].—Fletcher 1920, p. 263.—Singh 1953, p. 120.—Drake 1954a, p. 232 [Niger].—Patel and Kulkarny 1955, pp. 86–96, pls. 1, 2.—Thontadarya and Channa Basavanna 1959, p. 289.—Drake and Davis 1960, fig. 32.

    Urentius olivaceus Distant 1909a, p. 115; 1910a, p. 112.

    Urentius sentis Distant 1909a, p. 115; 1910a, p. 113, fig. 56.

    Urentius aegyptiacus Bergevin 1930, p. 18, fig. [Egypt].—Priesner and Alfieri 1953, p. 63.—Stichel 1960a, p. 299.

    Urentius hystricellus: Drake and Ruhoff 1960a, p. 89; 1962a, p. 156; 1962c, p. 133.

    TYPE: Holotype ♀; Ceylon; deposition unknown.

    DISTRIBUTION: Ceylon; India; Niger; Egypt; Kenya; Sudan; Senegal; Uganda; Southern Rhodesia.

    HOST PLANT: *Solanum melongena.*

    NOTE: (1) Taken at port-of-entry, Washington, D.C. on leaves of eggplant; (2) notes on egg laying [Thontadarya and Channa Basavanna]; (3) life history study [Patel and Kulkarny].

Urentius indicus Menon and Hakk (nom. nud.)

    Urentius indicus Menon and Hakk 1959b, p. 393.

Urentius pusaensis Menon and Hakk (nom. nud.)

    Urentius pusaensis Menon and Hakk 1959b, p. 393.

Urentius sarinae Hacker

Urentius sarinae Hacker 1929, p. 325, pl. 32, fig. 3 [Queensland].

TYPE: Sex unknown; Sarina, Queensland, Australia; Queensland Mus.

DISTRIBUTION: Australia (Queensland).

HOST PLANT: Unrecorded.

Urentius sidae Menon and Hakk (nom. nud.)

Urentius sidae Menon and Hakk 1959b, p. 393.

*Urentius vepris Drake

Urentius vepris Drake 1945, p. 100 [Transvaal; *Hermannia micropetela*].

TYPE: Holotype ♂; Commando Nek, Pretoria, Transvaal; British Mus.

DISTRIBUTION: South Africa (Transvaal).

HOST PLANT: *Hermannia micropetela*.

Urentius zizyphifolius Menon and Hakk (nom. nud.)

Urentius zizyphifolius Menon and Hakk 1959b, p. 393.

Genus VATIGA Drake and Hambleton

Vatiga Drake and Hambleton 1946a, p. 10.—Hurd 1946, p. 466.— Drake and Ruhoff 1960a, p. 88.

TYPE SPECIES: *Vatiga vicosana* Drake and Hambleton.

*Vatiga cassiae (Drake and Hambleton)

Tigava cassiae Drake and Hambleton 1934, p. 440 [Brazil; *Cassia*].— Costa Lima 1936, p. 130.—Monte 1941e, p. 144.

Vatiga cassiae: Drake and Hambleton 1946a, p. 10.

TYPE: Holotype ♂, macropterous; Viçosa, Minas Gerais, Brazil; Drake Coll. (USNM).

DISTRIBUTION: Brazil.

HOST PLANT: *Cassia* sp.

*Vatiga celebrata (Drake)

Leptopharsa celebratis Drake 1928a, p. 53 [Brazil].—Monte 1941e, p. 109.

Vatiga celebratis: Drake and Ruhoff 1960c, p. 29.

TYPE: Holotype ♂, macropterous; Rio Grande do Sul, Brazil; Drake Coll. (USNM).

DISTRIBUTION: Brazil.

HOST PLANT: Unrecorded.

*Vatiga illudens (Drake)   FIGURE 3

Atheas nigricornis (not Champion): Van Duzee 1907, p. 22.

Leptopharsa illudens Drake 1922c, p. 370 [Puerto Rico; Jamaica; Dominican Republic]; 1930b, p. 25 [Brazil].—Wolcott 1923, p. 246 [*Manihot*].—Drake and Bruner 1924a, p. 148 [Haiti; Cuba; *Manihot utilissima*].—Barber 1939, p. 370.—Monte 1941e, p. 113; 1942d, p. 108.—Bruner, Scaramuzza, and Otero 1945, p. 109 [*Manihot esculenta*].—Gomez-Menor 1956a, p. 112.

Atheas pallidus Barber 1923, p. 6.
Vatiga illudens: Drake and Hambleton 1946a, p. 10.—Silva 1956, p. 69 [*Manihot dulcis*].—Drake and Cobben 1960, p. 85, figs. 84a, b [St. Eustatius].

TYPE: Holotype ♀, macropterous; Mandeville, Jamaica; Drake Coll. (USNM).

DISTRIBUTION: Cuba; Haiti; Dominican Republic; Jamaica; Puerto Rico; Leeward Islands (St. Eustatius); Brazil.

HOST PLANTS: *Manihot dulcis; Manihot esculenta; Manihot utilissima; Manihot* sp.

*Vatiga illudens var. varianta (Drake)

Leptopharsa illudens var. *variantis* Drake 1930b, p. 25 [Brazil].—Monte 1940b, p. 378; 1941e, p. 113 [*Manihot dulcis*].
Vatiga illudens var. *variantis:* Drake and Hambleton 1946a, p. 10.— Silva 1956, p. 70.

TYPE: Holotype ♂, macropterous; Bahia, Brazil; Drake Coll. (USNM).
DISTRIBUTION: Brazil.
HOST PLANT: *Manihot dulcis.*

*Vatiga lonchocarpa (Drake and Hambleton)

Tigava lonchocarpa Drake and Hambleton 1944b, p. 125 [Brazil; *Lonchocarpus*].
Vatiga lonchocarpa: Drake and Hambleton 1946a, p. 10.

TYPE: Holotype ♀, macropterous; Viçosa, Minas Gerais, Brazil; Drake Coll. (USNM).
DISTRIBUTION: Brazil.
HOST PLANT: *Lonchocarpus* sp.

*Vatiga longula (Drake)

Leptopharsa longula Drake 1922c, p. 371, pl. 39, fig. 4 [Brazil].—Costa Lima 1936, p. 129.—Monte 1937a, p. 35; 1939b, p. 74 [*Bauhinia; Manihot utilissima*]; 1941e, p. 114.
Vatiga longula: Drake and Hambleton 1946a, p. 10.

TYPE: Holotype ♀; Chapada, Brazil; Carnegie Mus.
DISTRIBUTION: Brazil.
HOST PLANTS: *Bauhinia* sp.; *Manihot utilissima.*

*Vatiga manihotae (Drake)

Leptopharsa manihotae Drake 1922c, p. 371 [Trinidad; *Manihot*].—Drake and Bruner 1924a, p. 148.—Drake and Hambleton 1934, p. 445 [Brazil; *Manihot utilissima*].—Costa Lima 1936, p. 129.—Monte 1937a, p. 35, fig. 4; 1939b, p. 74 [Cuba]; 1941e, p. 115.
Vatiga manihotae: Drake and Hambleton 1946a, p. 10.

TYPE: Holotype ♀, macropterous; Trinidad, BWI; USNM.
DISTRIBUTION: Trinidad; Cuba; Brazil; Peru; Paraguay; Argentina.
HOST PLANTS: *Manihot utilissima; Manihot* sp.

*Vatiga pauxilla (Drake and Poor)

Leptopharsa pauxilla Drake and Poor 1939a, p. 32 [Argentina].

Vatiga pauxilla: Drake and Ruhoff 1960c, p. 29.

TYPE: Holotype ♀, macropterous; Empedrado, Corrientes, Argentina; Drake Coll. (USNM).

DISTRIBUTION: Argentina.

HOST PLANT: Unrecorded.

*Vatiga sesoris (Drake and Hambleton)

Tigava sesoris Drake and Hambleton 1942b, p. 77 [Brazil].

Vatiga sesoris: Drake and Hambleton 1946a, p. 10.

TYPE: Holotype ♂, macropterous; São Paulo, Brazil; Drake Coll. (USNM).

DISTRIBUTION: Brazil.

HOST PLANT: Unrecorded.

*Vatiga variana Drake and Hambleton

Vatiga variana Drake and Hambleton 1946a, p. 11 [Brazil].

TYPE: Holotype ♀, macropterous; Rio Grande do Sul, Brazil; Drake Coll. (USNM).

DISTRIBUTION: Brazil.

HOST PLANT: Unrecorded.

*Vatiga vicosana Drake and Hambleton

Vatiga vicosana Drake and Hambleton 1946a, p. 10 [Brazil].

TYPE: Holotype ♂, macropterous; Viçosa, Minas Gerais, Brazil; Drake Coll. (USNM).

DISTRIBUTION: Brazil.

HOST PLANT: Unrecorded.

Genus XENOTINGIS Drake

Xenotingis Drake 1923a, p. 105; 1927a, p. 57.—Drake and Ruhoff 1960a, p. 88.

TYPE SPECIES: *Xenotingis horni* Drake.

*Xenotingis bakeri Drake

Xenotingis bakeri Drake 1927a, p. 57 [Luzon].

TYPE: Holotype ♂, macropterous; Los Baños, Phillippine Islands; Drake Coll. (USNM).

DISTRIBUTION: Philippine Islands (Luzon).

HOST PLANT: Unrecorded.

Xenotingis horni Drake

Xenotingis horni Drake 1923a, p. 105, fig. 1 [Taiwan]; 1927a, pp. 57, 58.—Esaki 1926, p. 163.—Takeya 1951a, p. 21.

TYPE: Holotype ♀; Kosempo, Formosa, Japan; Horn Coll.

DISTRIBUTION: Taiwan.

HOST PLANT: Unrecorded.

*Xenotingis luzonana Drake

Xenotingis luzonana Drake 1954f, p. 8 [Luzon].

TYPE: Holotype ♀, macropterous; Mount Makiling, Luzon, Philippine Islands; Drake Coll. (USNM).

DISTRIBUTION: Philippine Islands (Luzon).

HOST PLANT: Unrecorded.

*Xenotingis malkini Drake

Xenotingis malkini Drake 1948e, p. 149 [New Guinea]; 1960, p. 378.

TYPE: Holotype ♂, macropterous; Hollandia, Dutch New Guinea; USNM.

DISTRIBUTION: New Guinea (Netherlands).

HOST PLANT: Unrecorded.

*Xenotingis papuana Drake

Xenotingis papuana Drake 1954f, p. 9 [Papua]; 1960, p. 379, fig. 27 [New Guinea].

TYPE: Holotype ♂; Kokoda, Papua; British Mus.

DISTRIBUTION: New Guinea (Papua; Northeast).

HOST PLANT: Unrecorded.

NOTE: Taken at light [Drake 1960].

Genus XYNOTINGIS Drake

Xynotingis Drake 1948a, p. 8.—Drake and Ruhoff 1960a, p. 88.

TYPE SPECIES: *Xynotingis hoytona* Drake.

*Xynotingis hoytona Drake

Xynotingis hoytona Drake 1948a, p. 8, fig. 3 [Japan].—Takeya 1951a, p. 19; 1953d, p. 173, pl. 6, fig. 3.—Drake and Maa 1953, p. 95.

TYPE: Holotype ♀, macropterous; Japan; Drake Coll. (USNM).

DISTRIBUTION: Japan.

HOST PLANT: Unrecorded.

Genus ZATINGIS Drake

Zatingis Drake 1928a, p. 44.—Drake and Ruhoff 1960a, p. 88.

TYPE SPECIES: *Zatingis extraria* Drake.

*Zatingis extraria Drake

Zatingis extraria Drake 1928a, p. 45 [Paraguay]; 1935, p. 16.

TYPE: Holotype ♂, macropterous; S. Bernardino, Paraguay; Drake Coll. (USNM).

DISTRIBUTION: Paraguay.

HOST PLANT: Unrecorded.

Genus ZEIRATINGIS Drake and Ruhoff

Zeiratingis Drake and Ruhoff 1961b, p. 173.

TYPE SPECIES: *Zeiratingis peirosa* Drake and Ruhoff.

681–552—64——29

*Zeiratingis dissita Drake and Ruhoff

Zeiratingis dissita Drake and Ruhoff 1961b, p. 174 [Borneo].

TYPE: Holotype ♂, macropterous; Sandakan, Borneo; Drake Coll. (USNM).

DISTRIBUTION: Greater Sunda Islands (Borneo).

HOST PLANT: Unrecorded.

*Zeiratingis peirosa Drake and Ruhoff

Zeiratingis peirosa Drake and Ruhoff 1961b, p. 173, figs. 18a, b [Viet-Nam].

TYPE: Holotype ♀, macropterous; Tonkin, Viet-Nam; Drake Coll. (USNM).

DISTRIBUTION: Viet-Nam.

HOST PLANT: Unrecorded.

Genus ZELOTINGIS Drake and Hambleton

Zelotingis Drake and Hambleton 1946a, p. 9.—Drake and Ruhoff 1960a, p. 89.

TYPE SPECIES: *Stenocysta aspidospermae* Drake and Hambleton.

*Zelotingis aspidospermae (Drake and Hambleton)

Stenocysta aspidospermae Drake and Hambleton 1934, p. 444 [Brazil; *Aspidosperma melanocalyx*].—Costa Lima 1936, p. 130.—Monte 1937a, p. 33; 1939b, p. 78; 1941e, p. 132.

Zelotingis aspidospermae: Drake and Hambleton 1946a, p. 10 [Paraguay].

TYPE: Holotype ♀, macropterous; Viçosa, Minas Gerais, Brazil; Drake Coll. (USNM).

DISTRIBUTION: Brazil; Paraguay.

HOST PLANT: *Aspidosperma melanocalyx*.

Genus ZOROTINGIS Drake and Ruhoff

Zorotingis Drake and Ruhoff 1961b, p. 168.

TYPE SPECIES: *Zorotingis scitula* Drake and Ruhoff.

*Zorotingis scitula Drake and Ruhoff

Zorotingis scitula Drake and Ruhoff 1961b, p. 169, fig. 15 [Mindanao].

TYPE: Holotype ♀, macropterous; Davao, Mindanao, Philippines; Drake Coll. (USNM).

DISTRIBUTION: Philippine Islands (Mindanao).

HOST PLANT: Unrecorded.

Tribe YPSOTINGINI, new tribe

TYPE GENUS: *Ypsotingis* Drake.

Genus BISKRIA Puton

Dictyonota (Biskria) Puton 1874c, p. 440.
Biskria: Lethierry and Severin 1896, p. 10.—Horváth 1906a, pp. 13, 34 (key).—Oshanin 1908, p. 413; 1912, p. 43.—Kiritshenko 1951, pp. 240, 245 (key).—Drake and Ruhoff 1960a, p. 40.—Stichel 1960a. p. 282 (key); 1960b, p. 392; 1960c, p. 131.

TYPE SPECIES: *Dictyonota (Biskria) gracilicornis* Puton.

*Biskria gracilicornis (Puton)

Dictyonota (Biskria) gracilicornis Puton 1874c, p. 440 [Algeria].—Lethierry and Puton 1876, p. 32.
Biskria gracilicornis: Horváth 1906a, p. 35.—Stichel 1960a, p. 282.

TYPE: Sex unknown; Biskria, Algeria; Paris Mus.
DISTRIBUTION: Algeria; French Somaliland (Dijibouti).
HOST PLANT: Unrecorded.

Biskria hispanica Gomez-Menor

Biskria hispanica Gomez-Menor 1955b, p. 250, figs. 1–2 [Spain].— Stichel 1960a, p. 283, figs. 66, 67.

TYPE: Sex unknown; El Escorial, Madrid, Spain; Inst. Ent. Madrid.
DISTRIBUTION: Spain.
HOST PLANT: Unrecorded.

Biskria horvathi Kiritshenko

Biscria [sic] *horvathi* Kiritshenko 1913a, p. 413 [Turkestan].

TYPE: Holotype ♂, macropterous; Termez, Turkestan, Russia; Leningrad Inst.
DISTRIBUTION: U.S.S.R. (Turkestan).
HOST PLANT: Unrecorded.

Biskria lepida Horváth

Biskria lepida Horváth 1905b, p. 562 [Tunisia]; 1906a, p. 35.—Stichel 1960a, p. 283.

TYPE: Holotype ♀; Feriana, Tunisia; Hungarian Mus.
DISTRIBUTION: Tunisia.
HOST PLANT: Unrecorded.

Biskria sareptana (Jakovlev)

Dictyonota sareptana Jakovlev 1876b, p. 67, pl. 2, fig. 7 [Russia].
Scraulia sareptana: Lethierry and Severin 1896, p. 8.
Biskria sareptana: Horváth 1906a, p. 35.—Kiritshenko 1951, p. 245.— Stichel 1960a, p. 283.

TYPE: Holotype ♂, macropterous; Sarepta, Russia; Leningrad Inst.
DISTRIBUTION: U.S.S.R.
HOST PLANT: Unrecorded.

Biskria sareptana var. adelpha Horváth

Biskria sareptana var. *adelpha* Horváth 1905b, p. 563 [Russia]; 1906a, p. 35.—Kiritshenko 1951, p. 245.—Stichel 1960a, p. 283.

TYPE: Sex unknown; Theodosia, Tauria, Russia; Hungarian Mus.

DISTRIBUTION: U.S.S.R. (Tauria).

HOST PLANT: Unrecorded.

Genus CHOROTINGIS Drake

Chorotingis Drake 1961b, p. 111.

TYPE SPECIES: *Chorotingis indigena* Drake.

Chorotingis indigena Drake   PLATE 51

Chorotingis indigena Drake 1961b, p. 111, pl. 6 [Queensland].

TYPE: Holotype ♂; Saint George's Sound, Queensland, Australia; Austr. Mus.

DISTRIBUTION: Australia (Queensland).

HOST PLANT: Unrecorded.

Genus DEREPHYSIA Spinola

Derephysia Spinola 1837, p. 166.—Fieber 1844, p. 99; 1861, p. 128.—Douglas and Scott 1865, p. 253.—Stål 1874, p. 48.—Vollenhoven 1878, p. 283.—Lethierry and Severin 1896, p. 10.—Horváth 1906a, pp. 13, 45 (key).—Oshanin 1908, p. 419; 1912, p. 43.—Stichel 1926, pp. 104, 108 (key); 1935, p. 348; 1938a, p. 404; 1960a, p. 290 (key); 1960b, p. 393; 1960c, p. 132.—Börner 1935, pp. 73, 76 (key).—China 1943, p. 246.—Kiritshenko 1951, pp. 241, 246 (key).—Drake and Ruhoff 1960a, p. 50.

TYPE SPECIES: *Tingis foliacea* Fallén.

Derephysia brevicornis Reuter

Derephysia brevicornis Reuter 1888, p. 224 [Greece]; 1891a, p. 25.—Horváth 1906a, p. 46.—Stichel 1960a, p. 290.

TYPE: Sex unknown; Greece; Helsin. Mus.

DISTRIBUTION: Greece.

HOST PLANT: Unrecorded.

*Derephysia cristata (Panzer)

Tingis cristata Panzer 1806, heft 99, tab. 19 [Germany].—Lamarck 1816, p. 504.—Le Peletier and Serville 1828, p. 653.—Brullé 1835, p. 338, pl. 25, fig. 5 [France].—Burmeister 1835, p. 259.—Herrich-Schaeffer 1835, p. 58; 1838, p. 70, pl. 130, figs. i–l.—Blanchard 1840, p. 112.

Galeatus cristata: Westwood 1840b, p. 121 [England].

Derephysia cristata: Fieber 1844, p. 100, pl. 8, figs. 28–33 [Czechoslovakia; Austria]; 1861, p. 128.—Scholz 1847, p. 121.—Herrich-Schaeffer 1850, p. 161.—Jakovlev 1874a, p. 10 [Russia].—Puton 1879c, p.

104.—Reuter 1891b, p. 184.—Hüeber 1893, p. 319.—Horváth 1906a, pp. 46, 47 [Hungary; Siberia; *Artemisia campestris*].—Mužik 1907, p. 56.—Stichel 1926, p. 109; 1938a, p. 406 [Poland]; 1960a, p. 292, fig. 84.—Scholte 1935, p. 31 [Netherlands].—Gulde 1938, p. 269.—Hoberlandt 1942, p. 125.—Kiritshenko 1951, p. 246.

Tingis (Derephysia) cristata: Flor 1860, p. 362 [Estonia; Latvia].

TYPE: Sex unknown; Mannheim, Germany; Berlin Mus.

DISTRIBUTION: Germany; Czechoslovakia; Austria; Hungary; Poland; Netherlands; France; England; U.S.S.R. (Estonia; Latvia; Siberia).

HOST PLANT: *Artemisia campestris*.

*Derephysia foliacea (Fallén)

Tingis foliacea Fallén 1807, p. 39 [*Chrysanthemum leucanthemum*]; 1829, p. 149.—Herrich-Schaeffer 1830, heft 118, tab. 18 [Germany]; 1835, p. 58; 1838, p. 70, pl. 129, fig. d; pl. 130, figs. m, n.

Derephysia foliacea: Spinola 1837, p. 116.—Fieber 1844, p. 99, pl. 8, figs. 23–27 [Sweden; Czechoslovakia; Italy; Austria; *Artemisia campestris*]; 1861, p. 128 [*Statice armeria*].—Sahlberg 1848, p. 135 [Finland].—Herrich-Schaeffer 1850, p. 161.—Costa 1855a, p. 11; 1855b, p. 233.—Mayr 1858, p. 572.—Frey-Gessner 1865, p. 232 [Switzerland].—Douglas and Scott 1865, p. 254, pl. 9, fig. 4.— Garbiglietti 1869, p. 275.—Gredler 1870, p. 76.—Jakovlev 1874a, p. 10 [Russia]; 1880b, p. 101; 1893, p. 294.—Siebke 1874, p. 23 [Norway].—Saunders 1875, p. 250; 1892, p. 130, pl. 12, fig. 4 [ivy; moss].—Reiber and Puton 1876, p. 68.—Vollenhoven 1878, p. 284, pl. 10, figs. 4, 4a [Netherlands].—Puton 1879c, p. 104.—Reuter 1882b, p. 117.—d'Antessanty 1890, p. 31.—Hüeber 1893, p. 317.— Horváth 1906a, pp. 45, 46 [Turkey; Turkestan; Siberia; *Thymus serpyllus*]; 1906d, p. 2.—Mužik 1907, p. 56.—Oshanin 1908, p. 419 [Algeria].—Jensen-Haarup 1912, p. 154, fig. 97 [Denmark].— Schumacher 1914, p. 257.—Lindberg 1919, p. 42; 1927, p. 15.— Reichensperger 1920, p. 61.—Sahlberg 1920, p. 82.—Butler 1923, p. 208 [ash; *Chenopodium;* Wales; Scotland; Ireland].—Stichel 1926, p. 108, fig. 299 [*Echium; Quercus*]; 1938a, p. 406 [Poland]; 1960a, p. 291, fig. 82 [Bulgaria; *Armeria vulgaris; Echium vulgare; Artemisia vulgaris; Hedera helix; Lonicera; Vaccinium myrtillus; Juncus; Carex*].—de Seabra 1931, p. 418, figs. 490, 491 [Portugal].—Börner 1935, p. 76, fig. 114.—Scholte 1935, p. 30, fig. 5 [*Plantago media*].—Gulde 1938, p. 268, fig. [*Thymus*].—Hoberlandt 1942, p. 125; 1943a, p. 118; 1943b, p. 123; 1955, p. 87.—Blöte 1945, p. 82 [Belgium; Tunisia; Yugoslavia].—Kiritshenko 1951, p. 246.—Novak and Wagner 1951, p. 70 [*Cydonia vulgaris*].—Stehlik 1952, p. 205.—Mancini 1953b, p. 186 [Albania]; 1953d, p. 16.—Štušak 1957b, pp. 136, 140, figs. 5, 13c [*Climacium dendroides*]; 1961a, p. 79, figs. 6, 16.—Southwood and Leston 1959, p. 146, pl. 18, fig. 3.

Campylosteira (*Derephysia*) *foliacea:* Kolenati 1856, p. 432 [*Artemisia;* Caucasus].

Tingis (*Derephysia*) *foliacea:* Flor 1860, p. 364 [France; England; Estonia; Latvia].

TYPE: Unknown.

DISTRIBUTION: England; Wales; Scotland; Ireland; Belgium; Netherlands; France; Portugal; Italy; Switzerland; Czechoslovakia; Germany; Austria; Poland; Sweden; Norway; Denmark; Finland; U.S.S.R. (Estonia; Latvia; Caucasus; Turkestan; Siberia); Albania; Bulgaria; Yugoslavia; Turkey; Algeria; Tunisia.

HOST PLANTS: *Armeria vulgaris; Artemisia campestris; Artemisia vulgaris; Artemisia* sp.; *Carex* sp.; *Chenopodium* sp.; *Chrysanthemum leucanthemum; Climacium dendroides; Cydonia vulgaris; Echium vulgare; Echium* sp.; *Hedera helix; Juncus* sp.; *Lonicera* sp.; *Plantago media; Quercus* sp.; *Statice ameria; Thymus serpyllus; Thymus* sp.; *Vaccinium myrtillus;* moss; ivy; ash.

NOTE: Eggs [Štusak].

Derephysia foliacea var. biroi Horváth

Derephysia foliacea var. *biroi* Horváth 1896, p. 326 [Yugoslavia]; 1906a, p. 47 [Hungary].

TYPE: Holotype ♀; Croatia; Hungarian Mus.

DISTRIBUTION: Yugoslavia; Hungary.

HOST PLANT: Unrecorded.

*Derephysia gardneri Drake and Poor

Derephysia gardneri Drake and Poor 1936b, p. 148 [India].

TYPE: Holotype ♀, macropterous; Chakrata District, Bodyar, India; Drake Coll. (USNM).

DISTRIBUTION: India.

HOST PLANT: Unrecorded.

Derephysia lugens Horváth

Derephysia lugens Horváth 1902a, p. 593 [Yugoslavia]; 1906a, p. 47 [Bulgaria].—Stichel 1938a, p. 406 [Albania]; 1960a, p. 291.— Mancini 1953b, p. 186.

TYPE: Holotype ♂; Vranja, Serbia; Hungarian Mus.

DISTRIBUTION: Yugoslavia; Albania; Bulgaria.

HOST PLANT: Unrecorded.

Derephysia nigricosta Horváth

Derephysia nigricosta Horváth 1905a, p. 272 [Spain]; 1906a, p. 47.— Ribaut 1937, p. 247 [France].—Stichel 1960a, p. 292.

Derephysia nigricostata [sic]: González 1948, p. 50.

TYPE: Sex unknown; Spain; Hungarian Mus.

DISTRIBUTION: Spain; Portugal; France.

HOST PLANT: Unrecorded.

Derephysia rectinervis Puton

Derephysia rectinervis Puton (*in* Puton and Lethierry 1887, p. 304) [Algeria].—Horváth 1906a, p. 47.—Stichel 1960a, p. 291.

TYPE: Sex unknown; Mecheria, Algeria; Paris Mus.

DISTRIBUTION: Algeria.

HOST PLANT: Unrecorded.

Derephysia sinuatocollis Puton

Derephysia foliacea var. *sinuatocollis* Puton 1879c, p. 104 [France].— Chicote 1880, p. 189 [Spain].

Derephysia sinuatocollis: Horváth 1906a, p. 46.—Stichel 1960a, p. 290 [Italy].

TYPE: Sex unknown; Hautes-Pyrenees, France; Paris Mus.

DISTRIBUTION: France; Spain; Italy.

HOST PLANT: Unrecorded.

Genus DICTYONOTA Curtis

Dictyonota Curtis 1827, tab. 154.—Laporte 1833, p. 50.—Fieber 1844, p. 91; 1861, p. 126.—Douglas and Scott 1865, p. 255.—Garbiglietti 1869, p. 274.—Walker 1873a, p. 177.—Stål 1874, p. 49.—Horváth 1874b, p. 432; 1906a, pp. 13, 36 (key).—Oshanin 1908, p. 413; 1912, p. 43.—Schumacher 1914, p. 257.—Parshley 1923b, p. 699.—Stichel 1926, pp. 103, 107 (key); 1935, p. 348; 1938a, p. 404; 1960a, p. 284 (key); 1960b, p. 392; 1960c, p. 131.—de Seabra 1931, pp. 406, 413 (key).—Scholte 1935, p. 21 (key).—Börner 1935, pp. 73, 75 (key).— Gulde 1938, p. 262.—China 1943, p. 246.—Blöte 1945, p. 81.—Hurd 1946, p. 461.—Kiritshenko 1951, pp. 240, 245 (key).—Singer 1952, p. 49.—Mancini 1953d, p. 15; 1954b, p. 11.—Gomez-Menor 1955b, p. 248.—Drake and Ruhoff 1960a, p. 51.

Scraulia Stål 1874, p. 50.—Lethierry and Severin 1896, p. 8 (in part).— Kirkaldy 1900, p. 241.—Drake and Ruhoff 1960a, p. 81.

TYPE SPECIES: *Dictyonota strichnocera* Fieber.

Subgenus DICTYONOTA (DICTYONOTA) Curtis

Dictyonota Curtis 1827, tab. 154.

Scraulia Stål 1874, p. 50.

Dictyonota (*Dictyonota*): Horváth 1906a, p. 36.—Oshanin 1908, p. 413; 1912, p. 43.—Drake and Ruhoff 1960a, p. 51.

TYPE SPECIES: *Dictyonota strichnocera* Fieber.

*Dictyonota albipennis von Baerensprung

Dictyonota albipennis von Baerensprung 1858, p. 207, pl. 2, fig. 12 [Italy].—Fieber 1861, p. 127.—Puton 1874a, p. 227; 1879c, p. 102 (in part) [France; Corsica]; 1886a, p. 5 [Tunisia].—Chicote 1880, p. 189 [Spain].—Horváth 1906a, p. 39.—Lindberg 1932a, p. 41 [Morocco; *Genista anglica*].

Scraulia albipennis: Lethierry and Severin 1896, p. 8 (in part).

TYPE: Sex unknown; Piedmont, Italy; Berlin Mus.

DISTRIBUTION: Italy; Corsica; France; Spain; Morocco; Tunisia.

HOST PLANT: *Genista anglica.*

*Dictyonota fuliginosa Costa

Dyctionota [sic] *fuliginosa* Costa 1855a, p. 10, pl. 6, fig. 5; 1855b, p. 232.—Stichel 1960d, p. 120.

Dictyonota fuliginosa: Costa 1863, pl. 1, fig. 6.—Garbiglietti 1869, p. 275 [Italy].—Puton 1874a, p. 227; 1879c, p. 101 [Corsica].—Saunders 1875, p. 251; 1892, p. 129, pl. 12, fig. 3 [broom].—Reiber and Puton 1876, p. 68.—Ferrari 1878, p. 84.—Chicote 1880, p. 189 [Spain].—Hüeber 1893, p. 316.—Horváth 1906a, p. 40 [Belgium; Netherlands; *Spartium scoparium*]; 1906d, p. 2.—Schumacher 1914, p. 257 [*Sarothamus*].—Reichensperger 1920, p. 61.—Butler 1923, p. 207.—Stichel 1926, p. 108; 1960a, p. 286, fig. 73 [Czechoslovakia].—de Seabra 1931, p. 416, figs. 486(1), 488 [Portugal].—Scholte 1935, p. 23, fig. 2.—González 1948, p. 49.—Seidenstücker 1954, p. 235 [Turkey].—Massee 1954, p. 260.—Southwood and Leston 1959, p. 145.—Scudder 1960, p. 22 [B.C.].

Dictyonota fieberi Fieber 1861, p. 127 [France].—Frey-Gessner 1865, p. 232 [Switzerland].—Douglas and Scott 1868, p. 245, pl. 2, fig. 2 [England].—Walker 1873a, p. 177 [Germany].

Scraulia fieberi: Stål 1874, p. 50.

TYPE: Unknown.

DISTRIBUTION: England; Netherlands; Belgium; France; Spain; Portugal; Corsica; Italy; Switzerland; Czechoslovakia; Germany; Turkey; Canada (B.C.).

HOST PLANTS: *Sarothamus* sp.; *Spartium scoparium;* broom.

NOTE: *Dictyonota fieberi* was a manuscript name of Förster used by Fieber (1861) thus giving Fieber the credit for the species. Species recently introduced in Canada.

*Dictyonota marmorea von Baerensprung

Dictyonota marmorea von Baerensprung 1858, p. 206, pl. 2, fig. 11 [Spain].—Fieber 1861, p. 127.—Puton 1874a, p. 227; 1879c, p. 102 [France; Corsica].—Ferrari 1878, p. 84.—Horváth 1906a, p. 40.—Lindberg 1932a, p. 41 [Morocco].

Scraulia marmorea: Stål 1874, p. 50.

TYPE: Sex unknown; Andalusia; Berlin Mus.

DISTRIBUTION: Spain; France; Corsica; Morocco.

HOST PLANT: Unrecorded.

*Dictyonota mitoris Drake and Hsiung

Dictyonota mitoris Drake and Hsiung 1936, p. 287 [China; ash].

TYPE: Holotype ♂, macropterous; Tientsin, China; Drake Coll. (USNM).

DISTRIBUTION: China.

HOST PLANT: Chinese ash.

*Dictyonota pakistana Drake and Maldonado

Dictyonota pakistana Drake and Maldonado 1959, p. 25, fig. 1 [Pakistan].—Drake and Davis 1960, fig. 35.

TYPE: Holotype ♂, macropterous; Lahore, West Pakistan; Drake Coll. (USNM).

DISTRIBUTION: Pakistan.

HOST PLANT: Unrecorded.

NOTE: Taken at light [Drake and Maldonado].

*Dictyonota pulchella Costa

Dictyonota pulchella Costa 1863, p. 9, pl. 1, fig. 7 [Italy].—Horváth 1906a, p. 39 [Spain; Algeria; Mauritania; *Genista scorpius*]; 1906d, p. 3.—Oshanin 1908, p. 414 [Morocco; Tunisia].—Stichel 1926, p. 108; 1960a, p. 284, fig. 70 [Bulgaria]; 1960d, p. 122.—de Seabra 1931, p. 415, figs. 486 (3–5), 487 [*Ulex*].—Ribaut 1932, p. 576.— Gulde 1938, p. 263 [*Genista*].

Dictyonota aubei Signoret 1865, p. 118 [France].

Scraulia aubei: Stål 1874, p. 50.

Dictyonota albipennis (not von Baerensprung): Ferrari 1878, p. 84.— Puton 1879c, p. 102 (in part).—Rey 1893, p. 97.

TYPE: Sex unknown; Italy; Naples Mus.

DISTRIBUTION: Italy; France; Spain; Portugal; Bulgaria; Algeria; Morocco; Mauritania; Tunisia.

HOST PLANTS: *Genista scorpius; Genista* sp.; *Ulex* sp.

*Dictyonota strichnocera Fieber

Dictyonota eryngii (not Latrielle): Curtis 1827, tab. 154, section iv [England; *Ulex*].

Tingis crassicornis (not Fallén): Herrich-Schaeffer 1835, p. 57.

Dictyonota crassicornis (not Fallén): Herrich-Schaeffer 1838, p. 74, pl. 129, fig. B.

Dictyonota strichnocera Fieber 1844, p. 95, pl. 8, figs. 4–7 [Czechoslovakia; Austria; Yugoslavia]; 1861, p. 127 [Germany].—Herrich-Schaeffer 1850, p. 157.—Mayr 1858, p. 571 [Hungary].—Costa 1863, p. 8, pl. 1, fig. 5 [Italy].—Douglas and Scott 1865, p. 256 [moss].— Frey-Gessner 1865, p. 232 [Switzerland].—Gredler 1870, p. 76.— Jakovlev 1876b, p. 67 [Russia].—Saunders 1875, p. 251; 1892, p. 129, pl. 12, fig. 2 [broom].—Vollenhoven 1878, p. 269, pl. 22, fig. 8 [Netherlands].—Ferrari 1878, p. 84.—Puton 1879c, p. 102 [France].—

Chicote 1880, p. 189 [Spain].—Rey 1893, p. 97.—Hüeber 1893, p. 316.—Kirkaldy 1900, p. 241.—Horváth 1906a, p. 40 [Belgium; Rumania; *Spartium scoparium*]; 1906d, p. 241.—Mužik 1907, p. 55.— Jensen-Haarup 1912, p. 153 [Denmark].—Butler 1922, p. 179; 1923, p. 206, fig.—Stichel 1926, p. 108; 1938a, p. 404 [Poland]; 1960a, p. 285 [Bulgaria; *Sarothamus scoparius; Pinus silvestris; Larix decidua*].—Scholte 1935, p. 23, fig. 1.—Hoberlandt 1943, p. 118.— Kiritshenko 1951, p. 245.—Štuśak 1957b, p. 140; 1961a, p. 77, fig. 5H.—Southwood and Leston 1959, p. 145, pl. 18, fig. 4; pl. 21, figs. 4; pl. 45, fig. 5; fig. 45.

Scraulia strichnocera: Stål 1874, p. 50.

Dictyonota idonea Jakovlev 1903c, p. 291 [Ukraine].

TYPE: Unknown.

DISTRIBUTION: England; Belgium; Netherlands; France; Spain; Italy; Switzerland; Czechoslovakia; Germany; Yugoslavia; Bulgaria; Denmark; Poland; Hungary; Austria; Rumania; U.S.S.R. (Ukraine).

HOST PLANTS: *Larix decidua; Pinus silvestris; Sarothamus scoparius; Spartium scoparium; Ulex* sp.; broom; moss.

NOTE: Life history study [Butler 1922]; eggs [Butler 1923]; eggs and immature stages [Štuśak].

Dictyonota teydensis Lindberg

Dictyonota teydensis Lindberg 1936b, p. 29, pl. 1, fig. 4 [Canary Islands].

TYPE: Sex unknown; Canary Islands; Helsin. Mus.

DISTRIBUTION: Canary Islands.

HOST PLANT: Unrecorded.

Subgenus DICTYONOTA (ALCLETHA) Kirkaldy

Dictyonota (not Curtis): Stål 1874, p. 49.—Lethierry and Severin 1896, p. 7.

Alcletha Kirkaldy 1900, p. 241.

Dictyonota (Alcletha): Horváth 1960a, p. 40 (key).—Oshanin 1908, p. 415; 1912, p. 43.—de Seabra 1931, pp. 414, 416 (key).—Börner 1935, p. 75 (key).—Stichel 1935, p. 348; 1960a, p. 286.—China 1943, p. 246.—Drake and Ruhoff 1960a, p. 52.

TYPE SPECIES: *Acanthia tricornis* Schrank.

*Dictyonota (Alcletha) aethiops Horváth

Dictyonota truncaticollis? (not Costa): Puton 1879c, p. 100 [France; Corsica].

Dictyonota aethiops Horváth 1905b, p. 563 [Algeria].—Novak and Wagner 1951, p. 70 [Yugoslavia].

Dictyonota (Alcletha) aethiops: Horváth 1906a, p. 41 [Spain].—Gulde 1938, pp. 263, 266.—Stichel 1906a, p. 286 [Sardinia].

Alcletha aethiops: Vidal 1937, p. 197 [Morocco].

TYPE: Unknown.

DISTRIBUTION: Spain; France; Corsica; Sardinia; Yugoslavia; Algeria; Morocco.

HOST PLANT: Unrecorded.

*Dictyonota (Alcletha) aridula Jakovlev

Dictyonota aridula Jakovlev 1902a, p. 66 [Crimea].—Drake and Ruhoff 1962d, p. 489.

Dictyonota tricornis (not Schrank): Horváth 1905b, p. 563 [Hungary].

Dictyonota (*Alcletha*) *aridula:* Horváth 1906a, p. 42 [Greece].—Kiritshenko 1951, p. 246.—Seidenstücker 1954, p. 235 [Turkey].—Hoberlandt 1955, p. 87.—Stichel 1960a, p. 288.

Dictyonota maroccana Ribaut 1939, p. 186 [Morocco].

Dictyonota (*Alcletha*) *maroccana:* Drake and Ruhoff 1962c, p. 141.

TYPE: Holotype ♀, macropterous; Eupatoria, Crimea, Russia; Leningrad Inst.

DISTRIBUTION: U.S.S.R. (Crimea); Turkey; Greece; Hungary; Morocco.

HOST PLANT: Unrecorded.

*Dictyonota (Alcletha) lugubris Fieber

Dictyonota lugubris Fieber 1861, p. 126 [Yugoslavia].

Dictyonota (*Alcletha*) *lugubris:* Horváth 1906a, p. 41, pl. 1, fig. 6.—Stichel 1960a, p. 286.

TYPE: Sex unknown; Serbia; Vienna Mus.

DISTRIBUTION: Yugoslavia.

HOST PLANT: Unrecorded.

*Dictyonota (Alcletha) pusana Drake and Maa

Dictyonota (*Alcletha*) *pusana* Drake and Maa 1955, p. 6 [India].

Dictyonota pusana: Lindberg 1958a, p. 78 [Borneo; Cape Verde Islands].

TYPE: Holotype ♀; Pusa, Bengal, India; British Mus.

DISTRIBUTION: India; Greater Sundra Islands (Borneo); Cape Verde Islands (São Nicolao).

HOST PLANT: Unrecorded.

NOTE: Taken on "potatoes in store" [Drake and Maa].

*Dictyonota (Alcletha) tricornis (Schrank)

Acanthia tricornis Schrank 1801, p. 67.

Tingis crassicornis Fallén 1807, p. 38 [Sweden]; 1829, p. 147.—Zetterstedt 1828, p. 480 [Lapland]; 1840, p. 269.—Brullé 1835, p. 339, pl. 25, fig. 6.

Tingis erythrophthalma Germar and Kaulfuss 1817, fasc. 3, tab. 25.—Schilling 1838, p. 106.

Dictyonota crassicornis: Curtis 1827, pl. 4, tab. 154 [England].—Fieber 1844, p. 92, pl. 7, figs. 42–47 [Austria; Czechoslovakia; Italy; *Artemisia campestris*]; 1861, p. 127 [*Thymus*].—Sahlberg 1848, p. 134 [Finland].—

Herrich–Schaeffer 1850, p. 157.—Flor 1860, p. 358 [Estonia; Latvia].—Douglas and Scott 1865, p. 255, pl. 9, fig. 5.—Frey–Gessner 1865, p. 232 [Switzerland].—Jakovlev 1869, p. 111 [Russia]; 1880b, p. 101; 1893, p. 294.—Siebke 1874, p. 23 [Norway].—Stål 1874, p. 49.—Saunders 1875, p. 250; 1892, p. 128, pl. 12, fig. 1 [Ireland].—Vollenhoven 1878, p. 268, pl. 9, figs. 4, 4a [Netherlands].—Puton 1879c, p. 100.—Bolivar and Chicote 1879, p. 166 [Spain].—Rey 1893, p. 97.—Hüeber 1893, p. 313.

Tingis pilicornis Herrich-Schaeffer 1830, heft 118, tab. 17 [Germany]; 1835, p. 57.

Piesma marginatum (not Wolff): Burmeister 1835, p. 258 [Hungary].

Dictyesthes (monomial) Amyot 1846, p. 181.

Dictyonota pilicornis: Herrich–Schaeffer 1838, p. 74, pl. 129, fig. 401.—Fieber 1844, p. 95, pl. 8, figs. 8–9.

Tingis marginata: Blanchard 1840, p. 112 [France].

Dictyonota erythrophthalma: Fieber 1844, p. 94, pl. 8, figs. 1–3 [*Senecio jacobaea*]; 1861, p. 127.—Herrich-Schaeffer 1850, p. 158.

Dyctinota [sic] *marginata:* Costa 1847a, p. 21; 1847c, p. 161.

Campylosteira (Derephysia) pilicornis: Kolenati 1856, p. 432 (no. 215) [Caucasus].

Dictyonota truncaticollis Costa 1863, p. 7, pl. 1, fig. 4.—Stål 1874, p. 49.—Puton 1886a, p. 4 [Tunisia].—Stichel 1960d, p. 122.

Monanthia lurida Garbiglietti 1869, p. 274.

Dictyonota dictyesthes Garbiglietti 1869, p. 275.—Drake and Ruhoff 1960a, p. 7.

Dictyonota erythrocephala Garbiglietti 1869, p. 275.

Dictyonota crassicornis var. *erythrophthalma:* Puton 1879c, p. 100.

Alcletha tricornis: Kirkaldy 1900, p. 241.

Dictyonota (Alcletha) tricornis: Horváth 1906a, p. 41 [Iran; Turkey; Siberia; Turkestan; Armenia; *Mentha; Artemisia*].—Butler 1923, p. 205 [Algeria; Wales; *Cytisus scoparius*].—de Seabra 1931, p. 416, figs. 486(2), 489 [Portugal].—Gulde 1938, pp. 262, 265, fig.—Kiritshenko 1951, p. 245.—Stehlik 1952, p. 205.—Hoberlandt 1955, p. 87.—Stichel 1960a, p. 287, fig. 76 [Balearic; Crete; Greece; Bulgaria; Sardinia; Sicily; Belgium; *Hieracium: Chrysanthemum; Echium vulgare*].

Dictyonota tricornis: Horváth 1906d, p. 1; 1916, p. 9 [Albania].—Mužik 1907, p. 55.—Reuter 1908, p. 89.—Jensen-Haarup 1912, p. 153, fig. 96 [Denmark].—Sahlberg 1920, p. 81.—Stichel 1926, p. 108, fig. 298 [*Verbascum; Echium*]; 1938a, p. 404 [Poland].—Scholte 1935, p. 23, fig. 3.—Novak and Wagner 1951, p. 70 [Yugoslavia].—Bator 1953, p. 325, pl. 2, fig. 3.—Strawinski 1953, p. 380.—Southwood and Leston 1959, p. 145, pl. 21, fig. 9; fig. 44.—Drake and Ruhoff 1962c, p. 141.

Dictyonota tricornis var. *americana* Parshley 1916a, p. 164 [Maine]; 1917b, p. 53; 1923a, p. 103; 1923b, p. 699 [N.S.].—Blatchley 1926, p. 472.—Proctor 1946, p. 74.—Bailey 1951, p. 30.—Lindberg 1958, p. 78 [Cape Verde; *Heliotropium erosum*].

Dictyonota ifranensis Vidal 1951, p. 63 [Morocco].

TYPE: Unknown.

DISTRIBUTION: England; Ireland; Wales; Netherlands; Belgium; France; Portugal; Spain; Italy; Sardinia; Sicily; Balearic Islands; Switzerland; Czechoslovakia; Austria; Germany; Poland; Denmark; Sweden; Norway; (Lapland); Finland; U.S.S.R. (Estonia; Latvia; Caucasus; Siberia; Turkestan; Armenia); Hungary; Albania; Greece; Crete; Bulgaria; Yugoslavia; Turkey; Iran; Algeria; Tunisia; Morocco; Cape Verde Islands (São Nicolao); U.S. (Maine); Canada (N.S.; N.B.).

HOST PLANTS: *Artemisia campestris; Artemisia* sp.; *Chrysanthemum* sp.; *Cytisus scoparius; Echium vulgare; Echium* sp.; *Heliotropium erosum; Hieracium* sp.; *Mentha* sp.; *Sedum acre; Senecio jacobaea; Thymus* sp.; *Verbascum* sp.

NOTE: (1) Myrmecophile, nymphs and adults found in nests of *Myrmica rubra* [Butler]; *Lasius niger* [Sahlberg]; (2) introduced into Canada and U.S.; (3) see Drake and Ruhoff 1960a, p. 7 re monomial system.

Dictyonota (Alcletha) tricornis var. cicur Horváth

Dictyonota tricornis var. *cicur* Horváth 1905b, p. 563 [Hungary].—Dobšik 1951, p. 40.

Dictyonota (Alcletha) tricornis var. *cicur:* Horváth 1906a, p. 42.—Stichel 1960a, p. 287 [Czechoslovakia].

TYPE: Holotype ♂; Kecskemét, Hungary; Hungarian Mus.

DISTRIBUTION: Hungary; Czechoslovakia.

HOST PLANT: Unrecorded.

Subgenus DICTYONOTA (ELINA) Ferrari

Dictyonota (Elina) Ferrari 1878, p. 84.—Horváth 1906a, p. 44.—Oshanin 1908, p. 417; 1912, p. 43.—Stichel 1935, p. 348; 1960a, p. 288.—Drake and Ruhoff 1960a, p. 52.

Elina: Lethierry and Severin 1896, p. 9.

TYPE SPECIES: *Dictyonota beckeri* Jakovlev.

*Dictyonota (Elina) beckeri Jakovlev

Dictyonota beckeri Jakovlev 1871, p. 25 [Russia].

Dictyonota (Elina) beckeri: Ferrari 1878, p. 84.—Puton 1895, p. 86.—Horváth 1906a, p. 44 [Rumania].—Kiritshenko 1951, p. 246.

TYPE: Holotype ♀, brachypterous; Astrakhan, Russia; Leningrad Inst.

DISTRIBUTION: U.S.S.R.; Rumania.

HOST PLANT: Unrecorded.

Dictyonota (Elina) fuentei Puton

Dictyonota (Elina) fuentei Puton 1895, pp. 86, 87 [Spain].—Horváth 1906a, p. 44.—Gomez-Menor 1955b, p. 256, fig. 4.—Stichel 1960a, p. 288, fig. 78.

TYPE: Sex unknown; Pozuelo de Calatrava, Prov. de Ciudad Real, Spain; Paris Mus.

DISTRIBUTION: Spain.

HOST PLANT: Unrecorded.

*Dictyonota (Elina) henschi Puton

Dictyonota putoni (not Stål) Ferrari 1878, p. 85.

Dictyonota (Elina) henschi Puton 1892, p. 72 [Hungary]; 1895, p. 87.— Horváth 1906a, p. 44.—Gulde 1938, p. 266.—Kiritshenko 1951, p. 246.

Dictyonota (Elina) putoni: Puton 1895, p. 87.

Dictyonota (Elina) eupatoriae Jakovlev 1902a, p. 67 [Russia].

Dictyonota henschi: Horváth 1905b, p. 565 [Italy].—Stichel 1926, p. 108; 1938a, p. 404 [Turkey].

TYPE: Sex unknown; Budapest, Hungary; Paris Mus.

DISTRIBUTION: Hungary; Italy; Turkey; U.S.S.R. (Crimea).

HOST PLANT: Unrecorded.

Dictyonota (Elina) iberica Horváth

Dictyonota (Elina) iberica Horváth 1905b, p. 564 [Spain]; 1906a, p. 44.— Stichel 1960a, p. 288.

TYPE: Sex unknown; Sierra de Espuna, Spain; Hungarian Mus.

DISTRIBUTION: Spain.

HOST PLANT: Unrecorded.

Dictyonota (Elina) marqueti Puton

Dictyonota (Elina) marqueti Puton 1879b, p. 297 [France]; 1879c, p. 103; 1895, p. 86.—Horváth 1906a, p. 45.—Stichel 1960a, p. 289.

TYPE: Sex unknown; Banyuls-sur-Mer, France; Paris Mus.

DISTRIBUTION: France.

HOST PLANT: Unrecorded.

Dictyonota (Elina) nevadensis Gomez-Menor

Dictyonota (Elina) nevadensis Gomez-Menor 1955b, p. 254, fig. 3 [Spain].—Stichel 1960a, p. 289, fig. 80.

TYPE: Sex unknown; Puerto de la Ragua, Sierra Nevada, Granada, Spain; Inst. Ent. Madrid.

DISTRIBUTION: Spain.

HOST PLANT: Unrecorded.

Dictyonota (Elina) sicardi Puton

Dictyonota (Elina) sicardi Puton 1894, p. 115 [Tunisia]; 1895, p. 87.—
Horváth 1906a, p. 44.

TYPE: Sex unknown; Teboursouk, Tunisia; Paris Mus.
DISTRIBUTION: Tunisia.
HOST PLANT: Unrecorded.

Subgenus DICTYONOTA (KALAMA) Puton

Dictyonota (Kalama) Puton (*in* Lethierry and Puton 1876, p. 34).—
Horváth 1906a, p. 42.—Oshanin 1908, p. 416; 1912, p. 43.—Drake
and Ruhoff 1960a, p. 53.
Kalama: Lethierry and Severin 1896, p. 10.

TYPE SPECIES: *Kalama coquereli* Puton.

Dictyonota (Kalama) brevicornis Ferrari

Dictyonota (Kalama) putonii var. *brevicornis* Ferrari 1884, p. 474 [Tunisia].
Dictyonota (Kalama) brevicornis: Horváth 1906a, p. 43.

TYPE: Sex unknown; Tunisia; Genova Mus.
DISTRIBUTION: Tunisia.
HOST PLANT: Unrecorded.

Dictyonota (Kalama) coquereli (Puton)

Kalama coquereli Puton (*in* Lethierry and Puton 1876, p. 34) [Algeria].
Dictyonota (Kalama) coquereli: Horváth 1906a, p. 44.

TYPE: Sex unknown; Algeria; Paris Mus.
DISTRIBUTION: Algeria.
HOST PLANT: Unrecorded.

*Dictyonota (Kalama) putonii Stål

Dictyonota putonii Stål 1874, p. 50 [Algeria].
Dictyonota putoni [sic]: Puton 1886a, p. 12 [Tunisia].
Kalama putoni [sic]: Lethierry and Severin 1896, p. 10.
Dictyonota (Kalama) putonii: Horváth 1906a, p. 43.

TYPE: Sex unknown; Bône, Algeria; Stockholm Mus.
DISTRIBUTION: Algeria; Tunisia.
HOST PLANT: Unrecorded.

Dictyonota (Kalama) reuteri Horváth

Dictyonota (Kalama) reuteri Horváth 1906a, p. 42 [Syria].

TYPE: Sex unknown; Kaifa, Syria; Helsin. Mus.
DISTRIBUTION: Syria.
HOST PLANT: Unrecorded.

*Dictyonota (Kalama) theryi (Montandon)

Kalama theryi Montandon 1897, p. 99 [Algeria].
Dictyonota (Kalama) theryi: Horváth 1906a, p. 43.

TYPE: Sex unknown; Algeria; Bucharest Mus.
DISTRIBUTION: Algeria.
HOST PLANT: Unrecorded.

Genus DICTYOTINGIS Drake

Dictyotingis Drake 1942a, p. 8.—Drake and Ruhoff 1960a, p. 53.

TYPE SPECIES: *Dictyotingis gibberis* Drake.

*Dictyotingis gibberis Drake

Dictyotingis gibberis Drake 1942a, p. 8 [India].—Drake and Davis 1960, fig. 37.

TYPE: Holotype ♂, macropterous; Madura, India; Drake Coll. (USNM).

DISTRIBUTION: India.

HOST PLANT: Unrecorded.

*Dictyotingis monticula Drake

Dictyotingis monticula Drake 1956h, p. 21 [India].

TYPE: Holotype ♀, macropterous; Naga Hills, Assam; Drake Coll. (USNM).

DISTRIBUTION: India..

HOST PLANT: Unrecorded.

Genus EUAULANA Drake

Euaulana Drake 1945, p. 96.—Drake and Ruhoff 1960a, p. 56.

TYPE SPECIES: *Euaulana ferritincta* Drake.

*Euaulana ferritincta Drake

Euaulana ferritincta Drake 1945, p. 96 [Queensland; Tasmania; Victoria].

TYPE: Holotype ♂, macropterous; Burleigh, Queensland, Australia; Drake Coll. (USNM).

DISTRIBUTION: Australia (Queensland; Tasmania; Victoria; New South Wales).

HOST PLANT: Unrecorded.

*Euaulana tasmaniae Drake

Euaulana tasmaniae Drake 1945, p. 97 [Tasmania]; 1954c, p. 72; 1961b, p. 111 [New South Wales; *Banksia robur minor*].—Drake and Ruhoff 1962b, p. 250 [South Australia; *Banksia*].

TYPE: Holotype ♀, macropterous; Hobart, Tasmania, Australia; Drake Coll. (USNM).

DISTRIBUTION: Australia (Queensland; Tasmania; New South Wales; South Australia).

HOST PLANTS: Cones of *Banksia robur minor; Banksia* sp.

Genus YPSOTINGIS Drake

Ypsotingis Drake 1947d, p. 229; 1958d, pp. 149–153.—Drake and Ruhoff 1960a, p. 88.

TYPE SPECIES: *Ypsotingis sideris* Drake.

*Ypsotingis bakeri Drake

Ypsotingis bakeri Drake 1958d, p. 149, pl. 45, figs. a, b [Borneo].— Drake and Davis 1960, fig. 36.

Type: Holotype ♂, macropterous; Sandakan, Borneo; Drake Coll. (USNM).

Distribution: Greater Sunda Islands (Borneo).

Host Plant: Unrecorded.

*Ypsotingis bornea Drake

Ypsotingis bornea Drake 1958d, p. 152 [Borneo].

Type: Holotype ♀, macropterous; Sandakan, Borneo; Drake Coll. (USNM).

Distribution: Greater Sunda Islands (Borneo).

Host Plant: Unrecorded.

*Ypsotingis luzonana Drake   Plate 52

Ypsotingis luzonana Drake 1958d, p. 150, pl. 46, figs. a, b [Luzon].

Type: Holotype ♂, macropterous; Mount Makiling, Luzon, Philippine Islands; Drake Coll. (USNM).

Distribution: Philippine Islands (Luzon).

Host Plant: Unrecorded.

Ypsotingis sideris Drake

Ypsotingis sideris Drake 1947d, p. 230, fig. [Viet-Nam]; 1947e, p. 67, fig. (color); 1948b, p. 45, fig. 1; 1958d, p. 149.

Type: Holotype ♀; Tonkin, Indochina; Mus. Heude.

Distribution: Viet-Nam.

Host Plant: Unrecorded.

Ypsotingis vicinitas Drake (emendation)

Ypsotingis vicinatis Drake 1948h, p. 74, fig. [Soemba]; 1958d, p. 153 [Java].

Type: Holotype ♀; Kananggar, Soemba Island, Netherlands East Indies; Leiden Mus.

Distribution: Lesser Sunda Islands (Soemba); Greater Sunda Islands (Java).

Host Plant: Unrecorded.

Subfamily VIANAIDINAE Kormilev

VIANAIDIDAE Kormilev 1955b, p. 466.—Drake and Ruhoff 1960a, p. 6 (as family).

VIANAIDANAE Drake and Davis 1960, pp. 8, 82, 84 (as subfamily).

Type Genus: *Vianaida* Kormilev = *Anommatocoris* China.

[Note: According to the rules, Vianaidinae must be retained as the proper subfamily name.]

Genus ANOMMATOCORIS China

Anommatocoris China 1945, p 126.—Drake and Davis 1960, pp. 84, 88.

Vianaida Kormilev 1955b, p. 468.

Type Species: *Anommatocoris minutissimus* China.

*Anommatocoris coleopteratus (Kormilev)   PLATE 55

Vianaida coleopterata Kormilev 1955b, p. 472, figs. 1–5 [Argentina; *Gleditsia triacanthos*].

Anommatocoris coleoptratus [sic]: Drake and Davis 1960, pp. 88, 89, figs. 5, 21–23, 26 a–b, 27, 72 a–c, 73.

TYPE: Holotype ♀, brachypterous; Tigre, Rio Juján, Buenos Aires Prov., Argentina; Drake Coll. (USNM).

DISTRIBUTION: Argentina.

HOST PLANT: Roots of *Gleditsia triacanthos* ("imported tree called 'Acacia negra' in Argentina").

NOTE: Myrmecophile; found in nest of *Acromyrmex lundi* (Guérin) [Kormilev].

*Anommatocoris minutissimus China   PLATES 54, 56c

Anommatocoris minutissimus China 1945, pp. 127, 128, figs. 1 a–d [Trinidad].—Drake and Davis 1960, pp. 88, 90, figs. 74 a-c.—Drake and Froeschner 1962, fig. 3.

TYPE: Sex unknown; Trinidad, British West Indies; British Mus.

DISTRIBUTION: Trinidad.

HOST PLANT: Unrecorded.

NOTE: Found in soil of cacao experimental plantation [China]; myrmecophile, associated with undetermined species of ant [Drake and Davis].

*Anommatocoris zeteki Drake and Froeschner   PLATE 56

Anommatocoris zeteki Drake and Froeschner 1962, p. 8, figs. 1, 2 [Canal Zone].

TYPE: Holotype ♂, brachypterous; Barro Colorado Island, Panama Canal Zone; USNM.

DISTRIBUTION: Panama (Canal Zone).

HOST PLANT: Unrecorded.

NOTE: Myrmecophile [Drake and Froeschner].

Genus THAUMAMANNIA Drake and Davis

Thaumamannia Drake and Davis 1960, p. 90.

TYPE SPECIES: *Thaumamannia manni* Drake and Davis.

*Thaumamannia manni Drake and Davis   PLATE 53

Thaumamannia manni Drake and Davis 1960, pp. 88, 92, figs. 75 a–c [Bolivia].

TYPE: Holotype ♀, brachypterous; Santa Cruz, Bolivia; USNM.

DISTRIBUTION: Bolivia.

HOST PLANT: Unrecorded.

NOTE: Myrmecophile; found in nest of undetermined species of ant [Drake and Davis].

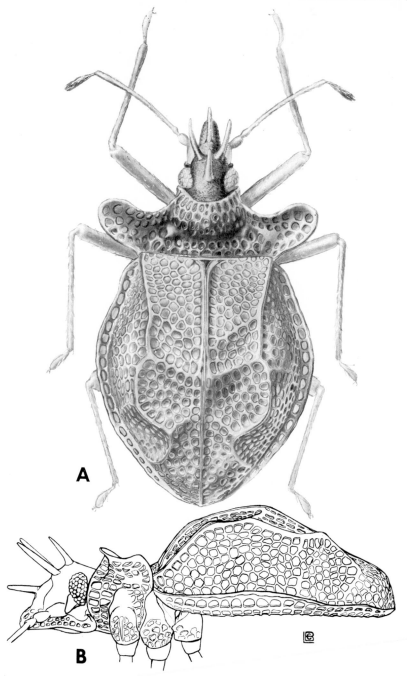

Alloeoderes davao Drake

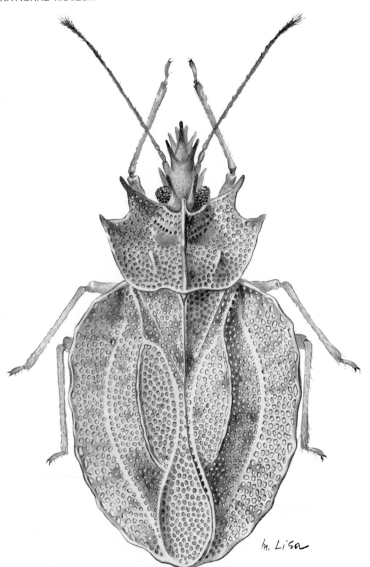

Phatnoma pacifica Kirkaldy

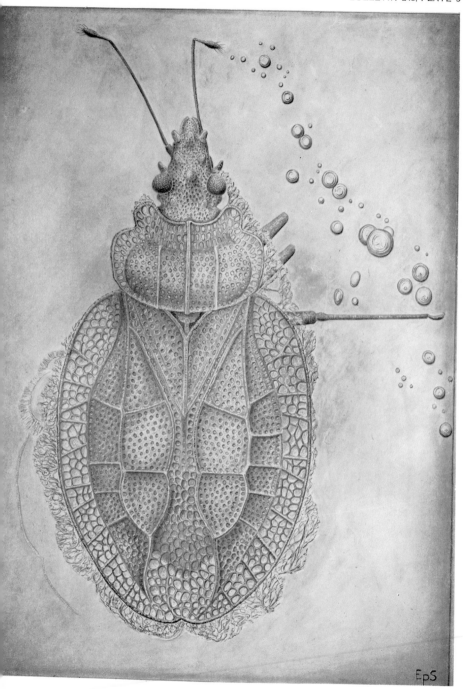

† *Phatnoma baltica* Drake (fossil in amber)

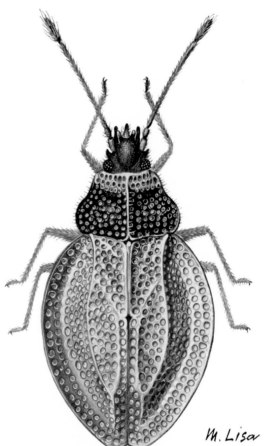

Zetekella pulla Drake and Plaumann

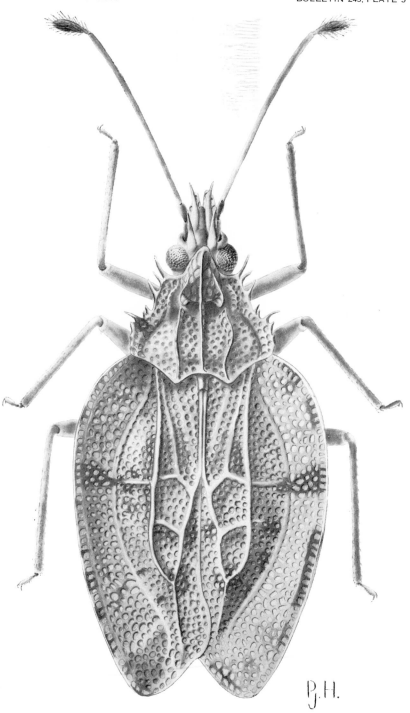

Ceratocader armatus (Hacker)

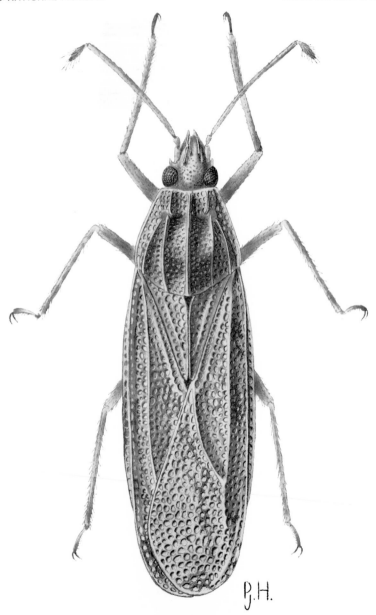

Cantacader tener Bergroth

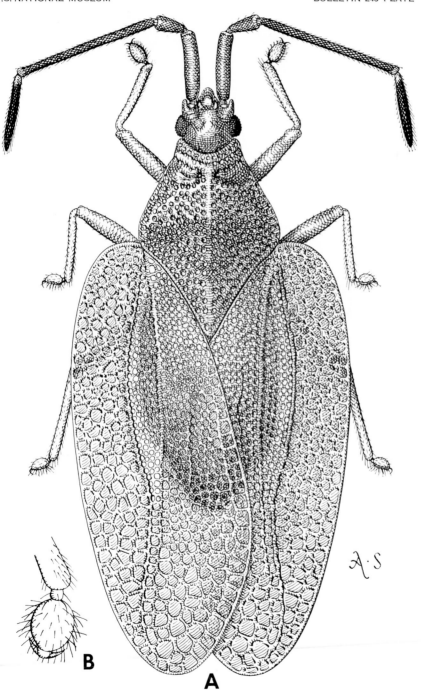

A·S

B

A

Litadea delicatula China

Litadea delicatula China, dorsal and ventral views of last nymphal instar

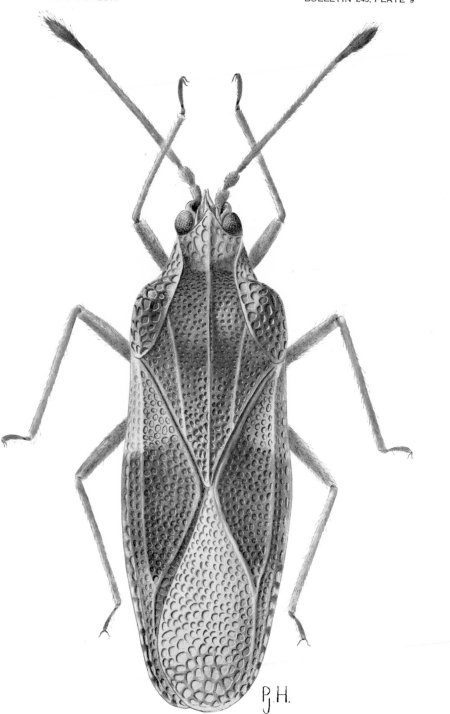

Cysteochila poecilia Drake and Ruhoff

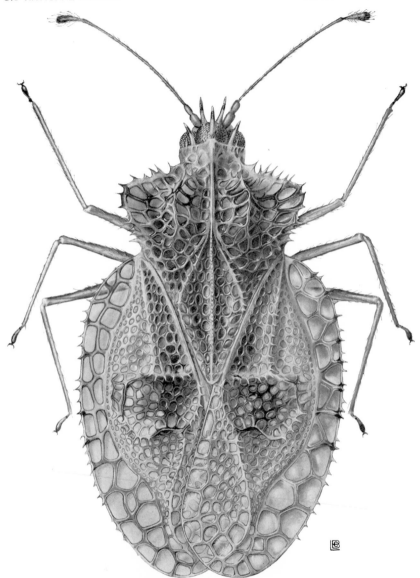

Ambotingis senta (Drake and Hambleton)

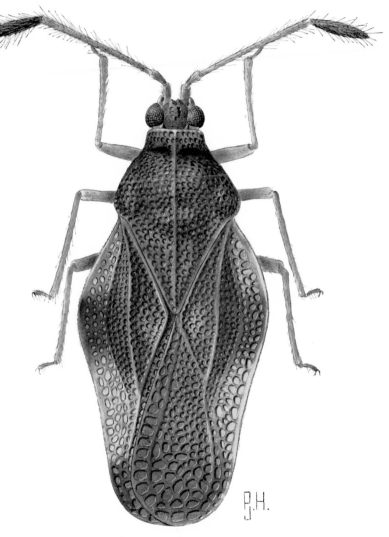

Eteoneus peroronus Drake

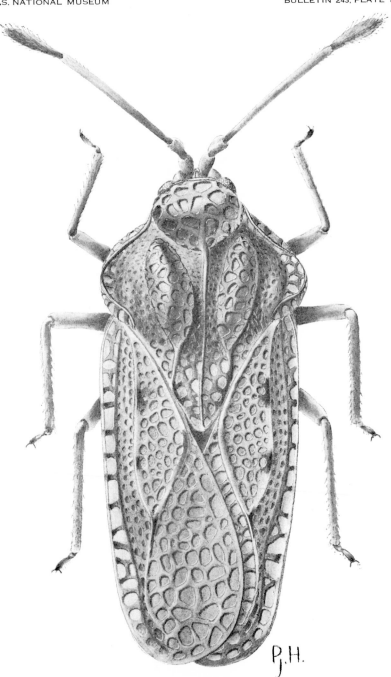

Alloeocysta approba Drake

Epimixia vittata Horváth

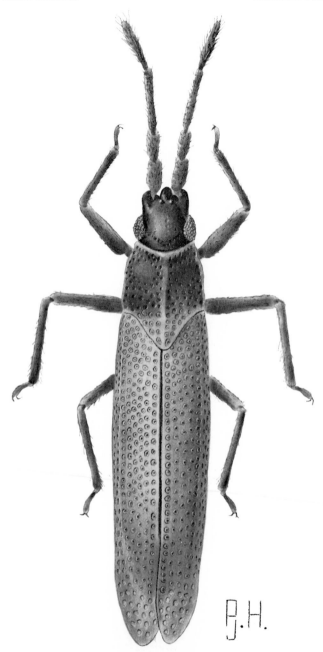

Agramma onar Drake

Lullius spinifemur Drake

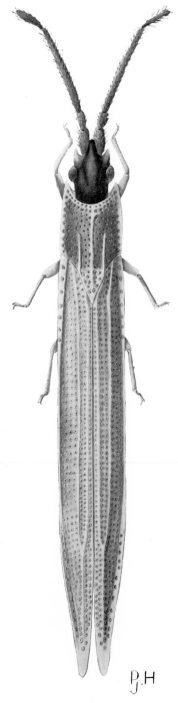

Perbrinckea brincki Drake

Leaf down-curl on *Dichapetalum cymosum* by feeding of *Onymochila dichapetali* (Horváth)

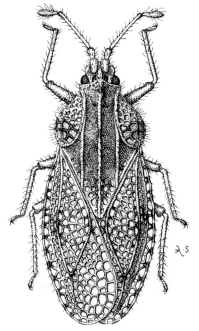

Onymochila dichapetali (Horváth)

Copium clavicorne (Linnaeus)

Copium clavicorne (Linnaeus), last nymphal instar

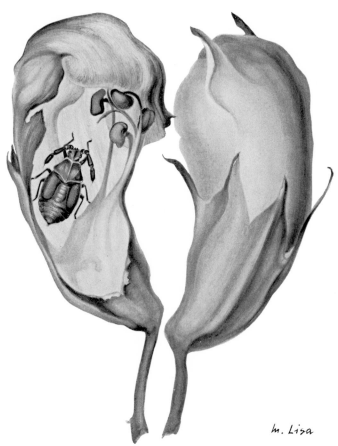

M. Lisa

Floral cecidia of *Copium clavicorne*, one side removed to expose inmate

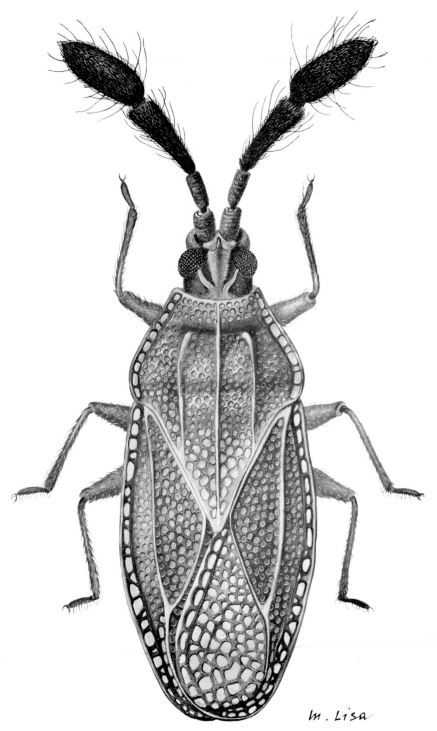

M. Lisa

Copium teucrii (Host)

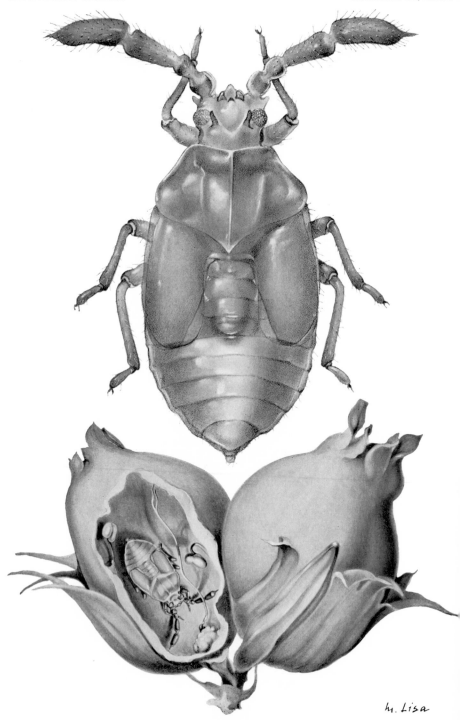

Copium teucrii (Host), last nymphal instar

Floral cecidia of *Copium teucrii*, one side removed to expose inmate

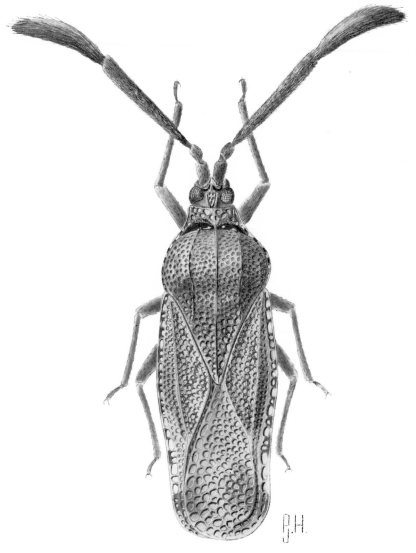

Paracopium hamadryas (Drake)

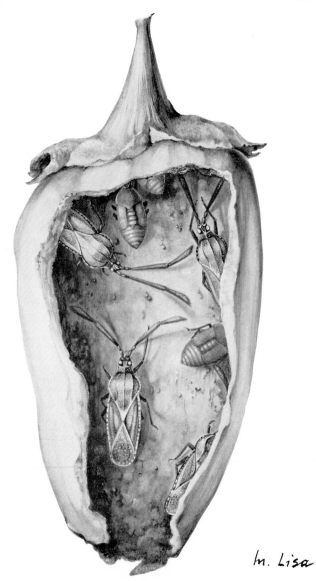

M. Lisa

Floral cecidium of *Paracopium hamadryas*, one side removed to show the seven inmates

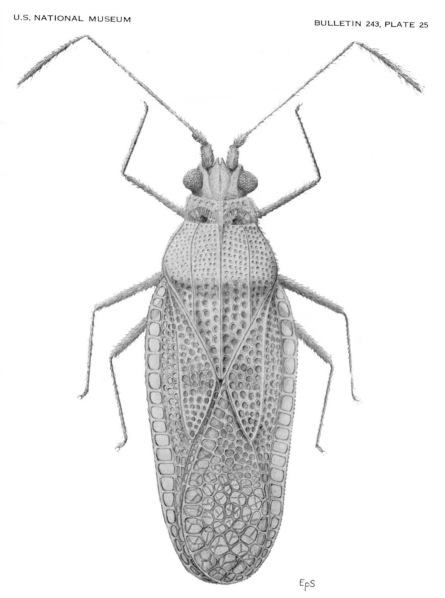

Perissonemia ecmeles Drake and Mohanasundarum

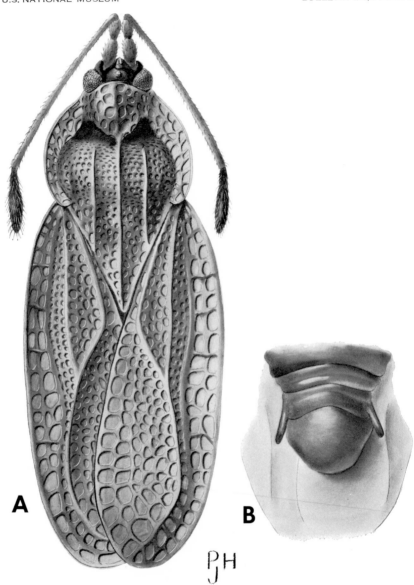

A

B

Dicrotingis digitalis (Drake)

Codotingis evanis Drake

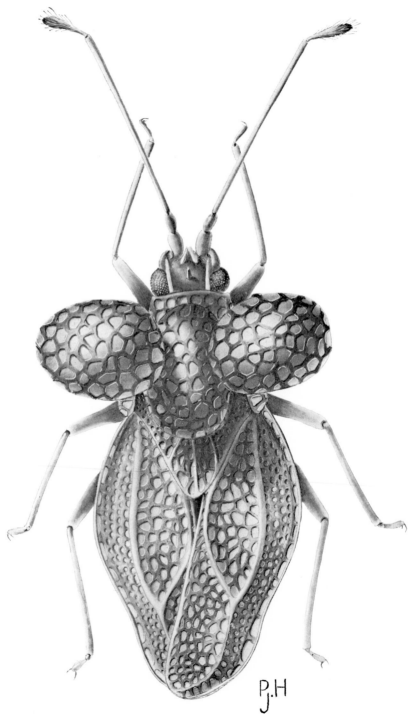

Diplocysta trilobata Drake and Poor

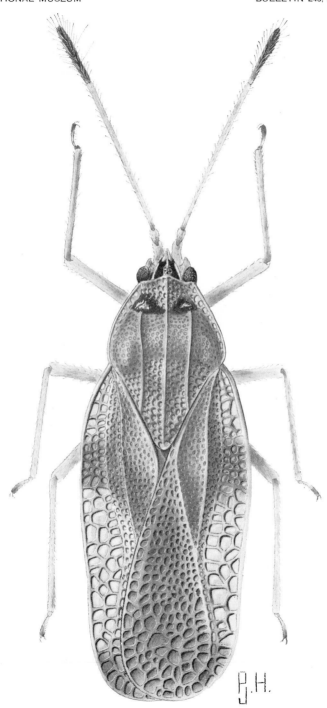

Hegesidemus otiosus Drake

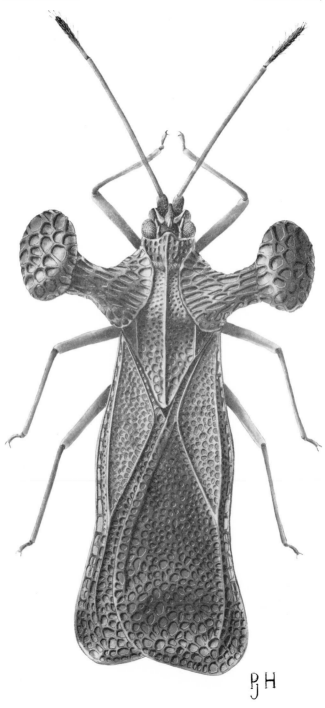

Diconocoris capusi (Horváth)

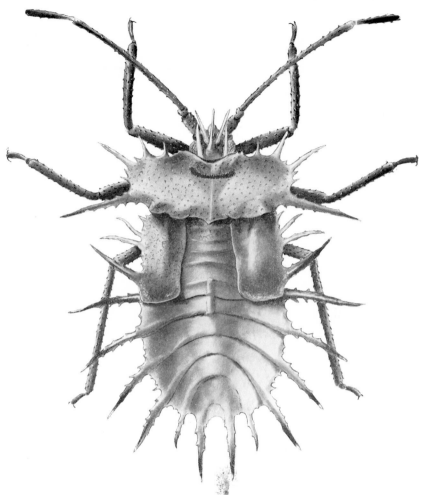

Diconocoris capusi (Horváth), last nymphal instar

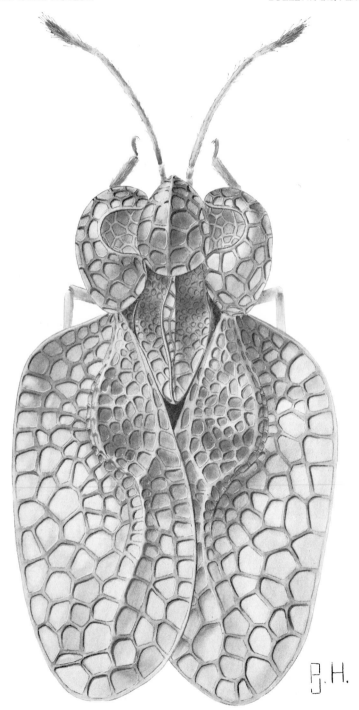

Australotingis franzeni Hacker

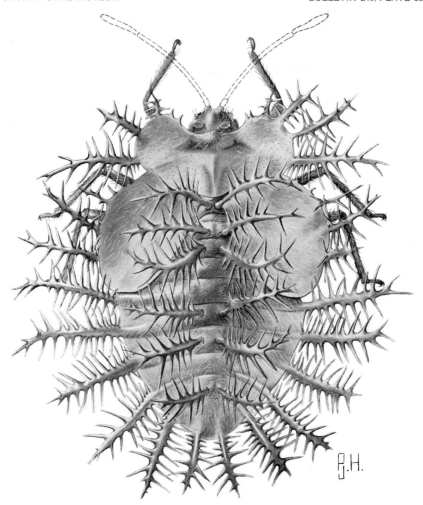

Australotingis franzeni Hacker, last nymphal instar

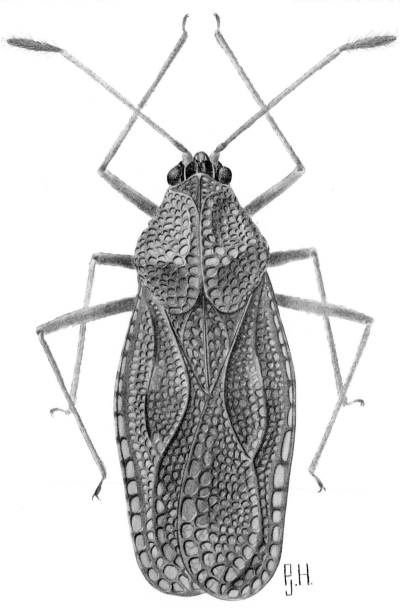

Dictyla picturata (Distant)

† *Dictyla veterna* (Scudder) (fossil in stone)

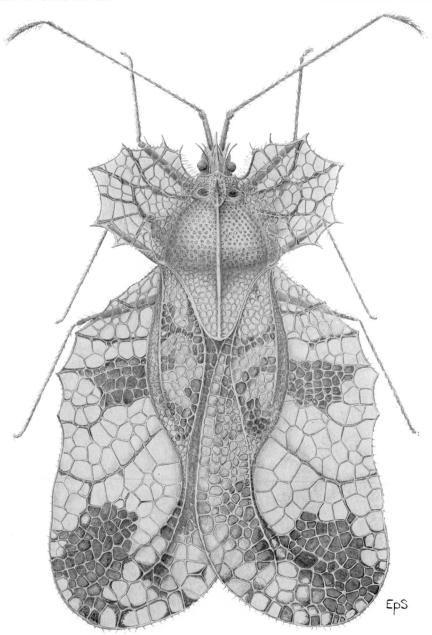

Ammianus alberti (Schouteden)

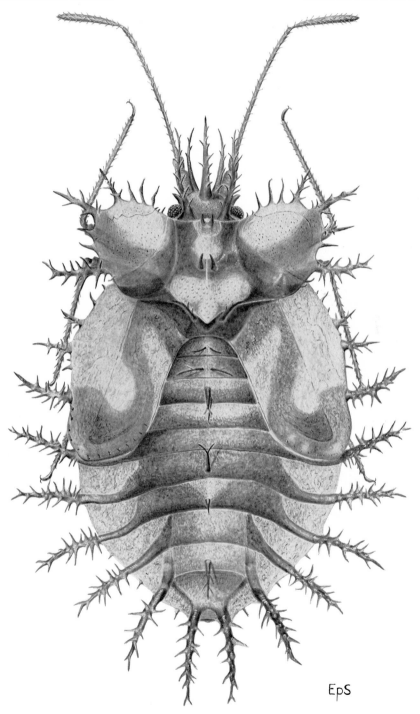

EpS

Ammianus alberti (Schouteden), last nymphal instar

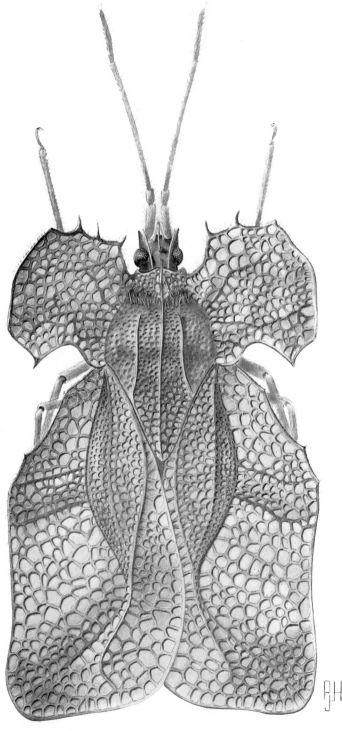

Ammianus dilatatus (Guérin-Méneville)

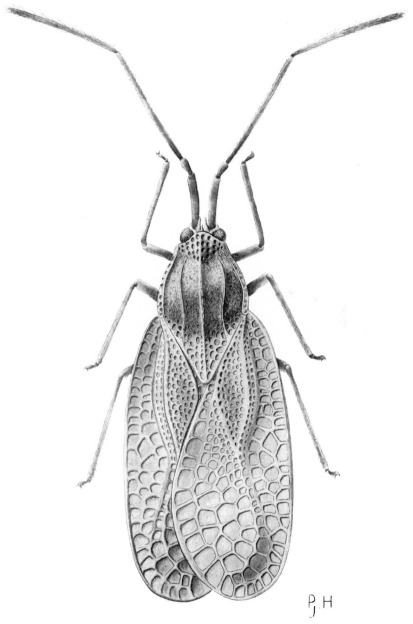

Mecopharsa hackeri Drake

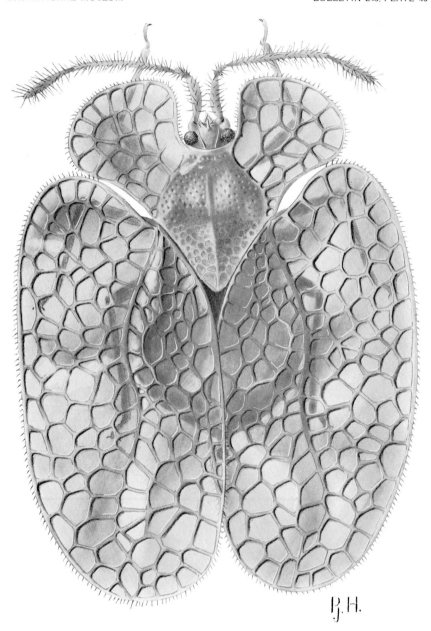

Planibyrsa montei Drake and Hambleton

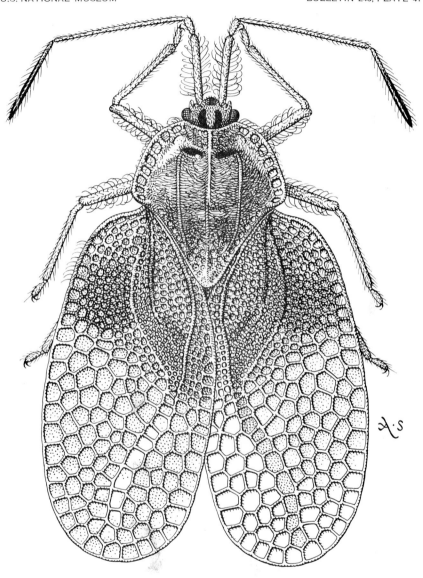

Nobarnus signatus (Distant)

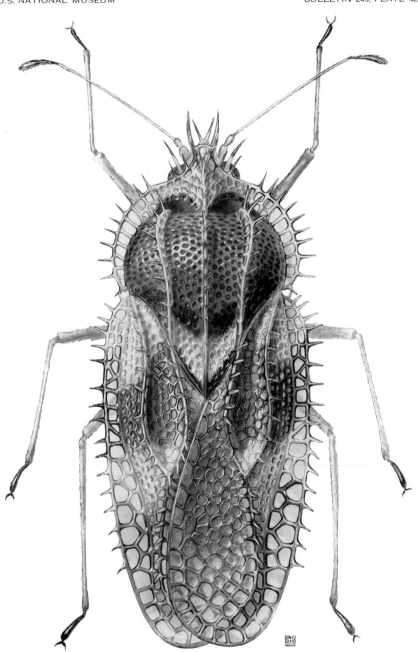

Inoma multispinosa Hacker

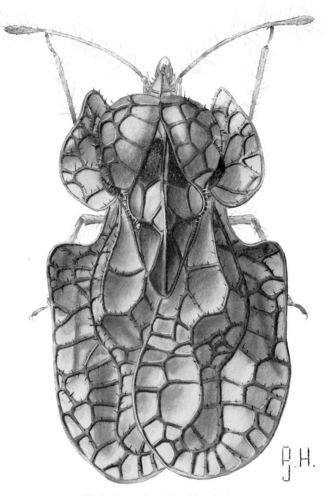

Hyalochiton colpochilus (Horváth)

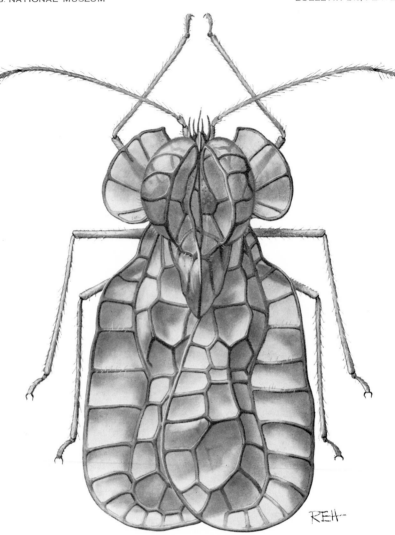

Galeatus spinifrons (Fallén)

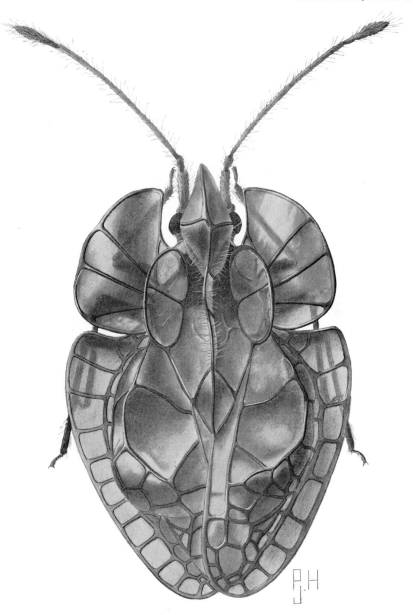

Galeatus sinuatus (Herrich-Schaeffer), brachypterous

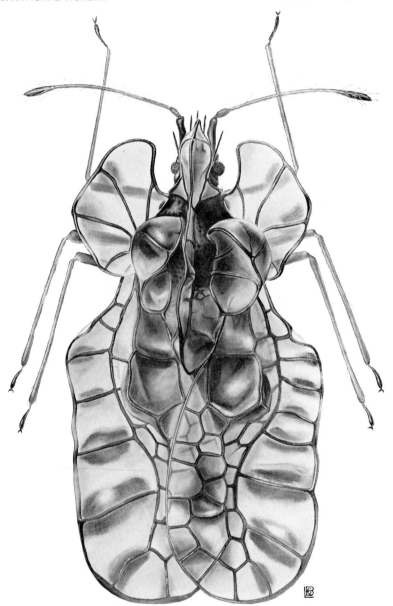

Galeatus maculatus (Herrich-Schaeffer), macropterous

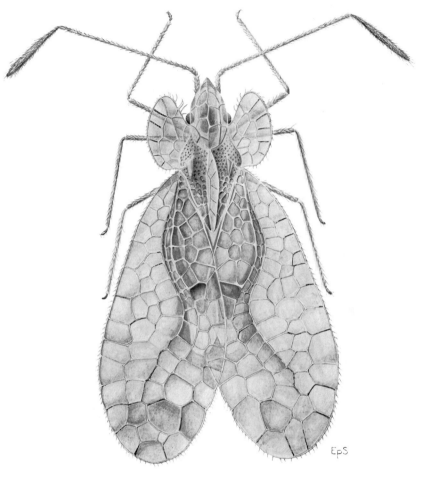

Stephanitis typica (Distant)

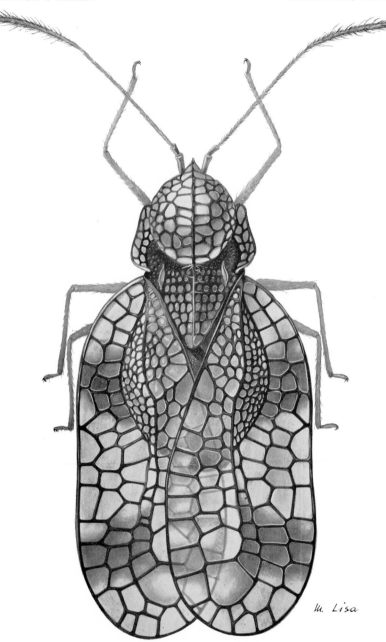

Stephanitis takeyai Drake and Maa

Holophygdon melanesica Kirkaldy

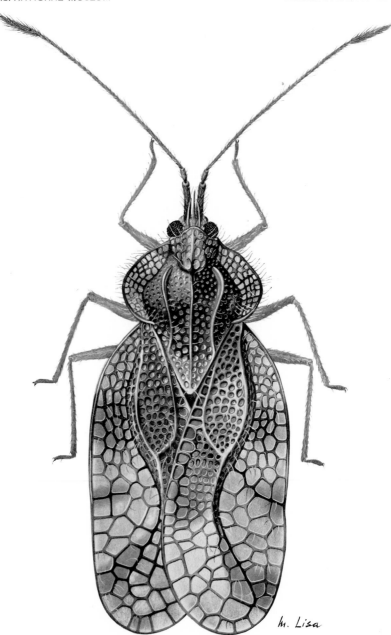

Gargaphia sororia Hussey

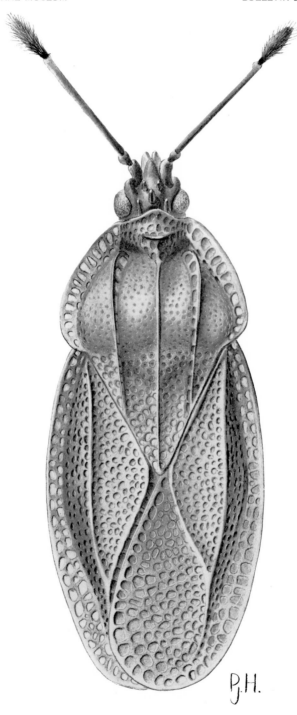

Chorotingis indigena Drake

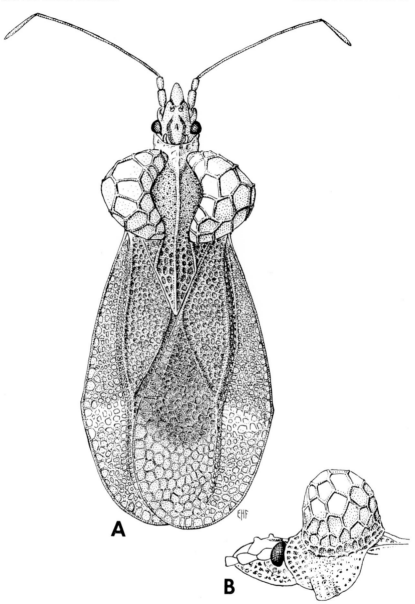

Ypsotingis luzonana Drake

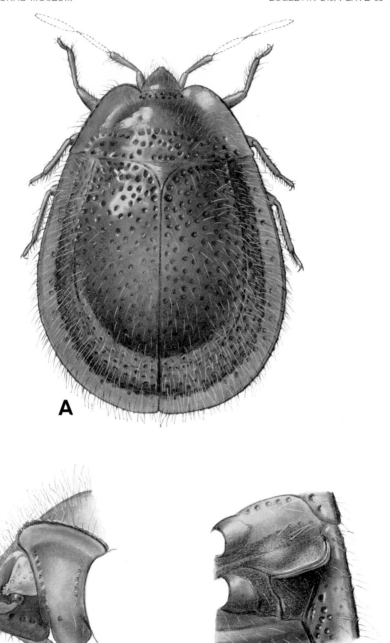

A

B

C

Thaumamannia manni Drake and Davis

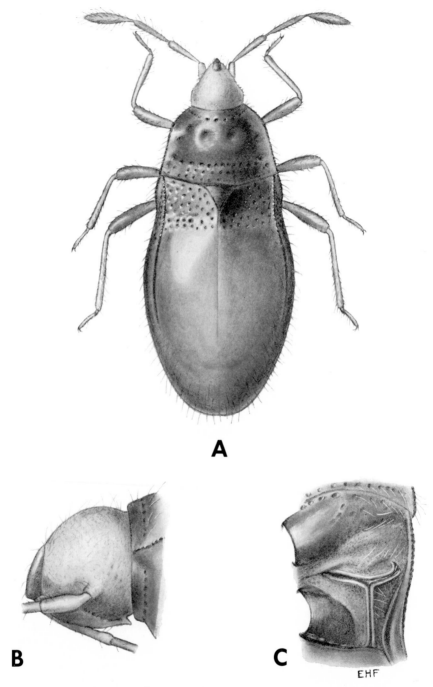

A

B

C

EHF

Anommatocoris minutissimus China

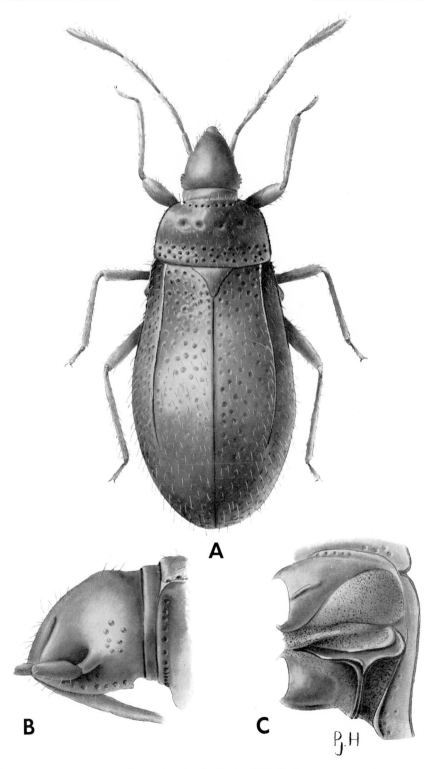

A

B

C

P.J.H

Anommatocoris coleopteratus (Kormilev)

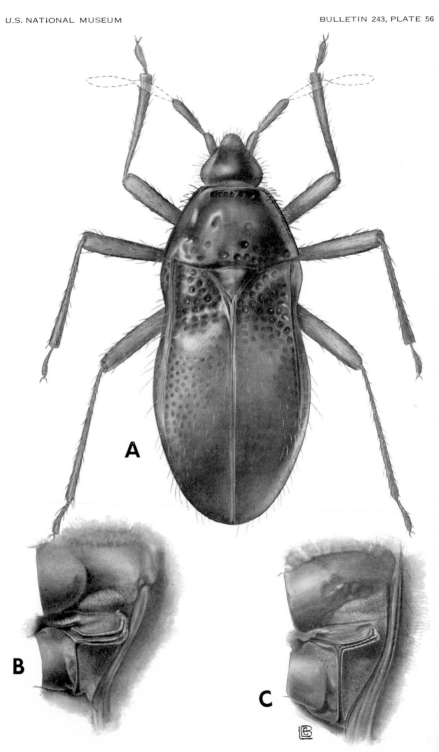

A, B, *Anommatocoris zeteki* Drake and Froeschner, and C, *A. minutissimus* China

Species Wrongly Classified as Tingidae

A number of species belonging to other families of Hemiptera have been wrongly described as Tingidae, or later mistakenly included as such in the literature. For convenience in finding and correcting these errors, the technical names of such species are entered below in alphabetical sequence. The correct family status is given in the second column opposite the trivial name. The asterisk (*) indicates the name of the author who corrected the error in the literature. The generic and specific names are also included in the index.

Agrammodes costatus Uhler.—Van Duzee 1916, p. 26; 1917b, p.   Piesmatidae
223.—Banks 1910, p. 55.

Copium guttatum Thunberg 1825, p. 10.—*Stål 1870b, p. 157.   Coreidae

Copium maculatum Thunberg 1825, p. 8.—*Stål 1870b, p. 157.   Coreidae

Copium serratum Thunberg 1825, p. 9.—Fallén 1829, p. 153.—   Coreidae
Burmeister 1835, p. 330.

Cymus basicornis Motschulsky.—Distant 1903b, p. 145.—*Bergroth   Lygaeidae
1921, p. 99.

Lasiocera Laporte 1833, p. 50.—*Fieber 1844, p. 21.   Reduviidae

Maynea maynei Schouteden.—Mayné and Ghesquière 1934, p. 20.   Aradidae

Metatropis aurita Breddin.—Zool. Rec. 1907, p. 380.   Berytidae

Opisthochasis albocostata Berg 1884, p. 100.—Pennington 1921, p.   Miridae
20.—*Drake and Poor 1938a, p. 103, fig. 1.

Phyllogasterotinginae Menon and Hakk 1959a, p. 392 [nom.   Coreidae
nud.].—Menon, Beri and Singh 1959, p. 286.

Phyllogasterotingis acheranthi Menon and Hakk 1959a, p. 392 [gen.,   Coreidae
sp., nom. nud.].—Menon, Beri and Singh 1959, p. 286.

Phyllotingis arida Walker 1873b, p. 3.—Lethierry and Severin   Aradidae
1896, p. 5.—*Champion 1898b, p. 5.

†*Tingiopsis reticulata* Bekker-Migdisova 1953, p. 461, fig. [fossil].—   Cercopidae
*Evans 1957, p. 289, fig. 6e.

Tingis alata (Fabricius).—Fabricius 1803, p. 125.   Aradidae

Tingis virescens (Fabricius).—Fabricius 1803, p. 127.—Fieber 1844,   Lygaeidae
p. 109.

445

Types and Their Locations

An endeavor has been made to record, whenever possible, pertinent data relative to the type (holotype or lectotype) of all species. These data include locality (as published in original description without change in geographic name), form (pterygopolymorphic), sex (male or female), and present deposition of the type specimen. When such information was not included in the original description or subsequent publications, the data on locality, wing development, and sex were obtained insofar as possible from the type specimens and labels thereon. When the type specimen is apparently "lost" or no information available on sex, or type locality, the term "unknown" is used.

As heretofore recorded in the pages, tingid types are lodged in museums, other institutions, and private collections in many countries. The full name and address of the museum or institution (including private collections) to which the abbreviations refer are as follows:

Amer. Mus.	American Museum Natural History, New York City, New York
Argentina Mus.	Museo Argentina de Ciencias Naturales, Buenos Aires, Argentina
Austr. Mus.	Australian Museum, Sydney, Australia
Berlin Mus.	Humboldt-Universitat zu Berlin Zoologisches Museum, Berlin, Germany
Bishop Mus.	Bernice P. Bishop Museum, Honolulu, Hawaii
British Mus.	British Museum (Natural History), London, England
Brussels Mus.	Institut Royal des Sciences naturelles de Belgique, Brussels, Belgium
Bucharest Mus.	Muzel de Istorie Naturala, Bucharest, Rumania
Cal. Acad.	California Academy of Sciences, San Francisco, California
Canada. Coll.	National Collection, Entomological Branch, Ottawa, Canada
Carnegie Mus.	Carnegie Museum, Pittsburgh, Pennsylvania
Cent. Afr. Mus.	Musée Royal de l'Afrique Centrale, Tervuren, Belgium (formerly Musée du Congo Belge)
Copenhagen Mus.	Universitets Zoologiske Museum, Copenhagen, Denmark
Cornell Univ.	Cornell University, Ithaca, New York
Coryndon Mus.	Coryndon Museum, Nairobi, Kenya
Drake Coll.(USNM)	Carl J. Drake Collection (United States National Museum)

446

Ent. Agr. Brazil	Servico de Entomologia Agricola do Instituto Biologico de Defensa Agricola, Rio de Janeiro, Brazil
Florida Univ.	University of Florida, Gainesville, Florida
Frankfort Mus.	Senckenbergische Naturforschende Gesellschaft, Frankfort a.M., Germany
Genova Mus.	Museo Civico di Storia Naturale, Genova, Italy
Hamburg Mus.	Zoologische Staatsinstitut und Zoologische Museum, Hamburg, Germany
Hawaii. Sugar Plant. Assn.	Hawaiian Sugar Planters Association, Honolulu, Hawaii
Helsin. Mus.	Kansaiimuseo, Helsinki, Finland
Heude Mus.	Museum Heude, Shanghai, China
Horn Coll.	Deutsches Entomologisches Institut, Berlin, Germany
Hungarian Mus.	Magyar Nemzeti Museum, Budapest, Hungary
Indian Mus.	Zoological Survey of India, Calcutta, India
Inst. Ent. Madrid	Instituto Español de Entomologica, Madrid, Spain
Inst. Fr. Afr. N.	Institut Francais d'Afrique Noire, Dakar, Senegal
Keil Coll.	In Copenhagen Museum
Kyushu Univ.	Kyushu Imperial University, Fukuoka, Japan
La Plata Mus.	Instituto del Museo de la Universidad Nacional de La Plata, La Plata, Argentina
Leiden Mus.	Rijksmuseum van Natuurlijke Historie, Leiden, Netherlands
Leningrad Inst.	Zoological Institute of Academy of Sciences, Leningrad, U.S.S.R.
Lingnan Surv.	Lingnan Natural History Survey, Canton, China
Lund Zool. Inst.	Zoological Institute, Lund University, Lund, Sweden
Lyon Mus.	Museum des Sciences Naturalles des Lyon, Rhone, France
Madagascar Sci. Inst.	Institut de Recherche Scientifique de Madagascar, Tenanarive, Malagasy Republic
Mancini Coll.	C. Mancini Collection in Genova Museum
MCZ	Museum of Comparative Zoology, Harvard University, Cambridge, Massachusetts
Michigan Univ.	Museum of Zoology, University of Michigan, Ann Arbor, Michigan
Monte Coll. (Mus. Nacional)	O. Monte Collection (Museum Nacional, Rio de Janeiro, Brazil)
Moscow Univ.	University of Moscow, Moscow, U.S.S.R.
Munich Mus.	Zoologische Sammlung des Bayerischen Staates, Munchen, West Germany

Naples Mus.	Musée Zoologique l'Université de Naples, Naples, Italy
Ohio State Univ.	Ohio State University, Columbus, Ohio
Oxford Mus.	Oxford Museum, Oxford, England
Parcs Nat. Inst.	Institut des Parcs Nationaux du Congo Belge, Brussels, Belgium
Paris Mus.	Museum National d'Histoire Naturelle, Paris, France
Prague Mus.	Národni Museum, Praha, Czechoslovakia
Queensland Mus.	Queensland Museum, Brisbane, Australia
Roubal Coll.	Jean Roubal, U.2, baterie 6, Praha, Czechoslovakia
Seidenstücker Coll.	Gustav Seidenstücker, Eichstätt, Bayern Römer Strasse 21, AOK, Germany
Snow Mus.	University of Kansas, Lawrence, Kansas
So. Afr. Mus.	South African Museum, Capetown, South Africa
So. Austr. Mus.	South Australian Museum, Adelaide, Australia
Stockholm Mus.	Naturhistoriska Rijsmuseet, Stockholm, Sweden
USNM	United States National Museum, Washington, D.C.
Vidal Coll.	J. P. Vidal Collection in Paris Museum
Vienna Mus.	Naturhistorisches Museum, Wien, Austria
Wagner Coll.	Edward Wagner, Mooreyhe 103, Hamburg, Germany

Host Plants

Most species of lacebugs are restricted to a single species of host plants or to a relatively small number of closely related plants. A few typical exceptions include the cotton or castor bean lacebug, *Corythucha gossypii* (Fabricius), the chrysanthemum lacebug, *Corythucha marmorata* (Uhler), the banana or coconut lacebug, *Stephanitis typica* (Distant), and the almond lacebug, *Monosteira unicostata* (Mulsant and Rey).

Since the technical and common names of host plants have been extracted directly from the literature, the determination of host plants as well as that of the tingid species concerned should be accredited to the authority as cited in the text. Except for corrections in spelling, the scientific names of plants are listed herein as printed in the literature, without nomenclatorial modernization or changes. The technical names of host plants are arranged alphabetically below the respective family names, which too are placed in alphabetical order.

ACANTHACEAE
Acanthus sp.
  Naochila kivuensis (Schouteden)
Anisacanthus thurberi
  Teleonemia huachucae Drake
Barleria cristata
  Habrochila darthula (Kirkaldy)
Barleria strigosa
  Habrochila darthula (Kirkaldy)
Bathysa stipulata
  Gargaphia patria (Drake and Hambleton)
Beloperone californica
  Teleonemia schwarzi Drake
Strobilanthes sp.
  Hegesidemus eliyanus Distant

ACERACEAE
Acer sp.
  Physatocheila harwoodi China
Acer creticum
  Physatocheila dumetorum (Herrich-Schaeffer)
Acer obtusifolium
  Physatocheila dumetorum (Herrich-Schaeffer)
Acer pennsylvanicum
  Corythucha pallipes Parshley

Acer platanoides
  Physatocheila harwoodi China
Acer pseudoplatanus
  Physatocheila harwoodi China
Acer saccharinum
  Corythucha pallipes Parshley
Acer saccharum
  Corythucha pallipes Parshley
Acer spicatum
  Corythucha pallipes Parshley

AESCULACEAE
Aesculus glabra
  Corythucha aesculi Osborn and Drake
Aesculus hippocastanum
  Corythucha aesculi Osborn and Drake
Aesculus octandra
  Corythucha aesculi Osborn and Drake

AGARICACEAE
Pholiota mutabilis
  Acalypta parvula (Fallén)

AMARANTACEAE
Achyranthes aspera
  Corythaica carinata Uhler

ANACARDIACEAE
Pistacia sp.
  Elasmotropis testacea (Herrich-Schaeffer)

449

Elasmotropis testacea var. *vicina* Horváth
  Tingis (Lasiotropis) hellenica (Puton)
Pseudospondias microcarpa
  Cysteochila ghesquierei Schouteden
Rhus laurina
  Teleonemia nigrina Champion
Rhus toxicodendron
  Corythucha padi Drake

ANNONACEAE

  Gargaphia concursa Drake
  Leptopharsa mira Drake and Hambleton
Annona cherimola
  Teleonemia morio (Stål)
Annona chrysophylla
  Haedus pallens Schouteden
Annona coriacea
  Idiostyla anonae (Drake and Hambleton)
Annona diversifolia
  Corythucha gossypii (Fabricius)
Annona muricata
  Corythucha gossypii (Fabricius)
  Haedus pallens Schouteden
  Stephanitis typica (Distant)
Annona reticulata
  Teleonemia morio (Stål)
Annona squamosa
  Corythucha gossypii (Fabricius)
  Teleonemia morio (Stål)
Rollinia silvatica
  Idiostyla rolliniae (Drake and Hambleton)
Uvaria rufa
  Stephanitis (Norba) nitor Drake and Poor

APOCYNACEAE

Paseala arnoldi Schouteden
Aspidosperma sp.
  Liotingis affinata Drake and Hambleton
  Liotingis aspidospermae Drake and Hambleton
  Liotingis evidens Drake
  Liotingis immaculata (Drake and Hambleton)

Aspidosperma melanocalyx
  Zelotingis aspidospermae (Drake and Hambleton)
Aspidosperma warmingii
  Leptopharsa sobrina Monte
Condylocarpon rauwolfiae
  Leptopharsa valida Drake and Hambleton
Forsteronia sp.
  Leptopharsa forsteroniae Drake and Hambleton
Nerium oleander
  Monosteira unicostata var. *buccata* Horváth

AQUIFOLIACEAE

Ilex sp.
  Leptoypha elliptica McAtee
  Leptoypha ilicis Drake

ARACEAE

Colocasia esculenta
  Stephanitis colocasiae Horváth
Raphidophora merrillii
  Cottothucha oceanae Drake and Poor
  Holophygdon melanesica var. *fusca* Drake and Poor

ARALIACEAE

Hedera helix
  Derephysia foliacea (Fallén)

ARISTOLOCHIACEAE

Aristolochia sp.
  Gargaphia flexuosa (Stål)

BERBERIDACEAE

Podophyllum peltatum
  Corythucha pallida Osborn and Drake

BETULACEAE

Alnus sp.
  Corythucha heidemanni Drake
  Corythucha pergandei Heidemann
  Physatocheila costata (Fabricius)
Alnus acuminata
  Atheas nigricornis Champion
  Corythucha decepta Drake
Alnus crispa
  Corythucha heidemanni Drake

Alnus glutinosa
  Corythucha pergandei Heidemann
  Monosteira unicostata (Mulsant and Rey)
  Physatocheila costata (Fabricius)
Alnus incana
  Corythucha bellula Gibson
  Corythucha pergandei Heidemann
  Physatocheila costata (Fabricius)
Alnus montana
  Physatocheila costata (Fabricius)
Alnus nepalensis
  Stephanitis gallarum Horváth
Alnus rugosa
  Corythucha pergandei Heidemann
Betula sp.
  Physatocheila costata (Fabricius)
Betula alba
  Corythucha pallipes Parshley
Betula lenta
  Corythucha pallipes Parshley
  Corythucha pergandei Heidemann
Betula lutea
  Corythucha heidemanni Drake
  Corythucha pallipes Parshley
  Corythucha pergandei Heidemann
Betula nigra
  Corythucha pergandei Heidemann
Betula papyrifera
  Corythucha pallipes Parshley
Betula populifolia
  Corythucha pergandei Heidemann
Carpinus caroliniana
  Corythucha lowyri Drake
Corylus sp.
  Corythucha bellula Gibson
  Corythucha coryli Osborn and Drake
Corylus americana
  Corythucha coryli Osborn and Drake
  Corythucha hewitti Drake
  Corythucha pergandei Heidemann
Corylus californica
  Corythucha hewitti Drake
Corylus rostrata
  Corythucha scitula Drake
Ostrya carpinifolia
  Physatocheila confinis Horváth

Ostrya virginiana
  Corythucha coryli Osborn and Drake
  Corythucha pallipes Parshley

BIGNONIACEAE

Acanthocheila hollandi Drake
Amblystira silvicola Drake
Dicysta amica Drake and Hambleton
Dicysta sagillata Drake
Planibyrsa elegantula (Drake)
Sphaerocysta angulata Monte
Sphaerocysta globifera (Stål)
Sphaerocysta inflata (Stål)
Tingis colombiana Drake
Adenocalymma sp.
  Dicysta lauta Drake and Hambleton
  Dicysta smithi Drake
  Dicysta vitrea Champion
Adenocalymma bracteatum
  Phymacysta tumida (Champion)
Anemopaegma prostratum
  Acanthocheila tumida Drake
Arrabidaea sp.
  Planibyrsa sodalis (Drake and Bondar)
Bignonia exoleta
  Acanthocheila visenda Drake and Hambleton
Chilopsis sp.
  Teleonemia barberi Drake
Jacaranda paucifoliata
  Teleonemia validicornis Stål
Mansoa glaziovii
  Dicysta vitrea Champion
Petastoma formosum
  Dicysta vitrea Champion
Petastoma samydoides
  Dicysta vitrea Champion
Pithecoctenium echinatum
  Teleonemia leitei Drake and Hambleton
Tecoma sp.
  Tingis americana Drake
  Tingis tecomae Monte

BOMBACACEAE

Bombax sp.
  Tigava bombacis Drake and Poor
  Tigava ferruginea Monte

Bombax munguba
  Eocader vegrandis Drake and Hambleton
Ceiba pentandra
  Tigava ceibae Drake and Poor
Chorisia sp.
  Tigava bombacis Drake and Poor
Chorisia speciosa
  Gargaphia lunulata (Mayr)
  Tigava bombacis Drake and Poor

BORAGINACEAE

Acysta praeclara Drake and Hambleton
Anchusa arvensis
  Dictyla echii (Schrank)
Anchusa officinalis
  Dictyla echii (Schrank)
  Octacysta echii (Fabricius)
Arnebia cornuta
  Physatocheila costata (Fabricius)
Cochranea anchusaefolia
  Dictyla parmata (Distant)
Cordia sp.
  Compseuta cordiae Drake
  Dictyla cheriana (Drake)
  Dictyla figurata (Drake)
  Dictyla loricata (Distant)
  Dictyla monotropida (Stål)
  Dictyla parmata (Distant)
  Naochila arete Drake and Mohanasundarum
  Tingis (Lasiotropis) beieri Drake
Cordia abyssinica
  Compseuta cordiae Drake
  Dictyla abyssinica (Drake)
  Horvathula uniseriata (Horváth)
Cordia alba
  Dictyla alia Drake and Cobben
Cordia alliodora
  Dictyla monotropida (Stål)
Cordia chrysocarpa
  Dictyla leroyi (Schouteden)
  Horvathula uniseriata (Horváth)
Cordia corymbosa
  Dictyla loricata (Distant)
  Dictyla parmata (Distant)
Cordia curassavica
  Dictyla parmata (Distant)

Cordia cylindristachya
  Dictyla parmata (Distant)
Cordia gerascanthus
  Dictyla monotropida (Stål)
Cordia millenii
  Horvathula uniseriata (Horváth)
Cordia myxa
  Compseuta lefroyi Distant
  Dictyla sauteri (Drake)
Cordia serrata
  Dictyla haitiensis (Drake and Poor)
Cordia tomentosa
  Dictyla monotropida (Stål)
Cordia verbenacea
  Dictyla parmata (Distant)
Cynoglossum sp.
  Dictyla echii (Schrank)
  Dictyla nassata (Puton)
  Dictyla triconula (Seidenstücker)
  Octacysta echii (Fabricius)
Cynoglossum creticum
  Dictyla putoni var. *pulla* (Horváth)
Cynoglossum officinale
  Dictyla echii (Schrank)
  Dictyla triconula (Seidenstücker)
Echinospermum lappula
  Dictyla platyoma (Fieber)
Echium sp.
  Derephysia foliacea (Fallén)
  Dictyla echii (Schrank)
  Dictyla putoni (Montandon)
  Dictyonota (Alcletha) tricornis (Schrank)
  Octacysta echii (Fabricius)
Echium altissimum
  Dictyla echii (Schrank)
  Dictyla putoni var. *pulla* (Horváth)
Echium candicans
  Dictyla indigena (Wollaston)
Echium creticum
  Dictyla echii (Schrank)
Echium hypertropicum
  Dictyla indigena (Wollaston)
Echium italicum
  Dictyla echii (Schrank)
  Octacysta echii (Fabricius)
Echium plantagineum
  Dictyla nassata (Puton)

Echium pustulatum
  Dictyla echii (Schrank)
Echium rubrum
  Dictyla echii (Schrank)
  Octacysta echii (Fabricius)
Echium sericeum
  Dictyla nassata (Puton)
Echium stenosiphon
  Dictyla indigena (Wollaston)
Echium vulgare
  Acalypta gracilis (Fieber)
  Derephysia foliacea (Fallén)
  Dictyla echii (Schrank)
  Dictyonota (Alcletha) tricornis (Schrank)
  Octacysta echii (Fabricius)
Ehretia acuminata
  Dictyla evidens (Drake)
Ehretia dicksonii
  Dictyla evidens (Drake)
Ehretia elliptica
  Dictyla ehrethiae (Gibson)
Ehretia laevis
  Naochila sufflata (Drake and Poor)
Ehretia taiwaniana
  Dictyla evidens (Drake)
Ehretia thyrsiflora
  Dictyla evidens (Drake)
Heliotropium erosum
  Dictyonota (Alcletha) tricornis (Schrank)
Lappula sp.
  Leptopharsa clitoriae (Heidemann)
Lycopsis arvensis
  Dictyla echii (Schrank)
Myosotis sp.
  Dictyla convergens (Herrich-Schaeffer)
  Dictyla lupuli (Herrich-Schaeffer)
  Dictyla platyoma (Fieber)
Myosotis cespitosa
  Dictyla convergens (Herrich-Schaeffer)
Myosotis lingulata
  Dictyla convergens (Herrich-Schaeffer)
Myosotis palustris
  Dictyla convergens (Herrich-Schaeffer)
  Dictyla lupuli (Herrich-Schaeffer)
  Dictyla platyoma (Fieber)
Onosma sp.
  Dictyla nassata (Puton)

Onosma echioides
  Campylosteira verna (Fallén)
Onosma visianii
  Dictyla putoni var. *pulla* (Horváth)
Pulmonaria sp.
  Dictyla echii (Schrank)
Symphytum sp.
  Dictyla echii (Schrank)
  Dictyla humuli (Fabricius)
  Dictyla platyoma (Fieber)
Symphytum officinale
  Dictyla humuli (Fabricius)
Tournefortia sp.
  Dictyla loricata (Distant)
Tournefortia sibirica
  Dictyla montandoni (Horváth)

BROMELIACEAE

Aechmea sp.
  Ambycysta gibbifera (Picado)
  Psilobyrsa aechemeae Drake and Hambleton
Vriesia hoehneana
  Psilobyrsa vriesiae Drake and Hambleton

CAPPARIDACEAE

Atamisquea emarginata
  Corythucha gossypii (Fabricius)
Capparis cynophallophora
  Corythucha gossypii (Fabricius)
Capparis flexuosa
  Corythucha gossypii (Fabricius)

CAPRIFOLIACEAE

Lonicera sp.
  Derephysia foliacea (Fallén)
Viburnum tinus
  Stephanitis chlorophana (Fieber)

CARICACEAE

Carica papaya
  Corythucha gossypii (Fabricius)

CARYOPHYLLACEAE

Gymnocarpos decandrum
  Sabestena alfierii Drake and Ruhoff
Herniaria sp.
  Acalypta parvula (Fallén)
Herniaria glabra
  Galeatus maculatus (Herrich-Schaeffer)

CASUARINACEAE

Casuarina sp.
  Epimixia veteris Drake
Casuarina equisetifolia
  Eocader bouclei (Bruner)

CHENOPODIACEAE

Chenopodium sp.
  Derephysia foliacea (Fallén)
Halogeton sativus
  Dictyla nassata (Puton)
Salsola pestifer
  Corythaica venusta (Champion)

CISTACEAE

Cistus albidus
  Urentius chobauti Horváth
Helianthemum lippii
  Urentius euonymus Distant

CLIMACIACEAE

Climacium americanum
  Acalypta lillianis Torre-Bueno
Climacium dendroides
  Acalypta parvula (Fallén)
  Derephysia foliacea (Fallén)

COMPOSITAE

Ambrosia sp.
  Gargaphia iridescens Champion
Ambrosia artemisiifolia
  Corythucha morrilli Osborn and Drake
Ambrosia tenuifolia
  Gargaphia subpilosa Berg
Ambrosia trifida
  Corythucha marmorata (Uhler)
Amphiachyris sp.
  Gargaphia solani Heidemann
Antennaria sp.
  Leptocysta sexnebulosa (Stål)
Antennaria dioica
  Galeatus spinifrons (Fallén)
Artemisia sp.
  Acalypta gracilis (Fieber)
  Derephysia foliacea (Fallén)
  Dictyonota (*Alcletha*) *tricornis* (Schrank)
  Galeatus scrophicus Saunders
  Tingis comosa (Takeya)
Artemisia absinthium
  Tingis crispata (Herrich-Schaeffer)

Artemisia campestris
  Acalypta gracilis (Fieber)
  Acalypta marginata (Wolff)
  Derephysia cristata (Panzer)
  Derephysia foliacea (Fallén)
  Dictyonota (*Alcletha*) *tricornis* (Schrank)
  Galeatus spinifrons (Fallén)
  Tingis crispata (Herrich-Schaeffer)
Artemisia dracunculoides
  Corythucha morrilli Osborn and Drake
Artemisia vulgaris
  Derephysia foliacea (Fallén)
  Galeatus spinifrons (Fallén)
  Tingis crispata (Herrich-Schaeffer)
Artemisia vulgaris v. indica
  Galeatus spinifrons (Fallén)
Aster sp.
  Corythucha marmorata (Uhler)
Aster macrophyllus
  Galeatus spinifrons (Fallén)
Baccharis sp.
  Corythucha baccharides Drake
Baccharis halimifolia
  Corythucha baccharides Drake
Baccharis mesoneura
  Leptobyrsa baccharidis Drake and Hambleton
  Leptobyrsa steini (Stål)
Baccharis pilularis
  Corythucha morrilli Osborn and Drake
Baccharis pingraea
  Coleopterodes brunnea Drake and Poor
  Coleopterodes liliputiana (Signoret)
Balsamorhiza sagittata
  Corythucha immaculata Osborn and Drake
Bidens pilosa v. radiata
  Leptopharsa machalana var. *vinnula* Drake and Hambleton
Cacalia thunbergii
  Cochlochila lewisi (Scott)
Carduus sp.
  Corythucha distincta var. *spinata* Osborn and Drake
  Tingis ampliata (Herrich-Schaeffer)
  Tingis cardui (Linnaeus)
  Tingis veteris Drake
  Tingis (*Tropidocheila*) *marrubii* Vallot

Carduus acanthoides
  Tingis cardui (Linnaeus)
Carduus crispus
  Tingis cardui (Linnaeus)
Carduus lanceolatus
  Corythucha distincta Osborn and Drake
  Stephanitis oberti (Kolenati)
  Tingis cardui (Linnaeus)
Carduus nutans
  Tingis cardui (Linnaeus)
Carthamus tinctorius
  Cochlochila bullita (Stål)
Cassinia leptophylla
  Cyperobia carectorum Bergroth
Centaurea paniculata
  Tingis grisea Germar
Centaurea rhenana
  Tingis grisea Germar
Centaurea solstitialis
  Tingis fuentei Horváth
Chrysanthemum sp.
  Catoplatus fabricii (Stål)
  Corythucha marmorata (Uhler)
  Dictyonota (*Alcletha*) *tricornis* (Schrank)
  Galeatus scitulus Drake and Maa
  Galeatus scrophicus Saunders
  Physatocheila costata (Fabricius)
Chrysanthemum indicum
  Galeatus spinifrons (Fallén)
Chrysanthemum leucanthemum
  Catoplatus fabricii (Stål)
  Derephysia foliacea (Fallén)
Chuquiragua glabra
  Phymacysta magnifica (Drake)
Cirsium sp.
  Tingis ampliata (Herrich-Schaeffer)
  Tingis demisea Horváth
  Tingis veteris Drake
  Tingis (*Lasiotropis*) *reticulata* Herrich-Schaeffer
Cirsium arvense
  Tingis ampliata (Herrich-Schaeffer)
Cirsium lanceolatum
  Tingis ampliata (Herrich-Schaeffer)
  Tingis cardui (Linnaeus)
Cirsium palustre
  Tingis ampliata (Herrich-Schaeffer)
  Tingis cardui (Linnaeus)

Cirsium vulgare
  Tingis cardui (Linnaeus)
Cnicus sp.
  Corythucha distincta Osborn and Drake
Crepis tectorum
  Tingis (*Tropidocheila*) *pilosa* Hummel
Dahlia sp.
  Corythucha gossypii (Fabricius)
Dahlia parryi
  Gargaphia condensa Gibson
Dahlia spinosa
  Gargaphia opacula Uhler
Echinops sp.
  Elasmotropis testacea (Herrich-Schaeffer)
  Elasmotropis testacea var. *platydera* Horváth
Echinops sphaerocephala
  Corythucha marmorata (Uhler)
  Elasmotropis testacea (Herrich-Schaeffer)
Echinops spinosa
  Galeatus scrophicus Saunders
  Tingis (*Lasiotropis*) *rotundipennis* Horváth
Egletes prostrata
  Corythucha morrilli Osborn and Drake
Erigeron canadensis
  Corythucha morrilli Osborn and Drake
Eupatorium sp.
  Galeatus spinifrons (Fallén)
Eupatorium intermedium
  Leptobyrsa baccharidis Drake and Hambleton
  Leptobyrsa steini (Stål)
Galactites tomentosa
  Tingis cardui (Linnaeus)
Helenium tenuifolium
  Teleonemia nigrina Champion
Helianthus sp.
  Corythucha marmorata (Uhler)
  Corythucha morrilli Osborn and Drake
Helianthus annuus
  Corythucha morrilli Osborn and Drake
  Gargaphia subpilosa Berg
Helianthus tuberosus
  Corythucha marmorata (Uhler)

Helichrysum angustifolium
  Copium teucrii (Host)
Helichrysum arenarium
  Galeatus spinifrons (Fallén)
Helichrysum italicum
  Copium intermedium (Rey)
Hieracium sp.
  Dictyonota (Alcletha) tricornis (Schrank)
  Galeatus maculatus (Herrich-Schaeffer)
  Galeatus spinifrons (Fallén)
  Lasiacantha capucina (Germar)
Hieracium murorum
  Acalypta nigrina (Fallén)
Hieracium pilosella
  Acalypta marginata (Wolff)
  Galeatus maculatus (Herrich-Schaeffer)
  Galeatus sinuatus (Herrich-Schaeffer)
Hymenoclea salsola
  Teleonemia schwarzi Drake
Lagascea mollis
  Corythucha morrilli Osborn and Drake
Lappa minor
  Tingis (Tropidocheila) pilosa Hummel
  Tingis (Tropidocheila) pilosa var. *amplicosta* (Montandon)
Launaea spinosa
  Galeatus scrophicus Saunders
Ligularia sibirica
  Cochlochila lewisi (Scott)
Mikania sp.
  Leptocysta sexnebulosa (Stål)
Mikania auricularis
  Gargaphia subpilosa Berg
Moquinia sp.
  Leptobyrsa tersa Drake and Hambleton
Moquinia polymorpha
  Leptobyrsa tersa Drake and Hambleton
Onopordon sp.
  Catoplatus carthusianus (Goeze)
Petasites japonica
  Cochlochila lewisi (Scott)
Pluchea indica
  Corythucha morrilli Osborn and Drake
Rudbeckia serotina
  Corythucha marmorata (Uhler)
Senecio sp.
  Tingis (Tropidocheila) pilosa Hummel

Senecio jacobaea
  Dictyonota (Alcletha) tricornis (Schrank)
  Oncochila scapularis (Fieber)
  Tingis (Lasiotropis) reticulata Herrich-Schaeffer
Serratula sp.
  Tingis cardui (Linnaeus)
Serratula atriplicifolia
  Tingis lasiocera Matsumura
Silybum sp.
  Tingis cardui (Linnaeus)
Solidago sp.
  Corythucha marmorata (Uhler)
  Melanorhopala clavata (Stål)
Solidago sempervirens
  Corythucha marmorata (Uhler)
Symphyopappus reticulatus
  Leptobyrsa ardua Drake
  Leptobyrsa steini (Stål)
Synedrella nodiflora
  Corythucha morrilli Osborn and Drake
Tanacetum sp.
  Corythucha marmorata (Uhler)
Verbesina sp.
  Teleonemia sacchari (Fabricius)
Verbesina encelioides
  Corythucha morrilli Osborn and Drake
Vernonia sp.
  Ammianus alberti subsp. *tricarinatus* (Schouteden)
  Corythucha agalma Drake and Cobben
  Leptocysta sexnebulosa (Stål)
  Nectocader gounellei (Drake)
  Phatnoma annulipes Champion
Vernonia conferta
  Ammianus alberti (Schouteden)
Vernonia polyanthes
  Phatnoma vernoniae Drake and Hambleton
  Teleonemia brevipennis Champion
Wedelia jacquini
  Corythucha morrilli Osborn and Drake
Xanthium sp.
  Corythucha morrilli Osborn and Drake
  Teleonemia scrupulosa Stål
Xanthium canadense
  Corythucha morrilli Osborn and Drake

Zinnia elegans
  Gargaphia torresi Costa Lima
  CONVOLVULACEAE
Ipomoea sp.
  Gargaphia deceptiva (Drake and Bruner)
  Gargaphia torresi Costa Lima
Ipomoea batatas
  Corythucha morrilli Osborn and Drake
  Leptocysta sexnebulosa (Stål)
  Teleonemia forticornis Champion
Ipomoea bonariensis
  Gargaphia subpilosa Berg
Ipomoea fistulosa
  Teleonemia brevipennis Champion
  CRASSULACEAE
Sedum acre
  Dictyonota (*Alcletha*) *tricornis* (Schrank)
  CUCURBITACEAE
Cucurbita moschata
  Teleonemia tricolor (Mayr)
Lagenaria leucantha
  Corythucha gossypii (Fabricius)
Sechium edule
  Teleonemia tricolor (Mayr)
Sicana odorifera
  Teleonemia tricolor (Mayr)
  CUPRESSACEAE
Cupressus sp.
  Elasmotropis testacea var. *vicina* Horváth
  CYPERACEAE
  Agramma confusum (Puton)
Carex sp.
  Acalypta platycheila (Fieber)
  Agramma laetum (Fallén)
  Agramma ruficorne (Germar)
  Derephysia foliacea (Fallén)
Eriophorum sp.
  Agramma tropidopterum Flor
Eriophorum angustifolium
  Agramma femorale Thomson
Rhynchospora alba
  Agramma femorale Thomson
  Agramma laetum (Fallén)
Schoenus albus
  Agramma femorale Thomson
  Agramma laetum (Fallén)

Scirpus holoschoenus
  Agramma atricapillum (Spinola)
  Agramma dubium var. *imbecillum* (Horváth)
Scleria myricocarpa
  Leptopharsa pensa Drake and Hambleton
  DICHAPETALACEAE
Dichapetalum cymosum
  Onymochila dichapetali (Horváth)
  DILLENIACEAE
Davilla rugosa
  Tingis silvacata Drake
  ERICACEAE
Andromedea sp.
  Stephanitis takeyai Drake and Maa
Azalea see *Rhododendron*
Calluna sp.
  Acalypta gracilis (Fieber)
  Galeatus spinifrons (Fallén)
Calluna vulgaris
  Acalypta marginata (Wolff)
  Acalypta nigrina (Fallén)
  Acalypta parvula (Fallén)
  Galeatus spinifrons (Fallén)
  Stephanitis oberti (Kolenati)
  Tingis (*Lasiotropis*) *reticulata* Herrich-Schaeffer
Chamaedaphne sp.
  Corythucha ciliata (Say)
Erica sp.
  Tingis (*Lasiotropis*) *reticulata* Herrich-Schaeffer
Erica vulgaris
  Galeatus maculatus (Herrich-Schaeffer)
  Tingis (*Lasiotropis*) *reticulata* Herrich-Schaeffer
Kalmia angustifolia
  Stephanitis rhododendri Horváth
Kalmia latifolia
  Physatocheila plexa (Say)
  Stephanitis pyrioides (Scott)
  Stephanitis rhododendri Horváth
Ledum palustre
  Stephanitis oberti (Kolenati)
Lyonia neziki
  Stephanitis takeyai Drake and Maa

Myrtillus niger
Stephanitis oberti (Kolenati)
Myrtillus uliginosus
Stephanitis oberti (Kolenati)
Pierus floribunda
Stephanitis rhododendri Horváth
Pierus japonica
Stephanitis rhododendri Horváth
Stephanitis takeyai Drake and Maa
Pieris ovalifolia
Stephanitis pyrioides (Scott)
Stephanitis takeyai Drake and Maa
Rhododendron sp.
Stephanitis caucasica Kiritshenko
Stephanitis oberti (Kolenati)
Stephanitis propinqua Horváth
Stephanitis pyrioides (Scott)
Stephanitis rhododendri Horváth
Rhododendron america
Stephanitis rhododendri Horváth
Rhododendron amoena
Stephanitis pyrioides (Scott)
Rhododendron amurasaki
Stephanitis pyrioides (Scott)
Rhododendron Antoon van Welie
Stephanitis rhododendri Horváth
Rhododendron benigeri
Stephanitis pyrioides (Scott)
Rhododendron calenulaceum
Stephanitis pyrioides (Scott)
Rhododendron caractacus
Stephanitis rhododendri Horváth
Rhododendron Cunningham's White
Stephanitis rhododendri Horváth
Rhododendron cynthia
Stephanitis rhododendri Horváth
Rhododendron Dr. V. H. Rutgers
Stephanitis rhododendri Horváth
Rhododendron everestianum
Stephanitis rhododendri Horváth
Rhododendron fastuosum
Stephanitis rhododendri Horváth
Rhododendron hatsugeri
Stephanitis pyrioides (Scott)
Rhododendron hinodegeri
Stephanitis pyrioides (Scott)
Rhododendron hollandia
Stephanitis rhododendri Horváth

Rhododendron hymenanthes var. heptamerum
Stephanitis hikosana Drake
Rhododendron indica
Stephanitis pyrioides (Scott)
Rhododendron kaempheri
Stephanitis pyrioides (Scott)
Rhododendron ledifolium alba
Stephanitis pyrioides (Scott)
Rhododendron maximum
Stephanitis rhododendri Horváth
Rhododendron Mme. de Bruin
Stephanitis rhododendri Horváth
Rhododendron Mme. Carvalho
Stephanitis rhododendri Horváth
Rhododendron Mme. Mason
Stephanitis rhododendri Horváth
Rhododendron mollis
Stephanitis pyrioides (Scott)
Rhododendron Mr. R. S. Holford
Stephanitis rhododendri Horváth
Rhododendron mucrunatum
Stephanitis pyrioides (Scott)
Rhododendron obtusum amoenum
Stephanitis pyrioides (Scott)
Rhododendron parsons gloriosum
Stephanitis rhododendri Horváth
Rhododendron Peter Koster
Stephanitis rhododendri Horváth
Rhododendron ponticum
Stephanitis pyrioides (Scott)
Rhododendron schilippenbachii
Stephanitis pyrioides (Scott)
Rhododendron shibori
Stephanitis pyrioides (Scott)
Rhododendron shirogeri
Stephanitis pyrioides (Scott)
Rhododendron Van der Hoop
Stephanitis rhododendri Horváth
Rhododendron yedoense pokhenense
Stephanitis pyrioides (Scott)
Rhododendron yodogawa
Stephanitis pyrioides (Scott)
Vaccinium sp.
Leptoypha ilicis Drake
Vaccinium myrtillus
Derephysia foliacea (Fallén)

Stephanitis oberti (Kolenati)
Stephanitis pyri (Fabricius)
Vaccinium uliginosum
Stephanitis oberti (Kolenati)
Vaccinium vitis-idaea
Stephanitis oberti (Kolenati)
Xolisma ferruginea
Leptoypha mcateei Drake

ERYTHROXYLACEAE

Erythroxylon sp.
Corycera rugulosa Drake
Corycera separata Drake and Hamble-
ton
Erythroxylon deciduum
Leptopharsa decens Drake and Hamble-
ton

EUPHORBIACEAE

Corythucha socia Monte
Gargaphia patricia (Stål)
Acalypha sp.
Gargaphia penningtoni Drake
Cnidoscolus sp.
Gargaphia lunulata (Mayr)
Croton sp.
Gargaphia concursa Drake
Gargaphia costalimai Monte
Gargaphia torresi Costa Lima
Haedus decellei Schouteden
Tingis (Lasiotropis) beieri Drake
Croton antisyphiliticus
Corycera spissa Drake
Croton flavens
Leptopharsa ruris Drake
Croton lobatus
Gargaphia penningtoni Drake
Croton pungens
Gargaphia mirabilis Monte
Croton urucurana
Gargaphia crotonae Drake and Hamble-
ton
Gargaphia decoris Drake
Dalechampia ficifolia
Gargaphia differitas Drake
Euphorbia cyparissias
Oncochila simplex (Herrich-Schaeffer)
Euphorbia gerardiana
Oncochila scapularis (Fieber)
Oncochila simplex (Herrich-Schaeffer)

Euphorbia heterophylla
Gargaphia lunulata (Mayr)
Glochidion sp.
Phatnoma veridica Drake and Maa
Hevea sp.
Cysteochila biseriata Schouteden
Cysteochila lueboensis Schouteden
Hevea brasiliensis
Leptopharsa heveae Drake and Poor
Jatropha sp.
Corythucha gossypii (Fabricius)
Jatropha gossypifolia
Corythucha gossypii (Fabricius)
Jatropha multifida
Corythucha gossypii (Fabricius)
Jatropha urens
Gargaphia niginervis Stål
Mallotus philippinensis
Trachypeplus jacobsoni Horváth
Trachypeplus malloti Drake and Poor
Manihot sp.
Atheas cearanus Monte
Vatiga illudens (Drake)
Vatiga manihotae (Drake)
Manihot dulcis
Vatiga illudens (Drake)
Vatiga illudens var. *varianta* (Drake)
Manihot esculenta
Vatiga illudens (Drake)
Manihot utilissima
Gargaphia lunulata (Mayr)
Vatiga illudens (Drake)
Vatiga longula (Drake)
Vatiga manihotae (Drake)
Ricinus communis
Corythaica cyathicollis (Costa)
Corythucha gossypii (Fabricius)
Corythucha spinosa (Dugès)
Gargaphia lunulata (Mayr)

FAGACEAE

Castanea americana
Corythucha arcuata (Say)
Castanea sativa
Stephanitis pyri (Fabricius)
Fagus grandifolia
Corythucha pallipes Parshley

Quercus sp.
Acalypta hellenica Reuter
Corthuchay arcuata (Say)
Corythucha cydoniae (Fitch)
Derephysia foliacea (Fallén)
Physatocheila costata (Fabricius)
Quercus acuminata
Corythucha arcuata (Say)
Quercus acutissima
Uhlerites debilis (Uhler)
Quercus alba
Corythucha arcuata (Say)
Quercus coccifera
Monosteira lobulifera Reuter
Physatocheila confinis Horváth
Stephanitis pyri (Fabricius)
Quercus dentata
Uhlerites debilis (Uhler)
Quercus dilatata
Physatocheila dryadis Drake and Poor
Quercus glandulifera
Uhlerites debilis (Uhler)
Quercus ilex
Monosteira lobulifera Reuter
Physatocheila confinis Horváth
Stephanitis pyri (Fabricius)
Quercus macrocarpa
Corythucha arcuata (Say)
Quercus muehlenbergii
Corythucha arcuata (Say)
Quercus prinoides
Corythucha arcuata (Say)
Quercus prinus
Corythucha arcuata (Say)
Quercus pubescens
Physatocheila confinis Horváth
Quercus rubra
Corythucha arcuata (Say)
Quercus serrata
Uhlerites debilis (Uhler)
Quercus suber
Catoplatus mamorensis Bergevin

FLACOURTIACEAE

Olmediella betschleriana
Leptopharsa dapsilis Drake and Hambleton

GERANIACEAE

Erodium sp.
Acalypta marginata (Wolff)
Acalypta nigrina (Fallén)
Acalypta parvula (Fallén)
Erodium circutarium
Acalypta gracilis (Fieber)

GNETACEAE

Ephedra sp.
Tingis lanigera (Puton)

GOODENIACEAE

Scaevola koenigii
Paracopium summervillei (Hacker)

GRAMINEAE

Agramma atricapillum var. *pallens* (Horváth)
Arusha horvathi Drake
Leptodictya (*Hanuala*) *plana* Heidemann
Leptopharsa lineata (Champion)
Tigava graminis Drake and Poor
Andropogon sp.
Hesperotingis antennata Parshley
Bambusa sp.
Corythucha spinosa (Dugès)
Leptodictya (*Hanuala*) *approximata* (Stål)
Leptodictya (*Hanuala*) *venezolana* Monte
Nyctotingis obsorni Drake
Bambusa vulgaris
Leptodictya (*Hanuala*) *bambusae* Drake
Cenchrus glaucus
Bako malayanus (Drake)
Cynodon dactylon
Bako malayanus (Drake)
Dendrocalamus strictus
Leptodictya (*Hanuala*) *bambusae* Drake
Ichnanthus leiocarpus
Aepycysta undosa Drake and Bondar
Merostachys sp.
Stephanitis mitrata (Stål)
Olyra sp.
Leptodictya (*Hanuala*) *austrina* Drake and Hambleton
Leptodictya (*Hanuala*) *comes* Drake and Hambleton
Leptodictya (*Hanuala*) *madra* Drake and Hambleton
Leptodictya (*Hanuala*) *nota* Drake and Hambleton

Leptodictya (*Hanuala*) *olyrae* Drake
Leptodictya (*Hanuala*) *solita* Drake and
  Hambleton
Olyra latifolia
  Leptodictya (*Hanuala*) *olyrae* Drake
Olyra micrantha
  Stephanitis olyrae Drake and Hamble-
  ton
Oryza sativa
  Bako malayanus (Drake)
Panicum lindheimeri
  Corythaica bellula Torre-Bueno
Panicum maximum
  Leptodictya (*Hanuala*) *dola* Drake and
  Hambleton
Panicum repens
  Bako malayanus (Drake)
Panicum turgidum
  Phaenotropis cleopatra (Horváth)
Paspalum sp.
  Leptodictya (*Hanuala*) *paspalii* Drake
  and Hambleton
Phyllostachys castilloni
  Leptodictya (*Hanuala*) *litigiosa* Monte
Psamma sp.
  Tingis (*Lasiotropis*) *reticulata* Herrich-
  Schaeffer
Saccharum officinarum
  Agramma formosanum (Matsumura)
  Leptodictya (*Hanuala*) *bambusae* Drake
Urochloa reptans
  Aconchus urbanus (Horváth)
Zea mays
  Corythucha salicata Gibson

HAMAMELIDACEAE
Hamamelis sp.
  Leptoypha costata Parshley

HERNANDIACEAE
Hernandia sp.
  Stephanitis subfasciata Horváth

HYDROPHYLLACEAE
Eriodictyon californicum
  Corythucha eriodictyonae Osborn and
  Drake

HYPERICACEAE
Hypericum sp.
  Catoplatus fabricii (Stål)

JUGLANDACEAE
Carya sp.
  Corythucha caryae Bailey
Carya illinoensis
  Corythucha juglandis (Fitch)
Carya olivaeformis
  Corythucha juglandis (Fitch)
Carya ovata
  Corythucha caryae Bailey
  Corythucha ciliata (Say)
Hicoria alba
  Leptoypha costata Parshley
Juglans cinerea
  Corythucha juglandis (Fitch)
Juglans nigra
  Corythucha juglandis (Fitch)
Juglans regia
  Stephanitis pyri (Fabricius)
Juglans sieboldiana
  Corythucha juglandis (Fitch)

JUNCACEAE
Juncus sp.
  Agramma atricapillum (Spinola)
  Agramma carinatum (Distant)
  Agramma confusum (Puton)
  Agramma fallax (Horváth)
  Agramma laetum (Fallén)
  Agramma melanoscele (Horváth)
  Agramma ruficorne (Germar)
  Agramma tropidopterum Flor
  Derephysia foliacea (Fallén)
Juncus acutus
  Agramma atricapillum (Spinola)
Juncus gerardi
  Agramma confusum (Puton)
Juncus maritimus
  Agramma atricapillum (Spinola)
  Agramma laetum (Fallén)
Luzula campestris
  Agramma laetum (Fallén)

LABIATAE
  Lasiacantha altimitrata (Takeya)
Ajuga sp.
  Lasiacantha capucina (Germar)
  Tingis (*Lasiotropis*) *reticulata* Herrich-
  Schaeffer
  Tingis (*Tropidocheila*) *caucasica* (Jakov-
  lev)

Ajuga chamaepytis
  Tingis (*Lasiotropis*) *ajugarum* (Frey-Gessner)
Ajuga genevensis
  Tingis (*Lasiotropis*) *ajugarum* (Frey-Gessner)
  Tingis (*Lasiotropis*) *reticulata* Herrich-Schaeffer
Ajuga iva
  Tingis (*Lasiotropis*) *ajugarum* (Frey-Gessner)
Ajuga reptans
  Tingis (*Lasiotropis*) *reticulata* Herrich-Schaeffer
Ballota nigra
  Tingis (*Tropidocheila*) *pilosa* Hummel
  Tingis (*Tropidocheila*) *pilosa* var. *amplicosta* (Montandon)
Betonica officinalis
  Hyalochiton colpochilus (Horváth)
Coleus sp.
  Cochlochila bullita (Stål)
Galeopsis tetrahit
  Tingis (*Tropidocheila*) *pilosa* Hummel
  Tingis (*Tropidocheila*) *pilosa* var. *amplicosta* (Montandon)
Hoslundia sp.
  Dictyla sjostedti (Horváth)
Hoslundia oppositifolia
  Naochila boxiana (Drake)
Keiskea japonica
  Copium japonicum Esaki
Leonurus cardiaca
  Tingis (*Tropidocheila*) *pilosa* Hummel
  Tingis (*Tropidocheila*) *pilosa* var. *amplicosta* (Montandon)
Marrubium sp.
  Tingis (*Tropidocheila*) *marrubii* Vallot
Marrubium vulgare
  Tingis cardui (Linnaeus)
  Tingis (*Tropidocheila*) *marrubii* Vallot
Mentha sp.
  Cochlochila bullita (Stål)
  Dictyonota (*Alcletha*) *tricornis* (Schrank)
Mosla punctata
  Copium japonicum Esaki
Ocium basilicum
  Cochlochila bullita (Stål)

Ocium canum
  Cochlochila bullita (Stål)
Ocium kilimandscharicum
  Cochlochila bullita (Stål)
Ocium sanctum
  Cochlochila bullita (Stål)
Phlomis sp.
  Hyalochiton multiseriatus (Reuter)
Phlomis fruticosa
  Tingis (*Lasiotropis*) *hellenica* (Puton)
Phlomis herba-venti
  Tingis (*Tropidocheila*) *granadensis* Horváth
Phlomis lynchitis
  Hyalochiton colpochilus (Horváth)
  Tingis (*Lasiotropis*) *trichonota* (Puton)
Phlomis pungens
  Tingis (*Tropidocheila*) *pauperata* (Puton)
Phlomis tuberosa
  Galeatus sinuatis (Herrich-Schaeffer)
Prunella vulgaris
  Teleonemia prunellae Drake and Hambleton
Salvia azurea
  Gargaphia solani Heidemann
Salvia officinalis
  Cochlochila bullita (Stål)
Salvia pitcheri
  Gargaphia solani Heidemann
Salvia verticillata
  Tingis (*Lasiotropis*) *reticulata* Herrich-Schaeffer
Satureja montana
  Lasiacantha gracilis (Herrich-Schaeffer)
Sideritis sp.
  Tingis (*Tropidocheila*) *stachydis* (Fieber)
Stachys sp.
  Tingis auriculata (Costa)
  Tingis (*Lasiotropis*) *ragusana* (Fieber)
  Tingis (*Tropidocheila*) *stachydis* (Fieber)
Stachys annua
  Tingis (*Tropidocheila*) *stachydis* (Fieber)
Stachys italica
  Tingis (*Lasiotropis*) *ragusana* (Fieber)
Stachys recta
  Tingis auriculata (Costa)
  Tingis (*Tropidocheila*) *stachydis* (Fieber)

Stachys salviaefolia
  Tingis (Lasiotropis) raguasana (Fieber)
Stachys sylvatica
  Tingis (Tropidocheila) pilosa Hummel
  Tingis (Tropidocheila) pilosa var. *amplicosta* (Montandon)
Teucrium sp.
  Copium clavicorne (Linnaeus)
  Copium horvathi Wagner
  Copium teucrii (Host)
  Hyalochiton komaroffii (Jakovlev)
Teucrium canum
  Copium clavicorne (Linnaeus)
Teucrium capitatum
  Copium teucrii (Host)
Teucrium chamaedrys
  Copium clavicorne (Linnaeus)
  Copium magnicorne (Rey)
  Copium teucrii (Host)
  Tingis (Tropidocheila) stachydis (Fieber)
Teucrium flavum
  Copium clavicorne (Linnaeus)
Teucrium marum
  Copium clavicorne (Linnaeus)
Teucrium montanum
  Copium clavicorne (Linnaeus)
  Copium magnicorne (Rey)
  Copium teucrii (Host)
Teucrium polium
  Copium bernardi Wagner
  Copium teucrii (Host)
Teucrium scordium
  Copium clavicorne (Linnaeus)
Teucrium scorodonium
  Copium clavicorne (Linnaeus)
  Copium reyi Wagner
Teucrium supinum
  Copium teucrii (Host)
Thymus sp.
  Acalypta gracilis (Fieber)
  Acalypta marginata (Wolff)
  Acalypta parvula (Fallén)
  Derephysia foliacea (Fallén)
  Dictyonota (Alcletha) tricornis (Schrank)
  Lasiacantha gracilis (Herrich-Schaeffer)
  Oncochila simplex (Herrich-Schaeffer)
Thymus montanus
  Lasiacantha capucina (Germar)

Thymus serpyllus
  Acalypta gracilis (Fieber)
  Acalypta nigrina (Fallén)
  Acalypta parvula (Fallén)
  Derephysia foliacea (Fallén)
  Lasiacantha capucina (Germar)

LAURACEAE

Aperula citriodora
  Stephanitis takeyai Drake and Maa
Camphora officinalis
  Pseudacysta perseae (Heidemann)
Cinnamomum camphora
  Stephanitis fasciicarina Takeya
  Stephanitis takeyai Drake and Maa
  Stephanitis (Norba) aperta Horváth
Cinnamomum pedunculatum
  Stephanitis (Norba) mendica Horváth
Lindera citriodora
  Stephanitis takeyai Drake and Maa
Lindera glauca
  Stephanitis ambigua Horváth
Lindera obtusiloba
  Stephanitis ambigua Horváth
  Stephanitis takeyai Drake and Maa
Lindera sericea
  Stephanitis takeyai Drake and Maa
Lindera umbellata
  Stephanitis takeyai Drake and Maa
Machilus sp.
  Stephanitis (Norba) esakii Takeya
Machilus gamblei
  Stephanitis gallarum Horváth
Machilus longifolia
  Stephanitis gallarum Horváth
Machilus pseudo-longifolia
  Stephanitis gallarum Horváth
Machilus thunbergii
  Stephanitis fasciicarina Takeya
  Stephanitis (Norba) aperta Horváth
  Stephanitis (Norba) esakii Takeya
  Stephanitis (Norba) exigua Horváth
Nectandra sp.
  Acysta nectandrae Drake and Hambleton
Ocotea sp.
  Pliobyrsa adversa (Drake and Hambleton)

Ocotea lanata
  Pliobyrsa inflexa (Drake and Hamble-
    ton)
Ocotea pretiosa
  Acysta ocoteae Drake and Hambleton
  Leptopharsa ocoteae Drake and Ham-
    bleton
Persea americana
  Pleseobyrsa chiriquensis (Champion)
Persea carolinensis
  Pseudacysta perseae (Heidemann)
Persea gratissima
  Pseudacysta perseae (Heidemann)
  Stephanitis (Norba) suffusa (Distant)
Tetrandenia dolichocarpa
  Stephanitis (Norba) esakii Takeya

LEGUMINOSAE

Atheas fuscipes Champion
Leptopharsa probala Drake and Ham-
    bleton
  Tigava gracilis Monte
  Tigava praecellens Stål
Acacia sp.
  Nethersia setosa (Hacker)
Acacia cavenia
  Coleopterodes liliputiana (Signoret)
Acacia riparia
  Teleonemia prolixa (Stål)
Aeschynomene sp.
  Atheas paganus Drake
Aeschynomene falcata
  Atheas ornatipes Drake and Hambleton
Aeschynomene nivea
  Atheas tristis Van Duzee
Amorpha fruticosa
  Gargaphia amorphae (Walsh)
  Leptopharsa oblonga (Say)
Arachis hypogaea
  Corythucha gossypii (Fabricius)
Astragalus sp.
  Galeatus scrophicus Saunders
Baptisia tinctoria
  Leptopharsa heidemanni (Osborn and
    Drake)
Bauhinia sp.
  Vatiga longula (Drake)
Bauhinia purpurea
  Cysteochila delineatus (Distant)

Bauhinia variegata
  Cysteochila ablusa Drake
Cajanus indicus
  Corythucha gossypii (Fabricius)
  Gargaphia penningtoni Drake
  Urentius euonymus Distant
Canavalia ensiformis
  Campylotingis bondari (Drake)
  Corythucha gossypii (Fabricius)
  Gargaphia lunulata (Mayr)
  Gargaphia opima Drake
Canavalia obtusifolia
  Gargaphia torresi Costa Lima
Cassia sp.
  Campylotingis mollis Drake and Bondar
  Gargaphia solani Heidemann
  Leptopharsa mira Drake and Hamble-
    ton
  Leptopharsa principis Drake and Ham-
    bleton
  Teleonemia brevipennis Champion
  Vatiga cassiae (Drake and Hambleton)
Cassia emarginata
  Corythucha gossypii (Fabricius)
Cassia fistula
  Gargaphia lunulata (Mayr)
Cassia imperialis
  Gargaphia lunulata (Mayr)
Ceratonia sp.
  Elasmotropis testacea var. *vicina* Hor-
    váth
  Tingis (Lasiotropis) hellenica (Puton)
Ceratonia siliqua
  Elasmotropis testacea (Herrich-Schaef-
    fer)
Cercis canadensis
  Gargaphia tiliae Walsh
Clitoria mariana
  Leptopharsa clitoriae (Heidemann)
Cytisus scoparius
  Dictyonota (Alcletha) tricornis (Schrank)
Dahlstedtia pinnata
  Corycera alboater Drake and Hamble-
    ton
Dalbergia sp.
  Leptopharsa tenuatis Drake

Derris elliptica
Amblystira fuscitarsis Champion
Amblystira opaca Champion
Desmodium sp.
Atheas austroriparius Heidemann
Atheas insignis Heidemann
Atheas mimeticus Heidemann
Leptopharsa machalana Drake and Hambleton
Leptopharsa machalana var. *vinnula* Drake and Hambleton
Dolichos lablab
Campylotingis bondari (Drake)
Gargaphia lunulata (Mayr)
Dorycnium suffruticosum
Phaenotropis parvula (Signoret)
Erythrina berteroana
Corythucha gossypii (Fabricius)
Falcata comosa
Leptopharsa oblonga (Say)
Ferreirea spectabilis
Campylotingis carvalhoi Drake and Hambleton
Campylotingis machaerii Drake and Hambleton
Genista sp.
Catoplatus fabricii (Stål)
Dictyonota pulchella Costa
Genista anglica
Dictyonota albipennis Baerensprung
Genista scorpius
Dictyonota pulchella Costa
Genista tinctoria
Catoplatus fabricii (Stål)
Gleditsia triacanthos
Anommatocoris coleopteratus (Kormilev)
Glycine max
Gargaphia lunulata (Mayr)
Hosackia crassifolia
Corythucha fuscigera (Stål)
Hymenaea stigonocarpa
Amblystira peltogyne Drake and Hambleton
Ichthyomethia grandifolia
Leptopharsa tenuis (Champion)
Ichthyomethia piscipula
Corythucha gossypii (Fabricius)

Indigofera sp.
Monosteira minutula Montandon
Kuhnistera sp.
Leptopharsa oblonga (Say)
Lathyrus nuttallii
Corythucha distincta Osborn and Drake
Lespedeza sp.
Leptopharsa clitoriae (Heidemann)
Lonchocarpus sp.
Vatiga lonchocarpa (Drake and Hambleton)
Lonchocarpus sericeus
Amblystira fuscitarsis Champion
Machaerium sp.
Atheas laetantis Drake and Hambleton
Campylotingis bondari (Drake)
Campylotingis jansoni (Drake)
Campylotingis lenatis Drake
Campylotingis machaerii Drake and Hambleton
Campylotingis prudens Drake and Hambleton
Campylotingis tantilla Drake
Corycera machaerii Drake and Hambleton
Leptopharsa prudens Drake and Hambleton
Machaerium angustifolium
Atheas flavipes Champion
Atheas laetantis Drake and Hambleton
Machaerium nictitans
Leptopharsa machaerii Drake and Hambleton
Machaerium oblongifolium
Teleonemia validicornis Stål
Machaerium oblongifolium v. subglabrum
Teleonemia validicornis Stål
Machaerium pedicillatum
Leptopharsa ogloblini Drake
Machaerium stipitatum
Leptopharsa gracilenta (Champion)
Machaerium villosum
Campylotingis prudens Drake and Hambleton
Medicago sp.
Galeatus spinifrons (Fallén)

Medicago lupulina
  Catoplatus fabricii (Stål)
Meibomia sp.
  Leptopharsa clitoriae (Heidemann)
Meibomia adscendens
  Gargaphia lunulata (Mayr)
Myrocarpus fastigiatus
  Acysta myrocarpi Drake and Poor
  Campylotingis clavata Drake and Hambleton
Oxytropis sp.
  Acalypta lillianis Torre-Bueno
Parosela citriodora
  Atheas nigricornis Champion
Parosela emoryi
  Gargaphia insularis Van Duzee
Peltogyne sp.
  Amblystira peltogyne Drake and Hambleton
Petalostemon sp.
  Leptopharsa oblonga (Say)
Petalostemon purpureum
  Atheas mimeticus Heidemann
Phaseolus sp.
  Gargaphia penningtoni Drake
  Gargaphia torresi Costa Lima
Phaseolus limensis
  Corythucha gossypii (Fabricius)
Phaseolus lunatus
  Campylotingis bondari (Drake)
  Gargaphia lunulata (Mayr)
  Gargaphia torresi Costa Lima
Phaseolus vulgaris
  Campylotingis bondari (Drake)
  Gargaphia lunulata (Mayr)
  Gargaphia subpilosa Berg
  Gargaphia torresi Costa Lima
Robina pseudoacacia
  Stephanitis pyri (Fabricius)
Sarothaumus sp.
  Dictyonota fuliginosa Costa
Sarothaumus scoparius
  Dictyonota strichnocera Fieber
Schrankia sp.
  Atheas austroriparius Heidemann
Spartium sp.
  Catoplatus fabricii (Stål)

Spartium junceum
  Aclypta nigrina (Fallén)
Spartium scoparium
  Dictyonota fuliginosa Costa
  Dictyonota strichnocera Fieber
  Monosteira unicostata (Mulsant and Rey)
Stylosanthes biflora
  Atheas insignis Heidemann
Swartzia sp.
  Leptopharsa mira Drake and Hambleton
Tamarindus indica
  Cysteochila endeca Drake
Tephrosia sp.
  Phaenotropis cleopatra (Horváth)
Ulex sp.
  Dictyonota pulchella Costa
  Dictyonota strichnocera Fieber
Vigna sinensis
  Campylotingis bondari (Drake)
Zornia diphylla
  Gargaphia lunulata (Mayr)

LILIACEAE

Yucca arborescens
  Corythucha caelata Uhler

LOGANIACEAE

Buddleia sp.
  Teleonemia brevipennis Champion
Buddleia asiatica
  Tingis buddleiae Drake

LYCOPODIACEAE

Stephanitis (*Norba*) *exigua* Horváth

MAGNOLIACEAE

Illicium religiosum
  Stephanitis svensoni Drake
Liriodendron sp.
  Melanorhopala infuscata Parshley

MALPIGHIACEAE

Byrsonima sp.
  Tingis neotropicalis Monte
Byrsonima sericea
  Ulotingis uniseriata (Drake)
Byrsonima verbascifolia
  Ulotingis uniseriata (Drake)
Malpighia glabra
  Phymacysta tumida (Champion)

Malpighia punicifolia
Phymacysta tumida (Champion)
Malpighia urens
Phymacysta tumida (Champion)
Stigmaphyllon sp.
Gargaphia lunulata (Mayr)

MALVACEAE

Compseuta picta Schouteden
Macrocorytha rhomboptera (Fieber)
Abelmoschus esculentus
Gargaphia lunulata (Mayr)
Abutilon sp.
Corythucha hispida Uhler
Gargaphia penningtoni Drake
Urentius euonymous Distant
Abutilon muticum
Urentius euonymus Distant
Abutilon pannosum
Urentius euonymus Distant
Abutilon umbellatum
Corythucha championi Drake and Cobben
Althaea rosea
Corythaica carinata Uhler
Ayenia magna
Corythucha championi Drake and Cobben
Callirhoe involucrata
Teleonemia scrupulosa Stål
Gossypium sp.
Corythaica costata Gibson
Corythaica monacha (Stål)
Corythucha gossypii (Fabricius)
Gargaphia subpilosa Berg
Gargaphia torresi Costa Lima
Gossypium arboreum
Gargaphia lunulata (Mayr)
Gossypium herbaceum
Gargaphia solani Heidemann
Hibiscus sp.
Corythucha gossypii (Fabricius)
Hibiscus esculentus
Corythucha gossypii (Fabricius)
Gargaphia acmonis Drake and Hambleton
Gargaphia lunulata (Mayr)
Hibiscus rosa-sinensis
Corythucha gossypii (Fabricius)

Hibiscus syriacus
Gargaphia torresi Costa Lima
Malva sp.
Gargaphia iridescens Champion
Malvaviscus arboreus
Leptopharsa rumiana Drake and Hambleton
Malvaviscus drummondii
Calotingis knighti Drake
Sida sp.
Gargaphia penningtoni Drake
Gargaphia torresi Costa Lima
Haedus sidae (Drake and Poor)
Sida acuta
Gargaphia penningtoni Drake
Sida cordifolia
Corythaica monacha (Stål)
Urentius euonymus Distant
Sida glomerata
Corythaica monacha (Stål)
Sida procumbens
Corythaica carinata Uhler
Sida rhombifolia
Corythaica monacha (Stål)
Sida ulmifolia
Corythaica monacha (Stål)
Sphaeralcea sp.
Corythucha sphaeralceae Drake
Sphaeralcea angustifolia
Teleonemia nigrina Champion
Sphaeralcea miniata
Corythaica cucullata (Berg)
Urena lobata
Gargaphia lunulata (Mayr)
Haedus vicarius (Drake)
Leptopharsa machalana var. *vinnula* Drake and Hambleton
Urena lobata v. sinuata
Haedus vicarius (Drake)
Wissadula sp.
Gargaphia penningtoni Drake
Gargaphia subpilosa Berg

MELASTOMATACEAE

Miconia sp.
Leptopharsa cognata Drake and Hambleton
Leptopharsa miconiae Drake and Hambleton

MENISPERMACEAE

Cissampelos glaberrima
  Gargaphia flexuosa (Stål)
Cissampelos tamoides
  Gargaphia flexuosa (Stål)
Cocculus sp.
  Stephanitis subfasciata Horváth
Cocculus trilobus
  Stephanitis subfasciata Horváth
Stephania hernandifolia
  Stephanitis queenslandensis Hacker

MONIMIACEAE

Mollinedia sp.
  Pliobyrsa mollinediae (Drake and Hambleton)
Siparuna guianensis
  Leptopharsa distincornis Drake

MORACEAE

Artocarpus incisa
  Nesocypselas dicysta Kirkaldy
Artocarpus integrifolia
  Alloiothucha artocarpi (Horváth)
  Leptopharsa angustata (Champion)
  Leptopharsa artocarpi Drake and Hambleton
  Leptopharsa vittipennis (Stål)
  Stephanitis typica (Distant)
  Stephanitis (*Menodora*) *chariesis* Drake and Mohanasundarum
Broussonetia papyrifera
  Corythucha ciliata (Say)
Chlorophora tinctoria
  Leptopharsa difficilis Drake and Hambleton
Ficus sp.
  Naochila kivuensis (Schouteden)
  Perissonemia ecmeles Drake and Mohanasundarum
  Tigava brevicollis Monte
Ficus elastica
  Leptopharsa fici Drake and Hambleton
Ficus subtriplinervia
  Leptopharsa fici Drake and Hambleton
Humulus sp.
  Dictyla humuli (Fabricius)
  Tingis (*Tropidocheila*) *pilosa* Hummel
Morus rubra
  Corythucha pallida Osborn and Drake

MUSACEAE

Musa sp.
  Stephanitis typica (Distant)
Musa paradisiaca
  Corythucha gossypii (Fabricius)
Musa paradisiaca v. sapientum
  Stephanitis typica (Distant)
  Stephanitis (*Menodora*) *sondaica* Horváth

MYOPORACEAE

Myoporum sandwicense
  Teleonemia scrupulosa Stål

MYRICACEAE

Myrica gale
  Stephanitis oberti (Kolenati)

MYRTACEAE

  Ulotingis decor Drake and Hambleton
  Ulotingis nitor Drake and Hambleton
Eugenia rhombea
  Hybopharsa colubra (Van Duzee)
Pimenta pimenta
  Hybopharsa colubra (Van Duzee)
Psidium sp.
  Gargaphia lunulata (Mayr)
Psidium guajava
  Ulotingis brasiliensis (Drake)

NYCTAGINACEAE

Pisonia sp.
  Acanthocheila armigera (Stål)
Pisonia aculeata
  Acanthocheila sigillata Drake and Bruner
Pisonia domingensis
  Acanthocheila spinicosta Van Duzee
Pisonia tomentosa
  Acanthocheila amigera (Stål)
Torrubia fragrans
  Acanthocheila spinicosta Van Duzee

OCHNACEAE

Ouratea sp.
  Acanthocheila armigera (Stål)

OLEACEAE

Adelia acuminata
  Leptoypha mutica (Say)
Chionanthus virginica
  Leptoypha mutica (Say)

Fraxinus sp.
Corythucha ciliata (Say)
Leptoypha mutica (Say)
Fraxinus americana
Leptoypha mutica (Say)
Fraxinus berlandierana
Leptoypha barberi Drake and Ruhoff
Fraxinus caroliniana
Leptoypha costata Parshley
Fraxinus mandshurica v. japonica
Leptoypha wuorentausi (Lindberg)
Fraxinus oregona
Leptoypha minor McAtee
Fraxinus pubinervis
Leptoypha wuorentausi (Lindberg)
Fraxinus rhynchophylla
Leptoypha wuorentausi (Lindberg)
Fraxinus velutina
Leptoypha minor McAtee
Jasminum sp.
Plerochila horvathi (Schouteden)
Jasminum dichotomum
Froggattia hargreavesi Drake
Jasmimum pubescens
Corythauma ayyari (Drake)
Ligustrum sp.
Stephanitis pyri (Fabricius)
Notelaea longifolia
Froggattia olivinia Froggatt
Olea sp.
Catoplatus dilatatus (Jakovlev)
Plerochila rutshurica Schouteden
Olea chrysophylla
Cysteochila pallens Horváth
Olea europaea
Froggattia olivinia Froggatt
Olastrida oleae Schouteden
Plerochila australis (Distant)
Plerochila horvathi (Schouteden)
Olea verrucosa
Cysteochila sordida (Stål)
Osmanthus americana
Leptoypha mcateei Drake

ORCHIDACEAE
(Intercepted at port-of-entry)
Cattleya dowiana var. aurea
Pleseobyrsa plicata (Champion)

Cattleya schroederae
Phatnoma barberi Drake
Phatnoma varians Drake
Epidendrum cochleatum
Phatnoma guatemalana Drake

PALMAE
Roystonea regia
Corythucha gossypii (Fabricius)
Thrinax wendlandiana
Allotingis binotata (Drake and Bruner)

PAPILIONACEAE
Campylotingis carvalhoi Drake and Hambleton
Tigava gracilis Monte
Tigava praecellens Stål

PASSIFLORACEAE
Passiflora caerulea
Corythaica cyathicollis (Costa)
Gargaphia lunulata (Mayr)
Passiflora foetida
Corythaica carinata Uhler
Passiflora violacea
Gargaphia lunulata (Mayr)

PHYTOLACCACEAE
Phytolacca acinosa
Cochlochila lewisi (Scott)

PINACEAE
Abies alba
Tingis (Tropidocheila) geniculata (Fieber)
Juniperus sp.
Physatocheila dumetorum (Herrich-Schaeffer)
Juniperus communis
Tingis (Tropidocheila) geniculata (Fieber)
Juniperus foetidissima
Tingis elongata (Fieber)
Juniperus phoenicea
Copium intermedium (Rey)
Tingis (Tropidocheila) griseola (Puton)
Larix decidua
Dictyonota strichnocera Fieber
Pinus sp.
Physatocheila dumetorum (Herrich-Schaeffer)
Tingis ampliata (Herrich-Schaeffer)

Pinus austriaca
  Tingis cardui (Linnaeus)
Pinus halepensis
  Monosteira unicostata (Mulsant and Rey)
Pinus monophylla
  Dictyla labeculata (Uhler)
Pinus sylvestris
  Dictyonota strichnocera Fieber
  Stephanitis oberti (Kolenati)
  Tingis cardui (Linnaeus)

PIPERACEAE

Piper nigrum
  Diconocoris distanti Drake

PLANTAGINACEAE

Plantago sp.
  Galeatus scrophicus Saunders
Plantago aristata
  Teleonemia nigrina Champion
Plantago cynops
  Acalypta gracilis (Fieber)
Plantago maritima
  Agramma confusum (Puton)
Plantago media
  Derephysia foliacea (Fallén)

PLATANACEAE

Platanus sp.
  Corythucha confraterna Gibson
Platanus occidentalis
  Corythucha ciliata (Say)

PLUMBAGINACEAE

Armeria vulgaris
  Derephysia foliacea (Fallén)
Statice sp.
  Agramma nigrum Fieber
  Tingis auriculata (Costa)
Statice armeria
  Derephysia foliacea (Fallén)
  Galeatus maculatus (Herrich-Schaeffer)

POLYGALACEAE

Bredemeyera sp.
  Amblystira pallipes (St°l)

POLYGONACEAE

Eriogonum sp.
  Corythaica venusta (Champion)
  Teleonemia nigrina Champion

POLYPORACEAE

Coriolus versicolor
  Acalypta musci (Schrank)
  Acalypta parvula (Fallén)
Polyporus hirsutus
  Acalypta parvula (Fallén)
Polyporus unicolor
  Acalypta musci (Schrank)
Trametes gibbosa
  Acalypta musci (Schrank)
  Acalypta parvula (Fallén)

POLYTRICHACEAE

Polytrichum sp.
  Acalypta lillianis Torre-Bueno

PROTEACEAE

Banksia robur minor
  Euaulana tasmaniae Drake
Protea sp.
  Sanazarius productus Distant
Roupala sp.
  Amblystira pensa Drake and Hambleton
  Corycera gibbosa Monte

RHAMNACEAE

Ceanothus sp.
  Corythucha obliqua Osborn and Drake
  Leptoypha minor McAtee
  Melanorhopala infuscata Parshley
Ceanothus americanus
  Gargaphia angulata Heidemann
  Melanorhopala infuscata Parshley
Ceanothus cordulatus
  Corythucha obliqua Osborn and Drake
Ceanothus sanguineus
  Corythucha obliqua Osborn and Drake
Zizyphus jujuba
  Monosteira minutula Montandon
Zizyphus spina-christi
  Monosteira minutula Montandon

ROSACEAE

Amelanchier sp.
  Corythucha cydoniae (Fitch)
Amelanchier canadensis
  Corythucha cydoniae (Fitch)
Amelanchier intermedia
  Corythucha cydoniae (Fitch)
  Corythucha juglandis (Fitch)

Amygdalus sp.
  Physatocheila dumetorum (Herrich-Schaeffer)
  Stephanitis pyri (Fabricius)
Amygdalus communis
  Monosteira unicostata (Mulsant and Rey)
Cerasus sp.
  Monosteira unicostata (Mulsant and Rey)
Chaenomeles sp.
  Corythucha cydoniae (Fitch)
Chaenomeles cathayensis
  Stephanitis nashi Esaki and Takeya
Chaenomeles japonica
  Stephanitis pyri (Fabricius)
Cormus sp.
  Stephanitis pyri (Fabricius)
Cormus tschonoskii
  Stephanitis nashi Esaki and Takeya
Cotoneaster hupehensis
  Corythucha cydoniae (Fitch)
Cotoneaster integerrima
  Stephanitis pyri (Fabricius)
Crataegus sp.
  Corythucha bellula Gibson
  Corythucha brunnea Gibson
  Corythucha cydoniae (Fitch)
  Physatocheila costata subsp. *smreczynskii* China
  Physatocheila dumetorum (Herrich-Schaeffer)
  Stephanitis nashi Esaki and Takeya
  Stephanitis pyri (Fabricius)
Crataegus albicans
  Corythucha bellula Gibson
Crataegus coccinea
  Corythucha cydoniae (Fitch)
Crataegus cordata
  Corythucha cydoniae (Fitch)
Crataegus crus-galli
  Corythucha cydoniae (Fitch)
  Stephanitis pyri (Fabricius)
Crataegus cuneata
  Stephanitis nashi Esaki and Takeya
Crataegus monogyna
  Monosteira unicostata (Mulsant and Rey)

Physatocheila dumetorum (Herrich-Schaeffer)
Crataegus neofluvialis
  Corythucha bellula Gibson
Crataegus oxyacantha
  Physatocheila dumetorum (Herrich-Schaeffer)
Crataegus parvifolia
  Corythucha cydoniae (Fitch)
Crataegus pruninosa
  Corythucha bellula Gibson
Crataegus punctata
  Corythucha bellula Gibson
Crataegus pyracantha
  Stephanitis pyri (Fabricius)
Crataegus tomentosa
  Corythucha cydoniae (Fitch)
Cydonia vulgaris
  Corythucha cydoniae (Fitch)
  Derephysia foliacea (Fallén)
  Monosteira unicostata (Mulsant and Rey)
  Stephanitis pyri (Fabricius)
Dryas sp.
  Acalypta lillianis Torre-Bueno
Heteromeles arbutifolia
  Corythucha incurvata Uhler
Kerria japonica
  Stephanitis nashi Esaki and Takeya
Malus sp.
  Corythucha cydoniae (Fitch)
  Stephanitis nashi Esaki and Takeya
Malus communis
  Stephanitis pyri (Fabricius)
Malus floribunda
  Stephanitis nashi Esaki and Takeya
Malus manschurica
  Leptoypha capitata (Jakovlev)
Mespilus oxyacantha
  Physatocheila dumetorum (Herrich-Schaeffer)
Persica vulgaris
  Monosteira unicostata var. *buccata* Horváth
Potentilla sp.
  Catoplatus nigriceps Horváth
  Galeatus maculatus (Herrich-Schaeffer)

Potentilla freyiana
  Stephanitis nashi var. *suigensis* Ŝaito
Prunus sp.
  Monosteira unicostata (Mulsant and Rey)
  Stephanitis nashi Esaki and Takeya
Prunus americana
  Corythucha pergandei Heidemann
Prunus amygdalus
  Monosteira unicostata (Mulsant and Rey)
Prunus armeniaca
  Stephanitis pyri (Fabricius)
Prunus avium
  Stephanitis pyri (Fabricius)
Prunus cerasus
  Gargaphia subpilosa Berg
  Monosteira unicostata (Mulsant and Rey)
  Stephanitis pyri (Fabricius)
Prunus demissa
  Corythucha padi Drake
Prunus domestia
  Physatocheila dumetorum (Herrich-Schaeffer)
Prunus lusitanica
  Stephanitis pyri (Fabricius)
Prunus mahaleb
  Stephanitis pyri (Fabricius)
Prunus marasca
  Stephanitis pyri (Fabricius)
Prunus padus
  Physatocheila dumetorum (Herrich-Schaeffer)
  Physatocheila costata subsp. *smreczynskii* China
Prunus persica
  Corythucha associata Osborn and Drake
  Corythucha gossypii (Fabricius)
  Gargaphia subpilosa Berg
  Monosteira unicostata (Mulsant and Rey)
  Stephanitis pyri (Fabricius)
Prunus serotina
  Corythucha associata Osborn and Drake
  Corythucha pruni Osborn and Drake
  Gargaphia tiliae (Walsh)

Prunus spinosa
  Physatocheila dumetorum (Herrich-Schaeffer)
Pyrus sp.
  Stephanitis nashi Esaki and Takeya
  Stephanitis pyri (Fabricius)
Pyrus americana
  Corythucha cydoniae (Fitch)
  Corythucha pallipes Parshley
Pyrus aria
  Stephanitis pyri (Fabricius)
  Tingis angustata (Herrich-Schaeffer)
Pyrus aucuparia
  Corythucha cydoniae (Fitch)
  Stephanitis pyri (Fabricius)
Pyrus communis
  Gargaphia lunulata (Mayr)
  Gargaphia subpilosa Berg
  Monosteira unicostata (Mulsant and Rey)
  Physatocheila confinis Horváth
  Physatocheila dumetorum (Herrich-Schaeffer)
  Physatocheila costata subsp. *smreczynskii* China
  Stephanitis pyri (Fabricius)
Pyrus malus
  Corythucha arcuata (Say)
  Corythucha salicata Gibson
  Monosteira unicostata (Mulsant and Rey)
  Physatocheila dumetorum (Herrich-Schaeffer)
  Physatocheila costata subsp. *smreczynskii* China
  Stephanitis pyri (Fabricius)
Pyrus mamorensis
  Monosteira unicostata (Mulsant and Rey)
Pyrus melanocarpa
  Corythucha cydoniae (Fitch)
Pyrus prunifolia
  Corythucha pergandei Heidemann
Pyrus ussuriensis
  Leptoypha capitata (Jakovlev)
  Stephanitis nashi Esaki and Takeya

Pyracantha coccinea
  Corythucha cydoniae (Fitch)
Rosa sp.
  Gargaphia lunulata (Mayr)
  Stephanitis pyri (Fabricius)
Rubus sp.
  Corythucha juglandis (Fitch)
Sorbus sp.
  Corythucha heidemanni Drake
  Corythucha juglandis (Fitch)
  Physatocheila costata subsp. *smreczynskii*
    China
Sorbus americana
  Corythucha juglandis (Fitch)
Sorbus aria
  Stephanitis pyri (Fabricius)
Sorbus aucuparia
  Physatocheila costata subsp. *smreczynskii*
    China
Sorbus cretica
  Tingis angustata (Herrich-Schaeffer)
Sorbus intermedia
  Physatocheila costata subsp. *smreczynskii*
    China
Sorbus torminalis
  Stephanitis pyri (Fabricius)
Vauquelinia californica
  Corythucha sagillata Drake

RUBIACEAE

Acanthotingis apicicornis Monte
Leptopharsa distinconis Drake
Leptopharsa divisa (Champion)
Leptopharsa flava Monte
Leptopharsa furculata (Champion)
Cephaelis hastisepala
  Leptopharsa fortis Drake and Hambleton
Cephalanthus sp.
  Corythucha cydoniae (Fitch)
  Corythucha floridana Heidemann
Cephalanthus occidentalis
  Corythucha cydoniae (Fitch)
  Corythucha floridana Heidemann
Cinchona sp.
  Teleonemia prolixa (Stål)
Diodia conferta
  Corythaica umbrosa (Monte)

Faramea sp.
  Leptopharsa farameae Drake and Hambleton
Faramea montevidensis
  Stephanitis farameae Drake and Hambleton
Galium sp.
  Lasiacantha capucina (Germar)
Guettarda viburnoides
  Pachycysta hambletoni Drake and Poor
Morinda sp.
  Dulinius conchatus Distant
Posqueria acutifolia
  Leptopharsa posoqueriae Drake and Hambleton
Psychotria sp.
  Leptopharsa fortis Drake and Hambleton
  Leptopharsa psychotriae Drake and Hambleton
Psychotria hancorniaefolia
  Leptopharsa ignota Drake and Hambleton
Psychotria suterella
  Leptopharsa hyaloptera (Stål)
Richardia brasiliensis
  Corythaica monacha (Stål)
  Corythaica umbrosa (Monte)
Rudgea sp.
  Leptopharsa perbona Drake
  Leptopharsa rudgeae Drake and Hambleton
Rudgea blanchetiana
  Leptopharsa nota Drake and Hambleton
Rudgea villiflora
  Leptopharsa furcata (Stål)
Sickingia tinctoria
  Gargaphia patria (Drake and Hambleton)

RUTACEAE

Citrus aurantium
  Leptobyrsa decora Drake
Citrus medica
  Corythucha gossypii (Fabricius)
Zanthoxylum martinicense
  Corythucha gossypii (Fabricius)

SALICACEAE

Populus sp.
Corythucha mollicula Osborn and Drake
Monosteira unicostata (Mulsant and Rey)
Stephanitis pyri (Fabricius)
Tingis populi Takeya
Tingis (*Tropidocheila*) *geniculata* (Fieber)

Populus alba
Monosteira unicostata (Mulsant and Rey)

Populus balsamifera
Corythucha elegans Drake

Populus candicans
Leptoypha minor McAtee

Populus grandidentata
Corythucha elegans Drake

Populus nigra
Monosteira unicostata (Mulsant and Rey)
Tingis lanigera (Puton)
Tingis populi Takeya

Populus tremula
Monosteira unicostata (Mulsant and Rey)
Physatocheila costata (Fabricius)
Tingis populi Takeya

Populus tremuloides
Corythucha elegans Drake

Salix sp.
Corythucha elegans Drake
Corythucha mollicula Osborn and Drake
Corythucha pallipes Parshley
Monosteira lobulifera Reuter
Monosteira unicostata (Mulsant and Rey)
Stephanitis takeyai Drake and Maa
Tingis populi Takeya

Salix discolor
Corythucha mollicula Osborn and Drake

Salix hookeriana
Corythucha mollicula Osborn and Drake

Salix koreensis
Tingis populi Takeya

Salix lasiandra
Corythucha salicata Gibson
Physatocheila variegata Parshley

Salix purpurea
Dictyla salicorum (Baba)

Salix scouleriana
Corythucha salicata Gibson

Salix sieboldiana
Corythucha pallipes Parshley

SAPINDACEAE

Serjania sp.
Amblystira pallipes (Stål)
Amblystira silvicola Drake
Gargaphia obliqua Stål
Gargaphia serjaniae Drake and Hambleton
Planibyrsa montei Drake and Hambleton

SAPOTACEAE

Lucuma sp.
Aristobyrsa latipennis (Champion)

SAXIFRAGACEAE

Hydrangea integra
Stephanitis hydrangeae Drake and Maa

Ribes sp.
Corythucha mollicula Osborn and Drake

Ribes nigrum
Stephanitis pyri (Fabricius)

Ribes oxyacanthoides
Corythucha bellula Gibson

SCROPHULARIACEAE

Adenostegia filifolia
Teleonemia nigrina Champion
Teleonemia notata Champion

Adenostegia pilosa
Teleonemia nigrina Champion
Teleonemia notata Champion

Penstemon sp.
Teleonemia montivaga Drake

Verbascum sp.
Dictyonota (*Alcletha*) *tricornis* (Schrank)
Tingis ampliata (Herrich-Schaeffer)
Tingis (*Lasiotropis*) *reticulata* Herrich-Schaeffer

Verbascum phlomoides
Tingis (*Lasiotropis*) *ragusana* (Fieber)

Verbascum thapsus
Tingis (*Lasiotropis*) *reticulata* Herrich-Schaeffer

SOLANACEAE

Brunfelsia sp.
  Gargaphia brunfelsiae Monte
  Gargaphia munda (Stål)
Brunfelsia hopeana
  Gargaphia brunfelsiae Monte
  Gargaphia munda (Stål)
Lycopersicum esculentum
  Corythaica costata Gibson
  Corythaica cyathicollis (Costa)
  Gargaphia solani Heidemann
Nicotiana tabacum
  Acanthocheila armigera (Stål)
Solanum sp.
  Corythucha fuscomaculata (Stål)
  Corythucha globigera Breddin
  Corythucha nobilis Drake and Bondar
  Gargaphia angulata Heidemann
  Gargaphia crotonae Drake and Hamble-
  ton
  Gargaphia decoris Drake
  Gargaphia iridescens Champion
  Gargaphia munda (Stål)
  Gargaphia nigrinervis Stål
  Gargaphia solani Heidemann
Solanum argillicolum
  Corythaica cyathicollis (Costa)
Solanum auriculatum (?)
  Gargaphia decoris Drake
Solanum balbisii
  Corythaica cyathicollis (Costa)
Solanum bonariense
  Corythaica cyathicollis (Costa)
Solanum capsicastrum
  Gargaphia oreades Drake
Solanum carolinense
  Gargaphia solani Heidemann
Solanum concinnum
  Gargaphia formosa (Stål)
Solanum dulcamara
  Galeatus spinifrons (Fallén)
Solanum elaeagnifolium
  Corythaica cyathicollis (Costa)
  Gargaphia solani Heidemann
Solanum gilo
  Corythaica cyathicollis (Costa)
Solanum grandiflorum
  Corythaica cyathicollis (Costa)

Solanum hindsianum
  Gargaphia gentilis Van Duzee
Solanum hirtum
  Corythaica cyathicollis (Costa)
Solanum juripeba
  Corythaica cyathicollis (Costa)
Solanum lycopersicum
  Corythaica cyathicollis (Costa)
  Corythucha gossypii (Fabricius)
Solanum melongena
  Corythaica carinata Uhler
  Corythaica cyathicollis (Costa)
  Corythucha gossypii (Fabricius)
  Gargaphia opacula Uhler
  Gargaphia solani Heidemann
  Urentius hystricellus (Richter)
Solanum nigrum
  Gargaphia oreades Drake
Solanum nigrum americanum
  Corythaica cyathicollis (Costa)
Solanum paniculatum
  Corythaica cyathicollis (Costa)
Solanum pulverulentum
  Corythaica cyathicollis (Costa)
Solanum quitoense
  Corythaica cyathicollis (Costa)
Solanum racemiflorum
  Corythaica cyathicollis (Costa)
Solanum racemosum
  Corythaica cyathicollis (Costa)
Solanum sisymbrifolium
  Corythaica cyathicollis (Costa)
Solanum tabacifolium
  Corythucha cyathicollis (Costa)
Solanum torvum
  Corythaica cyathicollis (Costa)
  Corythucha gossypii (Fabricius)
  Corythucha spinosa (Dugès)
  Tigava pulchella Champion
Solanum tuberosum
  Corythaica cyathicollis (Costa)
  Gargaphia solani Heidemann
  Gargaphia subpilosa Berg
Solanum variabile
  Corythaica cyathicollis (Costa)
Solanum verbascifolium
  Dictyla rasilis (Drake and Maa)

STAPHYLEACEAE
Staphylea trifolia
  Corythucha bulbosa Osborn and Drake
STERCULIACEAE
Hermannia micropetela
  Urentius vepris Drake
STYRACACEAE
Styrax japonica
  Stephanitis takeyai Drake and Maa
THYMELEACEAE
Pimelea sp.
  Oncophysa vesiculata (Stål)
TILIACEAE
Corchorus hirsutus
  Corythaica carinata Uhler
Tilia sp.
  Gargaphia tiliae (Walsh)
  Stephanitis pyri (Fabricius)
Tilia americana
  Corythucha juglandis (Fitch)
  Corythucha pallida Osborn and Drake
  Gargaphia tiliae (Walsh)
Tilia pubescens
  Gargaphia tiliae (Walsh)
Triumfetta sp.
  Gargaphia torresi Costa Lima
Triumfetta flavescens
  Compseuta montandoni Distant
Triumfetta grossulariaefolia
  Corythucha spinosa (Dugès)
Triumfetta rhombeaefolia
  Ammianus schoutedeni Distant
Triumfetta rhomboidea
  Corythucha fuscomaculata (Stål)
Triumfetta semitriloba
  Corythucha fuscomaculata (Stål)
TURNERACEAE
Piriqueta ovata
  Corythaica carinata Uhler
TYPHACEAE
Typha latifolia
  Agramma atricapillum (Spinola)
  Agramma intermedium (Wagner)
ULMACEAE
Celtis brasiliensis
  Atheas placentis Drake and Poor
  Corythucha pellucida Drake and Hambleton

Celtis crassifolia
  Corythucha pergandei Heidemann
Celtis ferruginea
  Corythucha pellucida Drake and Hambleton
Celtis mississippiensis
  Corythucha celtidis var. *mississippiensis* Drake
Celtis occidentalis
  Corythucha celtidis Osborn and Drake
Ulmus sp.
  Corythucha pergandei Heidemann
Ulmus americana
  Corythucha heidemanni Drake
  Corythucha ulmi Osborn and Drake
Ulmus campestris
  Stephanitis pyri (Fabricius)
Ulmus effusa
  Stephanitis pyri (Fabricius)
Ulmus fulva
  Corythucha heidemanni Drake
  Corythucha ulmi Osborn and Drake
Ulmus glabra camperdownii
  Corythucha ulmi Osborn and Drake
Ulmus thomasii
  Corythucha ulmi Osborn and Drake
UMBELLIFERAE
Caucalis daucoides
  Tingis auriculata (Costa)
  Tingis auriculata var. *dauci* Horváth
Daucus carota
  Tingis auriculata (Costa)
  Tingis auriculata var. *dauci* Horváth
Eryngium sp.
  Catoplatus carthusianus (Goeze)
  Catoplatus carthusianus var. *albidus* (Herrich-Schaeffer)
  Catoplatus horvathi (Puton)
Eryngium amethystinum
  Catoplatus carthusianus (Goeze)
Eryngium campestre
  Catoplatus carthusianus (Goeze)
  Catoplatus horvathi (Puton)
  Catoplatus nigriceps Horváth
Eryngium maritinum
  Catoplatus carthusianus (Goeze)

Seseli glaucum
 Catoplatus carthusianus (Goeze)
 Catoplatus carthusianus var. albidus
 (Herrich-Schaeffer)
Torilis arvensis
 Tingis auriculata (Costa)

URTICACEAE
Corythucha clara Drake and Hambleton
Boehmeria cylindrica v. drummondiana
 Leptopharsa machalana var. vinnula
 Drake and Hambleton
Boehmeria spicata
 Cysteochila fieberi (Scott)
Phyllostylon rhamnoides
 Dicrotingis digitalis (Drake)
Pipturus sp.
 Phatnoma veridica Drake and Maa

VACCINIACEAE
Myrtillus uliginosus
 Stephanitis oberti (Kolenati)

VERBENACEAE
Callicarpa americana
 Teleonemia belfragii Stål
Clerodendron sp.
 Paracopium hamadryas (Drake)
Clerodendron buchholzi
 Paracopium hamadryas (Drake)
Clerodendron giletii
 Paracopium bequaerti (Schouteden)
Clerodendron micans
 Paracopium dauphinicum Drake
Clerodendron phlomoides
 Paracopium cingalense (Walker)
Clerodendron subreniforme
 Paracopium hamadryas (Drake)
Duranta repens
 Teleonemia notata Champion
Gmelina arborea
 Tingis (Caenotingis) beesoni Drake
Gmelina leichardtii
 Lasiacantha compta (Drake)
Kalaharia (Clerodendron) spinescens
 Paracopium stolidum (Horváth)
Lantana sp.
 Compseuta lefroyi Distant
 Corythaica venusta (Champion)

Corythauma ayyari (Drake)
Habrochila africana Drake
Haedus pictus (Distant)
Naochila sufflata (Drake and Poor)
Phatnoma takasago Takeya
Teleonemia bifasciata Champion
Teleonemia carmelana (Berg)
Teleonemia elata Drake
Teleonemia notata Champion
Teleonemia variegata Champion
Lantana aculeata
 Teleonemia scrupulosa Stål
Lantana brasiliensis
 Teleonemia scrupulosa Stål
Lantana camara
 Corythucha spinosa (Dugès)
 Teleonemia limbata (Stål)
 Teleonemia prolixa (Stål)
 Teleonemia sacchari (Fabricius)
 Teleonemia scrupulosa (Stål)
 Teleonemia validicornis Stål
Lantana canescens
 Teleonemia sacchari (Fabricius)
 Teleonemia scrupulosa Stål
 Teleonemia syssita Drake and Cobben
Lantana involucrata
 Teleonemia sacchari (Fabricius)
Lantana montevidensis
 Teleonemia scrupulosa Stål
Lippia alba
 Teleonemia scrupulosa Stål
Lippia juncea
 Teleonemia carmelana (Berg)
Premna sp.
 Eteoneus esakii Drake
Premna gaudichaudii
 Berotingis guamensis (Drake)
 Berotingis yapensis (Drake)
Rhaphithamnus spinosus
 Teleonemia carmelana (Berg)
Tectona grandis
 Cochlochila nilgiriensis (Distant)
Verbena sp.
 Teleonemia nigrina Champion
Vitex heterophylla
 Cromerus kalshoveni Drake

Vitex pubescens
  Ammianus ravanus (Kirkaldy)
Vitex ruganda
  Dasytingis rudis Drake and Poor
Vitex trifolia
  Ammianus ravanus (Kirkaldy)
  Tingis buddleiae Drake

VITACEAE

Cissus japonica
  Cysteochila chiniana Drake

ZINGIBERACEAE

Alpina chinensis
  Stephanitis typica (Distant)

Alpina japonica
  Stephanitis typica (Distant)
Alpina nutans
  Stephanitis typica (Distant)
Alpina speciosa
  Stephanitis typica (Distant)
Elettaria cardamomum
  Stephanitis typica (Distant)
Hedychium sp.
  Stephanitis typica (Distant)
Zingiber kawagoii
  Stephanitis typica (Distant)
Zingiber mioga
  Stephanitis typica (Distant)

Host Plants Cited Only as Common Names

Alder
  Corythucha padi Drake
  Corythucha salicata Gibson
  Leptopharsa clitoriae (Heidemann)
  Physatocheila variegata Parshley
Ash
  Derephysia foliacea (Fallén)
  Dictyonota mitoris Drake and Hsiung
  Leptoypha drakei McAtee
Avocado
  Pleseobyrsa boliviana Drake and Poor
  Tigava pulchella Champion
Bamboo
  Leptodictya (Hanuala) comes Drake and Hambleton
  Leptodictya (Hanuala) cretata Champion
  Leptodictya (Hanuala) decor Drake and Hambleton
  Leptodictya (Hanuala) ecuadoris Drake and Hambleton
  Leptodictya (Hanuala) fraterna Monte
  Leptodictya (Hanuala) fuscocincta (Stål)
  Leptodictya (Hanuala) laidis Drake and Hambleton
  Leptodictya (Hanuala) litigiosa Monte
  Leptodictya (Hanuala) lucida Drake and Hambleton
  Leptodictya (Hanuala) nigrosis Drake and Hambleton
  Leptodictya ochropa (Stål)
  Leptodictya (Hanuala) parilis Drake and Hambleton
  Leptodictya (Hanuala) simulans Heidemann
  Leptodictya (Hanuala) tabida (Herrich-Schaeffer)
Bean
  Gargaphia angulata Heidemann
Bean, kidney
  Leptodictya (Hanuala) colombiana Drake
Broom
  Dictyonota fuliginosa Costa
  Dictyonota strichnocera Fieber

Cabbage
  Corythaica cyathicollis (Costa)
Cacao
  Amblystira machalana Drake
  Ammianus alberti (Schouteden)
  Dichocysta pictipes Champion
  Habrochila placida Horváth
  Phatnoma marmorata Champion
Camphor
  Stephanitis typica (Distant)
Chaparral
  Corythucha fuscigera (Stål)
Cherry
  Corythucha cerasi Drake
  Phymacysta tumida (Champion)
Coconut
  Stephanitis typica (Distant)
Coffee
  Habrochila ghesquierei Schouteden
  Habrochila placida Horváth
  Leptopharsa flava Monte
Cotton
  Dictyla monotropidia (Stål)
Cottonwood
  Physatocheila variegata Parshley
Ebony
  Corythucha morrilli Osborn and Drake
  Teleonemia scrupulosa Stål
Elm
  Tingis (Tropidocheila) gamboana Drake and Hambleton
Grapefruit
  Corythucha gossypii (Fabricius)
Grass
  Leptodictya (Hanuala) madelinae Drake
Hazelnut
  Corythucha padi Drake
Heath
  Agramma laetum (Fallén)
Heliotrope
  Cochlochila bullita (Stål)

Hickory
  Physatocheila plexa (Say)
  Physatocheila variegata Parshley
Hollyhock
  Corythucha distincta Osborn and Drake
  Gargaphia iridescens Champion
  Gargaphia solani Heidemann
  Sphaerocysta globifera (Stål)
Hops
  Acalypta barberi Drake
Ivy
  Derephysia foliacea (Fallén)
Jasmine
  Cochlochila exolenta Drake
Lemon
  Corythucha gossypii (Fabricius)
Loquat
  Corythucha cydoniae (Fitch)
Maize
  Gargaphia torresi Costa Lima
  Leptodictya (*Hanuala*) *bambusae* Drake
  Leptodictya (*Hanuala*) *tabida* (Herrich-Schaeffer)
Mango
  Corythucha gossypii (Fabricius)
Mangle
  Leptoypha morrisoni Drake
Maple
  Corythucha arcuata (Say)
Millet
  Kapiriella polita (Drake)
Moss
  Acalypta barberi Drake
  Acalypta brunnea (Germar)
  Acalypta carinata (Panzer)
  Acalypta cooleyi Drake
  Acalypta duryi Drake
  Acalypta gracilis (Fieber)
  Acalypta lillianis Torre-Bueno
  Acalypta marginata (Wolff)
  Acalypta mniophila Drake and Ruhoff
  Acalypta musci (Schrank)
  Acalypta musci var. *ditata* (Puton)
  Acalypta nigrina (Fallén)
  Acalypta nyctalis Drake
  Acalypta parvula (Fallén)
  Acalypta platycheila (Fieber)
  Acalypta pulchra Štušak

Acalypta saundersi (Downes)
Acalypta thomsonii Stål
Agramma laetum (Fallén)
Agramma ruficorne (Germar)
Campylosteira ciliata Fieber
Campylosteira falleni Fieber
Campylosteira verna (Fallén)
Derephysia foliacea (Fallén)
Dictyonota strichnocera Fieber
Esocampylia hackeri Drake
Gonycentrum tindalei (Hacker)
Lasiacantha capucina (Germar)
Nettle, sand
  Gargaphia iridescens Champion
Oak
  Corythucha cerasi Drake
  Corythucha floridana Heidemann
  Melanorhopala clavata (Stål)
  Physatocheila plexa (Say)
  Stephanitis querca Bergroth
Orange
  Corythucha gossypii (Fabricius)
Papaya
  Aconchus urbanus (Horváth)
Pea
  Gargaphia subpilosa Berg
Pear
  Corythucha cydoniae (Fitch)
Pepper
  Diconocoris greeni (Kirby)
  Diconocoris hewetti (Distant)
  Nesocypselas piperica Drake
Pine
  Physatocheila variegata Parshley
Pineapple
  Phatnoma marmorata Champion
  Phatnoma trinidadana Drake
Polony
  Leptopharsa milleri Drake
Poplar
  Corythucha salicata Gibson
Rose
  Corythucha arcuata (Say)
Sedge
  Cyperobia carectorum Bergroth
Snapdragon
  Teleonemia nigrina Champion

Soursop
  Corythucha gossypii (Fabricius)
Sugarcane
  Abdastartus sacchari Drake
  Leptodictya (Hanuala) tabida (Herrich-Schaeffer)
  Teleonemia sacchari (Fabricius)
Sugar beets
  Teleonemia nigrina Champion
Sunflower
  Galeatus scrophicus Saunders
Sweet potato
  Gargaphia torresi Costa Lima
Sycamore
  Corythucha salicata Gibson
Tea
  Habrochila chinensis Drake
  Stephanitis (Norba) chinensis Drake

Teak
  Amblystira machalana Drake
  Pontanus puerilis (Drake and Poor)
Thistle
  Gargaphia bimaculata Parshley
Tobacco
  Corythaica cyathicollis (Costa)
  Malala bulliens Distant
Tomato
  Corythaica monacha (Stål)
Walnut
  Corythucha padi Drake
Willow
  Gargaphia opacula Uhler
  Physatocheila plexa (Say)
Yautia
  Corythucha gossypii (Fabricius)

Literature Cited

The authors have seen the original publication of every title and reference listed in the bibliography, except two and these are so indicated. As customarily cited over the years, the dates of publications for a number of important papers are not always in agreement with the actual date of issue. For example, certain works of Herrich-Schaeffer, Costa, Stål, and Blanchard, as cited in the literature, do not at all times bear the same date or even the correct date of publication. The authority for and reference to the literature of such changes are cited [in brackets] just beneath the publication concerned.

ABBOTT, CYRIL E.
  1935. Notes on the oviposition and hatching of *Corythucha marmorata* Uhler. Bull. Brooklyn Ent. Soc., vol. 30, No. 1, p. 13.
Alfieri, A.: see PRIESNER and ALFIERI
AMYOT, CHARLES JEAN BAPTISTE
  1845–1847. Entomologie française. Rhynchotes. Méthode mononymique. Ann. Soc. Ent. France, ser. 2 (1845, vol. 3, pp. 369–492; 1846, vol. 4, pp. 73–192, 359–452; 1847, vol. 5, pp. 143–238, 453–524).
AMYOT, CHARLES JEAN B., and SERVILLE, JEAN GUILLAUMI AUDINET
  1843. Histoire naturelle des insectes. Hémiptères. Paris, lxvii +675 pp. Tingitides, pp. 295–303.
ANDRÉ, E.
  1876. *Euricera clavicornis-Canthophorus maculipes.* Feuille des Jeunes Naturalistes, No. 73, pp. 34–35.
  1878. Voyage d'un naturaliste. Deux kilomèters en six heures. Feuille des Jeunes Naturalistes, No. 87, pp. 25–27.
D'ANTESSANTY, GABRIEL
  1890. Catologue des hémiptères-hétéroptères de l'Aube. Mem. Soc. Acad. l'Aube, vol. 54, pp. 1–53.
D'ARAUJO E SILVA, ARISTOTELES G.
  1936. Alguns insectos com os seus respectivos hospedeiros. Rio de Janeiro, 30 pp. Tingidae p. 7.
DE ARAÚJO MENDONÇA, FLORIANO
  1949. Notas sôbre *Gargaphia lunulata* (Mayer, 1865) (*Gargaphia lasciva* Gibson). Boletím da Secretaria da Agricultura, Indústria e Comércio do Estado da Bahia, Serviço de Divulgação, vol. 45, No. 3, pp. 183–187, 15 figs.

482

Ascot, H. W.
   1930. Rhododendron bug (*Leptobyrsa rhododendri*). The Gardeners' Chronicle, Sept. 20, 1930, p. 238.

Ash, Charles R.
   1954. Tingoidea (Hemiptera) of Tippecanoe County, Indiana. Proc. Indiana Acad. Sci., vol. 63, p. 185, 1953.

Ashmead, William H.
   1886. On two new Hemiptera-Heteroptera. Canadian Ent., vol. 18, No. 1, pp. 18–20.
   1887. Hemipterological contributions (No. 1). Ent. Amer., vol. 3, pp. 155–156.

Baba, Shôsuke
   1925. "Dôsôkwai-Jihô," Nagano Agric. Exp. Station, vol. viii, No. 1, p. 3. [Publication not seen.]

Bachofen-echt, Adolf
   1949. Der Bernstein und seine Einschlüsse. Springer-Verlag. Vienna. 204 pp., 188 figs. Tingidae fig. 160.

von Baerensprung, Felix
   1858. Neue und seltene Rhynchoten der europäischen Fauna. Berliner Ent. Zeitschr., vol. 2, No. 2, pp. 188–208, 1 pl.

Bailey, Norman S. [see also Feldman and Bailey]
   1950. An Asiatic tingid new to North America (Heteroptera). Psyche, vol. 57, No. 4, pp. 143–145.
   1951. The Tingoidea of New England and their biology. Ent. Amer., vol. 31, pp. 1–140, 6 figs.
   1959. Additions to the bioecology of the New England Tingidae and Piesmidae (Heteroptera). Psyche, vol. 66, No. 4, pp. 63–69.

Baker, Carl F.: see Gillette and Baker

Balachowsky, Alfred, and Mesnil, L.
   1935–1936. Les Insectes nuisibles aux plantes cultivées leurs moeurs leur destruction, vol. 1 [1935], 1137 pp., 931 figs.; vol. 2 [1936], pp. 1138–1921, figs. 932–1369.

Banks, Nathan
   1909. Dates of Guérin's Iconographie règne animal. *In* Notes and News, Ent. News, vol. 20, No. 9, pp. 396–397.
   1910. Catalogue of the Nearctic Hemiptera-Heteroptera. Amer. Ent. Soc., Philadelphia, 103 pp. Tingitidae pp. 55–57.

Barber, Harry Gardner
   1906. Hemiptera from southwestern Texas. Brooklyn Inst. Arts and Sci. Bull. 1, No. 9, pp. 255–289.
   1910. Some Mexican Hemiptera-Heteroptera new to the fauna of the United States. Journ. New York Ent. Soc., vol. 18, No. 1, pp. 34–39.

1914.   Insects of Florida. 11. Hemiptera. Bull. Amer. Mus. Nat. Hist., vol. 33, art. 31, pp. 495–535.

1922a.   List of the superfamily Tingidoidea of New Jersey with synonymy and food plants. State of New Jersey Dept. Agric., Bur. Statistics and Inspection, circ. 54, pp. 16–17.

1922b.   Systematic treatment of the superfamily Tingidoideae of New Jersey. State of New Jersey Dept. Agric., Bur. Statistics and Inspection, circ. 54, pp. 18–24.

1923.   A preliminary report on the Hemiptera-Heteroptera of Porto Rico collected by the American Museum of Natural History. Amer. Mus. Nov., No. 75, pp. 1–13.

1925.   Hemiptera-Heteroptera from the Williams Galapagos Expedition. Zoologica, vol. 5, No. 21, pp. 241–254, 4 figs.

1934.   The Norwegian Zoological Expedition to the Galapagos Islands 1925, conducted by Alf Wollebaek. XI. Hemiptera-Heteroptera. Meddelelser fra det Zoologiske Mus., Oslo, No. 42, pp. 281–289.

1939.   Insects of Porto Rico and the Virgin Islands—Hemiptera-Heteroptera (excepting the Miridae and Coxidae). Scientific Survey of Porto Rico and the Virgin Islands. New York Acad. Sci., vol. 14, No. 3, pp. 263–441, 36 figs.

1954.   A report on the Hemiptera-Heteroptera from the Bimini Islands, Bahamas, British West Indies. Amer. Mus. Nov., No. 1682, pp. 1–18, 3 figs.

BARBER, HARRY G., and WEISS, HARRY B.
1922.   The lace bugs of New Jersey. State of New Jersey Dept. Agric., Bur. Statistics and Inspection, circ. 54, pp. 3–15, 8 figs.

BATOR, ADELHEID
1953.   Die heteropteren Nordtirols. Beiträge zur Entomologie, vol. 3, No. 3, pp. 323–333, 3 pls.

BEESON, CYRIL FREDERICK, and CHATTERJEE, N. C.
1940.   Possibilities of control of lantana (*Lantana aculeata* Linn.) by indigenous insect pests. Indian Forest Records, new ser., vol. 6, No. 3, pp. 41–84, 1939.

BEHR, L.
1952.   Über die Blütengalle des *Teucrium chamaedrys* L. Berichte der Deutschen Botanishchen Gesellschaft, vol. 65, No. 9, pp. 326–330, 6 figs.

BEKKER-MIGDISOVA, E. E.
1953.   Paleozoiskie ravnokrylyie voprosy filogenii otryada. Doklady Akad. Nauk S.S.S.R., Moscow, new ser., vol. 90, pp. 461–464, 2 figs.

BERENDT, GEORG CARL [see also GERMAR and BERENDT]
1845. Der Bernstein und die in ihm befindlichen Pflanzenreste der
Vorwelt. *In* Die im Bernstein befindlichen Organischen reste
der Vorwelt, vol. 1, No. 1, pp. 1–60.

BERG, CARLOS
1879a. Hemiptera Argentina. Anal. Soc. Cient. Argentina, vol. 7,
pp. 41–47. [Section that included Tingitidae; this publication was issued in parts then reprinted as an entire volume.]
1879b. Hemiptera Argentina enumeravit speciesque novas descripsit.
Bonariae, Hamburg. 316 pp. [Reprint.] Tingitidae pp.
135–137.
1884. Addenda et emendanda ad Hemiptera Argentina. Anal. Soc.
Cient. Argentina, 213 pp. Tingitidae pp. 99–104.
1891–1892. Nova Hemiptera faunarum Argentinae et Uruguayensis.
Anal. Soc. Cient. Argentina, vol. 32, No. 4, pp. 164–175; No.
5, pp. 231–243; No. 6, pp. 276–287; [1892] vol. 33, No. 1,
pp. 1–11; No. 2, pp. 43–50; No. 3, pp. 65–72; No. 4, pp.
98–104; No. 5, pp. 151–165; vol. 34, No. 2, pp. 82–96; No.
5, pp. 193–205. [Reprint 1892, 112 pp. Tingitidae pp.
99–102.]

BERGEVIN, ERNEST
1920. Description d'une espèce nouvelle de *Physatocheila* d'Algérie
[Hemip. Tingitidae]. Ann. Soc. Ent. France, vol. 88, pp.
412–413, 1 fig.
1922. Description d'une nouvelle espèce de *Catoplatus* (Hémiptère
Tingitidae) du Maroc Occidental. Bull. Soc. Sci. Nat.
Maroc, vol. 2, Nos. 5–6, pp. 108–109, 2 figs.
1928. Description d'une nouvelle espèce d'*Urentius* (Hémiptère
Tingitidae) du Hoggar. Bull. Soc. Hist. Nat. Afrique du
Nord, vol. 19, pp. 336–338, 1 fig.
1929. Description de deux espèces nouvelles d'hémiptères Tingitidae
provenant de la mission du Hoggar. Bull. Soc. d'Hist. Nat.
Afrique du Nord, vol. 20, pp. 114–116, 2 figs.
1930. Note sur trois espèces d'hémiptères recueillis en Egypte et
description d'une nouvelle espèce d'*Urentius* (Hémiptère
Tingitidae) et d'une nouvelle variété d'*Ommatissus binotatus*
Fieb. (Homoptère Cixiidae). Bull. Soc. Roy. Ent. Egypte,
new ser., fasc. 1, pp. 17–20, 1 fig.

BERGROTH, ERNST EVALD
1892. Notes synonymiques. Rev. Ent., vol. 11, pp. 262–264.
1894. Tingidae tres Madagascariensis. Rev. Ent., vol. 13, pp. 167–168.
1898. Eine neue Tingide. Wiener Ent. Zeitung, vol. 17, No. 1, p. 9.
1903. Rhynchota Aethiopica. Ann. Soc. Ent. Belgique, vol. 47,
pp. 287–297.

1908.   Neue Hemiptera aus Süd-Abyssinien. Rev. Russe Ent., Nos. 2–3, pp. 106–110, 1907.

1911.   On some recently described Hemiptera, chiefly from India. Ann. Soc. Ent. Belgique, vol. 55, pp. 184–189.

1912.   Tingidae duae novae Africanae. Ann. Soc. Ent. Belgique, vol. 56, pp. 145–146.

1914a. H. Sauter's Formosa-Ausbeute: Hemiptera Heteroptera I. Ent. Mitt., vol. 3, Nos. 10–12, pp. 353–364.

1914b. Zwei neue paläarktische hemipteren, nebst synonymischen Mitteilungen. Wiener Ent. Zeitung, vol. 33, Nos. 5–6, pp. 177–184.

1919.   Die Erscheinungsdata zweier hemipterologischen Werke. Ent. Mitt., vol. 8, Nos. 10–12, pp. 188–191. [Contains validation of publication dates of papers by Herrich-Schaeffer.]

1921.   On the types of the exotic Hemiptera Heteroptera described by V. Motschulsky. Rev. Russe Ent., vol. 17, pp. 96–109, 1917.

1922.   On some Neotropical Tingidae (Hem.). Ann. Soc. Ent. Belgique, vol. 62, pp. 149–152.

1924.   Some Heteroptera from the alpine region of central Luzon. Ann. Soc. Ent. Belgique, vol. 64, pp. 82–84.

1927.   Hemiptera Heteroptera from New Zealand. Trans. New Zealand Inst., vol. 57, pp. 671–684.

BERGROTH, ERNST, and SCHOUTEDEN, HENRI
1905.   Note sur les hémiptères recueillis à Kinchassa par M. Waelbroeck. Ann. Soc. Ent. Belgique, vol. 49. pp. 379–389, 1 fig.

Beri, Y. P.: see MENON, BERI, and SINGH

BERRY, PAUL A.
1959.   Entomología Económica de El Salvador. Servicio Cooperativo Agricola Salvadoreño Americano Ministerio de Agricultura y Ganadería Santa Tecla, El Salvador. Boletín Técnico 24, 255 pp., 187 figs.

BIANCHI, F. A.
1955a. *Corythucha morrilli. In* Minutes of the meeting, April 12, 1954, Hawaiian Entomological Society. Proc. Hawaiian Ent. Soc., vol. 15, No. 3, p. 378.

1955b. *Corythucha morrilli. In* Minutes of the meeting, August 9, 1954, Hawaiian Entomological Society. Proc. Hawaiian Ent. Soc., vol. 15, No. 3, p. 383.

BLANCHARD, EMILE
1840.   Histoire naturelle des animaux articulés, annelides, crustacés, arachnides, myriapodes et insectes., vol. 3, 672 pp., many plates. *Tingis,* pp. 112–113.

1846. Insectes du voyage dans l'Amérique Méridionale par Alcide d'Orbigny. Paris, 1837–1846, 222 pp., 32 pls. [See Sherborn and Woodward 1901, for the dates of this publication.]

BLANCHARD, EVERARD
1926. Sobre un Tingido nuevo para la fauna Argentina. Physis, vol. 8, pp. 361–363, 1 fig.

BLATCHLEY, WILLIS STANLEY
1926. Heteroptera or true bugs of eastern North America, with especial references to the faunas of Indiana and Florida. Nature Publ. Co., Indianapolis, 1116 pp., 215 text figs., 12 pls. Tingididae pp. 448–501, figs. 96–121.
1928. Notes on the Heteroptera of eastern North America with descriptions of new species, I. Journ. New York Ent. Soc., vol. 36, No. 1, pp. 1–23.

BLÖTE, HENDRICK COENAAD
1945. Catalogue of the Berytidae, Piesmidae and Tingidae in the Rijksmuseum van Natuurlijke Historie. Zoologische Mededeelingen, vol. 25, pp. 72–92, 1 fig.

BOLIVAR, IGNACIO, and CHICOTE, CÉSAR
1879. Enumeración de los hemipteros observados en España y Portugal. Ann. Soc. Española Hist. Nat., vol. 8, pp. 147–186.

BONDAR, GREGORIO [see also DRAKE and BONDAR]
1928. Amarellecimento das folhas do feijão causado pelo Tingitideo. Correio Agricola, vol. 6, Nos. 11–12, pp. 244–247, 3 figs.
1936. Tingitideo nocivo ás Anonaceas frutiferas no Brasil. O Campo, January, p. 51, 2 figs.

BÖRNER, CARL
1935. Ordnung. Schnabelkerfe, Rhynchóta (Hemiptera). In Die Tierwelt Mitteleuropas von P. Brohmer, P. Ehrmann, G. Ulmer, band 4, teil 1, insekten lief 3, pp. 1–113, 181 figs.

BOSQ, JUAN M.
1937. Lista preliminar de los hemipteros (heteropteros), especialmente relacionados con la agricultura nacional. Revista Soc. Ent. Argentina, vol. 9, pp. 111–134.

BOX, HAROLD E.
1953. List of sugar-cane insects. Commonwealth Institute of Entomology, 101 pp.

BREDDIN, GUSTAV
1901. Neue neotropische Wanzen und Zirpen. Soc. Ent., vol. 16, No. 11, pp. 82–84.
1907. Rhynchotographische Beiträge. Wiener Ent. Zeitung, vol. 26, pp. 93–97.

BREMOND, P.
  1938. Le Faux-Tigre des arbres fruitiers (*Monostira unicostata* Muls.) au Maroc. Rev. Pathologie Végétale et d'Entomologie Agricole de France, vol. 25, No. 4, pp. 294–307, 3 pls., 2 figs.

BRITTON, WILTON EVERETT
  1920. Check-list of the insects of Connecticut. State Geol. Nat. Hist. Surv., Connecticut, Bull. 31, 397 pp. Tingidae p. 77.

BROEK, M. VAN DEN, and SCHENK, P. J.
  1915. Dierlijke en Plantaardige Parasieten. Vol. 1. Ziekten en Beschadigingen der Tuinbouwgewassen ten dienste van tuinbouwscholen en -cursussen en de practijk. Groningen, J. B. Wolters. 382 pp.

BRUEL, W. E. VAN DEN
  1947. A propos du comportement en Belgique de *Stephanitis rhododendri* Horv. (Tingidae). Bull. Ann. Soc. Ent. Belgique, vol. 84, pp. 191–197, 1 fig.

BRULLÉ, AUGUSTE
  1835. Orthoptères et hémiptères. *In* Histoire naturelle des Insectes (Audouin et Brullé) leur classification et la description des espèces par M. A. Brullé. Paris. Vol. 4, 415 pp., pls.

BRUNER, STEPHEN C. [see also DRAKE and BRUNER]
  1940. A new tingitid from Cuba (Hemiptera). Mem. Soc. Cubana Hist. Nat., vol. 14, No. 3, pp. 245–247, 1 fig.

BRUNER, STEPHEN; SCARAMUZZA, L. C.; and OTERO, A. R.
  1945. Catalogo de los insectos que atacan a las plantas economicas de Cuba. Estación Experimental Agronomica Santiago de las Vegas, Provincia de la Habana. Bol. 63, pp. 1–246, 12 pls.

BUCHANAN-WHITE, FRANCIS
  1877. *Laccometopus clavicornis* L. and its relation to *Teucrium chamaedrys*. Entomologists' Monthly Mag., vol. 13, p. 283.
  1879. Description of new Hemiptera. (1). Linnean Soc. Journ. Zool., vol. 14, pp. 482–489.

Bueno: see TORRE-BUENO

BURMEISTER, HERMANN
  1835. Handbuch der Entomologie. Berlin. Vol. 2, 400 pp. Membranacei pp. 249–262.

BUTLER, ARTHUR GARDINER
  1877. Lepidoptera, Orthoptera, and Hemiptera. *In* Account of the zoological collection made during the visit of H.M.S. *Peterel* to the Galapagos Islands, by Albert Günther. Proc. Scientific Meetings Zool. Soc. London, pp. 86–91.

BUTLER, EDWARD A.
 1922. A contribution towards the life-history of *Dictyonota strichnocera*
 Fieb. Entomologists' Monthly Mag., vol. 58, No. 92, pp.
 179–182.
 1923. A biology of the British Hemiptera-Heteroptera. London.
 682 pp., many figs. Tingidae pp. 196–216, 3 figs.

BYERS, GEORGE W.
 1959. Types of Tingidae described by Torre-Bueno (Hemiptera).
 Ent. News, vol. 70, No. 7, pp. 191–193.

Campbell, T. G.: see CASHMORE and CAMPBELL

CARAYON, JACQUES [see also MONOD and CARAYON]
 1960. *Stethoconus frappai* n. sp. Miridé prédateur du Tingidé du
 caféier, *Dulinius unicolor* (Sign.), a Madagascar. Journ.
 d'Agriculture Tropicale et de Botanique Appliquée, vol. 7,
 Nos. 1–3, pp. 110–120, 5 figs.

Carrillo, José Luie: see GIBSON and CARRILLO

Carvalho, José C.: see DRAKE and CARVALHO

CASHMORE, A. B., and CAMPBELL, T. G.
 1946. The weeds problem in Australia: A review. Journ. Council
 for Scientific and Industrial Research., vol. 19, No. 1,
 pp. 16–31, 2 figs.

Castlenau, François Louis Nompar de Caumont de Laporte, Comte de:
 see LAPORTE

CEDERHIELM, JOHANN
 1798. Faunae ingricae prodromus exhibens methoicam descriptionem
 insectorum agri petropolensis praemissa mammalium, avium,
 amphibiorum et piscium enumeratione. 348 pp., 3 pls.
 Ryngota pp. 263–286.

CHAMPION, GEORGE CHARLES
 1897. Rhynchota. *In* Godman and Salvin, Biologia Centrali-
 Americana, vol. 2, pp. 1–32.
 1898a. Rhynchota. *In* Godman and Salvin, Biologia Centrali-
 Americana, vol. 2, pp. 33–193, 22 pls. Tingitidae pp. 33–48.
 1898b. Notes on American and other Tingitidae, with descriptions of
 two new genera and four new species. Trans. Ent. Soc.
 London, vol. 1, pp. 55–64, 2 pls.
 1924. The insects of Galapagos Islands. Entomologists' Monthly
 Mag., vol. 60, pp. 259–260.

Channa Basavanna, G. P.: see THONTADARYA and CHANNA BASAVANNA

Chatterjee, N. C.: see BEESON and CHATTERJEE

CHICOTE, CÉSAR [see also BOLIVAR and CHICOTE]
 1880. Adiciones á la enumeración de los hemípteros observados en
 España y Portugal. Anal. Soc. Española Hist. Nat., vol. 9,
 pp. 185–203.

CHINA, WILLIAM E.

1924. The Hemiptera-Heteroptera of Rodriguez, together with the description of a new species of *Cicada* from that island. Ann. Mag. Nat. Hist., ser. 9, vol. 14, pp. 427–453, 4 figs.

1926. Synonymic notes on Hemiptera. Entomologist, vol. 59, pp. 227–228.

1930. Heteroptera. *In* Insects of Samoa and other Samoan Terrestrial Artropoda, part II, Hemiptera, fasc. 3, pp. 81–162, 28 figs. British Museum (Natural History).

1936. A new species of the genus *Physatocheila* Fieb. (Heteroptera: Tingitidae) from Dorsetshire. Entomologists' Monthly Mag., vol. 72, pp. 270–272, 1 fig.

1938. Die Arthropodenfauna von Madeira nach den Ergebnissen der Reise von Prof. Dr. O. Lundblad Juli-August 1935. 3. Terrestrial Hemiptera. Arkiv för Zoologi, Svenska Vetenskapsakademien, vol. 30, No. 2, pp. 1–68, 23 text figs.; 1 pl.

1941. Genotype fixations in Hemiptera Heteroptera. Proc. Roy. Ent. Soc. London (B), vol. 10, part 7, p. 130.

1943. The generic names of the British Hemiptera-Heteroptera with a check list of the British species. *In* The generic names of British insects prepared by the Committee on Generic Nomenclature of Royal Entomological Society of London, part 8, pp. 211–342.

1945. A completely blind bug of the family Lygaeidae (Hemiptera-Heteroptera). Proc. Roy. Ent. Soc. London, vol. 14, parts 9–10, pp. 126–128, 1 fig.

1952. On the identity of *Physatocheila quadrimaculata* Wolff (Heteroptera: Tingidae). Entomologists' Monthly Mag., vol. 88, pp. 49–50, 1 fig.

CHINA, WILLIAM, and MILLER, N.C.E.

1955. Check-list of family and subfamily names in Hemiptera-Heteroptera. Ann. Mag. Nat. Hist., ser. 12, vol. 8, pp. 257–267.

1959. Check-list and keys to the families and subfamilies of the Hemiptera-Heteroptera. Bull. British Museum (Nat. Hist.), Entomology, vol. 8, No. 1, pp. 1–45.

CHITTENDEN, FRANK H.

1900. A new tingitid on bean. *In* Some insects injurious to garden crops, a series of articles dealing with insects of this class. U.S. Dept. Agric., Bull. 23, new ser., pp. 32–33, 1 fig.

COBBEN, RENÉ [see also DRAKE and COBBEN]
1948. Wantsennieuws uit midden Limburg. Natuurhistorisch Maandblad, vol. 37, Nos. 11–12, pp. 81–82, 1 fig.
1958a. Biotaxonomische Einzelheiten über Niederländische Wanzen (Hemiptera-Heteroptera). Tijdschrift voor Entomologie, deel 101, No. 1, pp. 1–46, 40 figs.
1958b. Einige Bemerkenswerten Wanzenfunde aus den Niederlanden (Hem.–Heteroptera). Natuurhistorisch Maandblad, vol. 47, pp. 15–21.

COCKERELL, THEODORE D. A.
1893. The entomology of the mid-Alpine zone of Custer County, Colorado. Trans. Amer. Ent. Soc., vol. 20, pp. 305–370.
1914. New and little-known insects from the Miocene of Florissant, Colorado. Journ. Geology, vol. 22, No. 7, pp. 714–724, 11 figs.
1921. Fossil arthropods in the British Museum. Ann. Mag. Nat. Hist., ser. 9, vol. 8, pp. 541–545, 5 figs.

Comstock, Anna Botsford: see COMSTOCK and COMSTOCK

COMSTOCK, JOHN HENRY
1880. The hawthorn Tingis (Corythucha arcuata, Say, var.), order Hemiptera; family Tingidae. U.S. Dept. Agric., Rep. of the Entomologist for 1879, pp. 221–222.

COMSTOCK, JOHN HENRY, and COMSTOCK, ANNA BOTSFORD
1895. A manual for the study of insects. Comstock Publ. Co., Ithaca, N.Y. 701 pp.

COSTA, ACHILLE
1847a. Cimicum regni neapolitani centurae. Napoli, Centuria 1, 76 pp., pl.
1847b. Cimicum regni neapolitani centuria secunda. 43 pp., 2 pls.
1847c.*Cimicum regni neapolitani centuria. Atti del Reale Istitute d'Icoraggiamento alle Scienze di Napoli, vol. 7, pp. 143–216.
1847d.*Cimicum regni neapolitani centuria secunda, decas prima, secunda, tertia, quatra, et quinta. Atti del Reale Istitute d'Icoraggiamento alle Scienze di Napoli, vol. 7, pp. 239–279.
1855a. Cimicum regni neapolitani centuria tertia et quartae fragmentum. 77 pp.
1855b.*Cimicum regni neapolitani. Centuria tertia et quartae fragmentum. Atti del Reale Istitute d'Icoraggiamento alle Scienze Naturali di Napoli, vol. 8, pp. 225–300.

---

*Cimicum regni neapolitani was originally published in various parts. Atti del Reale is a reprint of these using different pagination. See Stichel 1960d for dates of these publications.

1863. Additamenta as centurias cimicum regni neapolitani. 41 pp., 3 pls. (color).

1864. Annuario del Museo Zoologico della R. Universita di Napoli. Napoli, vol. 2, pp. 1–176, 4 pls. (color), 1862.

DE COSTA LIMA, ANGELO M.

1922. Nota sobre os insectos que atacam o algodoeiro no Brazil. Chacaras e Quintaes, vol. 25, No. 2, pp. 110–112, 6 figs.

1930. Supplemento ao 2 Catalogo systematico dos insectos que vivem nas plantas do Brasil e Ensaio de Bibliographia Entomologica Brasileira. O Campo, vol. 1, No. 8, pp. 84–91.

1936. Terceiro catalogo dos insectos que vivem nas plantas do Brasil. Rio de Janeiro. 460 pp. Tingidae pp. 124–131.

COTTON, RICHARD T.

1917. The eggplant lace-bug in Porto Rico. Journ. Dept. Agric. Porto Rico, vol. 1, No. 3, pp. 170–173.

CROSBY, CYRUS R., and HADLEY, C. H.

1915. The rhododendron lace-bug, *Leptobyrsa explanta* Heidemann. Journ. Econ. Ent., vol. 8, No. 4, pp. 409–414, 2 pls.

CURRIE, G. A., and FYFE, R. V.

1939. The lantana bug in Australia. Progress report. Journ. Council for Scientific and Industrial Research, vol. 12, No. 3, pp. 259–263.

CURTIS, JOHN

1823–1840. British entomology; being illustrations and descriptions of the genera of insects found in Great Britain and Ireland. London. 16 vols. (193 nos.), 770 pls. (color).

1833. Characters of some undescribed genera and species, indicated in the "Guide to an arrangement of British insects." Ent. Mag., vol. 1, pp. 186–199.

d'Antessanty: see ANTESSANTY

d'Araujo e Silva: see ARAUJO e SILVA, ARISTOTELES G.

Davis, Norman T.: see DRAKE and DAVIS

de Araújo Mendonça: see ARAÚJO MENDONÇA, FLORIANO

de Costa Lima: see COSTA LIMA

DE GEER, CHARLES

1773. Memoires pour servir a l'histoire des insectes. Vol. 3, Stockholm. 696 pp., 43 pls.

de Seabra: see SEABRA

de Serres: see SERRES

de Walsch: see WALSCH

DICKERSON, EDGAR L.,

1917. Notes on *Leptobyrsa rhododendri* Horv. Journ. New York Ent. Soc., vol. 25, No. 2, pp. 105–112, 1 pl.

DICKERSON, EDGAR L., and WEISS, HARRY B. [see also WEISS and DICKERSON]

  1916. Notes on *Leptoypha mutica* Say (Hemip.). Ent. News, vol. 27, pp. 308–310, 1 pl.

  1917. The azalea lace-bug, *Stephanitis pyrioides* Scott (Tingitidae, Hemiptera). Ent. News, vol. 28, pp. 101–105, pl. 1.

  1918. *Corythucha spinulosa* Gibson, a new lace-bug on wild cherry (Hem. Hom.). Ent. News, vol. 29, pp. 121–125, 1 pl.

DISTANT, WILLIAM LUCAS

  1888. Enumeration of the van Volxem collection of Rhynchota in the Brussels Museum, part 3. Ann. Soc. Ent. Belgique, vol. 32, pp. lxxviii–lxxxiii.

  1902a. XII. Rhynchotal miscellanea. Ann. South African Mus., vol. 2, No. 9, pp. 237–254, 1 pl.

  1902b. Rhynchotal notes. XIII. Heteroptera: Families Tingididae, Phymatidae and Aradidae. Ann. Mag. Nat. Hist., ser. 7, vol. 9, pp. 353–362.

  1903a. Contributions to a knowledge of the Rhynchota. Ann. Soc. Ent. Belgique, vol. 47, pp. 43–65.

  1903b. The fauna of British India including Ceylon and Burma, Rhynchota, vol. II (Heteroptera). Taylor and Francis, London. [1903 pp. 1–242; 1904 pp. 243–503]. Tingitidae pp. 122–145.

  1903c. Report on the Rhynchota. Part I, Heteroptera. Fasc. of Malayan Zoology, vol. 1, No. 2, pp. 219–273, 2 pls.

  1904. On the South African Tingididae and other heteropterous Rhynchota. Trans. South African Philos. Soc., vol. 14, No. 5, pp. 425–436, 1 pl.

  1907. Description of a new species of Tingididae from Honolulu. Etomologist, vol. 40, pp. 60–61.

  1908a. Description of a new tingid from Congo. Ann. Soc. Ent. Belgique, vol. 52, p. 220.

  1908b. XV. Rhynchota Malayana, part 1. Rec. Indian Mus., vol. 2, part 2, No. 15, pp. 127–151, 2 pls.

  1909a. New Oriental Tingididae. Ann. Soc. Ent. Belgique, vol. 53, pp. 113–123.

  1909b. Rhynchota (Heteroptera) from British India. Ann. Soc. Ent. Belgique, vol. 53, pp. 360–376.

  1909c. XI. Rhynchota Malayana, part 2. Rec. Indian Mus., vol. 3, part 2, No. 2, pp. 163–181, 2 pls.

  1910a. The fauna of British India, including Ceylon and Burma. Rhynchota, vol. V (Heteroptera: Appendix). Taylor and Francis, London. 362 pp., 214 figs. Tingidae pp. 100–126.

  1910b. Rhynchota Philippinensis, part 1. Philippine Journ. Sci., vol. 5, No. 1, pp. 57–66, 1 pl.

1910c. An introduced pest to rhododendrons. Zoologist, ser. 4, vol. 14, No. 166, pp. 395–396, 2 figs.

1911a. On some South African Rhynchota in the South African Museum. Ann. South African Mus., vol. 10, No. 2, pp. 39–49, 9 figs.

1911b. Rhynchota Indica (Heteroptera). Entomologist, vol. 44, pp. 269–271.

1913. The Percy Sladen Trust Expedition to the Indian Ocean in 1905, vol. 5, Rhynchota, part 1: suborder Heteroptera. Trans. Linnean Soc. London, vol. 16, No. 2, pp. 139–191, 3 pls.

1920. Rhynchota from New Caledonia. Ann. Mag. Nat. Hist., ser. 9, vol. 6, pp. 143–164.

Dobšík, B.

1951. Příspěvek k poznání ploštic Čsr. [Contribution a la connaissance des hétéroptères de Čsr. IV]. Entomologické Listy (Folia entomologica), vol. 13, Nos. 1–4, pp. 36–40, 1950.

Douglas, John W.

1877. The economy of *Laccometopus clavicornis*, Lin. Entomologists' Monthly Mag., vol. 13, pp. 236–237.

Douglas, John William, and Scott, John

1863. Descriptions of two new species. Entomologist's Ann. for 1863. London, pp. 143–146, 2 figs.

1865. The British Hemiptera. Vol. 1, Hemiptera-Heteroptera, 627 pp., 21 pls. Tingitidae pp. 243–264.

1868. British Hemiptera: additions and corrections. Entomologists' Monthly Mag., vol. 4, pp. 238–246, 1867–1868.

1869. British Hemiptera: additions and corrections. Entomologists' Monthly Mag., vol. 5, pp. 259–268, 1868–1869.

Downes, W.

1925. Lace bugs of British Columbia. Proc. Ent. Soc. British Columbia, No. 22, pp. 12–19, 1 pl.

1927a. A preliminary list of the Heteroptera and Homoptera of British Columbia. Proc. Ent. Soc. British Columbia, No. 23, pp. 1–22.

1927b. A new species of *Drakella* (Heteroptera-Tingitidae). Canadian Ent., vol. 59, p. 60.

Drake, Carl J. [see also Osborn and Drake]

1916. A new tingid from Tennessee. Ohio Journ. Sci., vol. 16, No. 7, pp. 326–328, 1 fig.

1917a. New and noteworthy Tingidae from the United States. Ohio Journ. Sci., vol. 17, No. 6, pp. 213–216.

1917b. Key to the nearctic species of *Gargaphia* with the description of a new species (Hem.-Het.). Ent. News, vol. 28, pp. 227–228.

1917c. The North American species of *Monanthia* (Tingidae). Bull. Brooklyn Ent. Soc., vol. 12, No.3, pp. 49–52, 1 fig.

1918a. Two new tingids from the West Indies (Hem.-Het.). Ohio Journ. Sci., vol. 18, No. 5, pp. 175–177.

1918b. The North American species of *Teleonemia* occurring north of Mexico. Ohio Journ. Sci., vol. 18, No. 8, pp. 323–332.

1918c. A new corn insect from California (Heteroptera). Journ. Econ. Ent., vol. 11, No. 4, p. 385.

1918d. Notes on North American Tingidae (Hem.-Het.). Bull. Brooklyn Ent. Soc., vol. 13, pp. 86–88.

1919a. On some North American Tingidae (Hemip.). Ohio Journ. Sci., vol. 19, No. 7, pp. 417–421.

1919b. On some Tingidae new to the fauna of Canada (Hemip.). Canadian Ent., vol. 51, pp. 159–160.

1919c. An undescribed *Teleonemia* from Florida and Jamaica (Hemip.). Florida Buggist, vol. 3, p. 24.

1920. Descriptions of new North American Tingidae. Ohio Journ. Sci., vol. 20, No. 3, pp. 49–54.

1921a. A new species of *Pachycysta* (Hem.-Het.). Bull. Mus. Hist. Nat., Paris., vol. 5, pp. 344–345, 1 fig.

1921b. Notes on some American Tingidae, with descriptions of new species. Florida Ent., vol. 4, pp. 49–54, 1 pl.

1922a. The genus *Dicysta* Champion (Hemiptera). Ann. Carnegie Mus., vol. 13, Nos. 3–4, pp. 269–273, 1 fig.

1922b. On some North and South American Tingidae (Hemip.). Florida Ent., vol. 5, No. 3, pp. 37–43, 48–50, 1 fig.

1922c. Neotropical Tingitidae with descriptions of three new genera and thirty-two new species and varieties (Hemiptera). Mem. Carnegie Mus., vol. 9, No. 2, pp. 351–378, 2 figs., 1 pl.

1922d. Heteroptera in the vicinity of Cranberry Lake. Tech. publ. No. 16, New York State College of Forestry, Syracuse Univ., vol. 22, No. 5, pp. 54–86, figs. 22–36.

1922e. Contribution toward the life history of *Galeatus peckhami* Ashmead. Tech. publ. No. 16, New York State College of Forestry, Syracuse Univ., vol. 22, No. 5, pp. 105–110, 1 pl.

1922f. The life history of the birch tingitid, *Corythucha pallipes* Parshley. Tech. publ. No. 16, New York State College of Forestry, Syracuse Univ., vol. 22, No. 5, pp. 111–116, 1 pl.

1923a. Some Tingitidae from Japan (Hemip.). Ohio Journ. Sci., vol. 23, No. 2, pp. 102–106, 1 fig.

1923b. Two new species of Cantacaderia (Hemip.-Tingitidae). Bull. Brooklyn Ent. Soc., vol. 18, No. 3, pp. 81–84, 1 fig.

1924. A new species of *Acanthocheila* from Bolivia (Hemiptera-Tingitidae). Bull. Brooklyn Ent. Soc., vol. 19, No. 3, p. 94.

1925a. An undescribed gall-making hemipteron (Tingitidae) from Africa. Amer. Mus. Nov., No. 158, pp. 1–2, 1 fig.

1925b. A new genus and new species of Tingitidae from Madagascar (Homopt.). Ent. Mitt., vol. 14, No. 2, pp. 107–109, 1 fig.

1925c. Concerning some Tingitidae from the Gulf States (Heteroptera). Florida Ent., vol. 9, pp. 36–39.

1926a. Notes on some Tingitidae from Cuba (Hemiptera). Psyche, vol. 33, No. 3, pp. 86–88.

1926b. The North American Tingitidae (Heteroptera) described by Stål. Ann. Carnegie Mus., vol. 16, Nos. 3–4, pp. 375–380, 1 pl.

1926c. An undescribed tingitid from Arizona (Hemiptera). Bull. Brooklyn Ent. Soc., vol. 21, No. 3, pp. 126–127.

1926d. The South American species of the genus *Tingis* Fabricius (Hemiptera). Ann. Carnegie Mus., vol. 17, No. 1, pp. 83–85.

1926e. On some Tingitidae from Java (Heteroptera). Treubia, vol. 8, Nos. 3–4, pp. 334–335.

1927a. Tingitidae from the Far East (Hemiptera). Philippine Journ. Sci., vol. 32, No. 1, pp. 53–59.

1927b. Two undescribed tingitids from Mexico. Bull. Brooklyn Ent. Soc., vol. 22, No. 2, pp. 116–117.

1927c. A new species of *Diplocysta* from the Philippines (Hemip.-Tingitidae). Pan-Pacific Ent., vol. 4, No. 1, p. 18.

1927d. Tingitidae from the Far East and Madagascar (Hemiptera). Philippine Journ. Sci., vol. 34, No. 3, pp. 307–312.

1928a. New and little known Neotropical Tingitidae. Iowa State Coll. Journ. Sci., vol. 3, No. 1, pp. 41–56.

1928b. A list of the insects of New York, families Piesmidae and Tingitidae. Cornell Univ. Agric. Exp. Sta., Mem. 101, pp. 99–103.

1928c. A synopsis of the American species of *Acalypta* (Hemip.-Tingitidae). Bull. Brooklyn Ent. Soc., vol. 23, No. 1, pp. 1–9, 2 figs.

1928d. Synonymical notes on tingitid genera with the descriptions of two new species from Haiti (Hemip.). Proc. Biol. Soc. Washington, vol. 41, pp. 21–24.

1928e. Some Tingitidae (Heteroptera) from Honduras. Occ. Pap. Mus. Zool., Univ. Michigan, No. 190, pp. 1–5, 1 fig.

1928f. Four undescribed tingitids from United States. Florida Ent., vol. 12, pp. 3–5.

1928g. A synopsis of the species of *Pachycysta* (Hemip: Tingitidae). Ent. News, vol. 39, pp. 184–185.

1928h. A new subgenus and species of *Tingis* from Burma (Hemip.). Indian Forest Records, vol. 8, No. 4, pp. 283–284.

1928i. Concerning some Tingitidae from Argentina with descriptions of five new species. Physis (Rev. Soc. Argentina Cienc. Nat.), vol. 9, pp. 72–76.

1929. Some Tingitoidea from Central and South America. Bull. Brooklyn Ent. Soc., vol. 24, No. 1, pp. 35–37, 1 fig.

1930a. Some Tingitidae (Hemiptera) from Brazil. Amer. Mus. Nov., No. 398, pp. 1–3.

1930b. Some Tingitidae from Brazil (Hemiptera). Bull. Brooklyn Ent. Soc., vol. 25, No. 1, pp. 25–26.

1930c. A new sugar-cane tingitid from Java and Sumatra (Hemiptera). Pan-Pacific Ent., vol. 7, No. 1, pp. 15–16.

1930d. Notes on American Tingitidae (Hemiptera). Bull. Brooklyn Ent. Soc., vol. 25, No. 5, pp. 268–272.

1930e. Concerning some Tingitidae from the Philippines (Hemiptera), with new species. Proc. Ent. Soc. Washington, vol. 32, No. 9, pp. 165–168.

1931a. Two new species of *Tigava* from South America, (Hemiptera, Tingitidae). Proc. Hawaiian Ent. Soc., vol. 7, No. 3, pp. 405–406.

1931b. The Cornell University Entomological Expedition to South America 1919 and 1920, scientific results. No. 5. Hemiptera-Tingitidae. Ann. Ent. Soc. America, vol. 24, No. 3, pp. 510–514.

1931c. Neotropical Tingitidae (Hemiptera). Ann. Mag. Nat. Hist., ser. 10, vol. 8, pp. 225–227, 1 fig.

1931d. An undescribed tingitid from Borneo and Strait Settlements (Hemiptera). Pan-Pacific Ent., vol. 8, No. 2, p. 96.

1931e. Concerning the genus *Leptodictya* Stål (Hemiptera, Tingitidae). Bol. Mus. Nac., Rio de Janeiro, vol. 7, No. 2, pp. 119–122.

1932. Notes on some American Tingitidae (Hemiptera). Psyche, vol. 39, No. 4, pp. 100–102.

1933. On some Tingitidae from South India including two new species (Hemiptera). Journ. Bombay Nat. Hist. Soc., vol. 36, No. 4, pp. 1015–1016.

1934a. An undescribed *Acalypta* from New York (Tingitidae: Hemiptera). Bull. Brooklyn Ent. Soc., vol. 29, No. 5, p. 196.

1934b. Un tingide nouveau provenant de Borneo et de Malacca. La Terre et La Vie, vol. 4, pp. 107–108, 1 fig. [Translation of 1931b.]

1935. American Tingitoidea (Hemiptera) in the Natural History Museum of Vienna. Sondar-Abdruck aus "Konowia," vol. 14, No. 1, pp. 9–20, 2 figs.

1936a. An undescribed tingitid from South India. Journ. Bombay Nat. Hist. Soc., vol. 39, No. 1, p. 145.

1936b. Some Tingitoidea from Argentina (Hemiptera). Travaux de l'Institut Zoologique de l'Académie des Sciences de l'URSS, vol. 3, pp. 699–701, 1 fig.

1937a. Some Tingitidae from China, East Indies and India. Lingnan Sci. Journ., vol. 16, No. 3, pp. 385–388, 3 figs.

1937b. Tingitidae from South China (Hemiptera). Lingnan Sci. Journ., vol. 16, No. 4, pp. 591–594, 1 fig.

1938a. Mexican Tingitidae (Hemiptera). Pan-Pacific Ent., vol. 14, No. 2, pp. 70–72.

1938b. Chinese Tingitidae (Hemiptera). Lingnan Sci. Journ., vol. 17, No. 2, pp. 195–197.

1939a. Three new species of Tingitidae (Hemiptera) from Australia. Pan-Pacific Ent., vol. 15, No. 2, pp. 87–88.

1939b. A new genus and species of tingitid (Hemiptera) from Formosa. Trans. Nat. Hist. Soc. Formosa, vol. 29, No. 191, pp. 205–206.

1939c. Chilean Tingitoidea (Hemiptera). Revista Ent., Rio de Janeiro, vol. 10, No. 2, pp. 330–334.

1939d. Seven new South American Tingitidae (Hemiptera). Revista Ent., Rio de Janeiro, vol. 10, No. 3, pp. 525–530.

1939e. A new tingitid from Palau Islands (Hemiptera). Mushi, vol. 12, pp. 102–103.

1939f. Two new tingitids (Hempitera) from Panama. Psyche, vol. 46, Nos. 2–3, pp. 68–69.

1940a. An undescribed *Corythucha* (Tingitidae-Hemip.) from Colorado. Ent. News, vol. 51, p. 172.

1940b. New American *Teleonemia* (Hemip.: Tingitidae). Revista Chilena Hist. Nat., vol. 44, pp. 242–243.

1941a. New American Tingitidae (Hemiptera). Journ. Washington Acad. Sci., vol. 31, No. 4, pp. 141–145.

1941b. Three new American Tingitidae (Hemiptera). Pan-Pacific Ent., vol. 17, No. 3, pp. 139–141.

1942a. New Tingitidae (Hemiptera). Iowa State Coll. Journ. Sci., vol. 17, No. 1, pp. 1–21.

1942b. New Australian Tingitidae (Hemiptera). Journ. Washington Acad. Sci., vol. 32, No. 12, pp. 359–364.

1943a. A list of species of *Monanthia* Lep. and Serv. of the Western Hemisphere, including description of a new species (Hemiptera: Tingidae). Proc. Ent. Soc. Washington, vol. 45, No. 6, pp. 141–142.

1943b. Concerning the genus *Lepturga* Stål (Hemiptera, Tingitidae). Revista Chilena Hist. Nat., vol. 45, pp. 175–177.

1944a. A new genus and ten new species of serenthiines (Hemiptera: Tingitidae). Proc. Ent. Soc. Washington, vol. 46, No. 3, pp. 67–76, 2 figs.

1944b. Concerning the American cantacaderinids (Hemiptera: Tingidae). Bol. Ent. Venezolana, vol. 3, No. 3, pp. 139–142, 1 fig.

1945. New Tingidae (Hemiptera). Bull. Southern California Acad. Sci., vol. 44, No. 3, pp. 96–100.

1946. A new tingid from Yap Island (Hemiptera). Mushi, vol. 17, No. 6, pp. 27–28.

1947a. Wissenschaftliche Ergebnisse der schwedischen entomologischen Reisen des Herrn Dr. A. Roman 1914–15 und 1923–24 in Amazonas. 17. Tingididae. Arkiv för Zoologi, vol. 39B, No. 3, pp. 1–2.

1947b. A new genus and two new species of Tingidae (Hemiptera). Bol. Mus. Nac., Rio de Janeiro, vol. 81, pp. 1–4, 1 fig.

1947c. Australian Tingidae (Hemiptera). Bull. Southern California Acad. Sci., vol. 46, No. 3, pp. 111–121, 3 figs.

1947d. Tingidae (Hemiptera) from the Orient and South Pacific. Musée Heude, Notes d'Entomologie Chinoise, vol. 11, No. 7, pp. 225–231, 4 figs.

1947e. *Ypsotingis sideria* Drake. Musée Heude, Fichier Entomologique Chinois, No. 67, fig. (color).

1947f. *Cantacader japanicus* Drake. Musée Heude, Fichier Entomologique Chinois, No. 68, fig. (color).

1947g. *Trachypeplus chinensis* Drake. Musée Heude, Fichier Entomologique Chinois, No. 69, fig. (color).

1947h. *Tingis coomani* Drake. Musée Heude, Fichier Entomologique Chinois, No. 70, fig. (color).

1948a. Some Tingidae (Hemiptera) from China, Japan and India. Musée Heude, Notes d'Entomologie Chinoise, vol. 12, No. 1, pp. 1–9, 3 figs.

1948b. New species of *Stephanitis* Stål including a list of species of the world (Hemiptera). Musée Heude, Notes d'Entomologie Chinoise, vol. 12, No. 6, pp. 45–56, 4 figs.

1948c. New American Tingidae (Hemiptera). Bol. Ent. Venezolana, vol. 7, Nos. 1–2, pp. 20–25.

1948d. Five new American Tingidae (Hemiptera). Bol. Ent. Venezolana, vol. 7, Nos. 1–2, pp. 15–19.

1948e. New genera and species of Tingidae (Hemiptera). Proc. Biol. Soc. Washington, vol. 61, pp. 149–156.

1948f. The genus *Compseuta* Stål (Hemiptera, Tingidae). Proc. Ent. Soc. Washington, vol. 50, No. 8, pp. 197–204, fig.

1948g. New Tingidae from the Orient and other regions (Hemiptera: Heteroptera). Musée Heude, Notes d'Entomologie Chinoise, vol. 12, No. 15, pp. 173–178.

1948h. New and little known Piesmidae and Tingidae (Hemiptera). Zoologische Mededeelingen, vol. 30, No. 4, pp. 73–76, 1 fig.

1948i. The genus *Cochlochila* Stål (Hemiptera: Tingidae). Musée Heude, Notes d'Entomologie Chinoise, vol. 12, No. 16, pp. 179–181.

1948j. American Tingidae (Hemiptera). Revista Ent., Rio de Janeiro, vol. 19, No. 3, pp. 429–436.

1950a. Concerning the Cantacaderinae of the world (Hemiptera: Tingidae). Arthropoda, vol. 1, Nos. 2–4, pp. 153–166, 3 figs.

1950b. A new tingid from the Canal Zone (Hemiptera). Proc. Ent. Soc. Washington, vol. 52, No. 6, pp. 299–300.

1951. New genera and species of Tingidae (Hemiptera) in the Hungarian National Museum. Ann. Hist. Nat. Mus. Nat. Hungarici, vol. 1, No. 1, pp. 165–178.

1952. The genus *Parada* Horváth (Hemiptera: Tingidae). Psyche, vol. 59, No. 4, pp. 143–147.

1953a. New Neogaean Tingidae (Hemiptera). Great Basin Nat., vol. 13, Nos. 1–2, pp. 13–16.

1953b. Synonymic data and description of new genera and species of Tingidae (Hemiptera). Great Basin Nat., vol. 13, Nos. 3–4, pp. 91–99.

1953c. Two new Tingidae (Hemiptera). Psyche, vol. 60, No. 4, pp. 151–154.

1953d. A new genus and new species of Tingidae (Hemiptera). Proc. Biol. Soc. Washington, vol. 66, pp. 211–224.

1954a. New Senegalese Tingidae (Hemiptera). Bull. Inst. Français d'Afrique Noire, vol. 16, No. 1, pp. 232–237.

1954b. A miscellany of new Tingidae (Hemiptera). Proc. Biol. Soc. Washington, vol. 67, pp. 1–15.

1954c. New genera and species of Tingidae from the Old World (Hemiptera). Philippine Journ. Sci., vol. 83, No. 1, pp. 69–73.

1954d. Four new species of American Tingidae (Hemiptera). Proc. Ent. Soc. Washington, vol. 56, No. 2, pp. 75–78.

1954e. Some tingids from the Belgian Congo (Hemiptera: Tingidae). Bull. Inst. Roy. Sci. Nat. Belgique, vol. 30, No. 17, pp. 1–10, 1 fig.

1954f. Tingidae: descriptions and synonymic data (Hemiptera). Great Basin Nat., vol. 14, Nos. 1–2, pp. 1–10.

1954g. New and little-known Hemiptera-Heteroptera, Tingidae, from Ethiopia. Ann. Mag. Nat. Hist, ser. 12, vol. 7, pp. 657–655, 4 figs.

1955a. Three new Tingidae (Hemiptera). Bull. Southern California Acad. Sci., vol. 54, No. 2, pp. 78–81, 1 fig.

1955b. Angolan Tingidae (Hemiptera). Publicações Culturais da Companhia de Diamantes de Angola, separata 27, pp. 83–90, 2 figs.

1955c. Some Tingidae from the French Cameroons (Hemiptera). Proc. Biol. Soc. Washington, vol. 68, pp. 105–108.

1955d. New Tingidae (Hemiptera) from the Belgian Congo. Bull. Inst. Roy. Sci. Nat. Belgique, vol. 31, No. 85, pp. 1–5, 1 fig.

1955e. A new genus and species of African lacebug (Tingidae: Hemiptera). Rev. Zool. Bot. Africaine, vol. 52, Nos. 3–4, pp. 280–282, 1 fig.

1956a. Tingidae (Hemiptera Heteroptera). National Albert Park, vol. 86, No. 1, pp. 3–9, 1 fig.

1956b. New African Tingidae (Hemiptera). Rev. Zool. Bot. Africaine, vol. 53, Nos. 1–2, pp. 109–113.

1956c. Three new species of Cantacaderinae from Africa (Hemiptera: Tingidae). Rev. Zool. Bot. Africaine, vol. 53, Nos. 1-2, pp. 13–16.

1956d. Hemiptera: Tingidae. *In* Insects of Micronesia, vol. 7, No. 2, Bernice P. Bishop Museum, pp. 101–116, 8 figs., map.

1956e. The genus *Bako* Schouteden (Hemiptera: Tingidae). Rev. Zool. Bot. Africaine, vol. 54, Nos. 1–2, pp. 63–66.

1956f. Hemiptera Heteroptera Tingidae and Saldidae. *In* South African Animal Life, vol. 3, pp. 421–433, 2 figs.

1956g. Four new species of gall-making lacebugs (Hemiptera: Tingidae). Philippine Journ. Sci., vol. 85, No. 4, pp. 471–475, 2 figs.

1956h. New African and Asian Tingidae (Hemiptera). Great Basin Nat., vol. 16, pp. 18–22.

1957a. Hemiptera: Tingidae. British Museum Expedition to Southwest Arabia 1937–1938. Vol. 1, Nos. 27–33, pp. 415–420, 3 figs.

1957b. The genus *Kapiriella* Schouteden (Hemiptera: Tingidae). Rev. Zool. Bot. Africaine, vol. 55, Nos. 1–2, pp. 205–218, 1 fig.

1957c. The genus *Belenus* Distant and its allies (Hemiptera: Tingidae). Quart. Journ. Taiwan Mus., vol. 10, No. 1, pp. 31–35.

1957d. A new pepper tingid from New Britain. Proc. Roy. Ent. Soc. London, vol. 26, Nos. 11–12, pp. 203–205, 2 figs.

1957e. Quelques Tingidae la Réunion (Hemiptera). Mém. Inst. Scient. Madagascar, ser. E, vol. 8, pp. 399–405, 1 fig.

1957f. Tingidae de Madagascar (Hemiptera). Le Naturaliste Malgache, vol. 9, No. 1, pp. 125–131.

1958a. Angolan Tingidae (Hemiptera) II. Publicações Culturais da Companhia de Diamantes de Angola, separata 38, pp. 99–110, 3 figs.

1958b. Tingidae (Hemiptera Heteroptera). National Upemba Park, vol. 50, No. 3, pp. 25–33, 1 fig.

1958c. Quelques Tingidae Malgaches (Hemiptera). Mém. Inst. Scient. Madagascar, ser. E, vol. 9, pp. 315–333, 2 figs.

1958d. Three new species of *Ypsotingis* (Hemiptera: Tingidae). Bull. Southern California Acad. Sci., vol. 57, No. 3, pp. 149–153, 2 pls.

1959. A new tingid from New Zealand (Hemiptera). Trans. Roy. Soc. New Zealand, vol. 87, parts 1–2, pp. 67–68, 1 fig.

1960. Tingidae of New Guinea (Hemiptera). Pacific Insects, vol. 2, No. 3, pp. 339–380, 27 figs.

1961a. A new genus and species of cantacaderine lace-bug from the Philippines (Hemiptera: Tingidae). Fieldiana, Zool. Chicago Nat. Hist. Mus., vol. 42, No. 9, pp. 115–118, 2 figs.

1961b. Some Australian Tingidae (Hemiptera), including new genera and species. Rec. Australian Mus., vol. 25, No. 6, pp. 107–113, 4 figs.

1961c. Tingidae from South Africa (Hemiptera). Trans. Roy. Soc. South Africa, vol. 36, No. 3, pp. 129–131, 4 pls.

DRAKE, CARL J., and BONDAR, GREGORIO

1932. Concerning Brasilian Tingitidae, Hemiptera. Bol. Mus. Nac., Rio de Janeiro, vol. 8, pp. 87–96, 1 fig.

DRAKE, CARL J., and BRUNER, STEPHEN C.

1924a. Concerning some Tingitidae occurring in the West Indies (Hemip.). Mem. Soc. Cubana Hist. Nat., "Felipe Poey," vol. 6, Nos. 3–4, pp. 144–154, 2 figs.

1924b. Notes on some Tingitidae from Cuba (Hemiptera). Mem. Soc. Cubana Hist. Nat., "Felipe Poey," vol. 6, Nos. 3–4, pp. 155–156.

DRAKE, CARL J., and CARVALHO, JOSÉ C.

1944. Four new American Tingitidae (Hemiptera). Bull. Brooklyn Ent. Soc., vol. 39, No. 1, pp. 41–44.

DRAKE, CARL J., and COBBEN, R. H.

1960. The Heteroptera of the Netherlands Antilles—V, Tingidae (lace bugs). Studies on the fauna of Curaçao and other Caribbean Islands, vol. 10, No. 54, pp. 67–97, figs, 74–89.

DRAKE, CARL J., and DAVIS, NORMAN T.

1958. The morphology and systematics of the Piesmatidae (Hemiptera) with keys to world genera and American species. Ann. Ent. Soc. America, vol. 51, No. 6, pp. 567–581, 34 figs.

1960. The morphology, phylogeny, and higher classification of the family Tingidae, including the description of a new genus and species of the subfamily Vianaidinae (Hemiptera: Heteroptera). Ent. Amer., vol. 39 (new ser.), pp. 1–100. 75 figs.

DRAKE, CARL J., and FRICK, D. M.

1939. Synonymy and distribution of the lantana lace bug (Hemiptera: Tingitidae). Proc. Hawaiian Ent. Soc., vol. 10, No. 2, pp. 199–202, 1 fig.

DRAKE, CARL J., and FROESCHNER, RICHARD C.

1962. A new myrmecophilous lacebug from Panama (Hemiptera: Tingidae). Great Basin Nat., vol. 22, Nos. 1–3, pp. 8–11, 3 figs.

DRAKE, CARL J., and GOMEZ-MENOR, JUAN

1954. Some Tingidae from Spanish Guinea (Hemiptera). "EOS," Revista Española Ent., vol. 30, Nos. 1–2, pp. 89–93, 1 fig.

DRAKE, CARL J., and HAMBLETON, EDSON J.

1934. Brazilian Tingitidae (Hemiptera). Part I. Revista Ent., Rio de Janeiro, vol. 4, No. 4, pp. 435–451, 2 figs.

1935. New Brazilian Tingitidae (Hemiptera). Part II. Arch. Inst. Biol., São Paulo, vol. 6, No. 16, pp. 141–154, 6 figs.

1938a. Concerning Brazilian Tingitidae (Hemiptera). Part III. Revista Ent., Rio de Janeiro, vol. 8, Nos. 1–2, pp. 44–68, 11 figs.

1938b. Brazilian Tingitoidea (Hemiptera). Part IV. Arch. Inst. Biol., São Paulo, vol. 9, No. 5, pp. 51–57, 2 figs., 2 pls.

1939. Twenty new Brazilian Tingitidae (Hemiptera). Part V. Arch. Inst. Biol., São Paulo, vol. 10, No. 9, pp. 153–163.

1940. New Brazilian Tingitidae (Hemiptera). Part VI. Revista Ent., Rio de Janeiro, vol. 11, Nos. 1–2, pp. 533–537.

1942a. Two new Peruvian Tingitidae (Hemiptera). Iowa State Coll. Journ. Sci., vol. 16, No. 2, pp. 329–330.

1942b. Seven new South American Tingitidae (Hemiptera). Revista Ent., Rio de Janeiro, vol. 13, Nos. 1–2, pp. 76–81.

1944a. Four new American Tingitidae (Hemiptera). Proc. Ent. Soc. Washington, vol. 46, No. 4, pp. 94–96.

1944b. Concerning Neotropical Tingitidae (Hemiptera). Journ. Washington Acad. Sci., vol. 34, No. 4, pp. 120–129, 1 fig.

1945. Concerning Neotropical Tingitidae (Hemiptera). Journ. Washington Acad. Sci., vol. 35, No. 11, pp. 356–367.

1946a. New species and new genera of American Tingidae (Hemiptera). Proc. Biol. Soc. Washington, vol. 59, pp. 9–16.

1946b. Three new species and a new genus of American Tingidae (Hemiptera). Ent. News, vol. 57, No. 5, pp. 121–125.

DRAKE, CARL J., and HSIUNG, TA SHIH
1936. An undescribed tingitid from the Chinese Ash (Hemiptera). Lingnan Sci. Journ., vol. 15, No. 2, pp. 287–288.

DRAKE CARL J., and HURD, MARGARET POOR
1945a. Notes on two Fijian tingitids (Hemiptera). Proc. Hawaiian Ent. Soc., vol. 12, No. 2, pp. 287–289, 1 fig.

1945b. New American Tingitidae (Hemiptera). Bol. Ent. Venezolana, vol. 4, No. 2, pp. 127–132, 1 fig.

DRAKE, CARL J., and LUTZ, JOHN C.
1953. Two undescribed Tingidae from India (Hemiptera). Bull. Brooklyn Ent. Soc., vol. 48, No. 4, pp. 104–106.

DRAKE, CARL J., and MAA TSING-CHAO
1953. Chinese and other Oriental Tingoidea (Hemiptera). Quart. Journ. Taiwan Mus., vol. 6, No. 2, pp. 87–101.

1954. Chinese and other Oriental Tingoidea (Hemiptera). Part II. Quart. Journ. Taiwan Mus., vol. 7, Nos. 1–2, pp. 111–118.

1955. Chinese and other Oriental Tingoidea (Hemiptera). Part III. Quart. Journ. Taiwan Mus., vol. 8, No. 1, pp. 1–11.

DRAKE, CARL J., and MALDONADO CAPRILES, J.
1959. A new tingid from Pakistan (Hemiptera). Bull. Brooklyn Ent. Soc., vol. 54, No. 1, pp. 25–26, 1 fig.

DRAKE, CARL J., and MAMET, J. RAYMOND
1956. Mauritian Tingidae (Hemiptera). Mauritius Inst. Bull., vol. 3, No. 5, pp. 300–302, 1 pl.

1961. The Mauritian gall tingid (Hemiptera). Mauritius Inst. Bull., vol. 5, No. 6, pp. 223–224, 1 fig.

DRAKE, CARL J., and MOHANASUNDARUM, M.
1961. New Tingidae from South India (Hemiptera). Great Basin Nat., vol. 21, No. 4, pp. 108–113, 3 figs.

DRAKE, CARL J., and PLAUMANN, FRITZ
1956. A new cantacaderid from Brazil (Hemiptera: Tingidae). Bull. Southern California Acad. Sci., vol. 55, No. 1, pp. 17–18.

DRAKE, CARL J., and POOR, MARGARET E.
1935. An undescribed rubber tingitid from Brazil (Hemiptera). Journ. Washington Acad. Sci., vol. 25, No. 6, pp. 283–284, 1 fig.

1936a. Tingitidae from Hainan Island (Hemiptera). Lingnan Sci. Journ., vol. 15, No. 3, pp. 439–443.

1936b. New Indian Tingitidae (Hemiptera). Indian Forest Records, vol. 2, No. 5, pp. 141–149, 1 fig.

1936c. The genera and genotypes of Tingitoidea of the Western Hemisphere. Iowa State Coll. Journ. Sci., vol. 10, No. 4, pp. 381-390.

1937a. Tingitidae from Malaysia and Madagascar (Hemiptera). Philippine Journ. Sci., vol. 62, No. 1, pp. 1–18, 1 pl.

1937b. Some Tingitidae (Hemiptera) from Oceania. Iowa State Coll. Journ. Sci., vol. 11, No. 4, pp. 397–404.

1937c. Concerning the genus *Leptobyrsa* Stål (Hemiptera). Proc. Biol. Soc. Washington, vol. 50, pp. 163–166.

1937d. The South American Tingitidae (Hemiptera) described by Stål. Mem. Carnegie Mus., vol. 11, No. 5, pp. 301–312, 1 pl. (15 figs.).

1938a. Nine new American Tingitidae (Hemiptera). Bull. Brooklyn Ent. Soc., vol. 33, No. 1, pp. 28–34, 1 fig.

1938b. Los "Tingitidae" (Hemiptera) de la colección Carlos Berg. Instituto del Museo de la Universidad Nacional de La Plata, Notas del Museo de La Plata, vol. 3, No. 10, pp. 103–109, 2 figs.

1939a. Seven new American Tingitidae (Hemiptera). Bull. Brooklyn Ent. Soc., vol. 34, No. 1, pp. 31–35.

1939b. Some Tingitidae from the Republic of Argentina (Hemiptera). Physis (Rev. Soc. Argentina Cienc. Nat.), vol. 17, pp. 95–98, 1 fig.

1939c. Some Tingitidae (Hemiptera) from the Eastern Hemisphere. Proc. Hawaiian Ent. Soc., vol. 10, No. 2, pp. 203–207, 1 fig.

1940. Six new South American Tingitidae (Hemiptera). Revista Ent., Rio de Janeiro, vol. 11, Nos. 1–2, pp. 226–231.

1941. Tingitidae from Amboina Island (Hemiptera). Pan-Pacific Ent., vol. 17, No. 4, pp. 160–165.

1942. Four new Tingitidae (Hemiptera) from Argentina. Entomología, Anal. Mus. Argentino Cienc. Nat., vol. 40, No. 158, pp. 299–302.

1943. Fijian Tingitidae (Hemiptera). Occ. Pap. Bernice P. Bishop Mus., vol. 17, No. 15, pp. 191–205, 7 figs.

DRAKE, CARL J., and RUHOFF, FLORENCE A.

1959. A new moss-feeding tingid from Mexico (Hemiptera). Bull. Brooklyn Ent. Soc., vol. 54, pp. 136–139, 1 fig.

1960a. Lace-bug genera of the world (Hemiptera: Tingidae). Proc. U.S. Nat. Mus., vol. 112, pp. 1–105, 5 figs., 9 pls.

1960b. The identification of *Acanthia humuli* Fabricius and related species (Hemiptera; Tingidae). Bull. Southern California Acad. Sci., vol. 59, part 2, pp. 70–75, 3 pls.

1960c. Tingidae: new genera, species, homonyms, and synonyms (Hemiptera). Great Basin Nat., vol. 20, Nos. 1–2, pp. 29–38, 5 figs.

1960d. An undescribed tingid from Arizona (Hemiptera). Journ. Kansas Ent. Soc., vol. 33, No. 4, pp. 152–154, 1 fig.

1960e. A necessary correction. Great Basin Nat., vol. 20, Nos. 3–4, p. 80.

1961a. The genus *Epimixia* Kirkaldy (Hemiptera: Tingidae). Trans. Roy. Soc. New Zealand, Zoology, vol. 1, No. 1, pp. 1–6, 2 pls.

1961b. New genera and new species of lacebugs from the Eastern Hemisphere (Hemiptera: Tingidae). Proc. U.S. Nat. Mus., vol. 113, No. 3455, pp. 125–183, 24 pls.

1961c. New species and taxonomic changes in the Tingidae (Hemiptera). Journ. Kansas Ent. Soc., vol. 34, No. 3, pp. 145–151, 3 figs.

1962a. Synonymic changes and four new species of Tingidae (Hemiptera). Bull. Southern California Acad. Sci., vol. 60, part 3, pp. 156–164, 3 pls., 1961.

1962b. Some Tingidae (Hemiptera) in the South Australian Museum. Rec. South Australian Mus., vol. 14, No. 2, pp. 249–252, 1 pl.

1962c. Taxonomic changes and descriptions of new Tingidae (Hemiptera). Bull. Southern California Acad. Sci., vol. 61, part 3, pp. 133–142, 2 figs.

1962d. Synonymic notes and descriptions of new Tingidae (Hemiptera). Studia Ent., vol. 5, fasc. 1–4, pp. 489–506, 3 figs.

DRAKE, CARL J., and SLATER, JAMES A.
1955. A new genus and four new species of African Tingidae (Hemiptera). Act. Ent. Mus. Nat. Prague, vol. 30, No. 443, pp. 49–53.

DRAKE, CARL J., and SMITHERS, C. N.
1958. Two new species of *Pogonostyla* (Hemiptera: Tingidae). Rev. Zool. Bot. Africaine, vol. 57, Nos. 3–4, pp. 313–316, 1 fig.

DUBOIS, MICHEL
1888. Catalogue des hémiptères de la Somme. Mem. Soc. Linnéenne Nord France, vol. 7, pp. 97–178 (1886-1888).

DUGÈS, ALFREDO
1889. *Tingis spinosa.* La Naturaleza, Sociedad Mexican de Historia Natural, ser. 2, vol. 1, pp. 207–209, 1 pl.

ESAKI, TEISO
1926. Verzeichniss der Hemiptera-Heteroptera der Insel Formosa. Ann. Mus. Nat. Hungarici, vol. 24, pp. 136–189.

1931.   Eine neue Gallenbildende Tingitiden-art. Bulteno Scienca de la Fakultato Terkultura Kjuŝu Imperia Universitato Fukuoka, Japanujo, vol. 4, pp. 244–250, 2 figs. (in Japanese), pp. 251–253 (in German).

1932.   Iconographia insectorum Japanicorum, Tokyo, 2 vols., illustrated. Tingidae vol. 1, pp. 1634–1637, 8 figs.

1954.   Iconographia insectorum Japanicorum, ed. 2, 1736 pp.

ESAKI, TEISO, and TAKEYA, CHOKU

1931.   Identification of a Japanese tingitid injurious to the pear tree. Mushi, vol. 4, pp. 51–59, 2 text figs., 3 pls.

1933.   A new tingitid from Formosa (Hemiptera: Tingitidae). Mushi, vol. 6, No. 1, pp. 1–3, 2 figs.

EVANS, JOHN W.

1957.   Some aspects of the morphology and inter-relationships of extinct and recent Homoptera. Trans. Roy. Ent. Soc. London, vol. 109, No. 9, pp. 275–294, 6 figs.

FABRICIUS, JOHANN C.

1775.   Systema entomologiae, sistens insectorum classes, ordines, genera, species, adiectis synonymis, locis, descriptionibus, observationibus. 832 pp. Ryngota pp. 673–745.

1781.   Species insectorum exhibentes eorum differentias specificas, synonyma auctorum, loca natalia, metamorphosin adiectis observationibus, descriptionibus. Vol. 2, 517 pp. Ryngota pp. 313–397.

1787.   Mantissa insectorum, sistens species nuper detectas adiectis synonymis, observationibus, descriptionibus, emendationibus. Vol. 2, 382 pp. Ryngota pp. 260–320.

1794.   Entomologia systematica emendata et aucta, secundum classes, ordines, genera, species adjectis synonimis, locis, observationibus, descriptionibus. Vol. 4, 472 pp. Ryngota pp. 1–229.

1803.   Systema rhyngotorum, secundum ordines, genera, species, adiectis synonymis, locis, observationibus, descriptionibus. 314 pp. *Tingis* pp. 124–127.

FALLÉN, CARL F.

1807.   Monographia cimicum Sveciae, 121 pp.

1826.   Supplementum monographiae cimicidum Sveciae. 16 pp.

1829.   Hemiptera Sveciae. Cimicides eorumque familiae affines. 186 pp. [pp. 1–16 published June 6, 1828, the remainder in 1829]. *Tingis* pp. 142–151, 153–154.

FELDMAN, ALBERT EDWARD, and BAILEY, NORMAN S.

1952.   The taxonomic value of the ovipositor in the New England species of the genus *Corythucha* Stål (Hemiptera: Tingidae). Psyche, vol. 59, No. 3, pp. 96–104, 18 figs.

FELT, EPHRAM PORTER
1904.   Injurious insects, chysanthemum lace bug *Corythuca marmorata*
        Uhler. New York State Mus. Bull. 76, Entomology 21, 19th
        report of state entomologist on injurious and other insects of
        the State of New York for 1903, pp. 125–129.
1910.   Rhododendron lace bug *Leptobyrsa explanata* Heid. New York
        State Mus. Bull. 141, 25th report of state entomologist on
        injurious and other insects of the State of New York for 1909,
        pp. 72–75, 1 fig.
1933.   Observations on shade tree insects. Journ. Econ. Ent., vol. 26,
        pp. 45–51.

FENTON, FREDERICK A.
1934.   Tingitoidea affecting cotton. Canadian Ent., vol. 66, pp.
        198–199.

FERRARI, PIETRO M.
1874.   Hemiptera agri Ligustici. Ann. Mus. Civ. Stor. Nat. Genova,
        vol. 6, pp. 116–208.
1878.   Hemiptera Ligustica adjecta et emendata. Ann. Mus. Civ.
        Stor. Nat. Genova, vol. 12, pp. 60–96.
1884.   Materiali per lo studio della fauna Tunisina raccolti da G. e L.
        Doria. 5. Rincoti. Ann. Mus. Civ. Stor. Nat. Genova, ser.
        2, vol. 1, No. 21, pp. 439–522.
1885.   Rhynchota Tridentina a March, Jacopo et Laura Doria lecta
        anno 1884. Ann. Mus. Civ. Stor. Nat. Genova, ser. 2, vol.
        2, pp. 401–422.

FIEBER, FRANZ XAVIER
1844.   Entomologische Monographien. Leipzig. 138 pp., 10 pls.
        Tingideae pp. 20–111.
1861.   Die Europäischen Hemiptera. Halbflügler (Rhynchota
        Heteroptera). Vienna, 444 pp., 2 pls. Tingididae pp. 35–36,
        116–132.
1864.   Neuere Entdeckungen in europäischen Hemiptera. Wiener
        Ent. Monatschr., vol. 8, No. 7, pp. 205–234.

FINK, DAVID E.
1915.   The eggplant lacebug. U.S. Dept. Agric., Bull. 239, pp. 1–5,
        7 figs.

FITCH, ASA
1857.   Third report of the noxious and other insects of the State of New
        York. Ann. Rep. New York State Agric. Soc. 1856, vol. 16,
        pp. 315–490.
1858.   Say's heteropterous Hemiptera (reprint of: Descriptions of new
        species of heteropterous Hemiptera of North America, by
        Thomas Say, New Harmony, Indiana. December 1831).

Fourth Rep. on noxious, beneficial, and other insects of State of New York, pp. 754–812.

1861. The quince tingis. Country Gentleman, vol. 17, No. 7, p. 114, 1 fig.

FIUZA, RENATO MUNIZ

1946. Inimigos e moléstias das "Leguminosas comestíveis cultivadas" no Estado da Bahia. Boletim da Secretaria de Agricultura, Indústria e Comércio, vol. 13, No. 4, pp. 335–345.

FLETCHER, T. BAINBRIGGE

1918. Report of the Proceedings of the Second Entomological Meeting, Pusa, 1917, 340 pp.

1920. Tingididae. Report of the Proceedings of the Third Entomological Meeting, Pusa, 1919, vol. 1, pp. 263–264.

FLOR, GUSTAV

1860. Die Rhynchoten Livlands in systematischer Folge beschrieben. Vol. 1, 826 pp. Tingididea pp. 317–371.

FÖRSTER, HORST

1959. Biotaxonomische Bemerkungen über *Physatocheila smreczynskii* China (Heteroptera, Tingidae). Entomologische Berichten Maandblad uitgegeven door de Nederlansche Entomologische Vereeniging, vol. 19, No. 4, pp. 75–77.

FOURCROY, ANTOINE FRANÇOIS

1785. Entomologia parisiensis. Vol. 1, 231 pp.

FRAUENFELD, GEORG RITTER

1853. Über die Pflanzenauswüchse von *Teucrium montanum* und *Laccometopus (Cimex) Teucrii.* Verh. Zool.-bot. Ver. Wien, vol. 3, pp. 157–161. [This title was copied from Hagen, p. 249, since the article is included in a series of notes entitled "Versammlung am 5 October 1853."]

FREY-GESSNER, EMIL

1865. Verzeichniss schweizerischer Insekten. Mitth. Schweizer. Ent. Ges., vol. 1, pp. 195–203, 225–244, 304–310.

1872. Hemipterologisches. Mitth. Schweizer. Ent. Ges., vol. 4, No. 1, pp. 20–25, 1 pl.

Frick, D. M.: see DRAKE and FRICK

FROESCHNER, RICHARD C. [see also DRAKE and FROESCHNER]

1944. Contributions to a synopsis of the Hemiptera of Missouri, Part III. Amer. Midl. Nat., vol. 31, No. 3, pp. 638–683, 3 pls.

FROGGATT, WALTER W.

1901. Notes on Australian Hemiptera (plant bugs). Agric. Gaz. New South Wales, vol. 12, pp. 1592–1601, 1 pl.

FUKUI NATURAL HISTORY SOCIETY
  1938. Genshoku Fukui-ken Knochu zufu. (Original color illustrations of insects collected in Fukui prefecture.) Tingidae tab. 50, figs. 34–36.

FULLAWAY, DAVID T.
  1951. *Teleonemia scrupulosa.* *In* Minutes of the meeting, April 19, 1950, Hawaiian Entomological Society. Proc. Hawaiian Ent. Soc., vol. 14, No. 2, p. 208.
  1958. Biological control of *Opuntia megacantha* and *Lantana camera* in Hawaii. Proc. Tenth International Congress of Entomology, Montreal, Aug. 17–25, 1956, vol. 4, pp. 549–552.

FYFE, R. V. [see also CURRIE and FYFE]
  1935. The lantana bug in Fiji. Agric. Journ., Dept. Agric. Fiji, vol. 8, No. 1, pp. 35–36.
  1937. The lantana bug, *Teleonemia lantanae* Distant. Journ. Council for Scientific and Industrial Research, vol. 10, No. 3, pp. 181–186, 4 pls.

GARBIGLIETTI, ANTONIO
  1869. Catalogus methodicus et synonymicus, hemipterorum heteropterorum (Rhyngota Fabr.) Italiae indigenarum. Bull. Soc. Ent. Italiana, vol. 1, pp. 41–52, 105–124, 181–198, 271–281.

GAUTIER, C.
  1925. A propos de l'hibernation de *Tingis pyri* Fabr. Bull. Soc. Ent. France, No. 18, pp. 321–322.
  1927a. Nouvelles recherches sur l'hibernation de *Tingis pyri* Fab. Bull. Soc. Ent. France, No. 1, pp. 12–13.
  1927b. A propos de *Stethoconus cyrtopeltis* Flor. [Hem. Capsidae] ennemi de *Tingis pyri* [Hem. Tingitidae]. Bull. Soc. Ent. France, No. 2, pp. 26–27.

de Geer: see DE GEER

GEOFFROY, ETIENNE LOUIS
  1762. Histoire abregée des insectes qui se trouvent aux environs de Paris. Vol. 1, pp. 1–523, 10 pls.

GERMAR, ERNST F.
  1817. Fauna insectorum Europae. Fasc. 13.
  1835. Fauna insectorum Europae. Fasc. 13–15.
  1836. Fauna insectorum Europae. Fasc. 16–18.

GERMAR, ERNST F., and BERENDT, GEORG C.
  1856. Die im Bernstein befindlichen Hemipteren und Orthopteren der Vorwelt. *In* Die im Bernstein befindlichen Organischen Reste der Vorwelt, vol. 2, No. 1, pp. 3–40, 3 pls.

GERMAR, ERNST F., and KAULFUSS, F.
1817. Augusti ahrensii fauna insectorum Europae. Fasc. 3, 25 tabs.
Gessner: see FREY-GESSNER
Ghesquière, J.: see MAYNE and GHESQUIÈRE
GIBSON, ARTHUR
1904. Basswood, or linden, insects. Thirty-fourth Ann. Rep. Ent.
Soc. Ontario, 1903, vol. 19, pp. 50–61, 10 figs.
GIBSON, EDMUND H.
1917. A new species of *Corythuca* from the Northwest (Heter., Tingitidae). Ent. News, vol. 28, p. 258.
1918. The genus *Corythucha* Stål (Tingidae: Heteroptera). Trans.
Amer. Ent. Soc., vol. 44, pp. 69–104.
1919a. The genus *Phatnoma* Fieber (Tingidae: Heteroptera). Trans.
Amer. Ent. Soc., vol. 45, pp. 181–185.
1919b. The genus *Gargaphia* Stål (Tingidae: Heteroptera). Trans.
Amer. Ent. Soc., vol. 45, pp. 187–201.
1919c. The genera *Corythaica* Stål and *Dolichocysta* Champion (Tingidae: Heteroptera). Proc. Biol. Soc. Washington, vol. 32,
pp. 97–104.
GIBSON, WILLIAM W., and CARRILLO, JOSÉ LUIS
1959. Lista de insectos en la coleccion entomologica de la Oficina de
Estudios Especiales, S.A.G. Secretaria de Agricultura y
Ganaderia, Oficina de Estudios Especiales, Mexico. Folleto
Miscelaneo No. 9, 254 pp. Tingididae p. 19.
GIEBEL, CHRISTOPH GOTTFRIED
1856. Fauna der Vorwelt mit steter Berücksichtigung der lebenden
Thiere, vol. 2, 511 pp. Rhyncota pp. 332–390.
GILLETTE, CLARENCE P., and BAKER CARL F.
1895. A preliminary list of the Hemiptera of Colorado. Colorado
Agric. Exp. Station Bull. 31, tech. ser. 1, pp. 1–137.
GMELIN, JOHANN FRIEDRICH
1790. Caroli a Linné Systema Naturae. Vol. 1, part 4, pp. 1517–
2224. [Date as cited by Library of Congress (U.S.)].
GOEZE, JOHANN A. E.
1778. Entomologische Beyträge zu des Ritter Linné zwölften Ausgabe
des Natursystems. Leipzig. Vol. 2, lxxix+352 pp.
GÖLDI, EMIL A.
1886. Beiträge zur Kenntniss der kleinen und kleinsten Glieder-
thierwelt Brasiliens. Mitth. Schweizer. Ent. Ges., vol. 7,
No. 6, pp. 231–255, figs.
GOMEZ-MENOR, JUAN [see also DRAKE and GOMEZ-MENOR]
1949. Las especies españolas del género *Monostira* Costa (Hemiptera
Tingidae). Bol. Real Soc. Española Hist. Nat.: Tomo
extraordinario, 1946, Madrid, pp. 157–164, 1 fig.

1950.   La "Chincheta" del Almendro (*Monostira unicostata* Mulsant). Boletín de Patología Vegetal y Entomología Argícola, vol. 17, pp. 97–109, 1949.

1954.   Tíngides que viven sobre el peral. Boletín de Patología Vegetal y Entomología Agrícola, vol. 20, pp. 369–392, 8 figs.

1955a. Hemípteros que atacan a los árboles y arbustos frutales. Boletín de Patología Vegetal y Entomología Agrícola, vol. 21, pp. 209–282, 1954–55.

1955b. Nuevas citas de especies y descripción de algunas nuevas de Piesmidos y Tingidos de España e Islas Canarias. "EOS." Revista Española Ent., vol. 31, Nos. 3–4, pp. 247–259, 4 figs.

1956a. Las "chinches de encaje" (Hemiptera Tingidae) con referencias a las especies mas conocidas de Marruecos. Tamuda, vol. 4, No. 1, pp. 104–123, 15 figs.

1956b. Las tribus de hemipteros de España. Consejo Superior de Investigaciones Cientificas Trabajos del Instituto Español de Entomologia. 147 pp., figs. Tingidae pp. 79–82.

GONZÁLEZ, S. MARTINEZ
1948.   Avance complementario (1) al estudio de las principales especies de tingidos de España. Bol. Real Soc. Española Hist. Nat., vol. 46, Nos. 1–2, pp. 49–51.

GOWDEY, CARLTON C.
1925.   Report of the Government Entomologist. Annual Rep. Dept. Science Agric. 31 December 1924. Jamaica, pp. 17–20.

1926.   Catalogus insectorum Jamaicensis. Ent. Bull. Dept. Agric. Jamaica, No. 4, part 1, 114 pp. Tingididae p. 35.

GREDLER, P. VINCEZ MARIA
1870.   Rhynchota Tirolensia. Verh. Zool.-Bot. Ges. Wien, pp. 69–108.

GREEN, E. ERNEST
1916.   The rhododendron tingid (*Stephanitis rhododendri* Horv.). Entomologists' Monthly Mag., vol. 52, p. 207.

GREEN, S.
1882.   *Tingis hystricellus.* Hardwicke's Science Gossip, No. 211, p. 161.

GUÉRIN-MÉNEVILLE, FELIX E.
1831.   Description of *Tingis dilatata.* Mag. Zool., tome 1, part 2, p. 8, fig.

1844.   Iconographie du Régne Animal de G. Cuvier, vol. 3, 576 pp., 104 pls. (insects vol. 2). Hemipteres, pp. 343–381 [see Kirkaldy 1910, and Banks 1909, for validation of date of publication].

1857.   Animaux articules. *In* de la Sagra, Histoire physique, politique, et naturelle de l'Ile de Cuba. Paris, 868 pp. *Tingis* pp. 408–410.

GULDE, JOHANN
1938. Die Wanzen Mitteleuropas. Hemiptera Heteroptera Mittel-
europas. Tiel 6, pp. 225–377, figs.
Haarup: see JENSEN-HAARUP
HACKER, HENRY
1927. New Tingitoidea (Hemiptera) in the Queensland Museum.
Mem. Queensland Mus., vol. 9, No. 1, pp. 19–32, pls. 6–10.
1928. New species and records of Australian Tingitoidea (Hemiptera).
Mem. Queensland Mus., vol. 9, No. 2, pp. 174–188, 1 text
fig., pls. 20–23.
1929. New species of Australian Tingitidae (Hemiptera). Mem.
Queensland Mus., vol. 9, No. 3, pp. 324–334, pls. 32–35.
Hadley, C. H.: see CROSBY and HADLEY
HAGLUND, C. J. EMIL
1895. Beiträge zur Kenntniss der Insektenfauna von Kamerun. 4.
Verzeichniss der von Yngve Sjöstedt im norwestlichen
Kamerungebiete eingesammelten Hemipteren. Kongl. Vet.
Akad. Förhandl., vol. 52, No. 7, pp. 445–479.
Hakk, S. Afsarul: see MENON and HAKK
Hambleton, Edson J.: see DRAKE and HAMBLETON
HARDY, ELMO
1954. *Corythuca morrilli.* *In* Notes and exhibitions minutes of the
meeting, August 10, 1953, Hawaiian Entomological Society.
Proc. Hawaiian Ent. Soc., vol. 15, No. 2, pp. 282–283.
HARRIS, HALBERT H.
1942. On the date of publication of Laporte's Essai. Pan-Pacific
Ent., vol. 18, No. 4, pp. 161–162.
Hedicke, H.: see ROSS and HEDICKE
HEER, OSWALD
1853. Die Insektenfauna der Tertiärgebilde von Oeningen und von
Radoboj in Croatien. Nouv. Mém. Soc. Helvétique Sci.
Nat., vol. 3, No. 4, pp. 1–138, 15 pls.
1865. Die Urwelt der Schweiz. Zurich. 622 pp., 11 pls., map, many
illustr.
1872. Monde Primitif de la Suisse. Genève et Bale. 801 pp., 11
pls., map, many illustr.
1876. The primeval world of Switzerland, vol. 2, 324 pp., many
illustr.
1879. Die Urwelt der Schweiz, ed. 2. Zurich. 714 pp., 417 figs.
HEIDEMANN, OTTO
1899a. [Tingitid from Santa Rita Mountains.] *In* minutes of meeting,
November 3, 1898, Washington Entomological Society.
Proc. Ent. Soc. Washington, vol. 4, p. 339.

1899b. A new species of Tingitidae. Canadian Ent., vol. 31, pp. 301–302.

1901. [On *Gargaphia undulata*.] *In* minutes of the meeting, November 1, 1900, Washington Entomological Society. Proc. Ent. Soc. Washington, vol. 4, p. 493.

1906. Account of a new tingitid. Proc. Ent. Soc. Washington, vol. 8, Nos. 1–2, pp. 10–13, 2 figs.

1908. Two new species of North American Tingitidae (Hemiptera-Heteroptera). Proc. Ent. Soc. Washington, vol. 10, Nos. 1–2, pp. 103–108, 1 pl.

1909. New species of Tingitidae and description of a new *Leptoglossus* (Hemiptera-Heteroptera). Bull. Buffalo Soc. Nat. Sci., vol. 9, pp. 231–238, 6 figs.

1911a. Some remarks on the eggs of North American species of Hemiptera-Heteroptera. Proc. Ent. Soc. Washington, vol.13, No. 3, pp. 128–140, 4 pls.

1911b. A new species of North American Tingitidae. Proc. Ent. Soc. Washington, vol. 13, No. 3, pp. 180–181, 1 fig.

1913a. The sugar-cane tingid from Mexico. Journ. Econ. Ent., vol. 6, No. 2, pp. 249–251, 1 fig.

1913b. Description of two new species of North American Tingitidae. Proc. Ent. Soc. Washington, vol. 15, No. 1, pp. 1–4, 2 figs.

1914. A new species of North American Tingitidae. Proc. Ent. Soc. Washington, vol. 16, No. 3, pp. 136–137, 1 fig.

1917. Two new species of lace-bugs (Heteroptera: Tingidae). Proc. Ent. Soc. Washington, vol. 18, No. 4, pp. 217–220, 3 figs, 1916.

HERRICH-SCHAEFFER, GOTTLIEB AUGUST

1830. Faunae Insectorum Germanicae Initia. Regensburg. Hefts 117–122, figs.

1835. Nomenclator entomologicus. Verzeichniss der Europaischen Insecten, vol. 1, pp. 1–116.

[See Bergroth 1919 for validation of dates of the following publications.]

1836-1850. Die Wanzenartigen Insekten,

1836. Vol. 3 (issues 3–6), pp. 34–114.
1837. Vol. 4 (issues 1–2), pp. 1–32.
1838. Vol. 4 (issues 3–5), pp. 33–92.
1840. Vol. 5 (issue 5), pp. 73–88.
1850. Vol. 9 (issues 3–4), pp. 97–192.

HESSE, A. J.

1925. Contributions to a knowledge of the fauna of South-West Africa. 4. A list of the heteropterous and homopterous Hemiptera of South-West Africa. Ann. South African Mus., vol. 23, part. 1, 190 pp., 8 pls. Tingididae pp. 88–90.

HIXSON, EPHRIAM
1942. A new pest of snapdragon and verbena. Journ. Econ. Ent., vol. 35, No. 4, pp. 605–606, 1 fig.

HOBERLANDT, LUDVIK
1942. Piesmatidae et Tingiditidae (Het.) a Dr. A. Hoffer in Moravia Meridionali collectae. Entomologické Listy (Folia entomologica), vol. 5, pp. 124–126.
1943a. Heteroptera Moraviae II. Časopis České Společnosti Ent., vol. 40, No. 2, pp. 116–119.
1943b. Heteroptera Bohemiae II. Časopis České Společnosti Ent., vol. 40, No. 2, pp. 120–124.
1944. De nova specie Alpina generis *Acalypta* Westw. (Het.). Entomologické Listy (Folia entomologica), vol. 7, pp. 33–36, 1 fig.
1949. Some Hemiptera Heteroptera collected in north and east Iraq. Acta Ent. Mus. Nat. Prague, vol. 26, No. 360, pp. 1–9, 13 figs.
1951. Hemiptera-Heteroptera collected by Mr. J. Houšká in Israel. Acta Ent. Mus. Nat. Prague, vol. 27, No. 381, pp. 5–34, 13 figs.
1952. On some Hemiptera-Heteroptera of Cyprus. Acta Ent. Mus. Nat. Prague, vol. 28, No. 403, pp. 109–116, 5 figs.
1955. Results of the zoological scientific expedition of the National Museum in Praha to Turkey. 18. Hemiptera IV. Terrestrial Hemiptera Heteroptera of Turkey. Acta Ent. Mus. Nat. Prague, suppl. 3, 264 pp.

HOFFMAN, WILLIAM E.
1935. Observations on a hesperid leaf-roller and a lacebug. Two pests of banana in Kwangtung. Lingnan Sci. Journ., vol. 14, No. 4, pp. 639–649, 4 figs.

HOPE, FREDERIC WILLIAM
1847. Observations on the fossil insects of Aix in Provence, with descriptions and figures of three species. Trans. Ent. Soc. London, vol. 4, No. 4, pp. 250–255, 1 pl.

HORVÁTH, GÉZA
1874a. Neue Heteroptera aus Ungarn. Berliner Ent. Zeitschr., vol. 18, pp. 332–336.
1874b. Énumération des tingides de Hongrie. Petites Nouv. Ent., 6 année, No. 108, p. 432.
1881a. Hemiptera nova vel minus cognita. Természetrajzi Füzetek, vol. 5, pp. 39–42; 217–225.
1881b. M. le docteur G. de Horváth adresse les remarques qui suivent sur divers hémiptères. *In* Séance du 23 Février 1881. Ann. Soc. Ent. France, ser. 6, vol. 1, pp. xxxii–xxxvi.

1885. Hémiptères nouveaux. Rev. Ent., vol. 4, pp. 320–324.

1889. Notes synonymiques et géographiques sur les hémiptères Paléarctiques. Rev. Ent., vol. 8, pp. 325–331.

1891. Hémiptères recueillis dans l'Arménie Russe avec la description d'espèces et variétés nouvelles. Rev. Ent., vol. 10, pp. 68–81.

1892a. Uebersicht der Hemipteren-Gattung *Campylostira* Fieb. Wiener Ent. Zeitung, vol. 11, pp. 309–313.

1892b. Chasses hivernales dans le midi de la France. Rev. Ent., vol. 11, No. 1, pp. 128–140.

1896. Hemiptera nova Palaearctica. Természetrajzi Füzetek, vol. 19, Nos. 3–4, pp. 322–329.

1897a. Description d'hémiptères nouveaux et notes diverses. Rev. Ent., vol. 16, pp. 81–92.

1897b. Species generis *Galeatus* Curt. Természetrajzi Füzetek, vol. 20, No. 3, pp. 455–460.

1898a. Quatre espèces et quatre variétés nouvelles d'héteroptères Paléarctiques. Rev. Ent., vol. 17, pp. 67–72.

1898b. Remarques synonymiques sur les hémiptères Paléarctiques. Rev. Ent., vol. 17, No. 4, pp. 275–281.

1899. Heteroptera nova Europae Regionumque confinium in Museo Nationali Hungarico asservata. Természetrajzi Füzetek, vol. 22, pp. 444–451.

1901. Hémiptères du voyage de M. Martinez Escalera dans l'Asie-Mineure. Természetrajzi Füzetek, vol. 24, pp. 469–485.

1902a. Tingitidae novae Palaearcticae. Természetrajzi Füzetek, vol. 25, pp. 593–600.

1902b. Descriptions of new Hemiptera from New South Wales. Természetrajzi Füzetek, vol. 25, pp. 601–612.

1903a. Trois Tingitides nouveaux d'Algerie. Rev. Ent., vol. 22, pp. 77–79.

1903b. Szerbia Hemiptera-Faunája. Ann. Mus. Nat. Hungarici, vol. 1, pp. 1–28.

1905a. Descripciones de algunos Hemipteros nuevos del centro de España. Bol. Real Soc. Española Hist. Nat., vol. 5, pp. 272–277.

1905b. Tingitidae novae vel minus cognitae e regione Palaearctica. Ann. Mus. Nat. Hungarici, vol. 3, pp. 556–572.

1906a. Synopsis Tingitidarum regionis Palaearcticae. Ann. Mus. Nat. Hungarici, vol. 4, pp. 1–118, 1 pl.

1906b. A new gall-inhabiting bug from Bengal. Entomologists' Monthly Mag., vol. 42, pp. 33–34.

1906c. Sur quelques hémiptères nuisibles de Cochinchine. Bull. Soc. Ent. France, pp. 295–297, 1 fig.

1906d. Les Tingitides d'Achille Costa. Ann. Mus. Zool. Univ. Napoli (nuova ser.), vol. 2, No. 10, pp. 1–3.

1906e. A palearktikus faunaterület Tingitidái. Matematikai és Természettudományi Ertesitö, Budapest, vol. 24, pp. 495–502.

1907. Hemiptera nova vel minus cognita e regione Palaearctica. Ann. Mus. Nat. Hungarici, vol. 5, pp. 289–323.

1908. Remarques sur quelques hémiptères de l'Amérique du Nord. Ann. Mus. Nat. Hungarici, vol. 6, pp. 554–569.

1909a. Hemipteres recueillis par M. Th. Becker aux îles Canaries. Ann. Mus. Nat. Hungarici, vol. 7, pp. 289–301.

1909b. Adnotationes synonymicae de hemipteris nonnullis extraeuropaeis. Ann. Mus. Nat. Hungarici, vol. 7, pp. 631–632.

1910. Hemiptera: Tingitidae und Aradidae. Wissenschaftliche ergebnisse der Schwedischen Zoologischen Expedition nach dem Kilimandjaro, dem Meru und den Umgebenden Massaisteppen Deutsch-Ostafrikas 1905–1906. Pp. 61–72.

1911a. Miscellanea hemipterologica I–V. Ann. Mus. Nat. Hungarici, vol. 9, pp. 327–338, 1 pl.

1911b. Hemiptera nova vel minus cognita e regione Palaearctica. Ann. Mus. Nat. Hungarici, vol. 9, pp. 573–610, 2 figs.

1911c. Hémiptères récoltés par M. le Dr. W. Innes Bey en Égypte. Bull. Soc. Ent. Egypte (1910), fasc. 3, pp. 99–117, 1 fig.

1911d. Nomenclature des familles des hémiptères. Ann. Mus. Nat. Hungarici, vol. 9, pp. 1–34.

1912a. Deux tingitides nouveaux du Congo Belge. Rev. Zool. Africaine, vol. 1, No. 3, pp. 353–355.

1912b. Species generis Tingitidarum *Stephanitis*. Ann. Mus. Nat. Hungarici, vol. 10, pp. 319–339, 3 figs.

1912c. Hemipteren aus Java. Tijdschr. voor Ent., vol. 55, pp. 338–346, 3 figs.

1915. Descrizione di tre specie nueve, innanzi ricordate, par G. Horváth, L. Navás e E. Meyerick. Appendice *in* Silvestri 1915. Boll. Lab. Zool. Portici, vol. 9, p. 331.

1916. Albánia Hemiptera-Faunája. Ann. Mus. Nat. Hungarici, vol. 14, pp. 1–16.

1918. Adatok a Balkán-Félsziget Hemiptera-Faunájának Ismeretéhez. Ann. Mus. Nat. Hungarici, vol. 16, pp. 321–340.

1923a. A new species of *Galeatus* from New Mexico (Hemiptera-Tingitidae). Ann. Carnegie Mus., vol. 15, No. 1, pp. 108–109.

1923b. A fertö-tónak és közvetlen környékének Hemiptera-Fuanája. Ann. Mus. Nat. Hungarici, vol. 20, pp. 182–199.

1924. Heteroptera nova Madagascariensia. Ann. Mus. Nat. Hungarici, vol. 21, pp. 188–194.

518   U.S. NATIONAL MUSEUM BULLETIN 243

1925a. Results of Dr. E. Mjöberg's Swedish Scientific Expeditions to
       Australia 1910–1913. 45. Tingitidae. Arkiv. för Zoologi, K.
       Svenska Vetenskapakademien, vol. 17A, No. 24, pp. 1–17,
       9 figs.
1925b. Wissenschaftliche Ergebnisse der Schwedischen Entomologi-
       schen Reise des Herrn Dr. A. Roman in Amazonas 1914–1915.
       Ent. Tidskr., vol. 46, pp. 219–220.
1926. Hemipterologische notizen aus Niederländisch-Indien. Treu-
       bia, vol. 8, Nos. 3–4, pp. 327–333, 3 figs.
1929. New Tingitidae from the Ethiopian region. Ann. Mag. Nat.
       Hist., ser. 10, vol. 3, pp. 319–236.

HOST, NICOLAS THOMAS
1788. *Cimex teucrii.* *In* Nicolai Josephi Jacquin Collectanea Austriaca
       ad botanicam, chemiam, et historiam naturalem spectantia,
       cum figuris. Vindobonae, vol. 2, pp. 255–259, fig.

HOUTTUYN, MARTIN
1765. Natuurlyke Historie of Uitvoerige Beschryving der Dieren,
       Planten en Mineraalen. Amsterdam, vol. 10.

HOWARD, LELAND OSSIAN
1898. Injury to chrysanthemums by *Corythuca irrorata.* *In* Some
       miscellaneous results of the work of the Division of Ento-
       mology, II. U.S. Dept. Agric., Div. Ent., Bull. 10, new series,
       p. 99.
1904. Identity of a tingitid found on chrysanthemum. *In* Some
       miscellaneous results of the work of the Division of Ento-
       mology, VII. U.S. Dept. Agric., Div. Ent., Bull. 44, p. 89.

Hsiung, Ta Shih: see DRAKE and HSIUNG

HÜEBER, THEODOR
1893. Fauna Germanica. Hemiptera Heteroptera. (Die Halbflügler
       der Schnabelkerfe: Wanzen). Ulm, vol. 3, pp. 291–520.

HUMMEL, ARVID DAVID
1825. Novae species variorum. Essais Entomologiques No. IV.
       St. Petersbourg, pp. 58–72.

HURD, MARGARET POOR [see also DRAKE and HURD]
1945. A monograph of the genus *Corythaica* Stål (Hemiptera: Tingi-
       dae). Iowa State Coll. Journ. Sci., vol. 20, No. 1, pp. 79–99,
       5 figs., 1 pl.
1946. Generic classification of North American Tingoidea (Hemiptera-
       Heteroptera). Iowa State Coll. Journ. Sci., vol. 20, No. 4,
       pp. 429–492, 8 figs.

HUSSEY, ROLAND F.
1922a. On some Hemiptera from North Dakota. Occ. Pap. Mus.
       Zool., Univ. Michigan, No. 115, pp. 1–23.

1922b. Hemiptera from Berrien County, Michigan.   Occ. Pap. Mus. Zool., Univ. Michigan, No. 118, pp. 1–39.

1957.   A new *Gargaphia* from Florida (Hemiptera: Tingidae).   Proc. Ent. Soc. Washington, vol. 59, No. 4, pp. 175–176.

IYENGAR, M. O. T.

1924.   The life-history of a tingid bug, *Monanthia globulifera*.   Report of the Proceedings of the Fifth Entomological Meeting, Pusa, 1923, pp. 296–299, pls. 27–28.

JAKOVLEV, B. E.

1869.   Materialien zur entomologischen fauna der Wolga-gegend. Horae Soc. Ent. Rossicae, vol. 6, pp. 109–126.

1871.   Matepialy dlya entomologicheskoi fauny privolzhskago kraya. Trudy Russkugo Entomologicheskheo Obshchestva, vol. 6, pp. 3–34.

1874a–1876b. Materialy dlya entomologicheskoi fauny evropeiskoi Rossi. Trudy Russkugo Entomologicheskheo Obshchestva, vol. 7, part 1, pp. 7–44, 1 pl.; 1876, vol. 8, part 1, pp. 46–82, 1 pl.

1874b. Hemiptera Heteroptera Astrakhanskago Kraya. Bull. Soc. Imp. Nat. Moscou, vol. 48, No. 1, pp. 218–277.

1875a. Poluzhestkokrylyĭa Hemiptera Heteroptera Astrakhanskago kraya. Bull. Soc. Imp. Nat. Moscou, vol. 49, No. 2, pp. 145–174.

1875b. Poluzhestkokrylyĭa Hemiptera Heteroptera Russkoi fauny. Bull. Soc. Imp. Nat. Moscou, vol. 49, No. 4, pp. 248–270.

1876a. Novyia poluzhestkokrylyĭa Hemiptera Heteroptera. Bull. Soc. Imp. Nat. Moscou, vol. 51, No. 3, pp. 85–124.

1877.   Poluzhestkokrylyĭa (Hemiptera Heteroptera) s vernoi persii. Trudy Russkugo Entomologicheskheo Obshchestva, vol. 10, pp. 67–98.

1880a. Novy ĭa poluzhestkokrylyĭa (Hemiptera Heteroptera) Russkoi fauny.   Bull. Soc. Imp. Nat. Moscou, vol. 55, No. 1, pp. 127–144.

1880b. Poluzhestkokrylyĭa (Hemiptera Heteroptera) kavkazskagokraya. Trudy Russkugo Entomologicheskheo Obshchestva, vol. 12, pp. 1–176.

1883.   Materialy dlya fauny poluzhestkokrylyĭa rossii i sos ĭe dnikli Stran. Bull. Soc. Imp. Nat. Moscou, vol. 58, No. 1, pp. 103–108.

1884.   Neue hemipteren der Russischen fauna. Rev. Mensuelle d'Entomologie Pure et Appliquée, vol. 1, No. 5, pp. 121–122.

1890.   Zur Hemipteren-Fauna Russlands und der angrenzenden Länder. Horae Soc. Ent. Rossicae (1889–1890), vol. 24, pp. 311–348.

1893.   Hemiptera Heteroptera des gouverments Irkutsk.   Horae Soc.
        Ent. Rossicae (1892–1893), vol. 27, pp. 282–310.
1901.   Hémiptères-hétéroptères nouveaux de la faune paléarctique.
        Rev. Russe Ent., vol. 1, pp. 33–35.
1902a. Hémiptères-hétéroptères nouveaux de la faune paléarctique. II.
        Rev. Russe Ent., vol. 2, pp. 63–70.
1902b. Notes sur divers hémiptères-hétéroptères de la faune Russe.
        I.   Rev. Russe Ent., vol. 2, pp. 274–277.
1903a. Hémiptères-hétéroptères nouveaux de la faune paléarctique.
        (IV).   Rev. Russe Ent., vol. 3, No. 1, pp. 1–4.
1903b. Hémiptères-hétéroptères nouveaux de la faune paléarctique.
        VI.   Rev. Russe Ent., vol. 3, Nos. 3–4, pp. 191–195.
1903c. Hémiptères-hétéroptères nouveaux de la faune paléarctique.
        VII.   Rev. Russe Ent., vol. 3, No. 5, pp. 289–293.

JENSEN-HAARUP, A. C.
1912.   Taeger.   Danmarks Fauna.   300 pp., 171 figs.

JOHNSON, C. G.
1936.   The biology of *Leptobyrsa rhododendri* Horvath (Hemiptera,
        Tingitidae), the rhododendron lacebug.   Ann. Applied
        Biol., vol. 23, pp. 342–368, 3 pls., 4 text figs.

JONES, THOMAS H.
1915.   Insects affecting vegetable crops in Porto Rico.   U.S. Dept.
        Agric. Bull. 192, pp. 1–11, 4 pls.

JORDAN, K. H. C.
1933.   Beiträge zur Biologie heimischer Wanzen (Heteropt.).
        Stettiner Ent. Zeitung, vol. 94, pp. 212–236, 30 figs.

KATO, M.
1933.   Three color illustrated insects of Japan.   Fasc. 5.   Heteroptera.
        48 pls.

Kaulfuss, F.: see GERMAR and KAULFUSS

KHAN, A. H.
1945.   On the lantana bug (*Teleonemia scrupulosa* Stål).   Indian Journ.
        Ent., vol. 6, Nos. 1–2, pp. 149–161.

KIRBY, WILLIAM F.
1891.   Catalogue of the described Hemiptera Heteroptera and Homop-
        tera of Ceylon, based upon the collection formed (chiefly at
        Pundaloya) by Mr. E. Ernest Green.   Journ. Linnean Soc.,
        vol. 24, Nos. 149–150, pp. 72–176, 3 pls.

KIRITSHENKO, ALEKSANDR N.
1913a. Hemiptera-Heteroptera turanica nova.   Rev. Russe Ent., vol.
        13, Nos. 3–4, pp. 397–415.
1913b. Analecta hemipterologica.   Rev. Russe Ent., vol. 13, Nos. 3–4,
        pp. 482–483.

1914. Hemiptera-Heteroptera turanica nova.III. Rev. Russe Ent., vol. 14, Nos. 2–3, pp. 181–202.

1915. Revisio critica hemipterorum heteropterorum palaearcticorum a V. Motschulsky descriptorum. Petrograd Ann. Mus. Zool. Acad. Sci., vol. 20, pp. 296–300.

1918. Hemiptera-Heteroptera Faunae Caucasicae, part 1. Mém. Mus. Caucase, ser. A, No. 6, 177 pp.

1931. *Leptoypha*, an American genus hitherto unknown as occurring in Palearctic Asia. Ann. Carnegie Mus., vol. 20, No. 2, pp. 269–270.

1939. *Stephanitis caucasicus* sp. n. Informatsionnyi biulleten' po voprosam karatina rastenii. Sluzhba vneshnego i vnutrennego karatina rastenii. Vsesoiuznaia gosudarstvennaia USSR, No. 4, p. 10. [Publication not seen; can not be located in the U.S.]

1951. Nastoyashchie Poluzhestkokrylyia Evropeïskoï chati S.S.S.R. Zoologische Institut Akademiia Nauk USSR. Faune del 'USSR, vol. 42, 423 pp., 416 figs. Tingitidae pp. 240–255, figs. 327–331.

1952. New and little known Hemiptera Heteroptera of Tadzhikistan. Trudy Zoologischeskii Institut Akademiia Nauk SSSR, vol. 10, pp. 140–198, 47 figs.

1959. Nastoyashchie Poluzhestkokrylyia (Hemiptera Heteroptera) Zapovedinka Tigrovaya Balka. Akademiya Nauk Tadzhikskoi SSR Institut Zoologii i Parazitologii, vol. 115, No. 1, pp. 97–110.

KIRKALDY, GEORGE W.

1900. Bibliographical and nomenclatorial notes on the Rhynchota. No. 1. Entomologist, vol. 33, No. 447, pp. 238–243.

1902. Memoirs on Oriental Rhynchota. Journ. Bombay Nat. Hist. Soc., vol. 14, pp. 46–58; 294–309, 3 pls.

1904. Bibliographical and nomenclatorial notes on the Hemiptera. No. 3. Entomologist, vol. 37, No. 498, pp. 279–283.

1905. Quelques tingides nouveaux ou peu connus [Hém.]. Bull. Soc. Ent. France, vol. 15, pp. 216–217.

1907. Biological notes on the Hemiptera of the Hawaiian Isles. No. 1. Proc. Hawaiian Ent. Soc., vol. 1, pp. 135–161, 4 figs.

1908a. Memoir on a few heteropterous Hemiptera from eastern Australia. Proc. Linnean Soc. New South Wales, vol. 32, No. 4, pp. 768–788, 1 pl., 1907.

1908b. A catalogue of the Hemiptera of Fiji. Proc. Linnean Soc. New South Wales, vol. 33, No. 2, pp. 345–391, pl. 1.

1908c. Notes on some Sinhalese Hemiptera. Ann. Soc. Ent. Belgique, vol. 52, pp. 9–16.

1908d. A list of the described Hemiptera (excluding Aleyrodidae and Coccidae) of the Hawaiian Islands. Proc. Hawaiian Ent. Soc., vol. 1, pp. 186–208, 1 pl.

1908e. On the interesting nature of heteropterous metamorphoses. Entomologist, vol. 41, pp. 58–59.

1910. [Confirmation of date of Guérin-Méneville's Iconographie.] Ent. News, vol. 21, No. 1, p. 47.

KNOWLTON, GEORGE F.

1931. Notes on Utah Heteroptera and Homoptera. Ent. News, vol. 42, pp. 40–43; 68–72.

1933. Notes on Utah Heteroptera. Ent. News, vol. 44, pp. 261–264.

KOLENATI, FRIDERICO A.

1856. Meletemata Entomologica, vol. 6. Bull. Soc. Imp. Nat. Moscou, vol. 29, No. 2, pp. 419–502, 1 pl.

KORMILEV, NICOLAS A.

1955a. Notas sobre "Tingidae" Neotropicales (Hemiptera). Revista Brasileira Biol., vol. 15, No. 1, pp. 63–68, 1 fig.

1955b. A new myrmecophil family of Hemiptera from the delta of Rio Paraná, Argentina. Revista Ecuatoriana Ent. Paras., vol. 2, Nos. 3–4, pp. 465–477. 1 pl.

KOTINSKY, JACOB

1921. Insects injurious to deciduous shade trees, and their control. U.S. Dept. Agric., Farmers' Bull. 1169, 100 pp., 64 figs.

KRAUSS, NOEL L. H.

1953. Notes on insects associated with *Lantana* in Cuba. Proc. Hawaiian Ent. Soc., vol. 15, No. 1, pp. 123–125.

Kulkarny, H. L.: see PATEL and KULKARNY

LAMARCK, JEAN BAPTISTE DE MONET

1816. Histoire naturelle des animaux sans vertèbres. Paris. Vol. 3, 586 pp.

LAMBERTIE, MAURICE

1906. Notules entomologiques et description d'une nouvelle espèce. Act. Soc. Linnéenne Bordeaux, ser. 7, pp. 23–29.

1911. Remarque sur quelques hémiptères. Proc. Soc. Linnéenne Bordeaux, vol. 65, pp. 93–95.

LAPORTE, FRANÇOIS LOUIS NOMPAR DE CAUMONT [COMTE DE CASTELNAU]

1833. Essai d'une classification systématique de l'ordre des hémiptères (hémiptères hétéroptères, Latr.). Mag. Zool., vol. 2, pp. 1–88, 4 pls. [See Harris 1942 for discussion of date of this publication.]

LATRIELLE, PIERRE A.

1804. Histoire naturelle, générale et particulière, des crustacés et des insectes. Paris. Vol. 12, 424 pp. *Tingis* pp. 250–255.

1807. Genera crustaceorum et insectorum secundum ordinem naturalem in familias disposita, iconibus exemplisque plurimis explicata. Paris. Vol. 3, 289 pp. *Tingis* pp. 139–140.

1810. Considérations générales sur l'ordre naturel des animaux composant les classes des crustacés, des arachnides, et des insectes. Paris. 444 pp. Cimicides pp. 255–259.

1829. Les crustacés, les arachnides et les insectes, distribués en familles naturelles, vol. 2. *In* Cuvier, Le Règne Animal, ed. 2, vols. 4–5, 556 pp., 5 pls. Hemiptera pp. 189–233.

LE CONTE, JOHN
1859. A description of the insects of North America by Thomas Say. Vol. 1, 412 pp., 54 pls.; vol. 2, 814 pp.

Lefroy: see MAXWELL-LEFROY

LEONARD, MORTIMER D., and MILLS, ALFRED S.
1931. Observations on the bean lace bug in Porto Rico. Journ. Dept. Agric. Puerto Rico, vol. 15, No. 3, pp. 309–323, 1 fig., 2 pls.

LE PELETIER DE SAINT FARGEAU, A. L. M., and SERVILLE, AUDINET
1828. [Genus *Tingis*] *in* Encyclopedie Methodique, vol. 10, pp. 652–653.

LESTON, DENNIS [see also SOUTHWOOD and LESTON]
1953. The eggs of Tingitidae (Hem.) especially *Acalypta parvula* (Fallén). Entomologists' Monthly Mag, vol. 89, pp. 132–134, 1 fig.

1954. The eggs of *Anthocoris gallarum-ulmi* (Deg.) (Hem. Anthocoridae) and *Monanthia humuli* (F.) (Hem. Tingidae) with notes on the eggs of Cimicoidea and "Tingoidea." Entomologists' Monthly Mag., vol. 89, pp. 99–102, 5 figs.

LESTON, DENNIS; PENDERGRAST, J. G.; and SOUTHWOOD, T. R. E.
1954. Classification of the terrestrial Heteroptera (Geocorisae). Nature, vol. 174, pp. 91–92.

LETHIERRY, LUCIEN, and PUTON, AUGUSTE [see also PUTON and LETHIERRY]
1876. Faunule des hémiptères de Biskra. Ann. Soc. Ent. France, ser. 5, vol. 6, pp. 13–56, 1 pl.

LETHIERRY, LUCIEN, and SEVERIN, GUILAUME
1896. Catalogue général des hémiptères. Berlin. Vol. 3, 275 pp. Tingidae pp. 1–26.

Lima: see de COSTA LIMA

LINDBERG, HÅKAN
1919. Ålands Hemiptera Heteroptera. Meddelanden Soc. Fauna Flora Fennica, vol. 46, pp. 33–55, 1919–1921.

1927.   Zur Kenntnis der heteropteren-fauna von Kamtschatka sowie der Amur- und Ussuri-Gebiete Ergebnisse einer von Y. Wuorentaus im Jahre 1917 unternommenen Forschungsreise. Acta Soc. Fauna Flora Fennica, vol. 56, No. 9, pp. 1–26, 1 pl., 3 text figs.

1930.   Zwei neue heteropteren aus Palästina. Netulae Ent., vol. 10, No. 3, pp. 69–71, 2 figs.

1932a. Inventa entomologica itineris Hispanici et Marocani, quod a. 1926 fecerunt Harald et Håkan Lindberg. XIII. Hemiptera Heteroptera (excl. Capsidae et Hydrobiotica). Soc. Scient. Fennica, Comment. Biol., vol. 3, No. 19, 53 pp., 2 pls.

1932b. Die Hemipterenfauna Petsamos. Memoranda Soc. Fauna Flora Fennica, vol. 7, pp. 193–235, 7 figs., 1931–1932.

1934.   Schwedisch-Chinesische Wissenschaftliche Expedition nach den Nordwestlichen Provinzen Chinas. 47. Hemiptera. 2. Hemiptera Heteroptera. Arkiv för Zoologi Svenska Veten-skapsakademien, band 27A, No. 28, 43 pp., 4 pls.

1936a. Drei neue Tingitiden aus Herrn A. Thérys Sammlung. Bull. Soc. Sci. Nat. Maroc, vol. 16, No. 1, pp. 81–85, 3 figs.

1936b. Die Heteropteren der Kanarischen Inseln. Soc. Scient. Fennica, Comment. Biol., vol. 6, No. 7, pp. 1–43, 2 pls.

1948.   On the insect fauna of the expedition of 1939 by Harald, Håkan and P. H. Lindberg. II. Heteroptera und Homoptera Cicadina der Insel Zypern. Soc. Scient. Fennica, Comment. Biol., vol. 10, No. 7, pp. 1–175, 54 figs.

1958a. Hemiptera Insularum Caboverdensium. Soc. Scient. Fennica, Comment. Biol., vol. 19, No. 1, pp. 1–246, 114 figs.

1958b. Hemiptera Heteroptera from Newfoundland, collected by the Swedish-Finnish Expedition of 1949 and 1951. Acta Zool. Fennica, vol. 96, pp. 1–25.

1960a. Supplementum Hemipterorum Insularum Canariensium. Soc. Scient. Fennica, Comment. Biol., vol. 22, No. 6, pp. 1–20.

1960b. Hemiptera from the Azores and Madeira. Report No. 6 from the Lund University Expedition in 1958 to the Azores and Madeira. Bol. Mus. Municipal Funchal, No. 13, art. 33, pp. 85–94.

LINDINGER, L.
1927.   Kleine Mitteilungen. Ent. Rundschau, vol. 44, No. 9, p. 36.

LINDROTH, CARL H.
1957.   The faunal connections between Europe and North America. John Wiley and Sons, New York. 344 pp.

LINNAEUS, CAROL
1746.   Fauna Svecica sistens animalia Sveciae regni: quadrupedia, aves, amphibia, pices, insecta, vermes distributa per classes,

et ordines, genera et species, cum differentiis specierum, synonymis autorum, nominibus incolarum, locis habitationum, descriptionibus insectorum. Stockholm. 411 pp., 2 pls. Hemiptera pp. 199–220.

1758. Systema naturae per regna tria naturae secundum classes, ordines, genera, species, cum characteribus, differentiis, synonymis, locis. Ed. 10, tome 1, 823 pp. Hemiptera pp. 434–457.

1761. Fauna Svecica sistens animalia Sveciae regni: mammalia, aves, amphibia, pices, insecta, vermes, distributa per classes et ordines, genera et species, cum differentiis specierum, synonymis auctorum, nominibus incolorum, locis natalium, descriptionibus insectorum. 578 pp. Hemiptera pp. 239–267.

1767. Systema naturae per regna tria naturae secundum classes, ordines, genera, species cum characteribus, differentiis, synonymis, locis. Ed. 12, tome 1, part 2, pp. 533–1327. Hemiptera pp. 687–743.

LINTNER, JOSEPH A.
1888. Fourth report on the injurious and other insects of the State of New York. New York State Mus. Nat. Hist. No. 41. Rep. State Entomologist of New York, 1887, 237 pp., 68 figs., Tingidae pp. 107–109.

Lott, Ralph B.: see WEISS and LOTT

LOUNSBURY, C. P.
1923. Report No. V.—Entomology. Journ. Dept. Agric., Union of South Africa, vol. 7, No. 6, pp. 542–549.

LUTZ, JOHN C. [see also DRAKE and LUTZ]
1929. *Corythucha decens* Stål in Pennsylvania (Heteropt.: Tingididae). Ent. News, vol. 40, p. 233.

MAA, T. (MAA TSING-CHAO) [see also DRAKE and MAA TSING-CHAO]
1957. Nymphal stages of certain Oriental Tingidae (Hemiptera). Quart. Journ. Taiwan Mus., vol. 10, Nos. 3, 4, pp. 117–133.

MABILLE, PAUL
1872. Notice bibliographique sur les travaux du Dr. P. Rambur. Ann. Soc. Ent. France, ser. 5, vol. 2, pp. 307–312.

MAEHLER, K. L.
1955. [*Teleonemia scrupulosa*], *in* Minutes of the meeting, April 12, 1954, Hawaiian Entomological Society. Proc. Hawaiian Ent. Soc., vol. 15, No. 3, p. 377.

Maldonado Capriles, J.: see DRAKE and MALDONADO CAPRILES

MAMET, J. RAYMOND [see also DRAKE and MAMET]
1957. A revised and annotated list of the Hemiptera (Heteroptera and Homoptera, excluding Sternorhyncha) of Mauritius. Mauritius Inst. Bull., vol. 5, part 2, pp. 31–81.

MANCINI, CESARE

1935. Raccolte entomologiche nell'Isola de Capraia faite da C. Mancini e F. Capra (1927–1931). Mem. Soc. Ent. Italiana, vol. 14, pp. 4–16.

1939a. Hemiptera. *In* Missione Biologica nel paese dei Borana. Rome. Vol. 3, No. 2, pp. 195–224, 7 figs.

1939b. Emitteri di Harrar. Boll. Soc. Ent. Italiana, vol. 71, pp. 161–163, 2 figs.

1939c. Hemiptera. Ann. Mus. Civ. Stor. Nat. Giacomo Doria, vol. 58, pp. 292–314.

1949a. Hemiptera Nota II. Spedizione Zoologica del Marchese Saverio Patrizi nel basso Guiba e nell'Oltregiuba. VI–VII, 1934. Ann. Mus. Civ. Stor. Nat. Giacomo Doria, vol. 63, pp. 218–234.

1949b. Emitteri eterotteri del Veronese. Mem. Mus. Civ. Stor. Nat. Verona, vol. 2, pp. 25–48.

1949c. Raccolte faunistiche compiute nel gargano da A. Ghigi e F. P. Pomini. Acta Pontificia Acad. Scient., vol. 13, No. 12, pp. 129–144.

1952. Emitteri dell'Isola del Giglio, 22. Materiali per una fauna dell'Arcipelago Toscano. Ann. Mus. Civ. Stor. Nat. Genova, vol. 66, pp. 1–32.

1953a. Missione Biologica Sagun-Omo diretta dal Prof. Edoardo Zavattari (1939) Hemiptera-Heteroptera. Ann. Mus. Civ. Stor. Nat. Genova, vol. 66, pp. 166–204.

1953b. Contributo alla conoscenza degli emitteri eterotteri dell'Albania. Ann. Naturhistorischen Mus. Wien, band 59 (1952–53), pp. 176–196.

1953c. Corologia emitterologica Italiana. Nota 1.—Emitteri eterotteri dell'Abruzzo. Boll. Assoc. Romana Ent., vol. 8, No. 2, pp. 22–27.

1953d. Corologia emitterologica Italiana. Nota II—Emitteri dell'Umbria. Mem. Soc. Ent. Italiana, vol. 32, pp. 5–33.

1954a. Contributo alla conoscenza degli emitteri dell'Eritrea. Atti Mus. Civ. Stor. Nat. Trieste, vol. 19, No. 3, pp. 137–159.

1954b. Corologia emitterologica Italiana. Nota III—Emitteri del Biellese. Mem. Soc. Ent. Italiana, vol. 33, pp. 5–18.

1956a. Emitteri eterotteri del gargano e delle tremiti con osservazioni sulle specie a distribuzione transadriatica. Istituto di Studi Adriatici Venezia. Mem. Biog. Adriatica, vol. 3, pp. 162–195, maps.

1956b. Emitteri dell'Abissinia. Fragmenta Ent., vol. 2, No. 8, pp. 65–96.

1959. Corologia emitterologica Italiana. Nota VI—Emitteri eterotteri, della Lombardia. Atti Soc. Italiana Sci. Nat. Mus. Civ. Stor. Nat. Milano, vol. 98, fasc. 2–3, pp. 223–283.
1960a. Miscellanea emitterologica. Ann. Mus. Civ. Stor. Nat. Giacomo Doria, vol. 71, pp. 102–110, 2 figs.
1960b. Corologia emitterologica Italiana. Nota V—Supplemento emitteri del Biellese e del 'Umbria. Ann. Mus. Civ. Stor. Nat. Giacomo Doria, vol. 71, pp. 111–118.

MARCHAL, PAUL
1917. Le tigre du rhododendron (Stephanitis rhododendri Horv.). Bull. Soc. Pathòlogie Végétale France, vol. 4, No. 2, pp. 93–95.

MASON, JAMES EARDLEY
1898a. Some Hemiptera-Heteroptera of the Isle of Man. The Naturalist, pp. 139–140.
1898b. Additions to the list of Hemiptera-Heteroptera of Lincolnshire. The Naturalist, pp. 209–210.

MASSEE, A. M.
1954. The Hemiptera-Heteroptera of Kent. Trans. Soc. British Ent., vol. 11, part 12, pp. 245–280.

MATHEN, K.
1960. Observations on Stephanitis typicus Distant a pest of coconut palm. 1. Description and life history. The Indian Coconut Journ., vol. 14, No. 1, pp. 8–27, 6 figs., 2 pls., 6 tables.

MATHUR, R. N.
1955. Immature stages of Tingis beesoni Drake (Heteroptera: Tingitidae). Entomologist, vol. 88, No. 1110, pp. 248–251, 6 figs.

MATSUMURA, SHÔNEN
1905. Thousand insects of Japan, vol. 2, pp. 1–213, 17 pls.
1908. Konchu Bunrui-gaku, vol. 1, pp. 147–148.
1910.* Schädlichen und nützlichen Insekten vom Zuckerrohr Formosas. The Keiseicha, Tokyo, Japan.
1911. Beschreibungen von am Zuckerrohr Formosas schädlichen oder nützlichen Insekten. Mem. Soc. Ent. Belgique, vol. 18, pp. 129–150.
1913.* Thousand insects of Japan, additamenta, I. p. 151.
1917.* Oyô Konchû-gaku, vol. 1, p. 440.
1930.* Illustrated thousands insects of Japan, vol. 1, rev. ed., pp. 158–164.
1931. 6000 illustrated insects of the Japanese Empire. 1467 pp.

MAXWELL-LEFROY, H.
1909. Indian insect life. Calcutta. 786 pp., 536 figs. Tingidae pp. 692–693.

* Saw only microfilm excerpts of these Japanese works.

MAYNÉ, R., and GHESQUIÈRE, J.
1934. Hémiptères nuisibles aux végétaux du Congo belge. Ann. Gembloux, Brussels, vol. 40, No. 1, pp. 3–41.

MAYR, GUSTAV L.
1858. Beiträge zur geographischen Verbreitung der Tingideen. Verh. Zool-Bot. Ges. Wien, vol. 8, pp. 567–572.
1865. Diagnosen neuer hemipteren. Verh. Zool.-Bot. Ges. Wien, vol. 15, pp. 429–446.
1866. Hemiptera. *In* Reise der Oesterreichischen Fregatta *Novara* um die Erde, in . . . 1857–59 . . . Zoologischer Theil, band 2, Abth. 5, 204 pp., 5 pls. Tingididae pp. 163–164.

McATEE, W. L.
1917a. Key to the Nearctic species of *Leptoypha* and *Leptostyla* (Heteroptera Tingidae). Bull. Brooklyn Ent. Soc., vol. 12, No. 3, pp. 55–64.
1917b. A few notes chiefly on the names of Nearctic Tingidae. Bull. Brooklyn Ent. Soc., vol. 12, No. 4, pp. 78–79.
1919. Corrections and additions to an article on *Leptoypha* and *Leptostyla* (Heteroptera; Tingidae). Bull. Brooklyn Ent. Soc., vol. 14, pp. 142–144.
1923. Tingitoidea of the vicinity of Washington, D.C. (Heteroptera). Proc. Ent. Soc. Washington, vol. 25, Nos. 7–8, pp. 143–151.

MEIXNER, ADOLF
1915. Die beiden Auflagen von Dr. G. W. F. Panzer's Faunae Insectorum Germanicae Initia. Ent. Mitt., vol. 4, pp. 268–278.

Mendonça: see DE ARAÚJO MENDONÇA, FLORIANO

Méneville: see GUÉRIN-MÉNEVILLE

MENON, M. G. R.; BERI, Y. P.; and SINGH, SARAN
1959. A new record of a tingid from Delhi. Indian Journ. Ent., vol. 21, part 4, pp. 286–287.

MENON, M. G. RAMDAS, and HAKK, S. AFSARUL
1959a. A new subfamily of Tingidae (Heteroptera: Tingoidea) from India. Proc. 46th Indian Science Congress, part III: abstract, p. 392.
1959b. A revision of the genus *Urentius* Distant, with descriptions of five new species (Heteroptera: Tingidae). Proc. 46th Indian Science Congress, part III: asbtract, p. 393.

Menon, K. P. V.: see NAGARAJ and MENON; also SHANTA, MENON, and PILLAI

Menor: see GOMEZ-MENOR

Mesnil, L.: see BALACHOWSKY and MESNIL

Miller, N. C. E.: see CHINA and MILLER

Mills, Alfred S.: see LEONARD and MILLS

Mohanasundarum, M.: see DRAKE and MOHANASUNDARUM

MONOD, THEODORE, and CARAYON, JACQUES
1958. Observations sur les *Copium* (Hemipt. Tingidae) et leur action Cécidogène sur les fleurs de *Teucrium* (Labiées). Arch. Zool. Exp. Gén., vol. 95, Notes et Revue, No. 1, pp. 1–31, 34 figs.

MONTANDON, ARNOLD L.
1887. Description d'hémiptères-hétéroptères nouveaux et notes sur quelques Hemiptera. Rev. Ent., vol. 6, pp. 64–68.
1892. Hémiptères-hétéroptères nouveaux. Rev. Ent., vol. 11, pp. 265–273.
1895. Contributions à la faune entomologique de la Roumanie, nouvelles espèces d'hémiptères-hétéroptères. Bull. Sci. Phisiques, vol. 11, pp. 159–162.
1897. Espèces d'hémiptères-hétéroptères d'Algérie et de Tunisie. Rev. Ent., vol. 16, pp. 97–104.

MONTE, OSCAR
1937a. Tingitideos de Bello Horizonte. Rodriguesia, vol. 8, pp. 29–36, 15 figs.
1937b. Os insectos damninhos. XLI—Um percevejo das Solanáceas (*Corythaica planaris*, Uhler). Chacaras e Quintaes, vol. 28, No. 1, pp. 79–80, 1 fig.
1937c. Notas hemipterologicas. O Campo, May 1937, pp. 70–72.
1937d. As especies do genero *Nectocader* (Hemiptera-Tingitidae). Revista Chilena Hist. Nat., vol. 41, pp. 111–115, 1 fig.
1938a. An undescribed *Gargaphia* from Venezuela. Revista Chilena Hist. Nat., vol. 42, pp. 292–294, 1 fig.
1938b. Tingitideos Neotrópicos. Bol. Biológico, new ser., vol. 3, Nos. 3–4, pp. 127–132, 1 fig.
1938c. Novas tingitideos. O Campo, February 1938, p. 64, 3 figs.
1938d. Sobre tingitideos de la Argentina. Anal. Soc. Cient. Argentina, vol. 126, pp. 387–392, 1 fig.
1939a. *Sphaerocysta brasiliensis* Monte (Hemiptera-Tingitidae). Bol. Biol., new ser., vol. 4, No. 3, pp. 516–518, 1 fig.
1939b. Lista preliminar dos tingitideos de Minas Gerais. Revista Soc. Brasileira de Agronomia, vol. 2, No. 1, pp. 63–87.
1940a. Descrição de um novo gênero e uma nova espécie de tingitideo (Hem.). Papéis Avulsos Dept. Zool., São Paulo, Brazil, vol. 1, pp. 13–16, 1 fig.
1940b. Notas sôbra alguns tingideos do Brazil. Arqu. Zool. Est. São Paulo, vol. 1, No. 2, pp. 375–382.
1940c. Some Tingitidae from Brazil (Hemiptera). Revista Chilena de Hist. Nat., vol. 43, pp. 190–195, 2 figs.
1940d. Contribucion al conocimiento de tingitidos de Venezuela. Revista Chilena de Hist. Nat., vol. 43, pp. 100–106, 1 fig., 1939.

1940e. Tingitideos novos ou pouco conhecidos da fauna Americana. Arqu. Inst. Biol., São Paulo, vol. 11, No. 34, pp. 283–300, 8 figs.

1940f. Notas sôbre *Gargaphia subpilosa* Berg (Hemiptera-Tingitidae). Arqu. Inst. Biol., São Paulo, vol. 11, No. 35, pp. 301–308, 1 fig.

1941a. Quatro novos tingitideos da Americo do Sul. Revista Brasil Biol., vol. 1, No. 4, pp. 373–378, 3 figs.

1941b. Sôbre a posição sistomática de *Leptodictya dohrni* Stål (Hemiptera Tingitidae). Arqu. Mus. Paranaense, vol. 1, No. 4, pp. 101–106, 1 fig.

1941c. Nótulas sôbre *Leptobyrsa steini* (Stål). Papéis Avulsos Dept. Zool., São Paulo, vol. 1, No. 21, pp. 203–208, 2 figs.

1941d. Sôbre tingitideos (Hemiptera) de Costa Rica com descrições de especies novas. Arqu. Inst. Biol., São Paulo, vol. 12, No. 8, pp. 93–100, 4 figs.

1941e. Catálogo dos tingitideos do Brazil. Arqu. Zool., São Paulo, vol. 2, No. 3, pp. 65–174, 1940.

1942a. Apontamentos sôbre tingitideos (Hemiptera) Americanos, especialmente do Brasil. Arqu. Inst. Biol., São Paulo, vol. 13, No. 9, pp. 91–98, 2 figs.

1942b. Tres novas espécies do gênero *Teleonemia* Costa (Hemiptera, Tingitidae). Revista Brasil Biol., vol. 2, No. 2, pp. 135–138, 2 figs.

1942c. Sinópse das espécies de *Megalocysta* (Hemiptera, Tingitidae). Revista Brasil Biol., vol. 2, No. 3, pp. 301–304, 3 figs.

1942d. Crítica sobre alguns gêneros e espécies de Tingitideos. Papéis Avulsos Dept. Zool., São Paulo, vol. 2, No. 6, pp. 103–115, 3 figs.

1943a. Sôbre tingitideos do Perú. Revista Brasil Biol., vol. 3, No. 1, pp. 105–108.

1943b. Descrições de duas novas espécies de *Teleonemia* da Argentina (Hemiptera-Tingitidae). Anal. Soc. Cient. Argentina, vol. 135, pp. 202–205, 1 fig.

1943c. Notas sobre um percevejo, praga de várias solanáceas cultivadas. O Biologico, São Paulo, vol. 9, No. 5, pp. 113–120, 1 fig.

1943d. Tingitideos Americanos (Hemiptera). Arqu. Inst. Biol., São Paulo, vol. 14, No. 19, pp. 263–272, 3 figs.

1944a. Concerning the genus *Tigava* Stål (Hemiptera, Tingitidae). Revista Brasil Biol., vol. 4, No. 2, pp. 157–159, 1 fig.

1944b. Concerning neotropical Tingitidae (Hemiptera). Revista Brasil Biol., vol. 4, No. 4, pp. 453–467, 8 figs.

1945a. Trés novas tingitideos. Revista Ent., vol. 16, Nos. 1–2, pp. 249–252, 1 fig.

1945b. Cultura do Tomateiro especialmenta as pragas e doenças e seu tratamento. Biblioteca Agrícola Popular Brasileira, pp. 1–88.

1946a. Revisão do gênero *Leptocysta* Stål (Hemiptera, Tingidae). Revista Brasil Biol., vol. 6, No. 3, pp. 325–331, 6 figs.

1946b. Novas espécies de tingitideos (Hemiptera) do Brasil. Revista Ent., vol. 17, Nos. 1–2, pp. 282–286.

1946c. Duas novas especies de tingitideos da Bolivia. Bol. Ent. Venezolana, vol. 5, No. 2, pp. 27–28.

1946d. Sôbre o gênero *Phatnoma* com a descrição de uma nova espécie e a lista de suas espécies. (Hem. Tingidae). Revista Brasil Biol., vol. 6, No. 2, pp. 247–254, 7 figs.

1947a. Notas sinonímicas. Papéis Avulsos Dept. Zool., São Paulo, vol. 8, No. 9, pp. 231–237, 5 figs.

1947b. Sobre tingideos Americanos com descrições de espécies novas (Hem.). Revista Ent., vol. 18, No. 3, pp. 429–432.

MONTROUZIER, XAVIER

1861. Essai sur la faune entomologique de la Nouvelle-Calédonie (Balde) et des îles des Pins, Art, Lifu, etc. Ann. Soc. Ent. France, series 4, vol. 1, pp. 59–74.

1864. [New Species]. *In* Perroud and Montrouzier. Essai sur la faune entomologique de Kanala (Nouvelle-Calédonie) et description de quelques espèces nouvelles ou peu connue. Ann. Soc. Linnéenne Lyon, vol. 11, pp. 46–256.

MORÓDER SALA, EMILIO

1920. Introducción al catálogo de los hemípteros de la región Valenciana. Anal. Inst. Gen. Téc. Valencia, vol. 7, No. 6, pp. 5–18, 3 pls.

MORRILL, AUSTIN W.

1903. Notes on the immature stages of some tingitids of the genus *Corythuca*. Psyche, vol. 10, No. 324, pp. 127–134, 1 pl.

MOTSCHULSKY, VICTOR

1863. Essai d'un catalogue des insectes de l'île Ceylan. Bull. Soc. Imp. Nat. Moscou, vol. 36, part 2, no. 3, pp. 1–153.

MOZNETTE, G. F.

1922. The avocado, its insect enemies and how to combat them. U.S. Dept. Agric., Farmers' Bull. 1261, 31 pp., 21 figs.

MÜLLER, PHILIPP LUDWIG

1774. Des Ritters Carl von Linné vollständiges Natursystem. Ed. 12, band 1, part 5, pp. 1–758, 22 pls.

MULSANT, ETIENNE, and REY, CLAUDIUS

1852a. Description de quelques hémiptères hétéroptères nouveaux ou peu connus. Ann. Soc. Linnéenne Lyon (1850–1852), pp. 76–140.

1852b. Description de quelques hémiptères hétéroptères nouveau ou peu connus. *In* Mulsant, Opuscules Entomologiques. Paris. Vol. 1, pp. 95–160. Tingides pp. 153–155. [Reprint of 1852a.]

MURATA, JUTARÔ
1928. Insect world, vol. 32, No. 7, p. 227; No. 8, p. 264.

MUŽIK, FRANTIŠEK
1907. České sit'natky Tingitidae. Časopis Česke Společnosti Ent. Acta Soc. Ent. Bohemiae, vol. 4, No. 1, pp. 46–64, 5 figs.

MYERS, JOHN G.
1926. Heteroptera in ocean drift. Psyche, vol. 33, Nos. 4–5, pp. 110–115.

NAGARAJ, A. N., and MENON, K. P. V.
1956. Note on the etiology of the wilt (root) disease of coconut palms in Travancore-Cochin. The Indian Coconut Journ., vol. 9, No. 3, pp. 161–165.

NOVÁK, OTTOMAR
1877a. Fauna der Cyprisschiefer des Egerer Tertiärbeckens. Sitz. Ber. Kaiserlichen Akad. Wiss., vol. 76, pp. 71–96, 3 pls.
1877b. Reprint of the above as a pamphlet.

NOVAK, PETAR, and WAGNER, EDUARD
1951. Prilog poznavanju faune Hemiptera Dalmacije (Hemiptera-Heteroptera). Godisnjak Bioloskog Instituta u Sarajevu, vol. 4, No. 1, pp. 59–80.

OBENBERGER, JAN
1958. Hemiptera. *In* Entomologie IV. Českoslov. Akad. Věd., Prague, pp. 8–215.

OLSEN, C. E.
1923. Distributional notes on Hemiptera (No. 1). Bull. Brooklyn Ent. Soc., vol. 18, No. 5, pp. 163–164.

ORIAN, ALFRED J. E.
1956. Hemiptera (Heteroptera and Homoptera excluding *Sternorhyncha*) of Mauritius. Ann. Mag. Nat. Hist., ser. 12, vol. 9, pp. 641–654.

OSBORN, HERBERT, and DRAKE, CARL J.
1915a. Additions and notes on the Hemiptera-Heteroptera of Ohio. Ohio Nat., vol. 15, No. 7, pp. 501–508.
1915b. Records of Guatemalan Hemiptera-Heteroptera with descriptions of new species. Ohio Nat., vol. 15, No. 8, pp. 529–541.
1916a. The Tingitoidea or " lace bugs" of Ohio. Ohio Biol. Surv., vol. 2, No. 4, Bull. 8, pp. 217–251, 9 figs., 4 pls.
1916b. Some new species of Nearctic Tingidae. Ohio Journ. Sci., vol. 17, No. 1, pp. 9–15, 3 figs.

1917a. Notes on Tingidae. Psyche, vol. 24, No. 5, pp. 155–161, 5 figs., 1 pl.

1917b. Notes on American Tingidae with descriptions of new species. Ohio Journ. Sci., vol. 17, No. 8, pp. 295–307, 2 figs.

OSHANIN, BASIL

1908. Verzeichnis der Palaearktischen Hemipteren, vol. 1, Heteroptera, 2. Tingididae-Acanthiidae, pp. 395–586. Tingididae pp. 395–462.

1912. Katalog der Paläarktischen Hemipteren (Heteroptera, Homoptera-Auchenorhyncha und Psylloideae). Berlin. 187 pp. Tingitidae pp. 42–46.

Otero, A. R.: see BRUNER, SCARAMUZZA, and OTERO

PANZER, GEORG WOLFGANG FRANZ

1793–1809. Faunae insectorum Germanicae initia oder Deutschlands Insecten. Nurnburg. [Hefts 1–12, 1793; 13–24, 1794; 25–36, 1796; 37–48, 1797; 49–60, 1798; 61–72, 1799; 73–84, 1801; 85–96, 1805; 97–108, 1809].
[1806. Revision der Insektenfaune Deutschlands nach dem system bearbeitet. Hefts 1–100.]
[See Meixner 1915 re second printing and revisions: Hefts 1–12, 1796; 13–24, 1799; 25–36, 1808; 37, 1810.]

PARSHLEY, HOWARD MADISON

1914. List of the Hemiptera-Heteroptera of Maine. Psyche, vol. 21, No. 5, pp. 139–149.

1916a. On some Tingidae from New England. Psyche, vol. 23, No. 6, pp. 163–168.

1916b. New and noteworthy Hemiptera from New England. Ent. News, vol. 27, pp. 103–106, 1 fig.

1917a. Notes on North American Tingidae (Hemiptera). Psyche, vol. 24, No. 1, pp. 13–24, 2 figs.

1917b. Fauna of New England. 14. List of the Hemiptera-Heteroptera. Occ. Pap. Boston Soc. Nat. Hist., vol. 7, pp. 1–125.

1917c. Insects in ocean drift. Canadian Ent., vol. 49, No. 2, pp. 45–48.

1919a. On some Hemiptera from western Canada. Occ. Pap. Mus. Zool., Univ. Michigan, vol. 71, pp. 1–35.

1919b. New England Hemiptera-Heteroptera new records. Canadian Ent., vol. 51, pp. 70–72.

1919c. Note on the sexes of the tingid *Melanorhopala clavata* Stål (Hemiptera). Bull. Brooklyn Ent. Soc., vol. 14, No. 3, pp. 102–103.

1920a. Hemipterological notices I. (Tingidae). Ent. News, vol. 31, pp. 271–273.

1920b. Hemiptera collected in western New England, chiefly from mountains. Psyche, vol. 27, No. 6, pp. 139–143.

1920c. Hemiptera from Peaks Island, Maine, collected by Mr. G. A. Moore. Canadian Ent., vol. 52, pp. 80–87.

1921. A report on some Hemiptera from British Columbia. Proc. Ent. Soc. British Columbia, vol. 18, pp. 13–24.

1922a. New England Hemiptera-Heteroptera new records II. Canadian Ent., vol. 53, pp. 233–239.

1922b. Report on a collection of Hemiptera-Heteroptera from South Dakota. South Dakota State Coll., Tech. Bull. 2, pp. 1–22.

1923a. Records of Nova Scotian Hemiptera-Heteroptera. Proc. Acadian Ent. Soc. for 1922, vol. 8, pp. 102–108.

1923b. Family Tingidae. *In* Britton, Guide to the insects of Connecticut. State Geol. Nat. Hist. Surv., Connecticut, Bull. 34, pp. 695–707, figs. 164–165, 1 pl.

PATEL, R. C., and KULKARNY, H. L.

1955. Bionomics of *Urentius echinus* Dist. (Hemiptera-Heteroptera: Tingidae) an important pest of brinjal (*Solanum melongena* L.) in North Gujarat. Journ. Bombay Nat. Hist. Soc., vol. 53, No. 1, pp. 86–96, 2 pls.

PEMBERTON, C.

1911. The California Christmas-berry tingis. Journ. Econ. Ent., vol. 4, pp. 339–346, 3 pls.

Pendergrast, J. G.: see LESTON, PENDERGRAST, and SOUTHWOOD

PENNINGTON, MILES STUART

1919. Descripción de un nuevo hemiptero. Physis (Rev. Soc. Argentina Cienc. Nat.), vol. 4, pp. 526–527, 2 figs.

1921. Lista de los hemipteros heteropteros de la Republica Argentina. Part 2. Buenos Aires, pp. 17–47.

PERKINS, R. C. L., and SWEZEY, O. H.

1924. The introduction into Hawaii of insects that attack lantana. Bull. Exp. Station Hawaiian Sugar Planters' Assoc., Ent. Ser., Bull. 16, appendix A, pp. 50–53.

PHILIPPI, RUDOLPH A.

1864. *Coleopterodes* Philippi, ein neues Geschlecht der Wanzen. Ent. Zeitung Stettin, vol. 25, pp. 306–308.

PICADO, C.

1913. Les Broméliacees Épiphytes considérées comme milieu biologique. Bull. Sci. France et Belgique, ser. 7, fasc. 3, pp. 215–360, 24 pls.

Pillai K. P.: see SHANTA, MENON, and PILLAI

Plaumann, Fritz: see DRAKE and PLAUMANN

POISSON, RAYMOND
1938. Aperçu sur la faune des insectes hémiptères de la région de Wimereux (Pas-de-Calais). Travaux de la Station Zoologique de Wimereux, vol. 13, pp. 587–595.
1951. Ordre des hétéroptères. *In* Grassé, Traité de Zoologie Anatomie, Systématique, Biologie, vol. 10, fasc. 2, pp. 1657–1803, figs. 1463–1591.

Poor, Margaret E.: see DRAKE and POOR

PORTOR, CAROLOS E.
1933. El genero *Nectocader* Drake, en Chile. Revista Chilena Hist. Nat., vol. 37, pp. 235–236.

PRIESNER, H.
1951. Two new Hemiptera-Heteroptera from Egypt. Bull. Soc. Fouad Ier d'Entomologie, vol. 35, pp. 137–139, 1 fig.

PRIESNER, H., and ALFIERI, A.
1953. A review of the Hemiptera Heteroptera known to us from Egypt. Bull. Soc. Fouad Ier d'Entomologie, vol. 37, 199 pp. Tingidae pp. 62–66.

PROCTOR, WILLIAM
1946. The insect fauna. *In* Biological Survey of the Mount Desert Region, Part 7. Wistar Inst. Anat. Biol., Philadelphia, pp. 1–566. Tingitidae pp. 74–75.

PROVANCHER, LEON
1886. Petite faune entomologique du Canada. Vol. 3, pp. 1–340, 5 pls. Tingitides pp. 156–161.

PUTON, AUGUSTE [see also LETHIERRY and PUTON; REIBER and PUTON]
1873. Notes pour servir à l'étude des hémiptères. Ann. Soc. Ent. France, ser. 5, vol. 3, pp. 11–26.
1874a. Notes pour servir à l'étude des hémiptères, part 2. Ann. Soc. Ent. France, ser. 5, vol. 4, pp. 213–230.
1874b. Hémiptères nouveaux. Petites Nouv. Ent. 6 année, No. 109, pp. 435–436.
1874c. Hémiptères nouveaux. Petites Nouv. Ent. 6 année, No. 110, pp. 439–440.
1876. Notes pour servir à l'étude des hémiptères. Ann. Soc. Ent. France, ser. 5, vol. 6, pp. 275–290.
1877. M. A. Puton adresse la description d'une nouvelle espèce d'hémiptère. *In* Séance du 11 Avril 1877. Ann. Soc. Ent. France, ser. 5, vol. 7, pp. lxv–lxxvi.
1878. M. le docteur Aug. Puton communique des descriptions de nouvelles espèces d'hémiptères de la famille des tingidides. *In* Séance du 24 Avril 1878. Ann. Soc. Ent. France, ser. 5, vol. 8, pt. 2, pp. lxii–lxxii.

1879a. M. Aug. Puton envoie la description d'une espèce nouvelle d'hémiptère. *In* Séance du 9 Avril 1879. Ann. Soc. Ent. France, ser. 5, vol. 9, pp. li–lxi.

1879b. Diagnoses d'hémiptères nouveaux. Petites Nouv. Ent., vol. 2, année 11, No. 213, p. 297.

1879c. Synopsis des hémiptères-hétéroptères de France, part 2. Tingidides, phymatides, aradides, hebrides, hydrometrides. Paris, pp. 83–159.

1880. Synopsis des hémiptères-hétéroptères de France, part 3. Remiremont, pp. 161–245.

1881. Enumération des hémiptères recoltés en Syrie par M. Abeille de Perrin avec la description des espèces nouvelles. Mitth. Schweizer. Ent. Ges., vol. 6, No. 3, pp. 119–129.

1884. Hémiptères nouveaux. Rev. Ent., vol. 3, pp. 312–313.

1886a. Énumération des hémiptères recueillis en Tunisie en 1883 et 1884 par MM. Valery Mayet et Maurice Sédillot. Exploration Scientifique de la Tunisie. 24 pp.

1886b. Catalogue des hémiptères (hétéroptères, cicadines et psyllides) de la faune Paléarctique. Ed. 3. Caen. 100 pp. Tingidides pp. 31–34.

1887. Hémiptères nouveaux ou peu connus de la faune Paléarctique. Rev. Ent., vol. 6, pp. 96–105.

1888. Hémiptères nouveaux ou peu connus et notes diverses. Rev. Ent., vol. 7, pp. 103–110.

1892. Descriptions de trois hémiptères nouveaux. Rev. Ent., vol. 11, pp. 71–72.

1894. Hémiptères nouveaux et notes diverses. Rev. Ent., vol. 13, pp. 114–116.

1895. Hémiptères nouveaux. Rev. Ent., vol. 14, No. 3, pp. 83–91.

1899. Catalogue des hémiptères (hétéroptères, cicadines et psyllides) de la faune Paléarctique. Ed. 4. Caen. 121 pp.

PUTON, AUGUSTE, and LETHIERRY, LUCIEN
1887. Hémiptères nouveaux de l'Algérie. Rev. Ent., vol. 6, pp. 298–311.

PUTSHKOV, V. G.
1960. K Ekologii Nekotorykh Maloizuchennykh vidov Nastoyashchikh Poluzhestkokrylykh. Rev. Ent. de l'URSS, vol. 39, No. 2, pp. 300–312.

RAMADE, F.
1960. Contribution a l'étude des Rhynchotes hétéroptères Terrestres de Provence. Ann. Soc. Ent. France, vol. 129, pp. 201–222.

RAMBUR, PIERRE
1839. Faune entomologique de l'Andalousie, vol. 2, lief 4, pp. 97–176. [See Mabille 1872 and British Museum catalogue, vol. 4, for dates of this publication.]

RAMOS, J. A.
1946. The insects of Mona Island (West Indies). Journ. Agric. Univ. Puerto Rico, vol. 30, No. 1, pp. 1–74, 2 pls.

RÉAUMUR, RENÉ A.
1737. Memoires pour servir a l'histoire des insectes. Paris. 532 pp.

RECLAIRE, A.
1940. Vervolg de Naamlijst der in Nederland en het omliggend gebied waargenomen wantsen (Hemiptera-Heteroptera). Tijdschrift voor Ent., vol. 83, pp. 103–119.

REED, EDWYN C.
1900. Sinopsis de los hemipteros de Chile. Primera parte: Heteropteros. Entomolojia Chilena. Revista Chilena Hist. Nat., vol. 4, No. 11, pp. 173–181.

REIBER, FERD, and PUTON, AUGUSTE
1876. Catalogue des hémiptères-hétéroptères de l'Alsace et de la Lorraine. Bull. Soc. Hist. Nat. Colmar, pp. 51–88.

REICHENSPERGER, AUGUST
1920. Rheinlands Hemiptera Heteroptera I. Verh. Naturh. Ver. Preuss. Rheinlande und Westfalens, vol. 77, pp. 35–77.

REMOLD, HEINZ
1959. Zum Auftreten von Serenthia minuta Horv. bei München (Hem. Het.). Nachrichtenblatt der Bayerischen Entomologen, vol. 8, No. 1, pp. 1–2, 1 fig.

REUTER, ODO M.
1874. Remarques synonymiques sur quelques hétéroptères. Ann. Soc. Ent. France, ser. 5, vol. 4, pp. 559–566.
1875. Remarques sur le catalogue des hémiptères d'Europe et du bassin de la Méditerranée par le Dr. A. Puton. Petites Nouv. Ent., 7 année, No. 137, p. 547.
1880a. Diagnoses hemiptorum novorum, II. Öfv. Finska Vet.-Soc. Förh., vol. 22, pp. 9–24.
1880b. Nya bidrag till Abo och Alands skärgards hemipter-fauna. Meddelanden Soc. Fauna Flora Fennica, vol. 5, pp. 160–236.
1881. Analecta hemipterologica. Zur Artenkenntniss, Synonymie und Geographischen Verbreitung palaearktischer Heteropteren. Berliner Ent. Zeitschr., vol. 25, pp. 155–196.
1882a. M. le Dr. O. M. Reuter adresse, par l'intermédiaire de M. L. Buquet, la description d'une nouvelle espèce d'hémiptère. In Bulletin des Séances de la Société Entomologique de

France, part 2, Séance du 26 Juillet 1882. Ann. Soc. Ent. France, ser. 6, vol. 2, pp. cxxii–cxxxii.

1882b. Finlands och den Skandinaviska Halföns Hemiptera Heteroptera. Ent. Tidskr., vol. 3, No. 1, pp. 65–81; No. 3, pp. 105–121; No. 4, pp. 163–172.

1885. Synonymische Bemerkungen über hemipteren. Berliner Ent. Zeitschr., vol. 29, pp. 39–47.

1886. [On *Orthosteira acutispinus*]. *In* Meddelanden fran Sällskapets sammanträden. Den 7 November 1885. Meddelanden Soc. Fauna Flora Fennica, vol 13, pp. 233–234.

1887. Ad cognitionem heteropterorum Madagascariensium. Ent. Tidskr., vol. 8, pp. 77–109.

1888. Heteroptera nova in Graecia a do E. V. Oertzen Lecta. Rev. Ent., vol. 7, pp. 223–228.

1890a. Adnotationes hemipterologicae. Rev. Ent., vol. 9, pp. 248–254.

1890b. Notes sur quelques hémiptères de Madère. Rev. Ent., vol. 9, pp. 260–262.

1891a. Griechische Heteroptera gesammelt von E. v. Oertzen und J. Emge. Berliner Ent. Zeitschr., vol. 36, No. 1, pp. 17–34.

1891b. Hemiptera Heteroptera fran trakterna kring Sajanska bärgskedjan insamlade af K. Ehnberg och R. Hammarström. Öfv. Finska Vet.-Soc. Förh., vol 33, pp. 166–208.

1900. Quelques hémiptères du Maroc. Bull. Soc. Ent. France, pp. 186–189.

1902. Miscellanea hemipterologica. Hemipterologische Mitteilungen. Öfv. Finska Vet-Soc. Förh., ser. B, vol. 44, pp. 141–188.

1908. Charakteristik und Entwickelungsgeschichte der Hemipteren-Fauna (Heteroptera, Auchenorrhynchia und Psillidae) der Palaearctischen Coniferen. Acta Soc. Scient. Fennicae, vol. 36, No. 1, pp. 1–129.

1912. Bemerkungen über mein neues Heteropterensystem. Öfv. Finska Vet.-Soc. Förh., vol. 54 (1911–1912), No. 6, pp. 1–62.

REY, CLAUDIUS [see also MULSANT and REY]

1888. Notes sur quelques hémiptères-hétéroptères et descriptions d'espèces nouvelles ou peu connues. Rev. Ent., vol. 7, pp. 189–198.

1893. Remarques en passant. Echange, Rev. Linnéenne, vol. 9, No. 105, p. 97.

RIBAUT, H.

1932. Espèces d'hémiptères nouvelles pour la France (troisième liste) description de formes inédites. Bull. Soc. Hist. Nat. Toulouse, vol. 64. pp. 575–580, 2 figs.

1937. Espèces d'hémiptères nouvelles pour la France, description
d'une espèce inédite. Bull. Soc. Hist. Nat. Toulouse, vol.
71, Nos. 1–2, pp. 247–251.

1939. Récoltes de R. Paulian et A. Villiers dans le haut atlas Maro-
cain, 1938. Bull. Soc. Sci. Nat. Maroc, vol. 19, Nos. 3–4,
pp. 186–190.

RICHTER, H. C.

1869. A new insect from Ceylon. Hardwicke's Science Gossip, p. 84,
1 fig.

ROEMER, JOHANN JACOB

1789. Genera insectorum Linnaei et Fabricii iconibus illustrata. 89
pp., 37 pls. Ryngota pp. 77–86.

ROONWAL, M. L.

1952. The natural establishment and dispersal of an imported insect
in India—the lantana bug *Teleonemia scrupulosa* Stål (=*lantanae* Distant) (Hemiptera, Tingidae), with a description of
its egg, nymphs and adult. Journ. Zool. Soc. India, vol. 4,
No. 1, pp. 1–16, 5 figs.

ROSS, H., and HEDICKE, H.

1927. Die Pflanzengallen (Cecidien) Mittel-und Nordeuropas ihre
Erreger und Biologie und Bestimmungstabellen. Jena. 348
pp., 10 pls.

ROSSI, PETER

1790. Fauna Etrusca, sistens insecta quae in Provinciis Florentinae
et Pisana praesertim collegit, vol. 2, 348 pp., 10 pls. Ryngota
pp. 212–267.

ROUBAL, JEAN

1958. Description d'une espèce nouvelle de Tingitidae de France
(Het.). Bull. Soc. Ent. France, vol. 63, Nos. 1–2, pp.
54–56, 1 fig.

RÜBSAAMEN, EWALD H.

1896. Über russische Zoocecidien und deren Erzeuger. Bull. Soc.
Imp. Nat. Moscou, new ser., tome 9, pp. 396–488, 6 pls.,
1895.

Ruhoff, Florence A.: see DRAKE and RUHOFF

SAHLBERG, JOHN

1878. Bidrag till Nordvestra Sibiriens Insektfauna, Hemiptera
Heteroptera insamlade under expeditionerna till obi och
Jenesej 1876 och 1877. Kongliga Svenska Vetenskaps-
Akademiens Handlingar, vol. 16, No. 4, pp. 1–39.

1920. Enumeration hemipterorum heteropterorum Faunae Fennicae. Ed. 2 Bidrag till Kännedom af Finlands Natur och
Folk, vol. 79, No. 2, pp. 1–226. Tingitidae pp. 77–87,
212.

SAHLBERG, REGINALD FERDINAND
1848. Monographia Geocorisarum Fenniae, quam, venia amplissimae facultatis philosophicae ad Universitatem Imperialem Alexandream in Fennia. 154 pp.

SAILER, REECE I.
1945. The bite of a lacebug, *Corythucha cydoniae* (Fitch). Journ. Kansas Ent. Soc., vol. 18, No. 2, p. 81.

SAITÔ, KÔZÔ
1933. On a new variety and unrecorded species of Tingitidae from Korea, with the food plants of Korean species. Journ. Chôsen Nat. Hist. Soc., vol. 15. pp. 5–7.
1934. Unrecorded insects to the fauna of Corea. Journ. Chôsen Nat. Hist. Soc., vol. 17, p. 69.

Sala: see MORÓDER SALA

SAUNDERS, EDWARD
1875. Synopsis of British Hemiptera-Heteroptera, part 1. Trans. Ent. Soc. London, part 2, pp. 117–159; part 4, pp. 245–309.
1876. Descriptions of new Hemiptera-Heteroptera. Entomologists' Monthly Mag., vol. 13, pp. 102–103, 1876–1877.
1892. The Hemiptera-Heteroptera of the British Islands. London. 350 pp., 29 pls. Tingididae pp. 120–137.

SAY, THOMAS
1825. Descriptions of new hemipterous insects collected in the expedition to the Rocky Mountains, performed by order of Mr. Calhoun, Secretary of War, under command of Major Long. Journ. Acad. Nat. Sci. Philadelphia, vol. 4, pp. 307–345. LeConte reprint 1859, pp. 237–260.
1832. Descriptions of new species of heteropterous Hemiptera of North America. New Harmony, Indiana. Fitch reprint 1858, pp. 755-812. LeConte reprint 1858, pp. 310–368.

Scaramuzza, L. C.: see BRUNER, SCARAMUZZA, and OTERO

Schaeffer: see HERRICH-SCHAEFFER

SCHELLENBERG, JOHANN RUDOLF
1800. Das Geschlecht der Land und Wasserwanzen. Zürich. 32 pp., 16 pls.

Schenk, P. J.: see VAN DEN BROEK and SCHENK

SCHILLING, PETER SAMUEL
1838. Bemerkungen über die Gattung *Tingis* oder Gitterwanze. Arbeiten und Veränderungen der schlesischen Gesellschaft für vaterländische Kultur im Jahr 1837, pp. 104–106.

SCHMIDT, MARTIN
1928. *Stephanitis rhododendri* Horv. (Hem. Ting.) in Deutschland. Zeitschr. Wiss. Insektenbiol., vol. 23, Nos. 8–9, pp. 205–206.

Scholte, A. M.
1935. De Nederlandsche Tingitiden in Woord en Beeld. Natuurhistorisch Maanblad, vol. 24, pp. 21–24, 29–32, 43–46, 60–62, 76–78, 90–92, 27 figs. (photos).

Scholz, Heinrich
1847. Prodromus zu einer Rhychoten-Fauna von Schlesien. Arbeiten und Veränderungen der Schlesischen Gessellschaft für vaterländische Kultur im Jahr 1846, pp. 104–164.

Schouteden, Henri [see also Bergroth and Schouteden]
1907. Note sur quelques hémiptères de l'Isle Maurice. Ann. Soc. Ent. Belgique, vol. 4, pp. 285–288.

1916a. Phyllontocheila nouveaux d'Afrique (Hem. Tingidae). Rev. Zool. Africaine, vol. 4, No. 3, pp. 271–277.

1916b. Tingides du Congo Belge. Rev. Zool. Africaine, vol. 4, No. 3, pp. 288–297.

1919. Tingides nouveaux du Congo Belge. Rev. Zool. Africaine, vol. 6, No. 1, pp. 138–144.

1923. Nouvelles notes sur les tingides du Congo Belge. Rev. Zool. Africaine, vol. 11, No. 1, pp. 82–110.

1953a. Habrochila Ghesquièrei nov. spec. parasite du caféier (Hem. Tingididae). Rev. Zool. Bot. Africaines, vol. 48, Nos. 1–2, pp. 104–105.

1953b. Espèces nouvelles du genre Cysteochila (Hem. Tingididae). Rev. Zool. Bot. Africaines, vol. 48, Nos. 1–2, pp. 115–123.

1953c. Haedus et Gitava nouveaux de l'est du Congo Belge (Hem. Tingididae). Rev. Zool. Bot. Africaines, vol. 48, Nos. 1–2, pp. 128–131.

1953d. Tingides congolais nouveaux. Rev. Zool. Bot. Africaines, vol. 48, Nos. 3–4, pp. 165–171.

1953e. Monanthia nouveaux du Congo Belge et du Ruanda. Rev. Zool. Bot. Africaines, vol. 48, Nos. 3–4, pp. 196–201.

1954. Tingides nouveaux du Congo Belge. Rev. Zool. Bot. Africaines, vol. 49, Nos. 1–2, pp. 140–141.

1955a. Tingides nouveaux africains. Rev. Zool. Bot. Africaines, vol. 52, Nos. 1–2, pp. 25–32.

1955b. Tingides nouveaux des collections du Musée Royal du Congo Belge. Rev. Zool. Bot. Africaines, vol. 52, Nos. 1–2, pp. 162–168.

1956. Un tingide nouveau du Ruanda, Olastrida oleae nov. gen. nov. spec. Rev. Zool. Bot. Africaines, vol. 53, Nos. 1–2, pp. 205–207.

1957a. tingides de Madagascar. Rev. Zool. Bot. Africaines, vol. 55, Nos. 1–2, pp. 82–89.

1957b. Un tingide nouveau genre *Haedus*. Rev. Zool. Bot. Africaines, vol. 55, Nos. 1–2, pp. 219–220.

1957c. Heteroptera Piesmidae et Tingidae. Contributions à l'étude de la faune entomologique du Ruanda-Urundi (Mission P. Basilewsky 1953). Ann. Mus. Roy. Congo Belge, Tervuren, ser. 8, vol. 58, pp. 311–318.

SCHRANK, FRANZ VON PAVLA

1781. Enumeratio insectorum Austriae indigenorum. 548 pp., 4 pls. Cimex pp. 262–290.

1782. Kritische revision des österreichischen Insectenverzeichnisses. Füessly Neues Magazin für die Liebhaber der Entomologie, vol. 1, pp. 135–168, 263–306.

1801. Fauna Boica. Nürnberg. 374 pp.

SCHUMACHER, FRIEDRICH

1912. Über eine Hemipternausbeute, gesammelt von Herrn E. Hintz im Kamerungebirge. Mitt. Zool. Mus. Berlin, vol. 6, No. 2, pp. 315–323.

1913. Eine neue paläarktische Gattung und Art aus der Familie der Tingitiden. Mitt. Zool. Mus. Berlin, vol. 6, No. 3, pp. 457–458.

1914. Verzeichnis der Hemipteren des Niederelbgebiets. Abhandlungen des Vereins für naturwissenschaftliche Unterhaltung, vol. 15, pp. 194–359.

1919. Die märkischen *Serenthia*-Arten. Deutsche Ent. Zeitschr., pp. 202–203.

SCOTT, JOHN [see also DOUGLAS and SCOTT]

1874. On a collection of Hemiptera Heteroptera from Japan. Descriptions of various new genera and species. Ann. Mag. Nat. Hist., ser. 4, vol. 14, pp. 289–304, 360–365, 426–452.

1880. On a collection of Hemiptera from Japan. Trans. Ent. Soc. London, part 4, pp. 305–317.

SCUDDER, SAMUEL HUBBARD

1881. The Tertiary lake-basin at Florissant, Colorado, between South and Hayden Parks. Bull. U.S. Geol. Geogr. Surv. Terr., vol. 6, No. 1, art. 11, pp. 279–300.

1890. The Tertiary insects of North America. U.S. Geol. Geogr. Surv. Terr., vol. 13, pp. 1–734, 28 pls.

1891. Index to the known fossil insects of the world including myriapods and arachnids. U.S. Geol. Surv. Bull. 71, 744 pp. Hemiptera pp. 380–450.

SCUDDER, G. G. E. [see also SOUTHWOOD and SCUDDER]

1960. *Dictyonota fuliginosa* Costa (Hemiptera: Tingidae) in the Nearctic. Proc. Ent. Soc. British Columbia, vol. 57, p. 22.

DE SEABRA, A. F.
1924. Observações sôbre algumas espécies raras ou pouco conhecidas de hemípteros heterópteros de Portugal. Memórias e Estudos do Museu Zoológico da Universidade de Coimbra, ser. 1, No. 2, pp. 5–19, 33 figs.
1931. Sinópse dos hemípteros heterópteros de Portugal. Tingitidae. Memórias e Estudos do Museu Zoológico da Universidade de Coimbra, ser. 1, No. 1, fasc. 10, pp. 405–445, figs. 482–515.

SEIDENSTÜCKER, GUSTAV
1954. *Monanthia triconula* n. sp. ve Güney Türkiyenin bazi tingid-türleri. Rev. Fac. Sci. Univ. d'Istanbul, vol. 19, fasc. 3, pp. 231–236, 3 figs.

DE SERRES, MARCEL
1829. Géognosie des terrains Tertiaires. Montpellier. 277 pp., 6 pls.

Serville, Audinet: see LE PELETIER and SERVILLE; also AMYOT and SERVILLE

Severin, Guilaume: see LETHIERRY and SEVERIN

SHANTA, P.; MENON, K. P. V.; and PILLAI, K. PATCHU
1960. Aetiology of the wilt (root) disease: investigation on its virological nature. The Indian Coconut Journ., vol. 13, No. 2, pp. 56–66.

SHARGA, U. S.
1953. Bionomics of *Monanthia globulifera* Walk. (Hemiptera-Heteroptera: Tingidae). Journ. Bombay Nat. Hist. Soc., vol. 51, No. 4, pp. 885–889, 5 figs.
1955. Genitalia and reproductive organs of *Monanthia globulifera* Wlk. (Hemiptera-Tingidae). Journ. Bombay Nat. Hist. Soc., vol. 53, No. 2, pp. 284–286, 1 pl.

SHERBORN, C. DAVIS, and WOODWARD, B. B.
1901. Notes on the dates of publication of the natural history portions of some French voyages. Part I, Amérique méridionale; Indes-Orientales; Pole Sud l'*Astrolabe* et la *Zélée*; la *Bonite*; la *Coquille* and l'*Uranie* et la *Physicienne*. Ann. Mag. Nat. Hist., ser. 7, vol. 7, No. 40, pp. 388–392.

SHINJI, ORIHEI
1938. Tingitids of Morioka, with description of a new species. Zool. Mag. Japan, vol. 50, p. 316.

SHIRÔZU, TAKAHI
1939. *Stephanitis typica* occurs in Japan. Mushi, vol. 11, p. 205.

SIEBKE, JOHANN HEINRICH
1874. Enumeratio insectorum Norvegicorum, Fasciculus 1, Catalogum hemipterorum et orthopterorum continens. 334 pp. Tingidae pp. 22–23.

SIGNORET, VICTOR

1861. Faune des hémiptères de Madagascar, part 2, hétéroptères. Ann. Soc. Ent. France, ser. 3, vol. 8, pp. 917–972, 1860. [See p. cxxxiv for dates of publication.]

1863. Révision des hémiptères du Chili. Ann. Soc. Ent. France, ser. 4, vol. 3, pp. 541–588, 3 pls.

1865. Descriptions de quelques hémiptères nouveaux. Ann. Soc. Ent. France, ser. 4, vol. 5, pp. 115–130.

1881. M. V. Signoret donne les descriptions de trois nouvelles espèces d'hémiptères. *In* Séance du 13 Avril 1881. Ann. Soc. Ent. France, ser. 6, vol. 1, pp. xlv–lv.

Silva, Aristoteles G. d'Araujo e: see ARAUJO E SILVA, ARISTOTELES G.

SILVA, PEDRITO

1956. Tingideos da Bahia (Insecta-Hemiptera). Bol. Inst. Biol. Bahia, vol. 3, No. 1, pp. 10–77, 29 figs.

SILVESTRI, FILIPPO

1915. Contributo alla conoscenza degli insetti dell' olivo dell' Eritrea e dell' Africa meridionale. Boll. Lab. Zool. Portici, vol. 9, pp. 240–333, 78 figs.

1934. Compendio di Entomologia Applicata (Agraria—Forestale—Medica—Veterinaria). Bellavista. Vol. 1, Nos. 1–28, pp. 1–448, 414 figs. Tingitidae pp. 256–260.

SIMMONDS, HUBERT W.

1929. The life history of *Teleonemia lantanae*. Agric. Journ., Dept. Agric., Fiji, vol. 2, No. 1, pp. 36–39, 1 pl.

SINGER, KARL

1952. Die Wanzen (Hemiptera-Heteroptera) des unteren Main-gebietas von Hanau bis Würzburg mit Einschluss des Spessarts. Mitteilungen des Naturwissenschaftlichen Museums der Stadt Aschaffenburg, new ser., vol. 5, 128 pp.

SINGH, BALWANT

1953. Order Hemiptera. Family Tingidae (part 16). *In* A systematic catalogue of the main identified entomological collection at the Forest Research Institute, Dehra Dun. Indian Forest Leaflet No. 121, part 3, Entomology. Forest Research Inst. Dehra Dun, pp. 117–120.

Singh, Saran: see MENON, BERI, and SINGH

Slater, James A.: see DRAKE and SLATER

SMITH, JOHN B.

1910. Insects of New Jersey. Ann. Rep. New Jersey State Mus. 1909. 880 pp., 340 figs. Hemiptera pp. 131–170.

Smithers, C. N.: see DRAKE and SMITHERS

SOARES, OMILIO M.
1941. Notas sobre parasitos do tomateiro, contendo a diagnose de *Anaphes tingitiphagus*, n. sp. (Himenoptera-Chalcidoidea)' Bol. Esc. Nac. Agron., Rio de Janeiro, No. 2, art. 7, pp. 259–267, 14 figs.

SOMES, M. P.
1916. Some insects of *Solanum carolinense* L., and their economic relations. Journ. Econ. Ent., vol. 9, pp. 39–44.

SOUTHWOOD, T. R. E., and LESTON, DENNIS [see also LESTON, PENDERGRAST, and SOUTHWOOD]
1959. Land and water bugs of the British Isles. Frederick Warne Co., London. 436 pp., illustr.

SOUTHWOOD, T. R. E., and SCUDDER, G. G. E.
1956. The bionomics and immature stages of the thistle lace bugs (*Tingis ampliata* H.-S. and *T. cardui* L.; Hem., Tingidae). Trans. Soc. British Ent., vol. 12, No. 3, pp. 93–112, 13 figs.

SPINOLA, MAXIMILIEN
1837. Essai sur les genres d'insectes appartenants à l'ordre des hémiptères, Lin., ou rhyngotes, Fab., et à la section des hétéroptères, Dufour. 383 pp. [Ed. 2 published 1840.] Tingidites pp. 161–170.

1852a. Hemipteros. *In* Gay, Historia física y política de Chile, Zoologia, vol. 7, pp. 113–320.

1852b. Tavola sinottica dei generi spettanti alla classe degli insetti Artroidignati, Hemiptera, Linn. Latr.—Rhyngota, Fab.— Rhynchota, Burm. Memorie di Matematica e di Fisica della Societá Italiana delle Scienze Residente in Modena, vol. 25, part 1, pp. 43–100.

STAHLER, N.
1946. A new lacebug in Florida. Journ. Econ. Ent., vol. 39, No. 4, pp. 545–546, 1 fig.

STÅL, CARL
1855a. Hemiptera fran Kafferlandet. Öfv. Kongl. Vet.-Akad. Förh., vol. 12, No. 1, pp. 27–46.

1855b. Nya Hemiptera. Öfv. Kongl. Vet.-Akad. Förh., vol. 12, pp. 181–192.

1858. Bidrag till Rio Janeiro-Traktens Hemipter-Fauna. I. Öfv. Kongl. Svenska Vet.-Akad. Handl., vol. 2, No. 7, pp. 1–84. [In the advertisements on the back of the original folder of "Hemiptera Fabriciana" (1868 and 1869) the publishers give the publication date of "Bidrag till Rio Janeiro-Traktens Hemipter-Fauna, vol. 1" as 1858. The present authors are accepting this date, which is in full accordance with Neave "Nomenclator Zoologicus (1939–1950)."]

1859. Hemiptera. Species novas descripsit. Konglica Svenska Fregatten Eugenies resa omkring Jorden 1851–1853. Vetenskapliga Iakttagelser II. Zoologi. Insecta, pp. 219–298.

1862. Hemiptera mexicana enumeravit speciesque novas descripsit. (cont.). Ent. Zeit. Stettin, vol. 23, pp. 289–325.

1865. Hemiptera Africana. Stockholm. Vol. 3, pp. 1–200

1868. Hemiptera Fabriciana, part 1. Kongl. Svenska Vet.-Akad. Handl., vol. 7, No. 11, pp. 1–148.

1870a. Hemiptera insularum Philippinarum. Bidrag till Philippinska öarmes hemipter-fauna. Öfv. Kongl. Vet.-Akad. Förh., vol. 7, pp. 607–776, 4 pls.

1870b. Enumeratio Hemipterorum, vol. 1. Kongl. Svenska Vet.-Akad. Handl., vol. 9, No. 1, pp. 1–232.

1873. Enumeratio Hemipterorum, vol. 3. Kongl. Svenska Vet.-Akad. Handl., vol. 11, No. 2, pp. 1–163.

1874. Genera Tingitidarum Europae disposuit. Kongl. Vet.-Akad. Förh., vol. 3, pp. 43–60.

STEHLIK, J. L.
1952. The fauna of Heteroptera of the Mountain High Jesenik. Acta Mus. Moraviae, vol. 37, pp. 131–248, 7 pls.

STEHR, WILLIAM C.
1938. The biology of *Corythucha aesculi* O. and D. (Hemiptera, Tingitidae) on the yellow buckeye, *Aesculus octandra* Marsh. Ohio Journ. Sci., vol. 38, No. 1, pp. 13–24, 3 figs.

STEPHENS, JAMES F.
1829a. The nomenclature of British insects; being a compendious list of such species as are contained in the Systematic catalogue of British insects. London. 68 pp.

1829b. A systematic catalogue of British insects, part 2, pp. 1–388. Cimicidae pp. 335–337.

STEYER,——
1915. *Stephanitis Rhododendri* Horvath (Hemip.) in Deutschland. Zeitschr. Angew. Ent., band 2, heft 2, pp. 434–435.

STICHEL, WOLFGANG
1926. Illustrierte Bestimmungstabellen der Deutschen Wanzen (Hemiptera-Heteroptera). Lief. 4, pp. 91–119, figs. 249–317.

1928. *Stephanitis rhododendri* Horv. und *St. azaleae* Horv.=*St. oberti* Kol.? (Hem. Ting.). Zeitschr. Wiss. Insektenbiol., vol. 23, Nos. 8–9, p. 206.

1935. Illustrierte Bestimmungstabellen der Deutschen Wanzen (Hemiptera-Heteroptera). Systematischer Katalog. Lief. 12, pp. 331–362.

1938a. Illustrierte Bestimmungstabellen der Deutschen Wanzen (Hemiptera-Heteroptera). Geographische Verbreitung, II. Lief. 14, pp. 363–426.

1938b. Illustrierte Bestimmungstabellen der Deutschen Wanzen (Hemiptera-Heteroptera). Geographische Verbreitung, III. Ergänzungen und Berichtigungen I. Lief. 15, pp. 427–458.

1960a. Illustrierte Bestimmungstabellen der Wanzen. II. Europa. Vol. 3, heft 9–11, pp. 264–352, figs. 1–222.

1960b. Illustrierte Bestimmungstabellen der Wanzen. II. Europa. Liste der Paläarkstischen Arten, vol. 3, heft 13–14, pp. 385–428.

1960c. Verzeichnis der Paläarktischen Hemiptera-Heteroptera. III. Cimicomorpha (Cimicoidea excl. Miridae—Reduvioidea—Saldoidea—Tingiodea) Pentatomomorpha (Aradoidea—Lygaeoidea—Pyrrhocoroidea). Berlin. Pp. 94–166.

1960d. Studien an zwei Hemipterologischen Werken. Mem. Soc. Ent. Italiana, vol. 38, pp. 115–126.

STRAWINSKI, KONSTANTY

1953. Badania nad pluskwiakami (Heteroptera) zyjacymi na lakach na przyklaszie materialu z Iwonicza. Ann. Univ. Marie Curie-Sklodowska Lublin-Polonia, sec. C, vol. 8, No. 10, pp. 357–401.

ŠTUSÁK, JOSEF M.

1957a. Beitrag zur Kenntnis der Eier der Tingiden (Heteroptera: Tingidae). Beiträge zur Entomologie, vol. 7, Nos. 1–2, pp. 20–28, 13 figs.

1957b. A contribution to the knowledge of some last nymphal instars of the Czechoslovakian lace bugs (Hemiptera-Heteroptera, Tingidae). Časopis Československé Společnosti Ent., vol. 54, No. 2, pp. 132–141, 15 figs.

1958. Zweiter Beitrag zur Kenntnis der Eier der Tingiden (Hemiptera Heteroptera, Tingidae). Časopis Československé Společnosti Ent., Acta Soc. Ent. Čechosloveniae, vol. 55, No. 4, pp. 361–371, 16 figs.

1959a. Zur Bionomie und Entwicklungsstadien der Art *Catoplatus carthusianus* (Goeze) (Hemiptera-Heteroptera, Tingidae). Časopis Československé Společnosti Ent., Acta Soc. Ent. Čechosloveniae, vol. 56, No. 1, pp. 52-64, 8 figs.

1959b. Early stages of the lace bug *Tingis grisea* Germar (Hemiptera-Heteroptera, Tingidae). Časopis Československé Společnosti Ent., Acta Soc. Ent. Čechosloveniae, vol. 56, No. 2, pp. 181–191, 8 figs.

1961a. Dritter Beitrag zur Kenntnis der Eier der Tingiden (Heteroptera, Tingidae). Časopis Československé Společnosti Ent., Acta Soc. Ent. Čechosloveniae, vol. 58, No. 1, pp. 71–88, figs.

1961b. *Acalypta pulchra* sp. n.—eine neue tingidenart aus Bulgarien (Heteroptera, Tingidae). Časopis Československé Společnosti Ent., Acta Soc. Ent. Čechosloveniae, vol. 58, No. 3, pp. 261–265, 3 figs.

Štusák, Josef M., and Štys, Pavel
1959. Investigations on the taxonomy and morphology of imagines and nymphs of some species of the genus *Monanthia* Le Peletier and Serville, 1825 (Hemiptera-Heteroptera: Tingidae). Acta Universitatis Carolinae-Biologica, No. 3, pp. 177–205, 46 figs.

Štys, Paval: see Štusák and Štys

Summers, H. E.
1891. The true bugs, or Heteroptera, of Tennessee. Bull. Agric. Exp. Station Univ. Tennessee, vol. 4, No. 3, pp. 75–96, 14 figs, 1 pl.

Swezey, Otto H. [see also Perkins and Swezey]
1924. Present status of lantana and its introduced insect enemies. *In* Perkins and Swezey, Bull. Exp. Station Hawaiian Sugar Planters' Assoc. Ent. Ser., Bull. 16, appendix C, pp. 72–82, 7 figs.

1945. Insects associated with orchids. Proc. Hawaiian Ent. Soc., vol. 12, No. 2, pp. 343–403.

Takahashi, Ryôichi
1936. Food habits and new habits of Formosan Psyllidae, with notes on peculiar food habits of Formosan phytophagous insects. Kontyû, vol. 10, pp. 295–296.

Takeya, Choku [see also Esaki and Takeya]
1930a. On a little-known tingitid, *Monanthia salicorum* (Baba) occurring in Japan (Hem. Heter.). Mushi, vol. 3, pp. 67–72, 1 pl.

1930b. Host plants of *Stephanitis globulifera* Matsumura. Mushi, vol. 3, p. 72.

1931. Some Tingidae of the Japanese Empire. Mushi, vol. 4, pp. 65–84, 3 pls.

1932. Some Corean lace bugs (Hemiptera, Tingitidae). Mushi, vol. 5, pp. 8–13, 1. pl.

1933. New or little-known lace bugs from Japan, Corea and Formosa (Hemiptera: Tingitidae). Mushi, vol. 6, pp. 32–39, 4 text figs, 1 pl.

1951a. A tentative list of Tingidae of Japan and her adjacent territories (Hemiptera). Kurume Univ. Journ. (Nat. Sci.), vol. 4, No. 1, pp. 5–28.

1951b. New *Stephanitis* species from Japan (Hemiptera: Tingidae). Sci. Bull., Kyushu Univ., vol. 13, Nos. 1–4, pp. 58–62, 2 figs.

1952. Notes on *Stephanitis typica* (Distant) in Japan (Hemiptera: Tingidae). Kurume Univ. Journ. (Nat. Sci.), vol. 4, No. 2, pp. 39–46, 1 fig.

1953a. Unrecorded piesmid and tingids of Manchuria (Hemiptera). Kurume Univ. Journ. (Nat. Sci.), vol. 5, No. 1, pp. 1–3, 1 fig.

1953b. An unrecorded tingid from Japan (Hemiptera). Kurume Univ. Journ. (Nat. Sci.), vol. 5, No. 1, pp. 4–7, 1 fig.

1953c. Variation of some morphological characters in *Stephanitis pyrioides* (Hemiptera: Tingidae). Kurume Univ. Journ. (Nat. Sci.), vol. 5, No. 1, pp. 8–12.

1953d. Notes on the Tingidae of Shikoku, Japan (Hemiptera). Trans. Shikoku Ent. Soc., vol. 3, No. 7, pp. 167–176, 1 fig., 1 pl.

THEOBALD, FRED V.

1911. An introduced rhododendron pest (*Stephanitis rhododendri* Horvath). Rep. Econ. Zool. for year ending Sept. 30, 1911. Journ. Southeastern Agric. College, Wye, Kent, No. 22, p. 206.

1913. Animals injurious to ornamental plants. Rep. Econ. Ent. for year ending Sept. 30, 1913. Journ. Southeastern Agric. College, Wye, Kent, No. 23, pp. 286–307, 9 figs.

THOMPSON, B. G., and WONG, KWAN LUN

1933. Western willow tingis, *Corythucha salicata* Gibson, in Oregon. Journ. Econ. Ent., vol. 26, pp. 1090–1095, 1 pl.

THOMSON, CARL G.

1871. Bidrag till Sveriges insect fauna. Opuscula Entomologica. Lund. Fasc. 4, pp. 361–452.

THONTADARYA, T. S., and CHANNA BASAVANNA, G. P.

1959. Mode of egg laying in Tingidae (Hemiptera). Nature, vol. 184, No. 4682, pp. 289–290.

THUNBERG, CARL P.

1822. Dissertatio entomologica de hemipteris rostratis capensibus. Part 2, pp. 1–8.

1825. Insectorum hemelytrorum tria genera illustrata. 10 pp.

TILDEN, JAMES W.

1950. Biological notes on *Corythucha morrilli* O. and D. (Hemiptera: Tingidae). Ent. News, vol. 61, pp. 135–137.

TORRE-BUENO, JOSE R.

1908. Hemiptera Heteroptera of Westchester County, N.Y. Journ. New York Ent. Soc., vol. 16, No. 4, pp. 223–238.

1910. Westchester Heteroptera. II. Additions, corrections and new records. Journ. New York Ent. Soc., vol. 18, No. 1, pp. 22–33.

1916. A new tingid from New York State. Bull. Brooklyn Ent. Soc., vol. 11, No. 2, pp. 39–40.

1917. A new species of tingid from New York. Bull. Brooklyn Ent. Soc., vol. 12, No. 1, pp. 19–20.

1924. A correction in *Acalypta* (Tingididae). Bull. Brooklyn Ent. Soc., vol. 19, No. 3, p. 93.

1925. Food plant of *Corythucha marmorata* Uhler. Bull. Brooklyn Ent. Soc., vol. 20, p. 179.

1926a. Further records of Heteroptera from Massachusetts. Bull. Brooklyn Ent. Soc., vol. 21, Nos. 1–2, pp. 53–55.

1926b. Some remarks, Al Vuelo, on tingitid names. Bull. Brooklyn Ent. Soc., vol. 21, No. 3, pp. 116–117.

1929. On some New England Heteroptera. Bull. Brooklyn Ent. Soc., vol. 24, No. 5, pp. 310–313.

1931. *Alveotingis grossocerata*. Bull. Brooklyn Ent. Soc., vol. 26, No. 3, p. 149.

1933. New records of Heteroptera from Arkansas. Bull. Brooklyn Ent. Soc., vol. 28, No. 5, p. 228.

1942. Maternal solicitude in *Gargaphia iridescens* Champion. Bull. Brooklyn Ent. Soc., vol. 37, No. 4, p. 131.

1946. On *Hesperotingis antennata* Drake. Bull. Brooklyn Ent. Soc., vol. 41, pp. 94–95.

TOWNSEND, CHARLES HENRY TYLER

1894. Notes on some southwestern Hemiptera. Canadian Ent., vol. 26, pp. 312–316.

1928. Insectos que atacan al Algodón y a la Caña de Azúcar en el Perú. Estacion Exp. Agric. Soc. Nac. Agraria, Lima, Peru, Bol. 1, 21 pp., 22 figs.

UHLER, PHILIP R.

1878. Notices of the Hemiptera Heteroptera in the collection of the late T. W. Harris, M.D. Proc. Boston Soc. Nat. Hist., vol. 19, pp. 365–446.

1884. Order VI—Hemiptera. *In* Kingsley, The Standard Natural History, vol. 2, pp. 204–296, figs. 286–341.

1886. Check-list of the Hemiptera Heteroptera of North America. Brooklyn Ent. Soc., 32 pp.

1889. Observations upon the Heteroptera collected in southern Florida by Mr. E. A. Schwarz. *In* Minutes of the meeting, March 1, 1888, Washington Entomological Society. Proc. Ent. Soc. Washington, vol. 1, pp. 142–144.

1893a. A list of the Hemiptera-Heteroptera collected in the island of St. Vincent by Mr. Herbert H. Smith; with descriptions of new genera and species. Proc. Zool. Soc. London, pp. 705–719.

1893b. Hemiptera and Heteroptera of the Death Valley expedition. *In* North American Fauna, No. 7, pp. 260–265. U.S. Dept. Agric., Div. Ornithology and Mammalogy.

1894a. On the Hemiptera-Heteroptera of the island of Grenada, West Indies. Proc. Zool. Soc. London, vol. 13, pp. 167–224.

1894b. Observations upon the heteropterous Hemiptera of Lower California, with descriptions of new species. Proc. California Acad. Sci., ser. 2, vol. 4, pp. 224–295.

1896. Summary of the Hemiptera of Japan, presented to the United States National Museum by Professor Mitzukuri. Proc. U.S. Nat. Mus., vol. 19, pp. 255–297.

1904. List of Hemiptera-Heteroptera of Las Vegas Hot Springs, New Mexico, collected by Messrs. E. A. Schwarz and Herbert S. Barber. Proc. U.S. Nat. Mus., vol. 27, pp. 349–364.

USINGER, ROBERT L.

1946a. Hemiptera Heteroptera of Guam. *In* Insects of Guam II, Bernice P. Bishop Mus. Bull. 189, pp. 11–103.

1946b. Biology and control of the ash lace-bug, *Leptoypha minor*. Journ. Econ. Ent., vol. 39, No. 3, pp. 286-289, 2 figs.

VALLOT, JEAN NICOLAS

1829. Notice sur differents insectes et differentes larves qui vivent sur les plantes. Académie des Sciences, Arts et Belles-lettres de Dijon, pp. 96–116.

van den Broek: see BROEK, VAN DEN
van den Bruel: see BRUEL, VAN DEN
van der Vecht: see VECHT, VAN DER
VAN DUZEE, EDWARD P.

1889. Hemiptera from Muskoka Lake district. Canadian Ent., vol. 21, No. 1, pp. 1–11.

1894. A list of the Hemiptera of Buffalo and vicinity. Bull. Buffalo Soc. Nat. Sci., vol. 5, No. 4, pp. 167–204.

1901. Notes on some Hemiptera from British Guiana. Trans. Amer. Ent. Soc., vol. 27, pp. 343–352.

1905. List of Hemiptera taken in the Adirondack Mountains. New York State Mus. Bull. 97, Rep. State Ent. 1904, pp. 546–556.

1907. Notes on Jamaican Hemiptera, a report on a collection of Hemiptera made on the island of Jamaica in the Spring of 1906. Bull. Buffalo Soc. Nat. Sci., vol. 8, No. 5, pp. 3–79.

1909. Observations on some Hemiptera taken in Florida in the spring of 1908. Bull. Buffalo Soc. Nat. Sci., vol. 9, pp. 149–230, figs.

1912. Synonymy of the Provancher collection of Hemiptera. Canadian Ent., vol. 44, No. 11, pp. 317–329.

1914.   A preliminary list of the Hemiptera of San Diego County, California. Trans. San Diego Soc. Nat. Hist., vol. 2, No. 1, pp. 1–57.

1916.   Check list of the Hemiptera (excepting the Aphididae, Aleurodidae and Coccidae) of America, north of Mexico. New York Ent. Soc., 111 pp.

1917a.   Report upon a collection of Hemiptera made by Walter M. Giffard in 1916 and 1917, chiefly in California. Proc. California Acad. Sci., ser. 4, vol. 7, No. 11, pp. 249–318.

1917b.   Catalogue of the Hemiptera of America north of Mexico excepting the Aphididae, Coccidae and Aleurodidae. Univ. California Publ., Tech. Bull., vol. 2, 902 pp. Tingididae pp. 209–224, 813–818.

1918.   New species of Hemiptera chiefly from California. Proc. California Acad. Sci., ser. 4, vol. 8, No. 7, pp. 271–308.

1923.   Expedition of the California Academy of Sciences to the Gulf of California in 1921. Hemiptera (true bugs, etc.). Proc. California Acad. Sci., ser. 4, vol 12, No. 11, pp. 123–200.

1936.   A report on some Heteroptera from the Hawaiian Islands, with descriptions of new species. Proc. Hawaiian Ent. Soc., vol. 9, No. 2, pp. 219–229.

VASILIEV, I.
1935.   Grushevye klopy roda *Stephanitis* kak vaediteli plodovstva. Pear-bugs as pest of fruit groves. Plant Proctection, vol. 7, pp. 151–152.

VECHT, JACOB VAN DER
1931.   De stand van het onderzoek der peper-insecten van Nederlandsch-Inde. "Landbouw." Tijdschrift der Vereeniging van Landbouwcounsulten in N-I, vol. 6, pp. 820–828.

1935.   Aanteekeningen over de pepernetwants (*Elasmognathus hewitti* Dist.). "Landbouw." Tijdschrift der Vereeniging van Landbouwcounsulten in N-I, vol. 10, pp. 484–493, 1 pl.

1953.   Het Lantana-Wantsje in Indonesie (*Teleonemia scrupulosa* Stål, Fam. Tingidae). Tijdschrift over Plantenziekten, vol. 59, pp. 170–173.

VIDAL, J. P.
1937.   Contribution à l'étude des hémiptères-hétéroptères du Maroc. Bull. Soc Hist. Nat. Afrique du Nord, vol. 28, pp. 185–208, 3 text figs., 2 pls.

1939.   Le faux tigre du poirier (*Monostira unicostata* Mls. Hem. Heter.). Bull. Soc. Hist. Nat. Afrique du Nord, vol. 30, pp. 27–32, 1 fig.

1951.   Hémiptères, hétéroptères nouveaux du Maroc. Bull. Soc. Sci. Nat. Maroc, vol. 31, pp. 57–64, 2 figs.

VILLERS, CAROL
1789. Caroli Linnaei Entomologia . . ., vol. 1, 765 pp., 3 pls.

VOLLENHOVEN, SAMUEL C. SNELLEN VAN
1878. Hemiptera Heteroptera Neerlandica. De inlandsche ware hemipteren (Land- en Waterwantsen). 368 pp., 22 pls. Tingididea pp. 265–286.
1879. Bijvoegsel tot de lijst der Inlandsche Hemiptera Heteroptera. Tijdschr. voor Ent., vol. 22, pp. 227–231, 2 pls.

von Baerensprung: see BAERENSPRUNG, VON

WADE, OTIS
1917. The sycamore lace-bug (*Corythucha ciliata* Say). Oklahoma Agric. Exp. Station Bull. 116, 16 pp., 7 figs.

WAGNER, EDUARD [see also NOVAK and WAGNER]
1941. Die deutschen *Serenthia*-Arten (Hem. Heteropt.). Verh. Ver. Naturw. Heimatforschung zu Hamburg, vol. 28, pp. 1–27, 11 figs.
1954. Revision der paläarktischen Arten der Gattung *Copium* Thbg. (Hem. Het. Tingidae). Deutsche Ent. Zeitschr., vol. 1, Nos. 3–5, pp. 200–209, 27 figs.
1955. Die Artberechtigung von *Copium magnicorne* Rey, 1888 (Hem. Het. Tingidae). Deutsche Ent. Zeitschr., vol. 2, Nos. 3–4, pp. 182–184, 6 figs.
1956. *Copium intermedium* Rey, 1888 (Hemipt. Het. Tingidae). Deutsche Ent. Zeitschr., vol. 3, No. 1, pp. 84–86, 6 figs.
1957. Eine neue *Copium* vom Balkan (Hem. Het. Tingidae). Boll. Soc. Ent. Italiana, vol. 87, Nos. 1–2, pp. 28–30, 5 figs.
1958. Deuzième contribution a la faune des hémiptères hétéroptères de France. Vie et Milieu, vol. 9, No. 2, pp. 236–247.
1960. Über *Physatocheila smreczynskii* China 1952 (Hem. Het. Tingidae). Mitt. Münchner Ent. Ges., pp. 83–92, 4 pls.

WALCKENAER, CHARLES ATHANASE
1802. Faune Parisienne, insectes; ou histoire abrégée des insectes des environs de Paris. Vol. 2, 440 pp.

WALKER, FRANCIS
1873a. Catalogue of the specimens of Hemiptera Heteroptera in the collection of the British Museum. Part VI, 210 pp.
1873b. Catalogue of the specimens of Hemiptera Heteroptera in the collection of the British Museum. Part VII, 213 pp.

DE WALSCH, J.
1960. Capture de l'hémiptère tingide *Orthostira parvula* Fallén. Bull. Ann. Soc. Roy. Ent. Belgique, vol. 96, Nos. 3–4, p. 38.

WALSH, BENJAMEN D.
1864. On phytophagic varieties and phrophagic species. Proc. Ent. Soc. Philadelphia, vol. 3, pp. 403–430.

WARNER, ROSE ELLA
1956.   A new record of the andromeda lace bug (*Stephanitis globulifera* (Matsumura)) from New Jersey. Journ. New York Ent. Soc., vol. 64, p. 6.

WEISS, HARRY B. [see also BARBER and WEISS; DICKERSON and WEISS]
1913.   Notes on the negative geotropism of *Corythuca ciliata* Say, *Adalia bipunctata* Linn, *Coccinella 9-notata* Hbst. and *Megilla fuscilabris* Muls. Journ. Econ. Ent., vol. 6, pp. 407–408.

1918.   Some new insect enemies of greenhouse and ornamental plants in New Jersey. New Jersey Agric. Exp. Station Circ. 100, pp. 1–19, 32 figs.

1919a. Notes on *Corythuca bulbosa* O. and D.   Ohio Journ. Sci., vol. 20, No. 1, pp. 17–20.

1919b. Notes on *Gargaphia tiliae* Walsh, the linden lace-bug.   Proc. Biol. Soc. Washington, vol. 32, pp. 165–168.

1921.   Notes on the life history and early stages of *Corythucha celtidis* O. and D.   Ohio Journ. Sci., vol. 21, No. 3, pp. 104–106.

1924.   *Corythucha marmorata* Uhler on seaside goldenrod (Hemiptera). Ent. News, vol. 35, p. 367.

WEISS, HARRY B., and DICKERSON, EDGAR L.
1918a. The early stages of *Corythucha pergandei* Heid. (Hem. Hom.). Ent. News, vol. 29, pp. 205–209, 2 figs.

1918b. The life-history and early stages of *Corythucha parshleyi* Gibson. Canadian Ent., vol. 50, No. 12, pp. 401–406, 1 pl.

WEISS, HARRY B., and LOTT, RALPH B.
1924.   Notes on *Corythucha marmorata* Uhler in New Jersey (Hemip.: Tingitidae).   Ent. News, vol. 35, p. 68.

WEISS, HARRY B., and WEST, ERDMAN
1924.   Notes on the false indigo lace bug, *Gelchossa heidemanni* Osborn and Drake, in New Jersey (Hemip.: Tingitidae).   Ent. News, vol. 35, pp. 56–60.

WELLHOUSE, WALTER H.
1919.   Lace bug on hawthorn, *Corythucha bellula* Gibson. Journ. Econ. Ent., vol. 12, No. 6, pp. 441–446, 2 figs.

West, Erdman: see WEISS and WEST

WESTWOOD, JOHN O.
1840a. An introduction to the modern classification of insects.   London. Vol. 2, 587 pp., 133 figs. Heteroptera, pp. 450–488.

1840b. Synopsis of the genera of British insects.   London. 158 pp. Heteroptera, pp. 119–134.

WHITE, RICHARD P.
1933.   The insects and diseases of rhododendron and azalea.   Journ. Econ. Ent., vol. 26, pp. 631–640, 2 pls.

White: see BUCHANAN-WHITE

WILSON, CHARLES E.
1923. Insect pests of cotton in St. Croix and means of combating them. Virgin Island Agric. Exp. Station Bull. 3, 20 pp., 21 figs.

WILSON, G. FOX
1925. Insect pests of rhododendrons. Journ. Roy. Hort. Soc., vol. 50, pp. 46–53, 4 figs.

WIRTNER, P. MODESTUS
1904. A preliminary list of the Hemiptera of western Pennsylvania. Ann. Carnegie Mus., vol. 3, pp. 183–232.

WOLCOTT, GEORGE N.
1923. Insectae Portoricensis. A preliminary annotated check-list of the insects of Porto Rico, with descriptions of some new species. Journ. Dept. Agric. Porto Rico, vol. 7, No. 1, 313 pp.

WOLFF, JOHANN FREDERIC
1801. Icones cimicum descriptionibus illustratae. Fasc. 2, pp. 43–84, 4 pls.
1804. Icones cimicum descriptionibus illustratae. Fasc. 4, pp. 125–166, 4 pls.

WOLLASTON, T. VERNON
1858. Brief diagnostic characters of undescribed Maderian insects. Ann. Mag. Nat. Hist., ser. 3, vol. 1, pp. 18–28, 113–125, 2 pls.

Wong, Kwan Lun: see THOMPSON and WONG
Woodward, B. B.: see SHERBORN and WOODWARD
WU, CHENFU F.
1935. Catalogus insectorum sinensium. Vol. 2. Fan Memorial Inst. Biol., 634 pp. Tingitidae pp. 449–450.

ZETTERSTEDT, JOHANN WILHELM
1828. Fauna insectorum Lapponica (Coleoptera, Orthoptera, Hemiptera). 563 pp.
1840. Insecta Lapponica descripta. 1140 pp. *Tingis* pp. 268–270.

ZIMMERMAN, ELWOOD C.
1948. Heteroptera. Insects of Hawaii, vol. 3. Univ. Hawaii Press, Honolulu. 255 pp.

General References

British Museum (Natural History)
    1903–1940. Catalogue of the books, manuscripts, maps, and drawings in
        the British Museum (Natural History).   5 vols. +3 suppl. vols.
HAGEN, HERMAN A.
    1862–1863. Bibliotheca entomologica. Leipzig. Vols. 1 and 2.
HORN, WALTHER, and SCHENKLING, S.
    1928–1929. Index litteraturae entomologicae. 1426 pp.
NEAVE, SHEFFIELD A.
    1939–1950. Nomenclator zoologicus. Vols. 1–6, supplements. (Covers
        years through 1945.)
Zoological Record.
    1864–1959. Zoological record, vols. 1–96 (section 13).

Index

[Genera and subgenera in CAPITALS, with synonyms followed by an asterisk (*); species and subspecies in roman, with synonyms in *italics*.]

602 INDEX

orientalis Horváth, Campylosteira, 104
orientis Drake, Physatocheila, 336
ornata Monte, Leptopharsa, 281
ornata Van Duzee [var.], Physatocheila, 338
ornatella (Stål), Compseuta, 125
ornatipes Drake and Hambleton, Atheas, 94
OROTINGIS Drake and Poor, 311
  eueides Drake, 312
  muiri Drake and Poor, 312
orta Drake and Maa, Cysteochila, 172
ORTHOSTEIRA* Fieber, 44
  acutangula Jakovlev, 44
  acutispinis Reuter, 49
  biseriata Thomson, 47
  cinerea Fieber, 51
  concinna Douglas and Scott, 44
  cylindricornis Thomson, 49
  ditata Puton [var.], 50
  elinoides Jakovlev, 47
  finitima Puton, 47
  gracilis Fieber, 47
  macrophthalma Fieber, 49
  macroptera Ferrari [var.], 53
  major Ferrari [var.], 53
  minor Ferrari [var.], 53
  pallescens Ferrari [var.], 53
  paradoxa Jakovlev, 350
  platycheila Fieber, 53
  propinqua Ferrari, 47
  reticosta Thomson, 47
  samara Puton, 54
  sordida Jakovlev, 55
  subtilis Reuter, 55
  suturalis Puton, 55
  uniseriata Puton, 56
Orthostira auct. (*see* Orthosteira)
osborni Drake, Nyctotingis, 307
oschanini Vasiliev, Stephanitis, 360
oscitans Drake and Maa, Cysteochila, 172
oscitantis Drake and Maa (*see* oscitans)
otaviana Drake, Cysteochila, 172
otiosus Drake, Haedus, 239
otiosus Drake, Hegesidemus, 241
OTTOICUS Drake, 312
  dissitus Drake, 312

outouana Drake and Maa, Stephanitis, 368
ovalis Distant, Axiokersos, 95
ovantis Drake and Hambleton, Leptopharsa, 282
ovata Champion, Phatnoma, 38
ovata Osborn and Drake, Acalypta, 48
ovata (Osborn and Drake), Acalypta, 46
ovatula (Jakovlev), Tingis, 407
oxyacanthae (Curtis), Physatocheila, 332

PACHYCYSTA Champion, 312
  adolpha Drake, 312
  championi Drake, 312
  diaphana Champion, 313
  hambletoni Drake and Poor, 313
  schildi Drake, 313
pacifica Drake, Corythucha, 160
pacifica Drake and Poor [misident.], Phatnoma, 38
pacifica Hacker [misident.], Phatnoma, 36
pacifica (Kirkaldy), Eritingis, 209, 210
pacifica Kirkaldy, Phatnoma, 38
pacis Drake and Hambleton, Leptopharsa, 282
padi Drake, Corythucha, 156
pagana Drake and Maa, Stephanitis, 368
paganus Drake, Atheas, 94
pagnana Drake, Perissonemia, 324
pakistana Drake and Maldonado, Dictyonota, 435
PALAUELLA Drake, 313
  gressitti Drake, 313
palawanus Drake and Maa, Cromerus, 163
paleipes Barber (*see* pallipes)
pallens Dobšik [var.], Catoplatus, 116
pallens (Horváth) [var.], Agramma, 65
pallens Horváth, Cysteochila, 173
pallens Monte, Leptopharsa, 282
pallens Schouteden [ssp.], Gitava, 236
pallens Schouteden, Haedus, 240
pallescens (Ferrari) [var.], Acalypta, 53
pallida (Garbiglietti), Tingis, 399
pallida (Kirby), Diconocoris, 179
pallida Osborn and Drake, Corythucha, 157
pallidulum (Schouteden), Agramma, 74

INDEX TO HOST PLANTS

[References to pp. 449–478 are to summary of host plants, arranged by family.]